Earth's Waters: Teacher's Edition

Contents in Brief

See Program Component List on page ii

Teacher's Edition

Student Edition

Prentice Hall Science Explorer

Series Tables of Contents

The Nature of Science and Technology

Life Science

From Bacteria to Plants

Animals

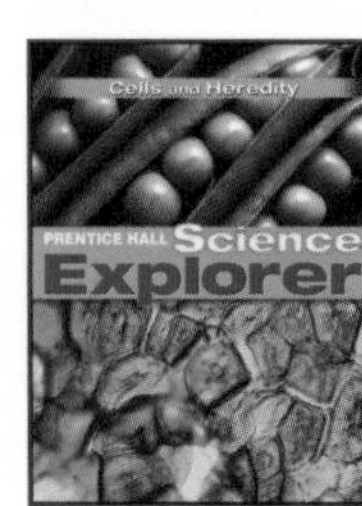

Cells and Heredity

Human Biology and Health

Environmental Science

Earth Science

Inside Earth

Earth's Changing Surface

Earth's Waters

Weather and Climate

Astronomy

Physical Science

Chemical Building Blocks

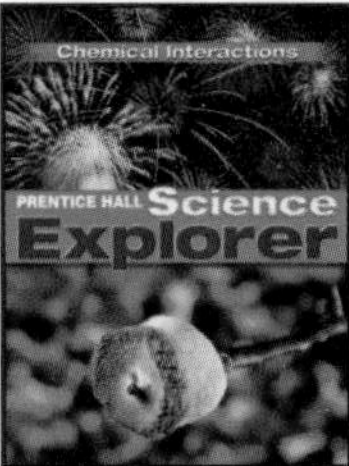

Chemical Interactions

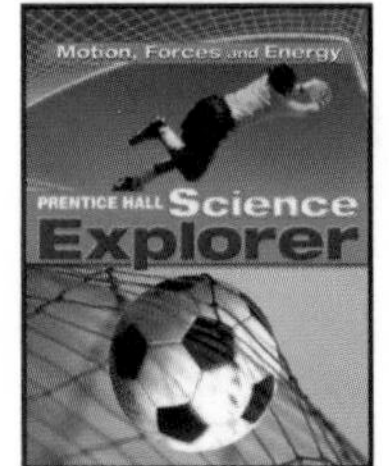

Motion, Forces, and Energy

Electricity and Magnetism

Sound and Light

Teacher's Edition

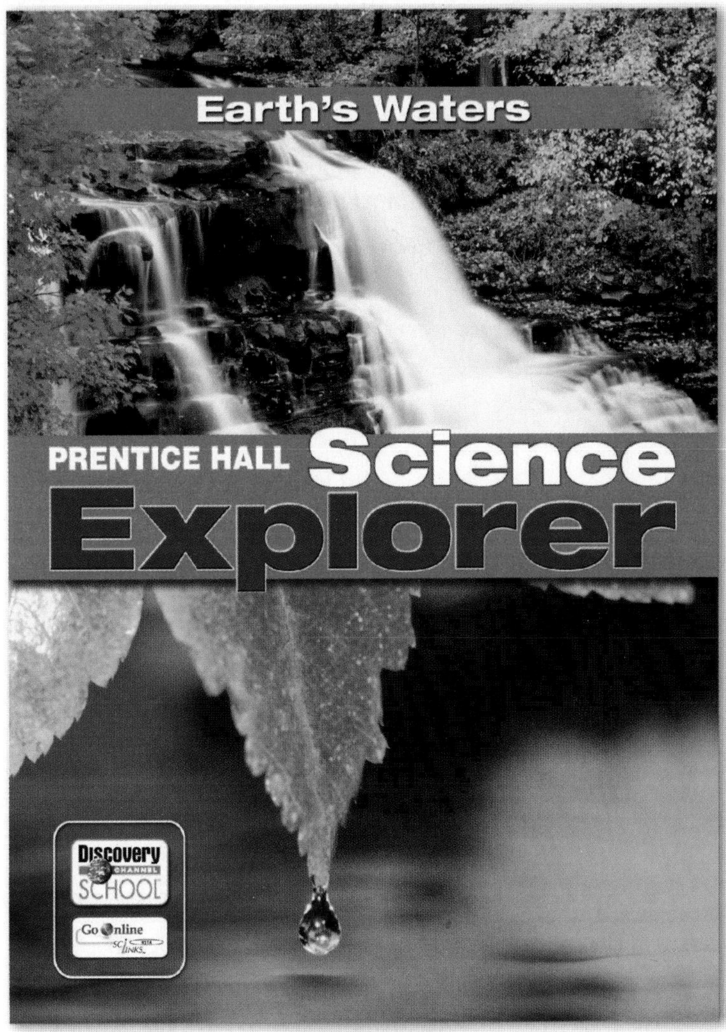

Needham, Massachusetts
Upper Saddle River, New Jersey

ISBN 0-13-181127-4

1 2 3 4 5 6 7 8 9 10 08 07 06 05 04

Pacing Options

PRENTICE HALL
TeacherEXPRESS™
Plan • Teach • Assess

SCIENCE EXPLORER offers many aids to help you plan your instruction time, whether regular class periods or block scheduling. Section-by-section lesson plans for each chapter include suggested times for Student Edition activities. TeacherExpress™ and the Lab zone™ Easy Planner CD-ROM will help you manage your time electronically.

Pacing Chart

	PERIODS	BLOCKS
Careers: Through the Lens of an Ocean Scientist	1	½
Chapter 1 Earth: The Water Planet		
Chapter 1 Project *Every Drop Counts*	Ongoing	Ongoing
1 Integrating Chemistry: The Properties of Water	1–2	½–1
2 Water on Earth	2–3	1–1½
3 Surface Water	2–3	1–1½
4 Wetland Environments	1–2	½–1
5 Water Underground	3–4	1–2
Chapter 1 Review and Assessment	1	½
Chapter 2 Freshwater Resources		
Chapter 2 Project *A Precious Resource*	Ongoing	Ongoing
1 Water Supply and Demand	3–4	1–2
2 Tech & Design: Water to Drink	2–3	1–1½
3 Freshwater Pollution	2–3	1–1½
4 Droughts and Floods	1–2	½–1
5 Integrating Physics: Water Power	1–2	½–1
Chapter 2 Review and Assessment	1	½
Chapter 3 Ocean Motions		
Chapter 3 Project *Design and Build an Erosion-Proof Beach*	Ongoing	Ongoing
1 Wave Action	2–3	1–1½
2 Integrating Space Science: Tides	1–2	½–1
3 Ocean Water Chemistry	2–3	1–1½
4 Currents and Climates	3–4	1–2
Chapter 3 Review and Assessment	1	½
Chapter 4 Ocean Zones		
Chapter 4 Project *At Home in the Sea*	Ongoing	Ongoing
1 Exploring the Ocean	3–4	1–2
2 Integrating Life Science: Ocean Habitats	1–2	½–1
3 Intertidal Zone	1–2	½–1
4 Neritic Zone and Open Ocean	2–3	1–1½
5 Resources From the Ocean	3–4	1–2
Chapter 4 Review and Assessment	1	½
Interdisciplinary Exploration: The Mississippi	2–3	1–2

Research-Based and Proven to Work

As the originator of the small book concept in middle school science, and as the nation's number one science publisher, Prentice Hall takes pride in the fact that we've always listened closely to teachers. In doing so, we've developed programs that effectively meet the needs of your classroom.

As we continue to listen, we realize that raising the achievement level of all students is the number one challenge facing teachers today. To assist you in meeting this latest challenge, Prentice Hall has combined the very best author team with solid research to create a program that meets your high standards and will ensure that no child is left behind.

With Prentice Hall, you can be confident that your students will not only be motivated, inspired, and excited to learn science, but that they will also achieve the success needed in today's environment of the No Child Left Behind (NCLB) legislation and testing reform.

On the following pages, you will read about the key elements found throughout *Science Explorer* that truly set this program apart and ensure success for you and your students.

As we continue to listen, we realize that raising the achievement level of all students is the number one challenge facing teachers today.

A Science Program Backed by Research

In developing Prentice Hall *Science Explorer*, we used research studies as a central, guiding element. Research on *Science Explorer* indicated key elements of a textbook program that ensure students' success: support for reading and mathematics in science, consistent opportunities for inquiry, and an ongoing assessment strand. This research was conducted in phases and continues today.

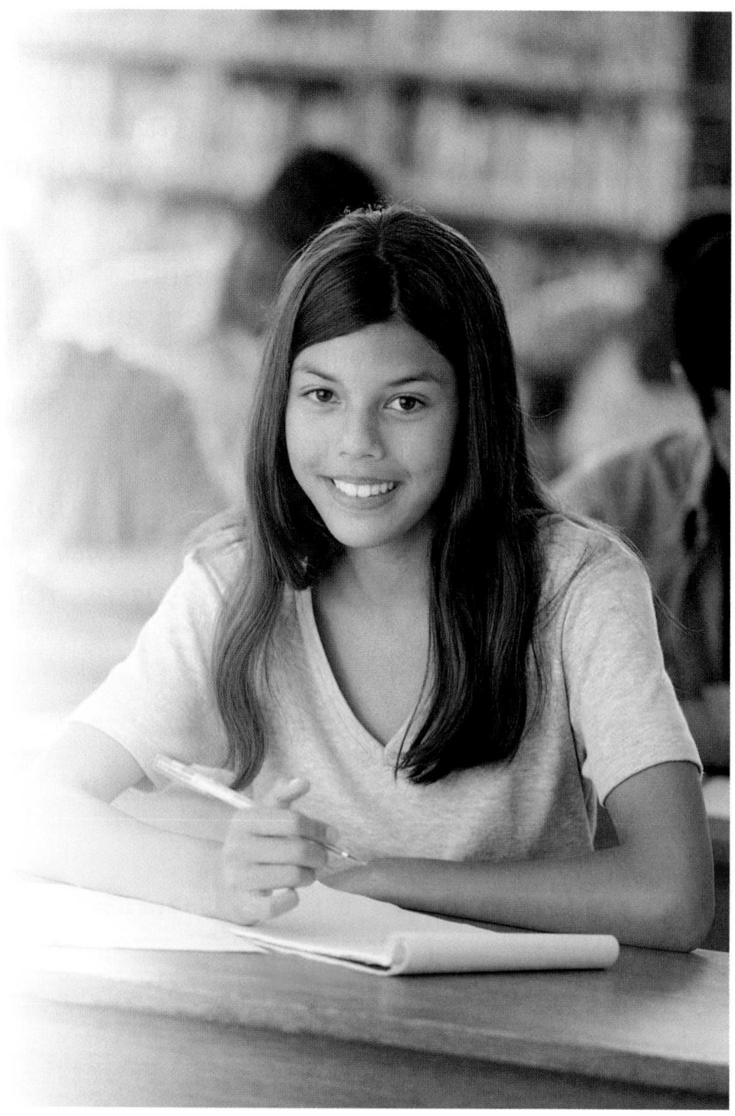

1. Exploratory: Needs Assessment

Along with periodic surveys concerning state and national standards as well as curriculum issues and challenges, we conducted specific product development research, which included discussions with teachers and advisory panels, focus groups, and quantitative surveys. We explored the specific needs of teachers, students, and other educators regarding each book we developed in Prentice Hall *Science Explorer*.

2. Formative: Prototype Development and Field-Testing

During this phase of research, we worked to develop prototype materials. Then we tested the materials by field-testing with students and teachers and by performing qualitative and quantitative surveys. In our early prototype testing, we received feedback about our lesson structure. Results were channeled back into the program development for improvement.

3. Summative: Validation Research

Finally, we conducted and continue to conduct long-term research based on scientific, experimental designs under actual classroom conditions. This research identifies what works and what can be improved in the next revision of Prentice Hall *Science Explorer*. We also continue to monitor the program in the market. We talk to our users about what works, and then we begin the cycle over again. The next section contains highlights of this research.

A Science Program With Proven Results

In a year-long study in 2000–2001, students in six states using Prentice Hall *Science Explorer* outscored students using other science programs on a nationally normed standardized test.

The study investigated the effects of science textbook programs at the eighth-grade level. Twelve eighth-grade science classes with a total of 223 students participated in the study. The selected classes were of similar student ability levels.

Each class was tested at the beginning of the school year using the TerraNova CTBS Basic Battery Plus, and then retested at the end of the school year. The final results, shown in the graph, show a significant improvement in test scores from the pre-test to the post-test evaluation.

- All tests were scored by CTB/McGraw-Hill, the publisher of the TerraNova exam. Statistical analyses and conclusions were performed by an independent firm, Pulse Analytics, Inc.

In Japan, Lesson Study Research has been employed for a number of years as a tool for teachers to improve their curriculum. In April 2003, Prentice Hall adapted this methodology to focus on a lesson from this edition. Our goal was to test the effectiveness of lesson pedagogy and improve it while in the program development stage. In all three classrooms tested, student learning increased an average of 10 points from the pre- to the post-assessment.

- Detailed results of these studies can be obtained at **www.PHSchool.com/research.**

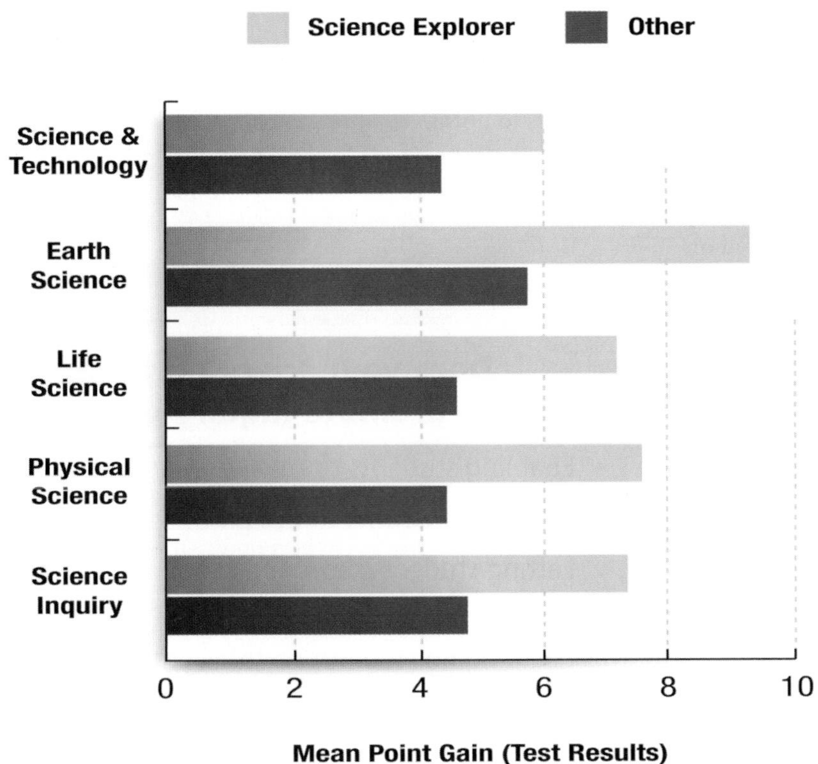

Inquiry

Foundational Research: Inquiry in the Science Classroom

"How do I know if my students are inquiring?" "If students are busy doing lots of hands-on activities, are they using inquiry?" "What is inquiry, anyway?" If you're confused, you are not alone. Inquiry is the heart and soul of science education, with most of us in continuous pursuit of achieving it with our students!

Michael J. Padilla, Ph.D.
Program Author of *Science Explorer*
Professor of Science Education
University of Georgia
Athens, Georgia

"Because inquiry is an intellectual pursuit, it cannot merely be characterized by keeping students busy and active."

Defining Science Inquiry

What is it? Simply put, inquiry is the intellectual side of science. It is thinking like a scientist—being inquisitive, asking why, and searching for answers. The National Science Education Content Standards define inquiry as the process in which students begin with a question, design an investigation, gather evidence, formulate an answer to the original question, and communicate the investigative process and results. Since it is often difficult to accomplish all this in one class period, the standards also acknowledge that at times students need to practice only one or two inquiry components.

Understanding Inquiry

The National Research Council in Inquiry and the National Science Education Standards (2000) identified several "essential features" of classroom inquiry. We have modified these essential features into questions to guide you in your quest for enhanced and more thoughtful student inquiry.

1. ***Who asks the question?*** In most curricula, these focusing questions are an element given in the materials. As a teacher you can look for labs that, at least on a periodic basis, allow students to pursue their own questions.
2. ***Who designs the procedures?*** To gain experience with the logic underlying experimentation, students need continuous practice with designing procedures. Some labs in which the primary target is content acquisition designate procedures. But others should ask students to do so.
3. ***Who decides what data to collect?*** Students need practice in determining the data to collect.
4. ***Who formulates explanations based upon the data?*** Students should be challenged to think—to analyze and draw conclusions based on their data, not just copy answers from the text materials.
5. ***Who communicates and justifies the results?*** Activities should push students not only to communicate but also to justify their answers. Activities also should be thoughtfully designed and interesting so that students want to share their results and argue about conclusions.

Making Time for Inquiry

One last question—Must each and every activity have students do all of this? The answer is an obvious and emphatic "No." You will find a great variety of activities in *Science Explorer*. Some activities focus on content acquisition, and thus they specify the question and most of the procedures. But many others stress in-depth inquiry from start to finish. Because inquiry is an intellectual pursuit, it cannot merely be characterized by keeping students busy and active. Too many students have a knack for being physically but not intellectually engaged in science. It is our job to help them engage intellectually.

Evaluator's Checklist

Does your science program promote inquiry by—

- ✔ Enabling students to pursue their own questions
- ✔ Allowing students to design their own procedures
- ✔ Letting students determine what data are best to collect
- ✔ Challenging students to think critically
- ✔ Pushing students to justify their answers

Inquiry in *Science Explorer*

Science Explorer offers the most opportunities to get students to think like a scientist. By providing inquiry opportunities throughout the program, *Science Explorer* enables students to enhance their understanding by participating in the discovery.

Student Edition Inquiry

Six lab and activity options are included in every chapter, structured from directed to open-ended—providing you the flexibility to address all types of learners and accommodate your class time and equipment requirements. As Michael Padilla notes, some activities focus on content acquisition, and thus the question and most of the procedures are specified. But many others stress in-depth inquiry from start to finish. The graph below shows how, in general, inquiry levels are addressed in the Student Edition.

Science Explorer encourages students to develop inquiry skills across the spectrum from teacher-guided to open-ended. Even more opportunities for real-life applications of inquiry are included in Science & Society, Science & Technology, Careers in Science, and Interdisciplinary Exploration features.

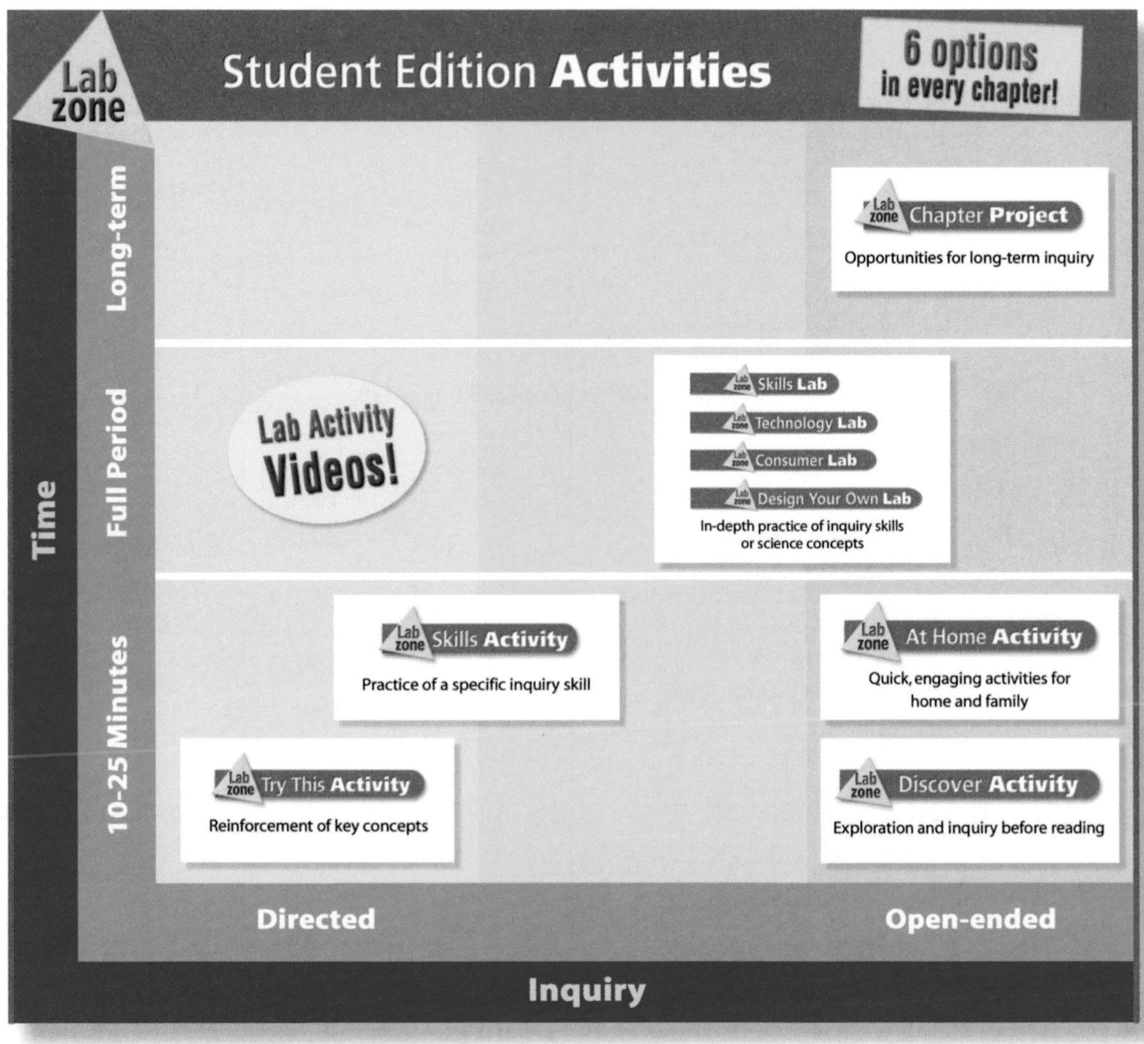

Inquiry Skills Chart

SCIENCE EXPLORER provides comprehensive teaching, practice, and assessment of science skills, with an emphasis on the process skills necessary for inquiry. This chart lists the skills covered in the program and cites the page numbers where each skill is covered.

Basic Process SKILLS				
	Student Text: Projects and Labs	**Student Text: Activities**	**Student Text: Caption and Review Questions**	**Teacher's Edition: Extensions**
Observing	18, 40–41, 47, 56, 66–67, 122–123, 165	6, 7, 11, 12, 19, 24, 27, 28, 32, 33, 34, 38, 61, 62, 68, 74, 78, 84, 87, 94, 97, 108, 116, 146, 150	30, 62, 154	6, 8, 11, 18, 21, 22, 28, 32, 34, 40–41, 46, 56, 61, 62, 66, 68, 78, 84, 94, 97, 108, 122–123, 148, 150, 153, 165
Inferring	18, 66–67, 122–123, 140, 165	9, 12, 21, 80, 82, 106, 116, 130, 141, 146, 155, 160	13, 22, 39, 44, 55, 63, 74, 90, 103, 107, 113, 116, 131, 145, 151, 163, 164, 170	9, 12, 18, 21, 23, 25, 51, 54, 66, 70, 72, 80, 82, 97, 122–123, 128, 130, 140–141, 142, 146, 155, 160
Predicting	41, 140, 165	36, 48, 54, 102	11, 28, 44, 107, 113, 121, 126	37, 48, 60, 62, 102, 104
Classifying	123	19, 24, 71, 158, 162	7, 17, 33, 44, 77, 126, 143, 145, 170	19, 24, 69, 71, 77, 85, 145, 158
Making Models	47, 56, 93, 114–115, 122–123, 129, 165	24, 32, 38, 61, 85, 87, 94, 99, 101, 121, 142, 164		7, 25, 32, 37, 38, 46, 51, 56, 61, 73, 74, 81, 82, 92, 99, 100, 122–123, 132, 136, 142, 152, 154, 156, 165
Communicating	18, 41, 56, 67, 115, 123, 140, 165			4, 12, 46, 53, 92, 128
Measuring	66, 114–115	6, 14, 48, 139		92, 114–115
Calculating	5, 18	14, 36, 54, 57, 58, 102, 110	55, 63, 90, 113, 126	4, 14, 15, 18, 57, 59, 110, 112, 113
Creating Data Tables	5, 18, 40–41, 66–67, 115			4
Graphing	40, 140	106, 139	44, 126, 139	4, 14, 36, 51, 54, 106, 135, 140
Advanced Process SKILLS				
Posing Questions	67	28, 84, 108	33, 170	28, 84
Developing Hypotheses	18, 40–41	85	33, 52, 77, 90, 101	40–41, 85
Designing Experiments	5, 40–41, 47, 56, 114–115, 123		27, 33, 55, 90	31, 40–41, 114–115, 147
Controlling Variables				

Advanced Process SKILLS (continued)				
	Student Text: Projects and Labs	Student Text: Activities	Student Text: Caption and Review Questions	Teacher's Edition: Extensions
Forming Operational Definitions				
Interpreting Data		36, 54, 106, 162	44, 58	4, 36, 54, 92, 104, 128
Drawing Conclusions	41, 56, 66–67	74, 118	44, 126, 170	18, 41, 56, 66, 74, 118
Critical Thinking SKILLS				
Comparing and Contrasting		78, 102, 108	10, 27, 33, 37, 44, 63, 77, 87, 90, 113, 121, 126, 139, 147, 149, 157	46, 78, 109, 133
Applying Concepts			17, 27, 44, 55, 63, 82, 83, 90, 95, 101, 107, 121, 126, 149, 157	7, 8, 10, 13, 14, 16, 21, 22, 23, 25, 26, 29, 32, 36, 37, 38, 51, 52, 53, 54, 59, 60, 61, 62, 69, 70, 71, 72, 73, 74, 75, 76, 80, 81, 82, 85, 86, 95, 96, 97, 98, 99, 100, 103, 104, 105, 106, 109, 110, 112, 117, 118, 119, 120, 131, 132, 134, 136, 137, 138, 142, 143, 144, 147, 148, 151, 152, 154, 155, 156, 159, 160, 161, 162, 163
Interpreting Diagrams, Graphs, Photographs, and Maps		36, 54, 162	13, 16, 21, 35, 39, 60, 70, 86, 99, 100, 109, 112, 117, 134, 137, 138, 139, 144, 159, 170	15, 59, 106, 162
Relating Cause and Effect		116, 150	11, 26, 53, 69, 90, 101, 110, 113, 121, 126, 139, 145, 148, 152, 157, 161, 170	46, 81, 116, 150
Making Generalizations			77, 107, 157, 170	
Making Judgments			17, 33, 55, 77, 83, 90, 149, 164	
Problem Solving	18, 40, 56, 66, 114, 122, 140, 165	162	39, 83, 87, 139	18, 114–115
Informational Organizational SKILLS				
Concept Maps			89	23, 42, 53, 81, 88, 124, 143, 163, 168
Compare/Contrast Tables			169	25, 110, 117, 155
Venn Diagrams				29
Flowcharts		57	63, 125	57, 75, 80
Cycle Diagrams			43	

The ***Science Explorer*** program provides additional teaching, reinforcement, and assessment of skills in the *Inquiry Skills Activities Book* and the *Integrated Science Laboratory Manual*.

A National Look at Science Education

Project 2061 was established by the American Association for the Advancement of Science (AAAS) as a long-term project to improve science education nationwide. A primary goal of Project 2061 is to define a "common core of learning"—the knowledge and skills we want all students to achieve. Project 2061 published *Science for All Americans* in 1989 and followed this with *Benchmarks for Science Literacy* in 1993. *Benchmarks* recommends what students should know and be able to do by the end of grades 2, 5, 8, and 12. Project 2061 clearly states that *Benchmarks* is not a curriculum but a tool for designing successful curricula.

The National Research Council (NRC) used *Science for All Americans* and *Benchmarks* to develop the National Science Education Standards (NSES), which were published in 1996. The NSES are organized into six categories (Content, Teaching, Assessment, Professional Development, Program, and System) to help schools establish the conditions necessary to achieve scientific literacy for all students.

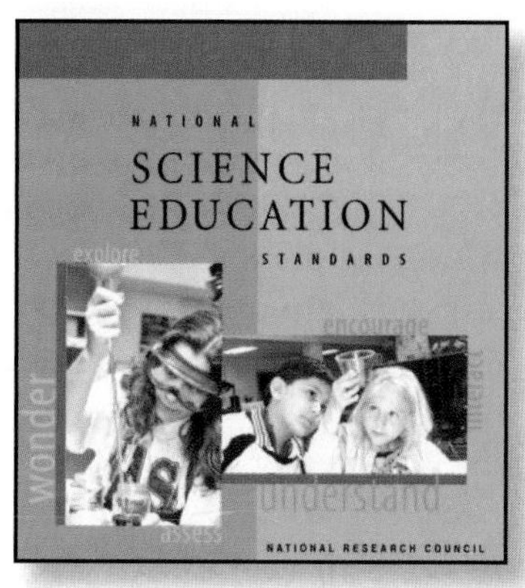

Michael Padilla, the program author of *Science Explorer,* guided one of six teams of teachers whose work led to the publication of *Benchmarks.* He also was a contributing writer of the National Science Education Standards. Under his guidance, *Science Explorer* has implemented these standards through its inquiry approach, a focus on student learning of important concepts and skills, and teacher support aligned with the NSES teaching standards.

Neither *Benchmarks* nor the NSES requires a single, uniform national curriculum, and in fact there is a great diversity nationwide in science curricula. The correlations that follow are designed to help you use the *Science Explorer* program to meet your particular curriculum needs.

Meeting the National Science Education Standards

EARTH: THE WATER PLANET

Science as Inquiry (Content Standard A)

- **Design and conduct a scientific investigation** Students design methods for tracking water use and soil testing. *(Chapter Project, Design Your Own Lab)*
- **Develop descriptions, explanations, predictions, and models using evidence** Students base their conclusions on what they observed. *(Skills Lab)*

Physical Science (Content Standard B)

- **Properties and changes of properties in matter** Students understand that water is the only substance that exists in three forms. *(The Properties of Water)*

Earth and Space Science (Content Standard D)

- **Structure of the Earth system** Earth's water is recycled naturally through the water cycle. Water is a solvent that moves through underground layers of soil and rock. *(Water on Earth, Water Underground)*

FRESHWATER RESOURCES

Science as Inquiry (Content Standard A)

- **Identify questions that can be answered through scientific investigations** Students observe how distillation can be used to obtain fresh water from salt water. *(Skills Lab)*
- **Design and conduct a scientific investigation** Students design and build a water treatment system. *(Chapter Project)*
- **Use appropriate tools and techniques to gather, analyze, and interpret data** Students observe and record data about water samples. *(Chapter Project)*

Physical Science (Content Standard B)

Transfer of energy The energy of moving water can be used to produce electricity. *(Water Power)*

Science and Technology (Content Standard E)

- **Identify appropriate problems for technological design** Students identify alternative sources of water. *(Water Supply and Demand)*
- **Design a solution or product** Students design a water treatment system. Students make water-distilling models. *(Chapter Project, Skills Lab)*

A National Look at Science Education *(continued)*

Science in Personal and Social Perspectives (Content Standard F)

● **Personal health** Drinking water must be treated before it is consumed. *(Water to Drink)*

● **Science and technology in society** The need for safe drinking water influences scientific technology. Students compare three types of treated water. *(Consumer Lab)*

OCEAN MOTIONS

Science as Inquiry (Content Standard A)

● **Design and conduct and investigation** Waves, tides, and currents move Earth's waters in different ways. Students will design and build a model to prevent shoreline erosion. Students will build an instrument to detect differences in water density. Students make models replicating ocean currents. *(Chapter Project, Technology Lab, Skills Lab)*

Physical Science (Content Standard B)

● **Motions and forces** Students illustrate how the motion of tides can be measured. *(Tides)*

● **Transfer of energy** The movement of water between high tide and low tide is a potential source of energy. *(Tides)*

Earth and Space Science (Content Standard D)

● **Structure of the Earth system** Oceans have a major effect on climate. *(Currents and Climates)*

Science and Technology (Content Standard E)

● **Design a solution or product** Students build a hydrometer. Students make a model replicating ocean currents. *(Technology Lab, Skills Lab)*

OCEAN ZONES

Science as Inquiry (Content Standard A)

● **Identify questions that can be answered through scientific investigation** Students will select a habitat and make a list of questions that can be answered through their investigation. *(Chapter Project)*

● **Use appropriate tools and techniques to gather, analyze, and interpret data** Students choose the materials needed to build their habitat models and sketch a design. *(Chapter Project)*

● **Use mathematics in all aspects of scientific inquiry** Students will use graphing, predicting, and inferring skills to determine the shape of the ocean floor. *(Skills Lab)*

Life Science (Content Standard C)

● **Populations and ecosystems** Scientists divide the ocean into different zones depending on physical conditions, relationships among organisms, and ocean food webs. *(Ocean Habitats)*

Science and Technology (Content Standard E)

● **Design a solution or product** Students make models illustrating ways to clean up an oil spill. *(Skills Lab)*

Science in Personal and Social Perspectives (Content Standard F)

● **Populations, resources, and environments** Ocean pollution caused by human activity reduces the amount of ocean resources available for use. *(Resources From the Ocean)*

Note: To see how the benchmarks are supported by *SCIENCE EXPLORER,* go to **PHSchool.com.**

Reading Comprehension in the Science Classroom

Q&A

Q: Why are science texts often difficult for students to read and comprehend?

A: In general, science texts make complex literacy and knowledge demands on learners. They have a more technical vocabulary and a more demanding syntax, and place a greater emphasis on inferential reasoning.

Q: What does research say about facilitating comprehension?

A: Studies comparing novices and experts show that the conceptual organization of experts' knowledge is very different from that of novices. For example, experts emphasize core concepts when organizing knowledge, while novices focus on superficial details. To facilitate comprehension, effective teaching strategies should support and scaffold students as they build an understanding of the key concepts and concept relationships within a text unit.

Q: What strategies can teachers use to facilitate comprehension?

A: Three complementary strategies are very important in facilitating student comprehension of science texts. First, guide student interaction with the text using the built-in strategies. Second, organize the curriculum in terms of core concepts (e.g., the **Key Concepts** in each section). Third, develop visual representations of the relationships among the key concepts and vocabulary that can be referred to during instruction.

Nancy Romance, Ph.D.
Professor of Science Education
Florida Atlantic University
Fort Lauderdale, Florida

"Effective teaching strategies should support and scaffold students as they build an understanding of the key concepts and concept relationships within a text unit."

Evaluator's Checklist

Does your science program promote reading comprehension with—

- ✔ Text structured in an outline format and key concepts highlighted in boldface type
- ✔ Real-world applications to activate prior knowledge
- ✔ Key concepts, critical vocabulary, and a reading skill for every section
- ✔ Sample graphic organizers for each section
- ✔ Relevant photos and carefully constructed graphics with questions
- ✔ Reading checkpoints that appear in each section
- ✔ Scaffolded questions in section assessments

Reading Support in *Science Explorer*

The latest research emphasizes the importance of activating learners' prior knowledge and teaching them to distinguish core concepts from less important information. These skills are now more important than ever, because success in science requires students to read, understand, and connect complex terms and concepts.

Before students read—

Reading Preview introduces students to the key concepts and key terms they'll find in each section. The **Target Reading Skill** is identified and applied with a graphic organizer.

During the section—

Boldface Sentences identify each key concept and encourage students to focus on the big ideas of science.

Reading Checkpoints reinforce students' understanding by slowing them down to review after every concept is discussed.

Caption Questions draw students into the art and photos, helping them connect the content to the images.

After students read—

Section Assessment revisits the **Target Reading Skill** and encourages students to use the graphic organizer.

Each review question is scaffolded and models the way students think, by first easing them into a review and then challenging them with increasingly more difficult questions.

Math in the Science Classroom

Why should students concern themselves with mathematics in your science class?

Good science requires good data from which to draw conclusions. Technology enhances the ability to measure in a variety of ways. Often the scientist must measure large amounts of data, and thus an aim of analysis is to reduce the data to a summary that makes sense and is consistent with established norms of communication—i.e., mathematics.

Calculating measures of central tendency (e.g., mean, median, or mode), variability (e.g., range), and shape (graphic representations) can effectively reduce 500 data points to 3 without losing the essential characteristics of the data. Scientists understand that a trade-off exists between precision and richness as data are folded into categories, and so margins of error can be quantified in mathematical terms and factored into all scientific findings.

Mathematics is the language used by scientists to model change in the world. Understanding change is a vital part of the inquiry process. Mathematics serves as a common language to communicate across the sciences. Fields of scientific research that originated as separate disciplines are now integrated, such as happened with bioengineering. What do the sciences have in common? Each uses the language of mathematics to communicate about data and the process of data analysis. Recognizing this need, *Science Explorer* integrates mathematics practice throughout the program and gives students ample opportunity to hone their math skills.

Clearly, mathematics plays an important role in your science classroom!

William Tate, Ph.D.
Professor of Education and Applied Statistics and Computation
Washington University
St. Louis, Missouri

"Mathematics is the language used by scientists to model change in the world."

Integrated Math Support

In the Student Edition

The math instruction is based on principles derived from Prentice Hall's research-based mathematics program.

Sample Problems, Math Practice, Analyzing Data, and a Math Skills Handbook all help to provide practice at point of use, encouraging students to Read and Understand, Plan and Solve, and then Look Back and Check.

Color-coded variables aid student navigation and help reinforce their comprehension.

In the Teacher's Edition

Math teaching notes enable the science teacher to support math instruction and math objectives on high-stakes tests.

In the Guided Reading and Study Workbook

These unique worksheets help students master reading and enhance their study and math skills. Students can create a record of their work for study and review.

Evaluator's Checklist

Does your science program promote math skills by—

- ✔ Giving students opportunities to collect data
- ✔ Providing students opportunities to analyze data
- ✔ Enabling students to practice math skills
- ✔ Helping students solve equations by using color-coded variables
- ✔ Using sample problems to apply science concepts

Technology and Design in the Science Classroom

Much of the world we live in is designed and made by humans. The buildings in which we live, the cars we drive, the medicines we take, and often the food we eat are products of technology. The knowledge and skills needed to understand the processes used to create these products should be a component of every student's basic literacy.

Some schools offer hands-on instruction on how technology development works through industrial arts curricula. Even then, there is a disconnect among science (understanding how nature works), mathematics (understanding data-driven models), and technology (understanding the human-made world). The link among these fields of study is the engineering design process—that process by which one identifies a human need and uses science knowledge and human ingenuity to create a technology to satisfy the need. Engineering gives students the problem-solving and design skills they will need to succeed in our sophisticated, three-dimensional, technological world.

As a complement to "science as inquiry," the National Science Education Standards (NRC, 1996) call for students at all age levels to develop the abilities related to "technology as design," including the ability to identify and frame a problem and then to design, implement, and evaluate a solution. At the 5–8 grade level, the standards call for students to be engaged in complex problem-solving and to learn more about how science and technology complement each other. It's also important for students to understand that there are often constraints involved in design as well as trade-offs and unintended consequences of technological solutions to problems.

As the *Standards for Technological Literacy* (ITEA, 2000) state, "Science and technology are like conjoined twins. While they have separate identities they must remain inextricably connected." Both sets of standards emphasize how progress in science leads to new developments in technology, while technological innovation in turn drives advances in science.

Ioannis Miaoulis, Ph.D.
President
Museum of Science
Boston, Massachusetts

"Engineering gives students the problem-solving and design skills they will need to succeed in our sophisticated, three-dimensional, technological world."

Evaluator's Checklist

Does your science program promote technology and design by—

- ✔ Incorporating technology and design concepts and skills into the science curriculum
- ✔ Giving students opportunities to identify and solve technological design problems
- ✔ Providing students opportunities to analyze the impact of technology on society
- ✔ Enabling students to practice technology and design skills

Technology and Design

Technology and Design in *Science Explorer*

How often do you hear your students ask: "Why do I need to learn this?" Connecting them to the world of technology and design in their everyday life is one way to help answer this question. It is also why so many state science curricula are now emphasizing technology and design concepts and skills.

Science Explorer makes a special effort to include a technology and design strand that encourages students to not only identify a need but to take what they learned in science and apply it to design a possible solution, build a prototype, test and evaluate the design, and/or troubleshoot the design. This strand also provides definitions of technology and engineering and discusses the similarities and differences between these endeavors and science. Students will learn to analyze the risks and benefits of a new technology and to consider the tradeoffs, such as safety, costs, efficiency, and appearance.

In the Student Edition

Integrated Technology & Design Sections

Sections throughout *Science Explorer* specifically integrate technology and design with the content of the text. For example, students not only learn how seismographs work but also learn what role seismographs play in society and how people use the data that are gathered.

Technology Labs

These labs help students gain experience in designing and building a device or product that meets a particular need or solves a problem. Students follow a design process of Research and Investigate, Design and Build, and Evaluate and Redesign.

Chapter Projects

Chapter Projects work hand-in-hand with the chapter content. Students design, build, and test based on real-world situations. They have the opportunity to apply the knowledge and skills learned to building a product.

Special Features

This technology and design strand is also reflected in Technology & Society and Science & Society features as well as Technology & History timelines. These highly visual features introduce a technology and its impact on society. For example, students learn how a hybrid car differs from a traditional car.

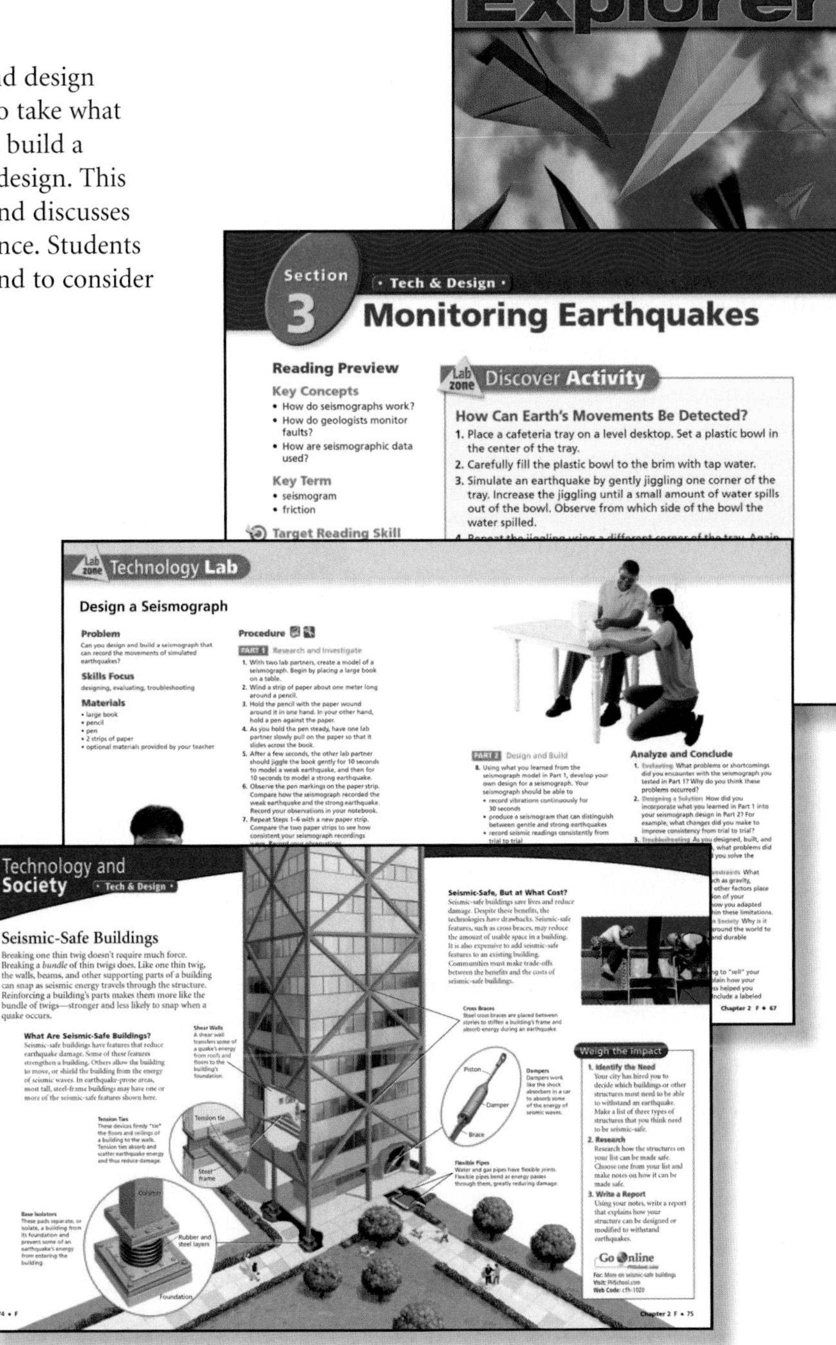

Assessment

Assessment in the Science Curriculum

No Child Left Behind clearly challenges school districts across the nation to raise expectations for all students with testing of student achievement in science beginning in 2007–2008.

A primary goal of NCLB is to provide classroom teachers with better data from scientifically valid assessments in order to inform instructional planning and to identify students who are at risk and require intervention. It has been a common practice to teach a science lesson, administer a test, grade it, and move on. This practice is a thing of the past. With the spotlight now on improving student performance, it is essential to use assessment results as a way to identify student strengths and challenges. Providing student feedback and obtaining student input is a valuable, essential part of the assessment process.

Assessment is a never-ending cycle, as is shown in the following diagram. Although you may begin at any point in the assessment cycle, the basic process is the same.

An important assessment strategy is to ensure that students have ample opportunities to check their understanding of skills and concepts before moving on to the next topic. Checking for understanding also includes asking appropriate, probing questions with each example presented. This enables students and teachers to know whether the skills or concepts being introduced are actually understood.

ASSESS: Use a variety of assessment tools to gain information and strengthen student understanding.

ANALYZE: Analyze assessment results to create a picture of student strengths and challenges.

TARGET: Choose a target to create a focused path on which to proceed.

STRATEGIZE: Identify strategies to achieve the target, create a plan for implementation, and choose assessments tools.

IMPLEMENT: Implement the plan with a focus on gathering and using assessment information throughout.

Eileen Depka
Supervisor of Standards and Assessment
Waukesha, Wisconsin

"Meeting the NCLB challenge will necessitate an integrated approach to assessment with a variety of assessment tools."

Evaluator's Checklist

Does your science program include assessments that—

- ✔ Are embedded before, during, and after lesson instruction
- ✔ Align to standards and to the instructional program
- ✔ Assess both skill acquisition and understanding
- ✔ Include meaningful rubrics to guide students
- ✔ Mirror the various formats of standardized tests

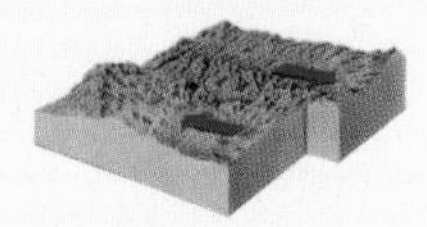

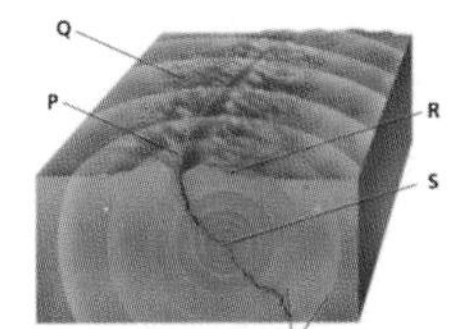

Assessment in *Science Explorer*

Science Explorer's remarkable range of strategies for checking progress will help teachers find the right opportunity for reaching all their students.

The assessment strategies in *Science Explorer* will help both students and teachers alike ensure student success in content mastery as well as high-stakes test performance. A wealth of opportunities built into the Student Edition help students monitor their own progress. Teachers are supported with ongoing assessment opportunities in the Teacher's Edition and an easy-to-use, editable test generator linked to content objectives. These integrated, ongoing assessment tools assure success.

Especially to support state and national testing objectives, Prentice Hall has developed test preparation materials that model the NCLB approach.

- **Diagnostic Assessment** tools provide in-depth analysis of strengths and weaknesses, areas of difficulty, and probable underlying causes that can help teachers make instructional decisions and plan intervention strategies.
- **Progress Monitoring** tools aligned with content objectives and state tests provide ongoing, longitudinal records of student achievement detailing individual student progress toward meeting end-of-year and end-of-schooling grade level, district, or state standards.
- **Outcomes** tools that mimic state and national tests show whether individual students have met the expected standards and can help a school system judge whether it has made adequate progress in improving its performance year by year.

Caption Questions enhance critical thinking skills

Reading Checkpoints reinforce students' understanding

Scaffolded Section Assessment Questions model the way students think

Comprehensive Chapter Reviews and Assessment provide opportunities for students to check their own understanding and practice valuable high-stakes test-taking skills

Exam*View*®, Computer Test Bank CD-ROM provides teachers access to thousands of modifiable test questions in English and Spanish

Test Preparation Blackline Masters and Student Workbook include diagnostic and prescription tools, progress-monitoring aids, and practice tests that help teachers focus on improving test scores.

Section 3 Assessment

Target Reading Skill Sequencing Refer to your flowchart about seismographs as you answer Question 1.

Reviewing Key Concepts

1. a. Defining What is a seismogram?
   b. Explaining How can geologists tell apart the different types of seismic waves on a seismogram?
   c. Comparing and Contrasting Two identical seismographs are located 1,000 km and 1,200 km from an earthquake's epicenter. How would the two seismograms for the earthquake compare?
2. a. Reviewing What changes are measured by the instruments used to monitor faults?
   b. Describing How are satellites used to measure movements along a fault?
   c. Inferring A satellite that monitors a fault detects an increasing tilt in the land surface along the fault. What could this change in the land surface indicate?
3. a. Listing What are three ways in which geologists use seismographic data?
   b. Explaining How do geologists use seismographic data to make maps of faults?
   c. Making Generalizations Why is it difficult to predict earthquakes?

Writing in Science

Dialogue Geologists in Alaska have just detected an earthquake and located the earthquake's epicenter. Write a dialogue in which the geologists notify a disaster response team that will help people in the earthquake area.

Chapter 2 F ◆ 65

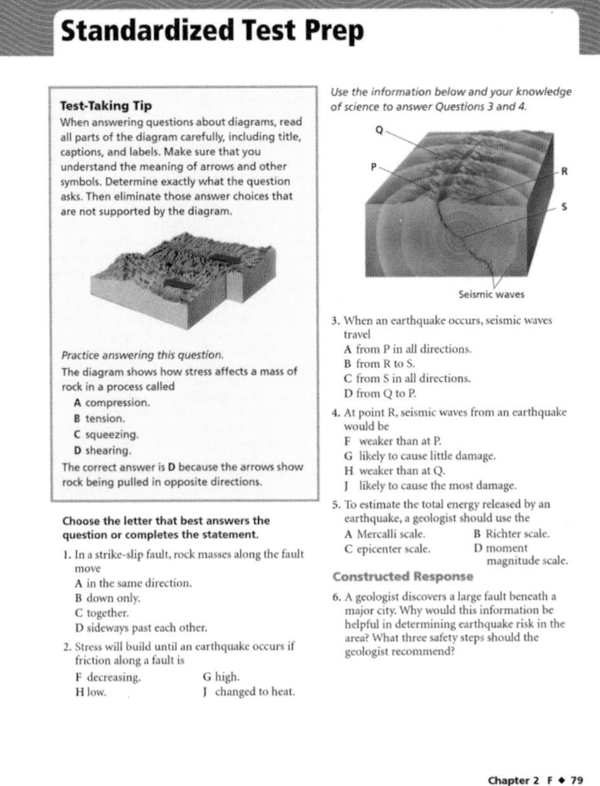

Standardized Test Prep

Test-Taking Tip
When answering questions about diagrams, read all parts of the diagram carefully, including title, captions, and labels. Make sure that you understand the meaning of arrows and other symbols. Determine exactly what the question asks. Then eliminate those answer choices that are not supported by the diagram.

Practice answering this question.
The diagram shows how stress affects a mass of rock in a process called
A compression.
B tension.
C squeezing.
D shearing.
The correct answer is D because the arrows show rock being pulled in opposite directions.

Choose the letter that best answers the question or completes the statement.

1. In a strike-slip fault, rock masses along the fault move
   A in the same direction.
   B down only.
   C together.
   D sideways past each other.
2. Stress will build until an earthquake occurs if friction along a fault is
   F decreasing. G high.
   H low. J changed to heat.

Use the information below and your knowledge of science to answer Questions 3 and 4.

3. When an earthquake occurs, seismic waves travel
   A from P in all directions.
   B from R to S.
   C from S in all directions.
   D from Q to P.
4. At point R, seismic waves from an earthquake would be
   F weaker than at P.
   G likely to cause little damage.
   H weaker than at Q.
   J likely to cause the most damage.
5. To estimate the total energy released by an earthquake, a geologist should use the
   A Mercalli scale. B Richter scale.
   C epicenter scale. D moment magnitude scale.

Constructed Response

6. A geologist discovers a large fault beneath a major city. Why would this information be helpful in determining earthquake risk in the area? What three safety steps should the geologist recommend?

Chapter 2 F ◆ 79

Master Materials List

SCIENCE EXPLORER offers an abundance of activity options in the Student Edition so you can pick and choose those that suit your needs. Prentice Hall has worked with Neo/SCI Corporation to develop Consumable Kits and Nonconsumable Kits that precisely match the needs of the ***SCIENCE EXPLORER*** labs. Use this Master Materials List or the Materials Ordering CD-ROM to help order your supplies. For more information on materials kits for this program, contact your local Prentice Hall sales representative or Neo/SCI Corporation at 1-800-526-6689 or **www.neosci.com**.

Consumable Materials

Description	Textbook Section(s)	Quantity per class
Agar, 0.5-ounce package	4-5(TT)	5
Aluminum foil, roll, 12" x 75"	2-1(Lab)	1
Bag, plastic, trash, large	2-2(DIS), 2-5(DIS)	10
Bag, sandwich, plastic, 4" x 6"	1-2(Lab)	15
Ball, Styrofoam, 2"	2-5(TT)	5
Balls	2-5(DIS)	5
*Bottle, plastic, 1-L	1-2(SA)	5
*Box, covered	4-1(DIS), 4-3(DIS)	10
*Can, empty	2-5(DIS)	5
Card, index, 3" x 5", blank	4-2(DIS)	30
*Carton, milk	4-2(TT)	5
Chalk, pkg/12	3-4(Lab)	1
Cheesecloth, squares, pkg	1-5(Lab)	1
Cork	2-5(DIS), 3-1(TT)	30
Cotton balls, pkg	4-5(Lab)	1
Cup, paper, 7 oz.	1-4(DIS), 2-2(Lab), 4-5(Lab)	30
Cup, plastic, 10 oz.	1-1(DIS), 1-1(TT), 1-2(SA), 2-4(SA), 3-4(DIS)	50
Dropper, plastic, pkg/10	1-1(DIS), 1-2(SA), 2-1(DIS), 4-5(Lab)	2
*Egg, whole, uncooked	3-3(DIS)	10
Feathers, pkg	4-5(Lab)	1
Fertilizer, liquid, 8 oz.	2-3(TT)	1
Filter, coffee	2-3(DIS)	5
Flour	4-4(DIS)	1
Food coloring, red, 30 mL	2-3(DIS), 3-4(Lab), 3-4(DIS), 4-5(TT)	1
Graph paper	4-1(Lab)	5
*Ice cubes, bag	1-2(DIS), 2-1(Lab), 3-3(Lab)	1
*Juice, fruit	4-5(TT)	1
*Labels, from household products	4-5(DIS)	15
*Leaves	1-2(Lab), 2-2(SA)	15
Lid, plastic, white	4-4(DIS)	5
Light-reflecting rheoscopic fluid, 400mL	3-4(Lab)	1
Marker, permanent, fine-point	1-3(SA), 2-3(DIS), 3-3(Lab), 3-4(Lab), 4-4(DIS), 4-5(Lab)	5
Modeling clay, white, 1 lb.	1-5(TT), 3-4(Lab)	1
*Newspaper	1-4(TT), 3-4(Lab)	5
Oil, vegetable, 16 oz.	1-1(DIS), 4-5(Lab)	1
Paper clip, pkg	4-4(DIS)	1
Paper, construction, blue, piece	3-4(Lab)	5
Paper, construction, red, piece	3-4(Lab)	5
*Paper towel, roll	1-1(DIS), 2-2(SA), 4-5(Lab)	1
Paper, wax, roll	1-1(DIS), 1-3(SA)	1
Pebbles, 2.75-lb. bag	1-2(Lab), 1-5(DIS), 1-5(Lab), 3-1(DIS)	1
*Pencil, unsharpened, with eraser	3-3(Lab), 4-1(Lab)	10
Pencil, wax	2-2(Lab)	5
pH paper, pkg/50	2-2(Lab)	1
pH color chart	2-2(Lab)	5
Plate, paper, 9"	2-3(DIS)	5
Plate, pie, aluminum, 9"	2-5(TT)	5
Pond culture, live, coupon for	1-3(DIS), 2-3(TT)	1
Potter's clay, powdered, pkg	1-5(Lab)	1
Salt, 737 g	2-1(Lab), 3-3(DIS), 3-3(Lab)	1
Sand, white, fine, 3 lb.	1-5(DIS), 1-5(TT), 1-5(Lab), 2-2(SA), 3-1(DIS), 3-1(SA)	1
Soap, liquid	2-2(Lab)	1
Soil, potting, 8 qt.	1-4(TT), 2-2(SA), 2-4(DIS)	1
Sponge	1-4(DIS), 1-4(TT), 2-3(DIS)	20
Spoon, plastic	2-1(DIS), 2-1(Lab), 2-4(DIS), 3-3(Lab)	20
*Sticks, wooden	4-5(Lab)	20
Straw, drinking	1-5(TT), 4-1(DIS)	60
Straw, drinking, jointed	3-4(Lab)	30

KEY: * = School Supplied

Quantities based on five groups of six students per class.

Master Materials List

Consumable Materials *(continued)*

Description	Textbook Section(s)	Quantity per class
String, roll	1-1(TT), 3-1(TT), 4-2(DIS), 4-4(DIS)	1
Sugar, 454 g	4-5(TT)	1
Tape, masking, roll	1-1(TT), 4-2(TT)	1
Thumbtack, pkg/100	3-3(Lab)	1
Tongue depressor	3-1(DIS)	5
Toothpick, pkg/250	2-5(TT)	1
Tube, plastic, 10 ft.	2-1(Lab), 2-2(TT)	5
Tubing, rubber, 250 cm	2-1(Lab)	1
Twist tie	1-2(Lab)	15
*Water, distilled	2-2(Lab)	1
*Water, mineral	2-2(Lab)	1
*Water, spring	2-2(Lab)	1
*Water, tap	2-2(Lab)	1

Nonconsumable Materials

Description	Textbook Section(s)	Quantity per class
Aquarium	3-1(TT)	5
*Balance	1-2(Lab), 3-3(Lab)	5
Ball, ping pong	4-3(DIS)	5
*Barrel, trash, large	2-2(DIS)	10
Basin	2-4(SA)	5
Beaker, 100-mL	1-5(Lab)	15
Beaker, 250-mL	2-1(Lab), 3-1(SA), 3-3(DIS), 2-2(Lab)	20
*Book	2-2(TT), 3-1(SA), 3-1(DIS)	15
Bowl, large	1-2(SA)	5
Bowl, small	2-1(DIS), 2-2(TT)	10
*Bucket, large, deep	4-4(DIS)	5
Container, plastic	3-4(DIS)	5
Coverslip, 1 oz.	1-3(DIS)	1
Flask, 500-mL	2-1(Lab)	5
Funnel	1-5(TT), 1-5(Lab), 2-4(SA)	15
*Glass, drinking	1-2(DIS)	5
*Graduated cylinder, 25-mL	2-2(Lab)	5
Graduated cylinder, 100-mL	4-5(Lab)	5
Graduated cylinder, 250-mL	1-2(SA), 3-3(Lab)	5
Hand lens	1-3(DIS), 1-5(Lab)	5
*Hole puncher	3-4(Lab)	5
*Hot plate	2-1(Lab), 2-2(Lab)	5
Jar, glass with lid	1-5(DIS), 2-2(SA), 2-3(TT)	10
Lamp	2-4(DIS)	5
Marble, 1/2"	2-5(DIS)	5
Measuring cup, 500-mL	2-1(DIS)	5
Meter stick	4-4(DIS)	5
*Microscope	1-3(DIS)	5
Microscope slides, pkg/72	1-3(DIS)	1
*Object, mystery	4-1(DIS)	5
Pan, loaf, aluminum	1-4(TT), 1-5(TT)	5
Pan, rectangular, baking, aluminum	1-4(DIS), 2-1(Lab), 2-4(DIS), 3-1(DIS), 3-1(SA), 3-4(Lab), 4-5(TT), 4-5(Lab)	20
*Pen, ball-point	4-2(TT)	5
Pitcher, large, with cover	1-1(TT), 2-2(DIS), 4-3(DIS)	5
Rack, test tube	2-2(Lab)	5
*Rock	4-3(DIS)	5
Rod, stirring	2-1(Lab), 3-3(DIS), 3-4(DIS), 4-5(TT)	5
Rubber band, assorted, pkg	1-5(Lab)	1
Rubber stopper	2-1(Lab)	5
Ruler, 15-cm	1-1(DIS), 2-2(Lab), 2-4(DIS), 3-3(Lab), 3-4(Lab)	5
*Saucepan	4-5(TT)	5
*Scissors	2-5(TT), 4-4(DIS)	5
Spool, wooden	2-5(DIS)	5
Spray bottle, with nozzle, 16-oz.	2-5(DIS)	5
*Stopwatch	1-5(Lab), 2-1(DIS)	5
Test tube with stopper	2-2(Lab)	20
Thermometer	3-3(Lab)	5
Washer, metal	3-1(TT)	75
Watering can	1-4(TT)	5

KEY: * = School Supplied

Quantities based on five groups of six students per class.

Earth's Waters

Book-Specific Resources

Student Edition
Interactive Textbook
Teacher's Edition
All-in-One Teaching Resources
Color Transparencies
Guided Reading and Study Workbook
Student Edition on Audio CD
Discovery Channel Video
Lab Activity Video
Consumable and Nonconsumable Materials Kits

Program Print Resources

Integrated Science Laboratory Manual
Computer Microscope Lab Manual
Inquiry Skills Activity Books
Progress Monitoring Assessments
Test Preparation Workbook
Test-Taking Tips With Transparencies
Teacher's ELL Handbook
Reading in the Content Area

Program Technology Resources

TeacherExpress™ CD-ROM
Interactive Textbook
Presentation Pro CD-ROM
ExamView®, Computer Test Bank CD-ROM
Lab zone™ Easy Planner CD-ROM
Probeware Lab Manual With CD-ROM
Computer Microscope and Lab Manual
Materials Ordering CD-ROM
Discovery Channel DVD Library
Lab Activity DVD Library
Web Site at PHSchool.com

Spanish Print Resources

Spanish Student Edition
Spanish Guided Reading and Study Workbook
Spanish Teaching Guide With Tests

Acknowledgments appear on page 214, which constitutes an extension of this copyright page.

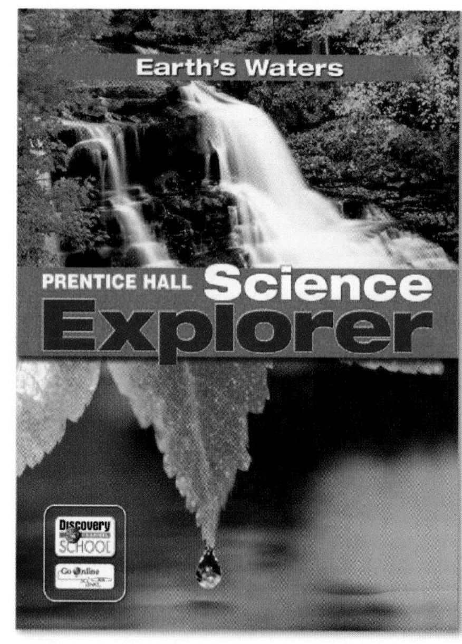

Cover
Brandywine Falls cascades down a rocky slope in Ohio (top). A water droplet falls from a maple leaf (bottom).

ISBN 0-13-115093-6
2 3 4 5 6 7 8 9 10 08 07 06 05 04

Program Authors

Michael J. Padilla, Ph.D.
Professor of Science Education
University of Georgia
Athens, Georgia

Michael Padilla is a leader in middle school science education. He has served as an author and elected officer for the National Science Teachers Association and as a writer of the National Science Education Standards. As lead author of Science Explorer, Mike has inspired the team in developing a program that meets the needs of middle grades students, promotes science inquiry, and is aligned with the National Science Education Standards.

Ioannis Miaoulis, Ph.D.
President
Museum of Science
Boston, Massachusetts

Originally trained as a mechanical engineer, Ioannis Miaoulis is in the forefront of the national movement to increase technological literacy. As dean of the Tufts University School of Engineering, Dr. Miaoulis spearheaded the introduction of engineering into the Massachusetts curriculum. Currently he is working with school systems across the country to engage students in engineering activities and to foster discussions on the impact of science and technology on society.

Martha Cyr, Ph.D.
Director of K–12 Outreach
Worcester Polytechnic Institute
Worcester, Massachusetts

Martha Cyr is a noted expert in engineering outreach. She has over nine years of experience with programs and activities that emphasize the use of engineering principles, through hands-on projects, to excite and motivate students and teachers of mathematics and science in grades K–12. Her goal is to stimulate a continued interest in science and mathematics through engineering.

Book Authors

Jan Jenner, Ph.D.
Science Writer
Talladega, Alabama

Thomas R. Wellnitz
Science Instructor
The Paideia School
Atlanta, Georgia

Contributing Writers

Jeffrey C. Callister
Former Earth Science Instructor
Newburgh Free Academy
Newburgh, New York

Barbara Brooks Simons
Science Writer
Boston, Massachusetts

Consultants

Reading Consultant

Nancy Romance, Ph.D.
Professor of Science Education
Florida Atlantic University
Fort Lauderdale, Florida

Mathematics Consultant

William Tate, Ph.D.
Professor of Education and Applied Statistics and Computation
Washington University
St. Louis, Missouri

H • iii

Reviewers

Tufts University Content Reviewers

Faculty from Tufts University in Medford, Massachusetts, developed *Science Explorer* chapter projects and reviewed the student books.

Astier M. Almedom, Ph.D.
Department of Biology

Wayne Chudyk, Ph.D.
Department of Civil and Environmental Engineering

John L. Durant, Ph.D.
Department of Civil and Environmental Engineering

George S. Ellmore, Ph.D.
Department of Biology

David Kaplan, Ph.D.
Department of Biomedical Engineering

Samuel Kounaves, Ph.D.
Department of Chemistry

David H. Lee, Ph.D.
Department of Chemistry

Douglas Matson, Ph.D.
Department of Mechanical Engineering

Karen Panetta, Ph.D.
Department of Electrical Engineering and Computer Science

Jan A. Pechenik, Ph.D.
Department of Biology

John C. Ridge, Ph.D.
Department of Geology

William Waller, Ph.D.
Department of Astronomy

Content Reviewers

Paul Beale, Ph.D.
Department of Physics
University of Colorado
Boulder, Colorado

Jeff Bodart, Ph.D.
Chipola Junior College
Marianna, Florida

Michael Castellani, Ph.D.
Department of Chemistry
Marshall University
Huntington, West Virginia

Eugene Chiang, Ph.D.
Department of Astronomy
University of California – Berkeley
Berkeley, California

Charles C. Curtis, Ph.D.
Department of Physics
University of Arizona
Tucson, Arizona

Daniel Kirk-Davidoff, Ph.D.
Department of Meteorology
University of Maryland
College Park, Maryland

Diane T. Doser, Ph.D.
Department of Geological Sciences
University of Texas at El Paso
El Paso, Texas

R. E. Duhrkopf, Ph.D.
Department of Biology
Baylor University
Waco, Texas

Michael Hacker
Co-director, Center for Technological Literacy
Hofstra University
Hempstead, New York

Michael W. Hamburger, Ph.D.
Department of Geological Sciences
Indiana University
Bloomington, Indiana

Alice K. Hankla, Ph.D.
The Galloway School
Atlanta, Georgia

Donald C. Jackson, Ph.D.
Department of Molecular Pharmacology, Physiology, & Biotechnology
Brown University
Providence, Rhode Island

Jeremiah N. Jarrett, Ph.D.
Department of Biological Sciences
Central Connecticut State University
New Britain, Connecticut

David Lederman, Ph.D.
Department of Physics
West Virginia University
Morgantown, West Virginia

Becky Mansfield, Ph.D.
Department of Geography
Ohio State University
Columbus, Ohio

Elizabeth M. Martin, M.S.
Department of Chemistry and Biochemistry
College of Charleston
Charleston, South Carolina

Joe McCullough, Ph.D.
Department of Natural and Applied Sciences
Cabrillo College
Aptos, California

Robert J. Mellors, Ph.D.
Department of Geological Sciences
San Diego State University
San Diego, California

Joseph M. Moran, Ph.D.
American Meteorological Society
Washington, D.C.

David J. Morrissey, Ph.D.
Department of Chemistry
Michigan State University
East Lansing, Michigan

Philip A. Reed, Ph.D.
Department of Occupational & Technical Studies
Old Dominion University
Norfolk, Virginia

Scott M. Rochette, Ph.D.
Department of the Earth Sciences
State University of New York, College at Brockport
Brockport, New York

Laurence D. Rosenhein, Ph.D.
Department of Chemistry
Indiana State University
Terre Haute, Indiana

Ronald Sass, Ph.D.
Department of Biology and Chemistry
Rice University
Houston, Texas

George Schatz, Ph.D.
Department of Chemistry
Northwestern University
Evanston, Illinois

Sara Seager, Ph.D.
Carnegie Institution of Washington
Washington, D.C.

Robert M. Thornton, Ph.D.
Department of Biology
University of California
Davis, California

John R. Villarreal, Ph.D.
College of Science and Engineering
The University of Texas – Pan American
Edinburg, Texas

Kenneth Welty, Ph.D.
School of Education
University of Wisconsin–Stout
Stout, Wisconsin

Edward J. Zalisko, Ph.D.
Department of Biology
Blackburn College
Carlinville, Illinois

iv ◆ H

Teacher Reviewers

David R. Blakely
Arlington High School
Arlington, Massachusetts

Jane E. Callery
Two Rivers Magnet Middle School
East Hartford, Connecticut

Melissa Lynn Cook
Oakland Mills High School
Columbia, Maryland

James Fattic
Southside Middle School
Anderson, Indiana

Dan Gabel
Hoover Middle School
Rockville, Maryland

Wayne Goates
Eisenhower Middle School
Goddard, Kansas

Katherine Bobay Graser
Mint Hill Middle School
Charlotte, North Carolina

Darcy Hampton
Deal Junior High School
Washington, D.C.

Karen Kelly
Pierce Middle School
Waterford, Michigan

David Kelso
Manchester High School Central
Manchester, New Hampshire

Benigno Lopez, Jr.
Sleepy Hill Middle School
Lakeland, Florida

Angie L. Matamoros, Ph.D.
ALM Consulting, Inc.
Weston, Florida

Tim McCollum
Charleston Middle School
Charleston, Illinois

Bruce A. Mellin
Brooks School
North Andover, Massachusetts

Ella Jay Parfitt
Southeast Middle School
Baltimore, Maryland

Evelyn A. Pizzarello
Louis M. Klein Middle School
Harrison, New York

Kathleen M. Poe
Fletcher Middle School
Jacksonville, Florida

Shirley Rose
Lewis and Clark Middle School
Tulsa, Oklahoma

Linda Sandersen
Greenfield Middle School
Greenfield, Wisconsin

Mary E. Solan
Southwest Middle School
Charlotte, North Carolina

Mary Stewart
University of Tulsa
Tulsa, Oklahoma

Paul Swenson
Billings West High School
Billings, Montana

Thomas Vaughn
Arlington High School
Arlington, Massachusetts

Susan C. Zibell
Central Elementary
Simsbury, Connecticut

Safety Reviewers

W. H. Breazeale, Ph.D.
Department of Chemistry
College of Charleston
Charleston, South Carolina

Ruth Hathaway, Ph.D.
Hathaway Consulting
Cape Girardeau, Missouri

Douglas Mandt, M.S.
Science Education Consultant
Edgewood, Washington

Activity Field Testers

Nicki Bibbo
Witchcraft Heights School
Salem, Massachusetts

Rose-Marie Botting
Broward County Schools
Fort Lauderdale, Florida

Colleen Campos
Laredo Middle School
Aurora, Colorado

Elizabeth Chait
W. L. Chenery Middle School
Belmont, Massachusetts

Holly Estes
Hale Middle School
Stow, Massachusetts

Laura Hapgood
Plymouth Community Intermediate School
Plymouth, Massachusetts

Mary F. Lavin
Plymouth Community Intermediate School
Plymouth, Massachusetts

James MacNeil, Ph.D.
Cambridge, Massachusetts

Lauren Magruder
St. Michael's Country Day School
Newport, Rhode Island

Jeanne Maurand
Austin Preparatory School
Reading, Massachusetts

Joanne Jackson-Pelletier
Winman Junior High School
Warwick, Rhode Island

Warren Phillips
Plymouth Public Schools
Plymouth, Massachusetts

Carol Pirtle
Hale Middle School
Stow, Massachusetts

Kathleen M. Poe
Fletcher Middle School
Jacksonville, Florida

Cynthia B. Pope
Norfolk Public Schools
Norfolk, Virginia

Anne Scammell
Geneva Middle School
Geneva, New York

Karen Riley Sievers
Callanan Middle School
Des Moines, Iowa

David M. Smith
Eyer Middle School
Allentown, Pennsylvania

Gene Vitale
Parkland School
McHenry, Illinois

H • v

Contents

Earth's Waters

vi ◆ H

Reference Section

VIDEO

Enhance understanding through dynamic video.

Preview Get motivated with this introduction to the chapter content.

Field Trip Explore a real-world story related to the chapter content.

Assessment Review content and take an assessment.

Get connected to exciting Web resources in every lesson.

SCI LINKS NSTA Find Web links on topics relating to every section.

Active Art Interact with selected visuals from every chapter online.

Planet Diary® Explore news and natural phenomena through weekly reports.

Science News® Keep up to date with the latest science discoveries.

Experience the complete textbook online and on CD-ROM.

Activities Practice skills and learn content.

Videos Explore content and learn important lab skills.

Audio Support Hear key terms spoken and defined.

Self-Assessment Use instant feedback to help you track your progress.

H • vii

Activities

Lab zone™ Chapter Project — Opportunities for long-term inquiry

Lab zone Discover Activity — Exploration and inquiry before reading

Lab zone Try This Activity — Reinforcement of key concepts

Lab zone Skills Activity — Practice of specific science inquiry skills

viii ◆ H

Labs — In-depth practice of inquiry skills and science concepts

At-Home Activity — Quick, engaging activities for home and family

• Tech & Design • Design, build, test, and communicate

Math — Point-of-use math practice

active art — Illustrations come alive online

H • ix

Careers in Science

Through the Lens of an Ocean Scientist

Inquiry and Ocean Science

Marine biologist Norbert Wu photographs marine life all over the world. This article shows how he uses inquiry skills such as observing, inferring, and communicating in his work. Although ocean life is discussed elsewhere in this book, students need not have previous knowledge of this topic to understand this real-world application of scientific inquiry.

Build Background Knowledge

Recalling experiences with cold water

Remind students that swimming in cold water can be uncomfortable. Ask: **How did you feel when you entered the water?** *(Cold, shocked)* **Why?** *(Heat was transferred from my body to the water.)* **How can divers swim in the frigid water near Antarctica?** *(Polar divers wear diving suits that keep them dry; warm clothing worn under the suits retain body heat.)*

Introduce the Career

Before students read the feature, let them read the title, examine the pictures, and read the captions on their own. Then ask: **What questions came into your mind as you looked at these pictures?** *(Students might suggest questions like these: "What types of animals live in ocean waters near Antarctica?" "Why do so many fish swim near seamounts?" and "Why do anglefish clean manta rays?")* Point out to students that just as they have questions about what they are seeing, scientists too have questions about what they observe.

Careers in **Science**

Through the Lens of an Ocean Scientist

Norbert Wu dives for his photographs. (He took all the photographs in this feature.) A trained marine biologist, he roams the underwater world looking for the perfect shot. "Photography has become a way of life for me," Norbert says. "At my best, I am both a scientist and an artist. Photographing new life forms and learning about the connections between different species makes my work a blend of science and art. Taking an in-depth look at the habits and behavior of marine life has become my specialty."

Norbert has followed the trail of manta rays slowly circling the top of an undersea mountain off the Mexican coast. He's photographed octopuses and snails on coral reefs. He's swum with jellyfish in the Antarctic Ocean.

"I went as far south as you can go and still have ocean," Norbert says. "And I fell in love with Antarctica. When you first get there at the beginning of the Antarctic spring, the water is clearer than anywhere in the world. It's really the last untouched place on Earth. That's what draws me back.

In Antarctica, a diver glides toward a jellyfish.

Talking With Norbert Wu

What protects divers from the cold?

Underwater photography in polar seas is a challenge. For one thing, it's very cold. In Antarctica, scientists used to wear wet suits—suits that allow a thin layer of water to touch the skin. Now divers use dry suits, which are waterproof and sealed at the neck and wrists. You can wear long underwear or polyester fleece underneath. Dry suits make polar diving bearable, but it's never very pleasant.

Background

History of Science In 1902, Willy Heinrich became the first person to dive in Antarctica and the first person to dive beneath Antarctic ice. Heinrich served on a German research vessel named the *Gauss,* which was commanded by Erich von Drygalski. After the ship became temporarily frozen in pack ice, Heinrich dove several times to make repairs. He also made observations about the underside of the pack ice. Diving in the Antarctic for solely scientific purposes did not occur until more than 50 years later.

Norbert is shown below with his dogs Ange, a labrador, and Sam, a golden retriever.

Career Path

Norbert Wu attended Stanford University in California, where he received a bachelor's degree and master's degree in electrical and mechanical engineering. He then returned to the subject he loved in high school—marine biology. He attended graduate school at Scripps Institution of Oceanography in San Diego. In 1999, Norbert received a Pew Marine Conservation Fellowship to photograph threatened underwater habitats.

How did you become an underwater photographer?

After college, I decided to pursue a career in marine biology. I got a job with a scientist working off the San Blas Islands near Panama. I counted sea urchins and measured coral growth. Before the trip, I'd never had any interest in photography. But I brought along books on photography, as well as an underwater flash and camera system.

My career didn't happen overnight. I returned to California to continue graduate school in marine biology. I sold some photographs taken at San Blas and gradually my career in photography just took over.

How do you locate ocean organisms?

You learn the places in the world where particular ocean organisms are found. In the waters of Antarctica, you find seals, penguins, and jellyfish. Squid come up in the waters off California at certain times of the year. Local guides can also put you exactly on the right site to locate ocean organisms.

If you dive a reef every day, you get to know the organisms that live there. During the months I spent on the San Blas Islands, I was able to return again and again to photograph an octopus or a flamingo tongue snail. Being able to spend weeks, rather than a few weekends, makes a big difference in the photographs.

Explore the Career

Choose from among the teaching strategies on these pages as you help your students explore the practical application of inquiry skills in the real world.

Help Students Read

Preview Before students read the feature, ask them to preview the headings. Make certain that students understand that the headings are questions and that what follows each heading is an answer. Ask: **Who answered the questions?** *(Norbert Wu)*

Use Maps Have students identify Antarctica on a map. Explain that the continent is almost entirely covered by glaciers. Show students the shelves of glacier ice that extend over the sea at some places. Also indicate areas where open water exists, especially during the Antarctic summer. Ask: **Why might Norbert Wu and other ocean scientists enjoy diving here?** *(The region is pristine and beautiful. The oceans are not well explored, and many organisms have yet to be described and photographed.)*

Build Inquiry Skills Tell students that they have been hired as scientists on a marine research vessel. Their job is to describe marine life and understand how marine organisms interact with their environment. Challenge each student to develop a research plan that is designed to accomplish these goals. After students have finished their plans, work as a class to summarize their ideas.

Background

Facts and Figures Coral reefs are the most diverse habitat in the oceans. In addition to the coral, soft coral, algae, and other organisms that are anchored to the reef, a variety of swimming organisms, such as fish and turtles, feed around the reef. The warm, shallow water in which reefs grow is ideal for diving and studying animals. Although most reefs are well explored, much remains to be learned about these complex ecosystems.

Research Have students research mutualism, the mutually beneficial relationship between two species. Ask: **How do manta rays benefit from the activities of the clarion angelfish?** *(The fish remove parasites from the manta rays.)* **How do the angelfish benefit?** *(The parasites on the manta rays are a source of food for the angelfish.)* Have students identify other examples of mutualism.

Show Examples Gather a collection of photographs of marine organisms in their natural habitats, or ask students to collect the photos. Have students examine each photograph and speculate about how it was taken. Ask: **Why are these photographs important?** *(People can observe organisms that they otherwise might never see; scientists can study organisms and habitats in still photos; the photos provide a visual record of marine life.)*

Use Maps On a map, show students the location of Cocos Island. Tell them that this region is a protected marine park and has been designated a UNESCO (United Nations Educational, Scientific and Cultural Organization) World Natural Heritage Site.

How is your science background useful?

You need to know how ocean animals behave and how different animals interact with each other. I've taken pictures of manta rays coming to a seamount to be cleaned of parasites by bright orange clarion angelfish. Parasites are small organisms that live on and can harm another organism like a manta ray. As the manta rays swoop past the seamount, the angelfish come out from their shelter, dance about, and flash their bright orange bodies as if signaling their arrival. The manta rays may pause and allow the angelfish to go all about their bodies, picking off parasites.

Why are you interested in an animal's behavior?

Understanding an ocean animal's behavior and its reactions is essential just to get near enough for a picture. Because of the limited visibility underwater, I am usually close to my subjects—often no more than a meter away. As a diver, the noise of your bubbles tells animals you're there. So an underwater photographer must move slowly and act in ways that won't threaten or frighten animals.

What do you do on a typical diving trip?

Most of my diving trips last two to three weeks. Once I'm there, almost all my time is on a boat or getting ready to go underwater. My next trip is to Cocos Island, in Costa Rica, where I will photograph seamounts. Seamounts are undersea mountain tops that serve as gathering places for marine life. They attract some of the ocean's largest and most exciting animals.

Seamounts form in areas of volcanic action, where the ocean floor abruptly rises to the surface. These volcanic hot spots can be close to the coast or hundreds of miles offshore. In the Cocos, there are a lot of sharks to photograph—hammerheads and white-tipped reef sharks as well as manta rays and snappers.

Schooling snappers and blue-striped snappers swim around a seamount off the Cocos Island in the Pacific Ocean.

Background

Facts and Figures Seamounts are mountains on the ocean floor that do not extend above water level. Most seamounts form at hot spots, regions within a tectonic plate where magma melts through the crust above it. Because of seafloor spreading, seamounts can be carried away from a hot spot after they form. If a volcanic island is carried away from a hot spot, it might sink below sea level to form a flat-topped, wave-cut seamount called a guyot.

Clarion angelfish clean manta rays near a seamount off the coast of Mexico.

What new technology do you use in your work?

Two new technologies have made a big difference—closed-circuit rebreathers and digital cameras. A rebreather recycles your exhaled breath in a closed loop, so you can breathe the unused oxygen you took in during earlier breaths. You can get up to twelve hours on one tank of oxygen. If you can breathe an oxygen-rich mixture in the ocean, you can stay deeper, longer.

With digital cameras, I can also stay down a long time without running out of film. I can put a memory card in the camera and take 300 or 500 exposures. (A large roll of film takes just 36 exposures.)

What would you tell students?

I've talked to young people a good deal. I'm amazed at how much they know about the world and the environment. I'd tell students that any subject you're passionate about is going to lead to good things. I'm very lucky. I've been able to combine a lot of things I love into my career—biology and diving and photography.

◄ Norbert on Antarctic ice

Writing in Science

Career Link For Norbert, one key to taking great scientific photographs is being at the right place at the right time. To do that, he says you need "an understanding of your subject's behavior." Choose an animal you know. In a paragraph, describe the right time and place to take a good photograph of that animal. Explain your choice.

For: More on this career
Visit: PHSchool.com
Web Code: cfb-3000

Show Examples Bring a digital camera to class. Allow students to examine the memory card, and explain that photographic data are stored on the card. Ask: **How are digital cameras different from film cameras?** *(Data are stored digitally in a digital camera. An image does not exist inside the camera. In an ordinary camera, film is exposed to light to form an image.)*

Discuss Refer students to Norbert Wu's remarks about pursuing a career about which one is passionate. Ask: **What topics are you passionate about? Do you think that you will pursue a career that will allow you to enjoy your passion? How can you prepare for this career while you are in school?** Remind students that with hard work and determination, most goals are attainable.

Writing in Science

Writing Skill Exposition

Scoring Rubric

4 Exceeds expectations by writing a paragraph describing the right time and place to photograph an animal and explaining how this choice relates to the animal's behavior; includes thoughtful cause-and-effect reasoning

3 Meets expectations by writing a paragraph that satisfies the criteria

2 Writes a paragraph that contains minor errors of reasoning

1 Writes a paragraph that is incomplete or that contains major errors

Go Online PHSchool.com

For: More on this career
Visit: PHSchool.com
Web Code: cfb-3000

Students can research this career and others that are related to the subject of ocean science.

Chapter at a Glance

PRENTICE HALL TeacherEXPRESS™ Plan • Teach • Assess

Lab zone Chapter Project *Every Drop Counts*

Technology | **Local Standards**

All in One Teaching Resources

- Chapter Project Teacher Notes, pp. 38–39
- Chapter Project Student Introduction, pp. 40–41
- Chapter Project Student Worksheets, pp. 42–43
- Chapter Project Scoring Rubric, p. 44

The Properties of Water

1–2 periods
1/2–1 block

H.1.1.1 Describe how the chemical structure of water molecules causes them to stick together.

H.1.1.2 Describe some of water's unusual properties.

H.1.1.3 Identify the three states in which water exists on Earth.

Water on Earth

2–3 periods
1–1 1/2 blocks

H.1.2.1 State how people and other living things use water.

H.1.2.2 Describe how Earth's water is distributed.

H.1.2.3 Explain how Earth's water moves through the water cycle.

Surface Water

2–3 periods
1–1 1/2 blocks

H.1.3.1 Tell what a river system is.

H.1.3.2 Explain how ponds and lakes form.

H.1.3.3 Describe the changes that occur in ponds and lakes.

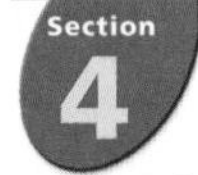

Wetland Environments

1–2 periods
1/2–1 block

H.1.4.1 Describe the common types of freshwater wetlands.

H.1.4.2 Identify human activities that threaten the Florida Everglades.

H.1.4.3 Explain important functions that wetlands serve.

Water Underground

3–4 periods
1–2 blocks

H.1.5.1 Describe how water moves through underground layers of soil and rock.

H.1.5.2 Explain how people obtain water from an aquifer.

Review and Assessment

All in One Teaching Resources

- Key Terms Review, p. 89
- Transparency H14
- Performance Assessment Teacher Notes, p. 96
- Performance Assessment Scoring Rubric, p. 97
- Performance Assessment Student Worksheet, p. 98
- Chapter Test, pp. 99–101

Test Preparation

Test Preparation Blackline Masters

Chapter Activities Planner

For more activities

Student Edition	Inquiry	Time	Materials	Skills	Resources
Chapter Project, p. 5	Open-Ended	Ongoing (2 weeks)	All in One **Teaching Resources** See p. 38.	Calculating, creating data tables	**Lab zone Easy Planner** All in One **Teaching Resources** Support pp. 38–39
Section 1					
Discover Activity, p. 6	Guided	15 minutes	Water, 2 plastic cups, vegetable oil, paper towel, scissors, meter stick, 2 pieces of wax paper, 2 plastic droppers	Observing	**Lab zone Easy Planner**
Try This Activity, p. 9	Guided	20 minutes	String, scissors, water, pitcher, plastic cup, tape	Inferring	**Lab zone Easy Planner**
Section 2					
Discover Activity, p. 12	Guided	10 minutes	Ice water, pitcher, clear drinking glass	Inferring	**Lab zone Easy Planner**
Skills Activity, p. 14	Guided	30 minutes	Water, 1-liter clear plastic bottle, large bowl, 5 plastic cups, graduated cylinder, calculator, dropper	Calculating	**Lab zone Easy Planner**
Skills Lab, p. 18	Guided	40 minutes	3 plastic sandwich bags, balance, 3 small pebbles, 3 twist ties	Observing, calculating, inferring	**Lab zone Easy Planner** **Lab Activity Video** Skills Lab: *Water From Trees,* pp. 62–63
Section 3					
Discover Activity, p. 19	Open-Ended	20 minutes	Pond water, plastic petri dish, hand lens, microscope, plastic dropper, slide, coverslip	Classifying	**Lab zone Easy Planner**
Skills Activity, p. 21	Open-Ended	10 minutes	No special materials are required.	Inferring	**Lab zone Easy Planner**
Skills Activity, p. 24	Guided	10 minutes	Wax paper, permanent marker, water	Classifying	**Lab zone Easy Planner**
Section 4					
Discover Activity, p. 28	Guided	15 minutes	2 dry kitchen sponges, water, pan, 2 paper clips	Observing	**Lab zone Easy Planner**
Try This Activity, p. 32	Guided	20 minutes	Newspaper, loaf pan, damp soil, water, watering can, sponge	Observing	**Lab zone Easy Planner**
Section 5					
Discover Activity, p. 34	Guided	10 minutes	Pebbles, clear jar, ruler, dry sand, water	Observing	**Lab zone Easy Planner**
Try This Activity, p. 38	Guided	20 minutes	Newspaper, loaf pan, modeling clay, moist sand, funnel, plastic straw, scissors, water	Making models	**Lab zone Easy Planner**
Design Your Own Lab, pp. 40–41	Part 1: Guided; Part 2: Open-Ended	40 minutes	Hand lens, 100 mL of sand, stopwatch, 3 rubber bands, 3 100-mL beakers, 300 mL of water, 100 mL of pebbles, 100 mL of powdered potter's clay, 3 squares of cheesecloth, 3 large funnels	Observing, developing hypotheses, designing experiments	**Lab zone Easy Planner** **Lab Activity Video** All in One **Teaching Resources** Design Your Own Lab: *Soil Testing,* pp. 86–88

Section 1 The Properties of Water

 *1–2 periods, 1/2–1 block*

ABILITY LEVELS
L1 Basic to Average
L2 For All Students
L3 Average to Advanced

Objectives

H.1.1.1 Describe how the chemical structure of water molecules causes them to stick together.

H.1.1.2 Describe some of water's unusual properties.

H.1.1.3 Identify the three states in which water exists on Earth.

Local Standards

Key Terms

• polar molecule • capillary action • surface tension • solution • solvent • specific heat • evaporation • condensation

Preteach

Build Background Knowledge

Show a glass of liquid water containing ice, and relate that to the states of water and why ice floats.

 *What Are Some Properties of Water?* L1

Targeted Print and Technology Resources

All in One Teaching Resources

L2 Reading Strategy: Building Vocabulary

Presentation-Pro CD-ROM

Instruct

The Structure of Water Use an illustration to analyze how the charges on water molecules attract one another to stick together.

Key Properties of Water Relate the polarity of water to why water dissolves other substances.

Changing State Use labeled diagrams to identify and explain the differences in the three states of water.

Targeted Print and Technology Resources

All in One Teaching Resources

L2 Guided Reading, pp. 47–50

L2 Transparencies H1, H2, H3

www.SciLinks.org Web Code: scn-0811

Student Edition on Audio CD

Assess

Section Assessment Questions

Have students use their definitions of key terms to answer the questions.

Reteach

Use illustrations to relate the structure of water to its properties and changes of state.

Targeted Print and Technology Resources

All in One Teaching Resources

• Section Summary, p. 46

L1 Review and Reinforce, p. 51

L3 Enrich, p. 52

Section 2 Water on Earth

 *2–3 periods, 1–1 1/2 blocks*

ABILITY LEVELS
L1 Basic to Average
L2 For All Students
L3 Average to Advanced

Objectives

H.1.2.1 State how people and other living things use water.
H.1.2.2 Describe how Earth's water is distributed.
H.1.2.3 Explain how Earth's water moves through the water cycle.

Key Terms

• photosynthesis • habitat • groundwater • water cycle • transpiration • precipitation

Local Standards

Preteach

Build Background Knowledge

Elicit reasons that the body needs water and what other living things need water.

 *Where Does the Water Come From?* L1

Targeted Print and Technology Resources

All in One Teaching Resources

L2 Reading Strategy Transparency H4: Identifying Main Ideas

Presentation-Pro CD-ROM

Instruct

All Living Things Need Water Use a questioning strategy to help students consider how living things use water.

Distribution of Earth's Water Use an illustration to identify where Earth's water is distributed and in what forms.

The Water Cycle Use a labeled diagram to sequence the flow of water through the water cycle.

Lab zone Skills Lab *Water From Trees* L2

Targeted Print and Technology Resources

All in One Teaching Resources

L2 Guided Reading, pp. 55–59
L2 Transpareny H5
L2 Skills Lab: *Water From Trees,* pp. 62–63

Lab Activity Video/DVD
Skills Lab: *Water From Trees*

PHSchool.com Web Code: cfp-4024

Student Edition on Audio CD

Assess

Section Assessment Questions

Have students use their graphic organizers with main ideas and details to answer the questions.

Reteach

Use the figures to summarize the distribution of Earth's water and the parts of the water cycle.

Targeted Print and Technology Resources

All in One Teaching Resources

• Section Summary, p. 54
L1 Review and Reinforce, p. 60
L3 Enrich, p. 61

Section 3 Surface Water

 *2–3 periods, 1–1 1/2 blocks*

ABILITY LEVELS
- L1 Basic to Average
- L2 For All Students
- L3 Average to Advanced

Objectives

H.1.3.1 Tell what a river system is.
H.1.3.2 Explain how ponds and lakes form.
H.1.3.3 Describe the changes that occur in ponds and lakes.

Key Terms

• tributary • watershed • divide • reservoir • nutrient
• eutrophication

Local Standards

Preteach

Build Background Knowledge

Encourage students to describe rivers, lakes, and ponds they have seen.

 *What's in Pond Water?* L1

Targeted Print and Technology Resources

All in One Teaching Resources
- L2 Reading Strategy Transparency H6: Outlining

Presentation-Pro CD-ROM

Instruct

River Systems Use a diagram to define a river system and identify its parts.

Ponds and Lakes Ask leading questions to help students explain how ponds and lakes form.

How Lakes Can Change Describe how ponds and lakes change with the seasons and how the buildup of nutrients leads to eutrophication.

Targeted Print and Technology Resources

All in One Teaching Resources
- L2 Guided Reading, pp. 66–69
- L2 Transparencies H7, H8, H9

PHSchool.com Web Code: cfd-3013

Student Edition on Audio CD

Assess

Section Assessment Questions

Have students use their completed outlines of the section to answer the questions.

Reteach

As a class, make a chart comparing and contrasting rivers, ponds, and lakes.

Targeted Print and Technology Resources

All in One Teaching Resources
- Section Summary, p. 65
- L1 Review and Reinforce, p. 70
- L3 Enrich, p. 71

Section 4 Wetland Environments

 *1–2 periods, 1/2–1 block*

ABILITY LEVELS
L1 Basic to Average
L2 For All Students
L3 Average to Advanced

Objectives

H.1.4.1 Describe the common types of freshwater wetlands.
H.1.4.2 Identify human activities that threaten the Florida Everglades.
H.1.4.3 Explain important functions that wetlands serve.

Local Standards

Key Terms

• wetland

Preteach

Build Background Knowledge

Assess students' knowledge of the similarities and differences between the types of wetlands.

 *Wet or Dry?* L1

Targeted Print and Technology Resources

All in One Teaching Resources

L2 Reading Strategy Transparency H10: Asking Questions

Instruct

Types of Wetlands Compare and contrast the three types of wetlands.

The Everglades: A Wetland Analyze how farming, development, and the introduction of new species are threatening the Everglades.

Importance of Wetlands Ask questions to help students consider the ways that wetlands help wildlife and people.

Targeted Print and Technology Resources

All in One Teaching Resources

L2 Guided Reading, pp. 74–76

www.SciLinks.org Web Code: scn-0814

Student Edition on Audio CD

Assess

Section Assessment Questions

Have students use their flowcharts with questions and answers to answer the questions.

Reteach

Use photos and illustrations to review the organisms that live in wetlands and how wetlands are important to people.

Targeted Print and Technology Resources

All in One Teaching Resources

• Section Summary, p. 73
L1 Review and Reinforce, p. 77
L3 Enrich, p. 78

Section 5 Water Underground

 *3–4 periods, 1–2 blocks*

ABILITY LEVELS
- L1 Basic to Average
- L2 For All Students
- L3 Average to Advanced

Objectives

H.1.5.1 Describe how water moves through underground layers of soil and rock.

H.1.5.2 Explain how people obtain water from an aquifer.

Local Standards

Key Terms

• permeable • impermeable • saturated zone • water table • unsaturated zone • aquifer • artesian well

Preteach

Build Background Knowledge

Show a bottle of spring water, and ask students where spring water comes from.

 *Where Does the Water Go?* L1

Targeted Print and Technology Resources

All in One Teaching Resources

L2 Reading Strategy Transparency H11: Previewing Visuals

Presentation-Pro CD-ROM

Instruct

How Water Moves Underground Use a labeled cross-section of soil layers to describe how water moves underground.

Bringing Up Groundwater Use a diagram to explain how people get water from an aquifer.

 *Soil Testing* L2

Targeted Print and Technology Resources

All in One Teaching Resources

L2 Guided Reading, pp. 81–83

L2 Transparencies H12, H13

L2 Design Your Own Lab: *Soil Testing,* pp. 86–88

Lab Activity Video/DVD
Design Your Own Lab: *Soil Testing*

www.SciLinks.org Web Code: scn-0815

Student Edition on Audio CD

Assess

Section Assessment Questions

Have students use the questions and answers they developed for previewing a visual to answer the questions.

Reteach

Summarize the connection between saturated and unsaturated zones and permeable and impermeable layers beneath Earth's surface.

Targeted Print and Technology Resources

All in One Teaching Resources

• Section Summary, p. 80

L1 Review and Reinforce, p. 84

L3 Enrich, p. 85

Chapter 1 Content Refresher

Section 1 The Properties of Water

Water Molecules and Liquid Water A hydrogen atom consists of a proton and an electron. In a water molecule, the electrons of the two hydrogen atoms are usually found close to the oxygen atom. The result is that each hydrogen atom tends to behave like a free proton, with a positive charge. This positive charge, in turn, causes a strong attraction to the negative oxygen atoms of nearby water molecules.

In liquid water, the water molecules are constantly moving at a variety of speeds and in all directions. As a result, some molecules are moving upward. The fastest of these can escape the attraction of the other water molecules. These fast-moving molecules can escape into the air through the surface of the liquid; that is, they evaporate. Evaporation occurs at all temperatures. If enough heat is added to raise the temperature of liquid water to 100°C, the water boils. Now even molecules moving at an average speed can escape the attraction of other water molecules, and a change of state occurs throughout the liquid. Therefore, though both evaporation and boiling represent changes of state, boiling is different from evaporation in two ways: (1) boiling occurs only at the boiling point, but evaporation occurs at all temperatures; and (2) boiling occurs throughout the liquid, but evaporation occurs only at the surface.

When water freezes, it expands. This phenomenon is responsible for much of the change that occurs on Earth's surface through the process called frost weathering. Water seeps into the cracks in rocks and then freezes and thaws with changes in temperature. Over time, this process widens the cracks, breaking off pieces of the rock.

Address Misconceptions

Some students think that when a solute "disappears" into a solvent, the original components can never be separated, as in a chemical reaction. However, dissolving is a physical process, and the solute is not changed. For a strategy for overcoming this misconception, see **Address Misconceptions** in The Properties of Water.

Section 2 Water on Earth

Water Sources on Earth Most of the ice that makes up about three-quarters of Earth's fresh water can be found at the poles. Ice around the North Pole includes sea ice covering much of the Arctic Ocean, as well as continental glaciers covering Greenland. But the continental glaciers on Antarctica contain most of the world's ice—90 percent of it. Fresh water locked up as ice is not available for human consumption.

Not all of Earth's groundwater is available for human use, either. Below a certain depth, it is not practical to raise groundwater to the surface. Therefore, only shallow groundwater is considered available. Scientists estimate that between Earth's surface and 4 km below the surface there are more than 8 million cubic kilometers of fresh water. About half of the population of the United States gets at least some of its fresh water from groundwater resources.

Antarctica's Ice

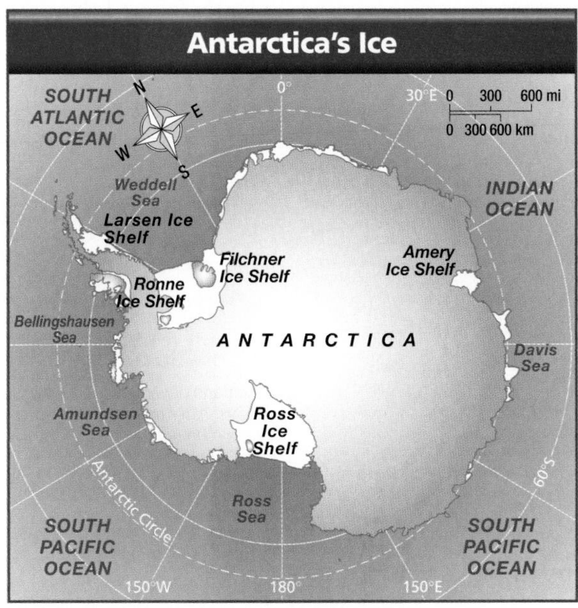

The Water Cycle Within the water cycle, water circulates in three loops: (1) the surface runoff loop, (2) the evaporation-transpiration loop, and (3) the groundwater loop. The last two loops tend to purify water, whereas the first loop does not. The water in the first loop runs off quickly, instead of filtering through soil and rock.

Section 3 Surface Water

River Systems Tributaries in river systems form distinctive drainage patterns. The most common pattern, found in the major watersheds of the United States, is a *dendritic* (treelike) pattern, with streams branching irregularly like branches on a tree. In a *radial* drainage pattern, all of the streams flow outward from a center point, like the spokes on a wheel. A radial pattern is most often found on isolated volcanic cones and uplifted domes of Earth's crust. A *rectangular* drainage pattern develops when the underlying bedrock is crisscrossed by joints and faults. The streams in this pattern form many right-angle bends. In a *trellis* drainage pattern, the streams are almost parallel to one another, making the system look rather like a garden trellis.

Other terms that are used to describe a river system are the stages of its development: youth, maturity, and old age. A single river may include all three stages. At the headwaters, where the fast-moving water erodes the underlying land, the river is young. A young river has waterfalls, rapids, a narrow V-shaped valley, and a steep slope. A mature river erodes its sides more than its bottom, creating a flood plain. A mature river has a gentler slope and a smoother riverbed. An old river has a flood plain that is much wider than the width of its meanders, and the river may shift course frequently. Oxbow lakes and natural levees are common. These stages are relative; an "old" river may be more recently formed than some "young" rivers.

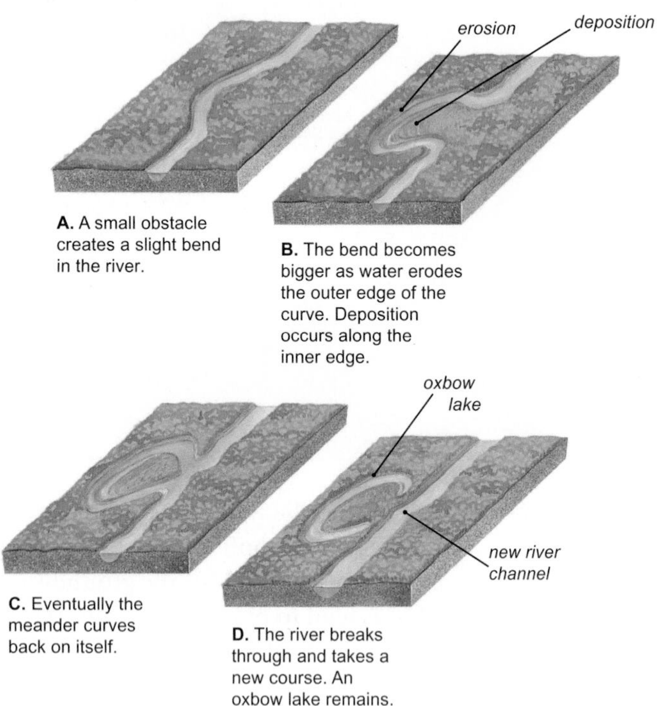

A. A small obstacle creates a slight bend in the river.

B. The bend becomes bigger as water erodes the outer edge of the curve. Deposition occurs along the inner edge.

C. Eventually the meander curves back on itself.

D. The river breaks through and takes a new course. An oxbow lake remains.

Ponds and Lakes These bodies of water are characterized by specific zones. Lakes have three major zones; ponds have two. The shallow water along the edge of a pond is called the littoral zone. More photosynthesis occurs in the littoral zone than anywhere else in the pond, in part because nutrients wash into the pond from the land and feed the algae and plants there. The open water away from the shore is called the limnetic zone. Free-floating photosynthetic bacteria and algae and animal-like protists inhabit the limnetic zone, as well as fish and other animals. Lakes have these same two zones, but a lake also has an area of deep water called the *profundal* zone. Sunlight does not reach the deeper parts of this zone, so no plants or algae live there. Particles of food and the remains of dead organisms drift down into the profundal zone. Bacteria decompose the wastes and release the nutrients into the water.

Section 4 Wetlands Environments

Characteristics of Wetlands Not all wetlands are wet throughout the year. Wetlands can be identified by their characteristic soil and by the specific types of water-tolerant plants that grow there. The soil in a wetland is waterlogged, at least for part of the year, and so contains very little oxygen. Because these conditions limit decomposition, wetland soil is generally rich in organic materials. In many swamps and bogs, this accumulated and partially decomposed plant matter forms layers of peat.

A fascinating group of plants commonly found in swamps and bogs is carnivorous plants. These plants have adapted to wetland soil, which lacks nitrogen, by having special organs to capture and digest insects that supply nitrogen. Common insectivorous plants found in bogs include pitcher plants and sundews.

Section 5 Water Underground

Aquifer Depletion Taking more groundwater from an aquifer than can be naturally recharged is known as aquifer depletion. Dry wells are not the only serious consequence. When water is depleted from an aquifer, the land above it may settle, a condition called subsidence. In California's San Joaquin Valley, for example, aquifer depletion has caused some land areas to sink nearly 10 meters in a 50-year period. When groundwater is depleted in coastal areas, salt water is drawn into the aquifer. This makes the groundwater salty and unfit for drinking.

Aquifer depletion results mainly from withdrawing water for irrigation. With traditional irrigation methods, more than 50 percent of the water applied to fields simply evaporates. Recent advances in irrigation technology are improving the efficiency of water use.

The High Plains Aquifer The High Plains aquifer lies beneath about 174,000 square miles of Colorado, Kansas, Nebraska, New Mexico, Oklahoma, South Dakota, Texas, and Wyoming. The entire aquifer comprises three major geologic units, or portions: the Ogallala Formation, the Arikaree Group, and the White River Group. Each of these portions was formed during a different geologic age in Earth's distant past. The Ogallala is the principal water-yielding portion of the entire aquifer. The water from the High Plains aquifer is used for all purposes, including industry, farming, and household. About 30 percent of the ground water used for irrigation in the United States comes from the High Plains aquifer.

Before 1940, agriculture in the Great Plains depended less on irrigation. As a result, during times of drought, crops failed; the ground dried up, wind-driven dust storms formed, and soil was blown away. The problem was perhaps most severe during the Dust Bowl days of the Great Depression in the 1930s. To avoid such disastrous dust storms and erosion, changes were made in the way people farmed. One of those changes was to use water from wells for irrigation. However, the aquifer that supplies those wells depends on rainfall for recharge. Because more water is drawn from the aquifer than can be replaced by rain in this typically dry climate, water levels in the High Plains aquifer have been steadily falling. By 1980, water levels in areas beneath Texas, Oklahoma, and southwestern Kansas had dropped more than 100 feet. In response to these falling water levels, in 1988 the U.S. Geological Survey (USGS) began to monitor groundwater and the water level in the aquifer. As part of this program, several government agencies at the Federal, State, and local level regularly check more than 8,000 wells in the High Plains.

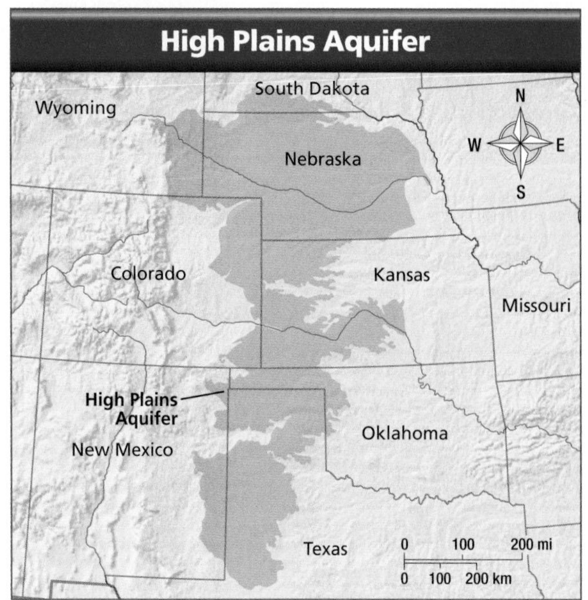

Help Students Read

Predicting

Previewing to Predict Content

Strategy Activate students' prior knowledge, provide a motivation for reading, and set the stage for confirming or correcting preconceptions. This strategy helps students develop and apply logic in predicting and analyzing what they read. Always avoid asking for predictions on topics about which students cannot be expected to have enough prior knowledge to make a valid prediction. Begin by assigning a section in this chapter and implementing the strategies below.

Example

1. Have students preview the section by skimming the headings, visuals, and boldfaced material. Ask students what they already know about this topic.

2. Then, ask students to predict what they might learn about the topic. List students' predictions on the board.

3. Tell students to read the section, taking notes as they come across information that supports or contradicts their predictions.

4. After they have read the section, discuss what they learned that proves or disproves their predictions. Point out that it is not unusual for people to have incorrect ideas about a topic before studying it, but that by making and then confirming or disproving predictions, they can replace their own misunderstandings with correct information.

5. Have students work with partners to repeat the process with other sections.

Interactive Textbook

- Complete student edition
- Video and audio
- Simulations and activities
- Section and chapter activities

Chapter 1 Earth: The Water Planet

Chapter Preview

1. **The Properties of Water**
   Discover *What Are Some Properties of Water?*
   Try This *Follow That String*
   At-Home Activity *Observing Water's Properties*
2. **Water on Earth**
   Discover *Where Does the Water Come From?*
   Skills Activity *Calculating*
   Active Art *The Water Cycle*
   Skills Lab *Water From Trees*
3. **Surface Water**
   Discover *What's in Pond Water?*
   Skills Activity *Inferring*
   Skills Activity *Classifying*
   At-Home Activity *The Knuckle Divide*
4. **Wetland Environments**
   Discover *Wet or Dry?*
   Try This *A Natural Filter*
   At-Home Activity *Runoff*
5. **Water Underground**
   Discover *Where Does the Water Go?*
   Analyzing Data *Uses of Water*
   Try This *An Artesian Well*
   Design Your Own Lab *Soil Testing*

These waterfalls in the Pacific Northwest show the abundance of water on Earth.

4 ◆ H

Lab zone Chapter **Project** L3

Objectives

This project will enhance students' understanding of the importance of water and water resources by tracking how much water is used at their homes and at a local place of business. After this Chapter Project, students will be able to

- calculate water usage in the home and in another building for one week
- create data tables about home water use and graph the data
- interpret data collected from a home water meter and from another building in the community
- communicate the results of the project in a presentation to the class

Skills Focus

Calculating, creating data tables, making and interpreting graphs, interpreting data, communicating

Project Time Line 2 weeks

All in One Teaching Resources

- Chapter Project Teacher Notes
- Chapter Project Worksheet 1
- Chapter Project Worksheet 2
- Chapter Project Scoring Rubric

Developing a Plan

During the first week, discuss how to make data tables, tell students to begin making measurements at home, and have students look for a building to study. Students may ask parents or other adults for help. The second week will be spent collecting data on water use in the residential building. Set aside time for students to prepare their presentations.

Possible Materials

Students may want to use colored markers or other art materials to make their graphs. They may also choose to mount their graphs on poster board. Encourage them to use a word processing program to print labels for the presentation.

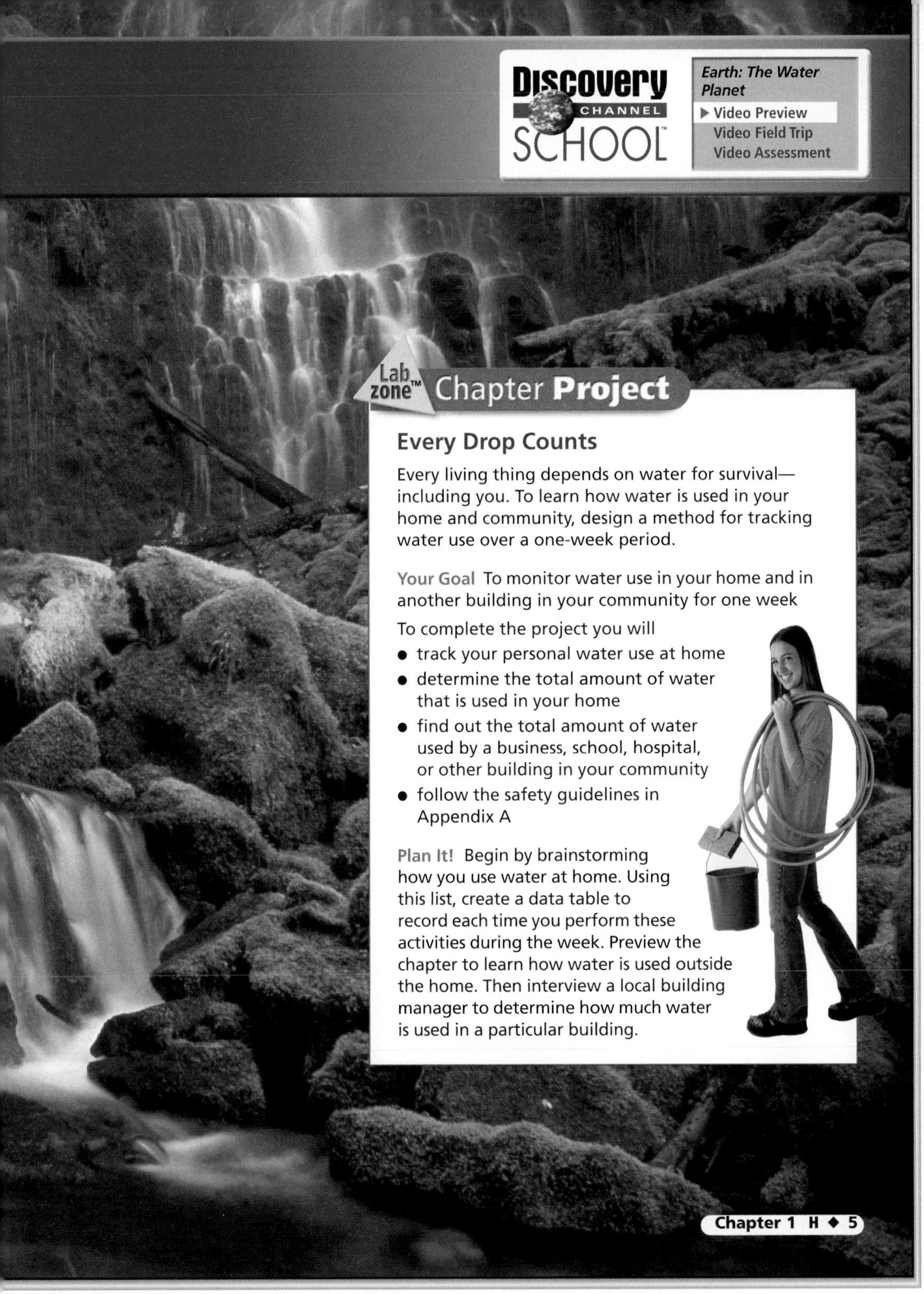

Discovery Channel School

Earth: The Water Planet

▶ Video Preview

Video Field Trip

Video Assessment

Lab zone™ Chapter Project

Every Drop Counts

Every living thing depends on water for survival—including you. To learn how water is used in your home and community, design a method for tracking water use over a one-week period.

Your Goal To monitor water use in your home and in another building in your community for one week

To complete the project you will

- track your personal water use at home
- determine the total amount of water that is used in your home
- find out the total amount of water used by a business, school, hospital, or other building in your community
- follow the safety guidelines in Appendix A

Plan It! Begin by brainstorming how you use water at home. Using this list, create a data table to record each time you perform these activities during the week. Preview the chapter to learn how water is used outside the home. Then interview a local building manager to determine how much water is used in a particular building.

Earth: The Water Planet

Show the Video Preview to introduce the Chapter Project and overview the chapter content. Discussion question: **How has human development affected the Everglades?** *(Human demands for freshwater and the effects of pesticides that have entered the waters of the Everglades have caused problems for the thousands of diverse organisms that live there.)*

Possible Shortcuts

- Have students do only the home study for two weeks or monitor only their individual water use.
- Assign a small group to monitor a small building and report to the class.

Launching the Project

Ask: **What are some ways that you and your family use water daily at home?** *(Flushing toilets, taking baths and showers, brushing teeth, cleaning dishes, washing clothes, watering the lawn, washing the car, and so on)* List these on the board. Challenge students to estimate how many liters of water each of them uses in one day. After students have shared their estimates, tell them that in the United States, residential water use averages about 300 L per day.

Performance Assessment

The Chapter Project Scoring Rubric will help you evaluate how well students complete the Chapter Project. You may want to share the scoring rubric with your students so that they will know what is expected of them. Students will be assessed on

- how completely and accurately they collect data from their homes and a second building
- how accurate and neat their graphs are
- how thorough and interesting their class presentations are
- their participation in groups

Section 1

The Properties of Water

Objectives

After this lesson, students will be able to

H.1.1.1 Describe how the chemical structure of water molecules causes them to stick together.

H.1.1.2 Describe some of water's unusual properties.

H.1.1.3 Identify the three states in which water exists on Earth.

Target Reading Skill

Building Vocabulary Explain that knowing the definitions of key terms helps students understand what they read.

Answers

Have students write what they know about each key term before they read the definitions in the section. Explain that connecting what they already know about key terms helps them remember the terms. As students read each passage that contains key terms, remind them to write the definitions in their own words.

All in One Teaching Resources

- Guided Reading Study Worksheet: *The Properties of Water, Use Target Reading Skills*

Preteach

Build Background Knowledge L1

Physical Properties

Hold a clear glass filled with water in your hand and, as students watch, place two large ice cubes in the water. Ask: **How is the ice in the glass related to the liquid?** *(Ice is the solid state of liquid water.)* **Why do you think the ice floats?** *(Some students may know that ice is less dense than liquid water.)* Challenge students to describe other properties of water. Address any misconceptions by stating that they will learn more about the properties of water in this section.

Section 1

Integrating Chemistry

The Properties of Water

Reading Preview

Key Concepts

- How does the chemical structure of water molecules cause them to stick together?
- What are some of water's unusual properties?
- What are the three states in which water exists on Earth?

Key Terms

- polar molecule
- capillary action
- surface tension
- solution
- solvent
- specific heat
- evaporation
- condensation

Target Reading Skill

Building Vocabulary A definition states the meaning of a word or phrase by telling about its most important feature or function. After you read this section, reread the paragraphs that contain definitions of Key Terms. Use all the information you have learned to write a definition of each Key Term in your own words.

Lab zone Discover Activity

What Are Some Properties of Water?

1. Pour a small amount of water into a plastic cup. Pour an equal amount of vegetable oil into a second cup.
2. Cut two strips of paper towel. Hold the strips so that the bottom of one strip is in the water and the other is in the oil.
3. After one minute, measure how high each substance rose up the paper towel.
4. Using plastic droppers, place equal-sized drops of water and oil next to each other on wax paper.
5. Observe the shape of the two drops from the side.
6. Follow your teacher's instructions for disposing of the oil.

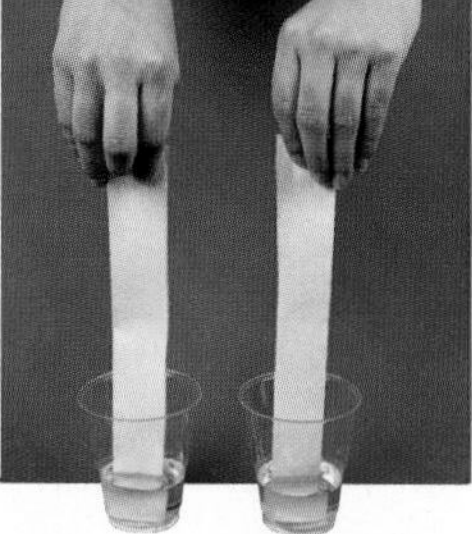

Think It Over

Observing What differences do you notice between the water and the oil in each experiment?

How would you describe water to someone who had never seen it before? You might say that pure water has no color, no taste, and no odor. You might even say that water is a rather plain, ordinary substance. But if you asked a chemist to describe water, the chemist would say that water is very unusual. Its properties differ from those of most other familiar substances.

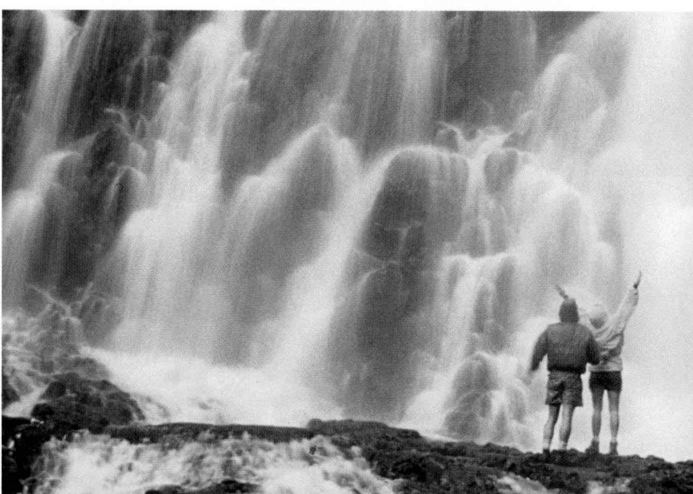

Hikers awed by waterfalls in Yosemite National Park ▶

Lab zone Discover Activity

Skills Focus Observing L1

Materials water, 2 plastic cups, vegetable oil, paper towel, scissors, meter stick, 2 pieces of wax paper, 2 plastic droppers

Time 15 minutes

Tips Students need only a small amount of water and oil in the cups. You may want to cut the strips of paper towel before class begins.

Think It Over The water moves up the paper towel faster than does the oil, and the water forms a taller, rounder drop on the wax paper than the oil does.

The Structure of Water

Could you and the chemist possibly be talking about the same substance? To understand the chemist's description of water, you need to know something about water's chemical structure.

Like all matter, water is made up of atoms. Just as the 26 letters of the alphabet combine in different ways to form all the words in the English language, about 100 types of atoms combine in different ways to form all types of matter.

Atoms attach together, or bond, to form molecules. Two hydrogen atoms bonded to an oxygen atom form a water molecule. A short way of writing this is to use the chemical formula for water, H_2O.

Figure 1 shows how the hydrogen and oxygen atoms are arranged in a water molecule. Each end of the molecule has a slight electric charge. The oxygen end has a slight negative charge. The hydrogen ends have a slight positive charge. A molecule that has electrically charged areas is a **polar molecule.** Because water consists of polar water molecules, it is called a polar substance.

Have you ever played with bar magnets? If so, then you know that the opposite poles of two magnets attract each other. The same is true with polar molecules, except that an electric force rather than a magnetic force causes the attraction. **The positive hydrogen ends of one water molecule attract the negative oxygen ends of nearby water molecules. As a result, the water molecules tend to stick together.**

Reading Checkpoint **Describe the arrangement of the atoms in a water molecule.**

For: Links on water properties
Visit: www.SciLinks.org
Web Code: scn-0811

FIGURE 1
The Structure of Water
Each water molecule has two positive ends and one negative end. The positive ends of one water molecule are attracted to the negative end of another molecule.
Classifying *What makes water a polar substance?*

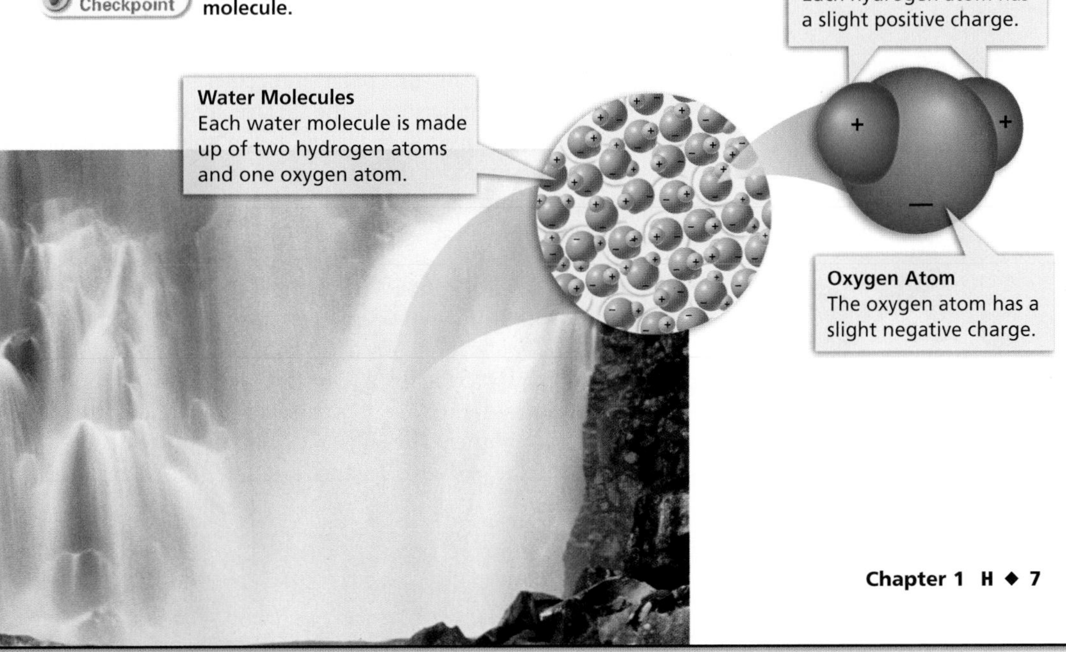
Hydrogen Atoms
Each hydrogen atom has a slight positive charge.
Water Molecules
Each water molecule is made up of two hydrogen atoms and one oxygen atom.
Oxygen Atom
The oxygen atom has a slight negative charge.

Differentiated Instruction

English Learners/Beginning L1
Vocabulary: Prior Knowledge Explain that the scientific meaning of the word *property* is "quality," not real estate or other possessions, and that water has special properties. To help these learners identify some properties of water both in English and in their native language, provide a pan of water for students to touch and observe. **learning modality: verbal**

English Learners/Intermediate L2
Vocabulary: Science Glossary Pronounce and define the key terms in this section. As students read, have them write sentences that use each term in English and in their native language. Have students practice pronunciation by reading their sentences aloud. **learning modality: verbal**

Instruct

The Structure of Water

For: Links on water properties
Visit: www.SciLinks.org
Web Code: scn-0811

Download a worksheet that will guide students' review of Internet resources on water properties.

Teach Key Concepts L2
How Water Molecules Stick Together

Focus Remind students that a molecule is a group of atoms that are joined as a single unit.

Teach Refer students to Figure 1. Ask students to describe the charges. *(Hydrogen atoms have a positive charge, and the oxygen atom has a negative charge.)* Ask: **What is a molecule that has charged areas called?** *(Polar)* **Why do water molecules tend to stick together?** *(The positive hydrogen ends of one molecule attract the negative oxygen ends of other molecules.)*

Apply Ask: **Why do beads of water stick to other substances?** *(The charged ends are attracted to the charged parts of molecules of other substances.)* **learning modality: visual**

All in One Teaching Resources
- Transparency H1

Independent Practice L2
All in One Teaching Resources
- Guided Reading and Study Worksheet: *The Properties of Water*

Student Edition on Audio CD

Monitor Progress L2
Drawing Challenge students to draw, cut out, and model how three water molecules attract one another.

Answers

Figure 1 A water molecule has a slight positive charge at the hydrogen end and a slight negative charge at the oxygen end.

Reading Checkpoint Two hydrogen atoms bonded to an oxygen atom form a water molecule.

Key Properties of Water

Teach Key Concepts L2

Polarity Determines Properties

Focus Review the structure of a water molecule.

Teach Ask: **Why do many substances dissolve in water?** *(The charged ends of the water molecule attract the charged ends of other polar substances.)* Refer students to Figure 2. Ask: **Why does the water rise in the tube?** *(The molecules stick to the sides of the tube and pull other water molecules up with them.)* **How is the insect able to stay on the water?** *(The polar molecules pull on one another to form a tight surface.)* **How does polarity affect the temperature of water?** *(A great deal of heat is required to raise the temperature of water because of the strong attraction between water molecules.)*

Apply Ask: **If water will not dissolve a particular substance, what can you infer about that substance?** *(That it is nonpolar—it has no charged parts to be attracted to water molecules)* **learning modality: verbal**

Observing Surface Tension L2

Materials water, bowl, pepper, liquid detergent

Time 20 minutes

Focus Ask: **What effect does detergent have on the surface tension of water?**

Teach Challenge students to find the answer. They will discover that the pepper floats on the surface of the water. When detergent is added, some of the pepper will sink, and much of it will move to the side of the bowl. Ask: **What can you conclude?** *(Detergent lowers water's surface tension.)*

Apply Ask: **How does this characteristic of detergent help clean soiled materials?** *(Detergent helps water penetrate soiled materials more completely.)* **learning modality: kinesthetic**

FIGURE 2
Three Properties of Water
The attraction among the polar water molecules is responsible for water's unusual properties.

Capillary Action: Water rises in a tube.

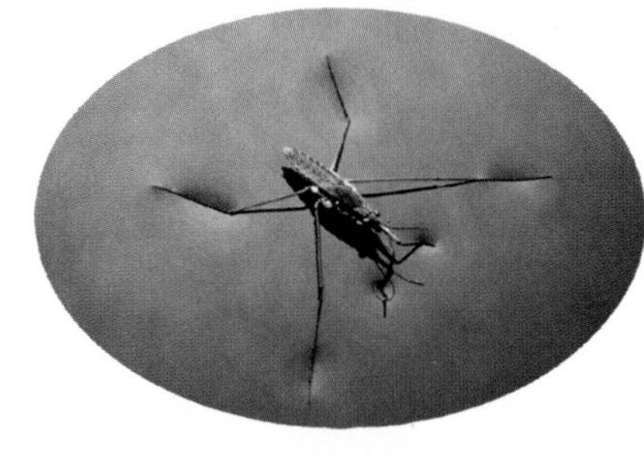

Surface Tension: The tightness of the water's surface keeps a water strider from sinking.

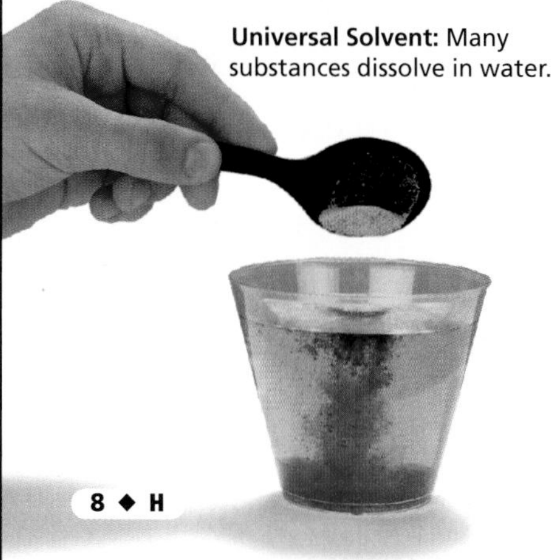

Universal Solvent: Many substances dissolve in water.

Key Properties of Water

Many of water's unusual properties occur because of the attraction among the polar water molecules. **The properties of water include capillary action, surface tension, the ability to dissolve many substances, and high specific heat.**

Capillary Action Just as water molecules stick to one another, they also stick to the sides of a tube, such as a straw. The next time you see a drink with a straw in it, look closely at the level of the liquid outside and inside the straw. You will see that the liquid rises higher inside the straw. As water molecules are attracted to the straw, they pull other water molecules up with them. Similarly, water will climb up into the pores of a brick or a piece of wood.

The combined force of attraction among water molecules and with the molecules of surrounding materials is called **capillary action.** Capillary action allows water to move through materials with pores inside.

Capillary action also causes water molecules to cling to the fibers of materials like paper and cloth. You may have seen outdoor or athletic clothing that claims to "wick moisture away from the skin." Capillary action along the cloth's fibers pulls water away from your skin. By pulling the water away from your skin, the fibers keep you dry.

Surface Tension Have you ever watched water striders skate across the surface of a pond without sinking? They are supported by the surface tension of the water. **Surface tension** is the tightness across the surface of water that is caused by the polar molecules pulling on one another. The molecules at the surface are being pulled by the molecules next to them and below them. The pulling forces the surface of the water into a curved shape. Surface tension also causes raindrops to form round beads when they fall onto a car windshield.

Universal Solvent What happens when you make a fruit drink from a powdered mix? As you stir the powder into the water, the powder seems to disappear. When you make the fruit drink, you are making a solution. A **solution** is a mixture that forms when one substance dissolves another. The substance that does the dissolving is called the **solvent.** In this example, the water is the solvent.

Many substances dissolve in water because water is polar. The charged ends of the water molecule attract the molecules of other polar substances. Water dissolves so many substances that it is called the "universal solvent." It can dissolve solids, such as sugar, and liquids, such as bleach. Water can also dissolve many gases, including oxygen and carbon dioxide. Substances that have molecules with no charged regions are called nonpolar substances. Nonpolar substances do not dissolve well in water.

Specific Heat It is a steamy summer day. The air is hot, the sidewalk is hot, and the sandy beach is hot. But when you jump into the ocean, the water is surprisingly cool! If you go for an evening swim, however, the water is warmer than the cool air.

You feel this difference in temperature because of water's unusually high specific heat. **Specific heat** is the amount of heat needed to increase the temperature of a certain mass of a substance by 1°C. Compared to other substances, water requires a lot of heat to increase its temperature.

Water's high specific heat is due to the strong attraction among water molecules. Other substances, such as air and rocks, have weaker attractions between their molecules. The temperature of each of these substances rises more quickly than that of water that is heated the same amount.

One effect of water's high specific heat is that land areas located near large bodies of water experience less dramatic temperature changes than areas far inland. In summer, the sun's heat warms the land more quickly than the water. The warm land heats the air above it to a higher temperature than the air over the ocean. As a result, the air is warmer inland than on the coast. The opposite effect occurs in winter—land loses heat more quickly than water, so the air above the land is cooler.

Why does water have a high specific heat?

Lab zone Try This Activity

Follow That String

Do this activity over a sink.

1. Cut a piece of string as long as your arm. Wet the string.
2. Fill a pitcher with water. Tie the string to the handle.
3. Drape the string across the spout and let the other end dangle into a plastic cup. Tape the end of the string inside the cup.

4. Hold the cup below the pitcher so that the string is pulled tight. As your partner gently pours the water into the cup, slowly move the cup to the right of the spout, keeping the string tight.

Inferring How do water's polar molecules cause it to follow the string?

FIGURE 3
Why Water Stays Cool
Although the air is hot, the water offers cool relief. Water's high specific heat keeps it from heating up as quickly as other materials.

H ◆ 9

Address Misconceptions L1

Solvents and Solutes

Focus Many students think that when a solute "disappears" into a solvent, the original components can never be separated.

Teach Stir several spoonfuls of sugar into a cup of water. Students will observe that the sugar disappears and that the water remains clear. Then pour some of the solution into a small saucer in a warm spot. After the water evaporates in a day or two, students can observe the residue of sugar that remains.

Apply Explain that the sugar was still present in the solution because a chemical change did not take place. Dissolving is a physical process. The sugar atoms were pulled apart by the water, but they were not changed into another substance. **learning modality: visual**

Lab zone Try This Activity

Skills Focus Inferring L2

Materials string, scissors, water, pitcher, plastic cup, tape

Time 20 minutes

Tips Students should keep tension on the string and pour the water slowly.

Expected Outcome As the students slowly move the cup away from the pitcher, the water should flow down the string into the cup. Water molecules flowing from the pitcher are attracted to the water molecules on the string.

Extend Students can explore whether the height at which the pitcher is held affects how the water flows down the string. **learning modality: kinesthetic**

Monitor Progress L2

Oral Presentation Invite students to explain each of the properties of water and provide examples that they have seen or experienced.

Answer

Reading Checkpoint The high specific heat of water is the result of strong attraction among water molecules, so the temperature of water does not increase as quickly as that of other substances.

Changing State

Teach Key Concepts L1

The Three States of Water

Focus Remind students that water, like all matter, is composed of molecules.

Teach Refer students to Figure 4. Explain that the state of matter depends on how close the molecules are to one another. Ask students to describe the three states of water. *(The solid state is ice, the liquid state is water that can flow, and the gas state is water vapor in the air.)* Ask: **Why can't a solid flow like a gas or a liquid?** *(The molecules in a solid are held rigidly in place, unlike the molecules of a liquid or a gas.)* **How is the arrangement of molecules of liquid water different from that of molecules in water vapor?** *(The molecules of liquid water are much closer together than the molecules of water vapor.)* **What factor is responsible for most of the changes of state from solid to liquid to gas and back again?** *(Temperature)*

Apply Show a glass of water with ice in it. Ask: **Which is more dense, liquid or solid water?** *(Liquid)* **Why is this fact important for organisms that live in ponds and small lakes during the winter?** *(If ice were denser, ponds and lakes would freeze from the bottom up and become solid ice throughout. Organisms would not survive.)* Tell students that water is unlike most other substances, which shrink rather than expand when they change into the solid state. **learning modality: logical/mathematical**

All in One Teaching Resources

- Transparency H2

Solid
The molecules in solid ice are close together and form a rigid structure.

Liquid
The molecules move more freely, and the water takes the shape of its container.

Gas
The molecules in water vapor move very freely and spread out to fill a space.

FIGURE 4
The Three States of Water
Water commonly exists as a solid, a liquid, and a gas.
Comparing and Contrasting
In which state do the molecules move the slowest? The fastest?

Changing State

It's a hot, humid summer day. To cool down, you put some ice cubes in a glass and add cold water. You are interacting with water in three different states, or forms: solid, liquid, and gas. **The ice is solid water, the familiar form of water is a liquid, and the water vapor in the air is a gas.** Water is the only substance on Earth that commonly exists in all of these different states. Figure 4 shows how the arrangement of the water molecules differs in each state.

Boiling and Evaporation If you've ever poured water into a pot, you've seen how the liquid takes the shape of the container. This is true because the molecules in liquid water move freely, bouncing off one another.

What happens if you place the pot of water on a stove and heat it? As more energy is added to the liquid water, the speed of the molecules increases and the temperature rises. At 100°C, the water boils and a change of state occurs. The molecules have enough energy to escape the liquid and become invisible water vapor. The molecules in a gas move even more freely than those in a liquid.

Another way that liquid water can become a gas is through evaporation. **Evaporation** is the process by which molecules at the surface of a liquid absorb enough energy to change to the gaseous state. If you let your hair air-dry after going swimming, you are taking advantage of evaporation.

Differentiated Instruction

Special Needs L1

Using Analogies To help students understand differences among the three states of water, display pictures of (1) a densely packed military formation, (2) a milling crowd of people, (3) soccer players dispersed on a field. The pictures represent the molecular arrangements of the states of matter—solid, liquid, and gas, respectively. Ask students to tell how each picture is similar to one of the states of matter. Ask students to think of other analogies for the arrangement of water molecules in the three different states. **learning modality: visual**

Condensation As water vapor cools down, it releases some of its energy to the surroundings. The molecules slow down and the temperature decreases. As the temperature of the gas reaches 100°C, the water vapor begins to change back to the liquid state. The process by which a gas changes to a liquid is called **condensation.** When you fog up a window by breathing on it, you are seeing the effects of condensation. The invisible water vapor in your breath is cooled by the window and forms drops of liquid water.

Freezing If those drops of liquid water cooled, the molecules would lose energy. They would start to move more and more slowly. At 0°C, the liquid water freezes, changing into solid ice. If you have ever observed an icicle forming from water dripping off a roof, you have seen this change of state in progress.

Melting Suppose that you put an ice cube in a pot and place it on the stove. As you heated it, the molecules in the ice would start moving faster. The temperature would rise. When the temperature reached 0°C, the solid ice would melt and become liquid water.

What is condensation?

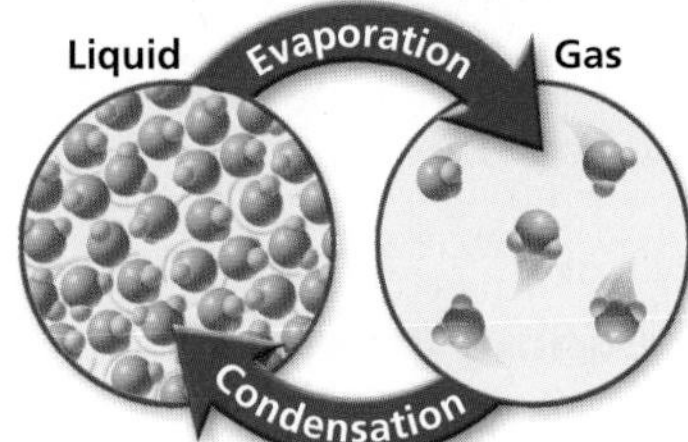

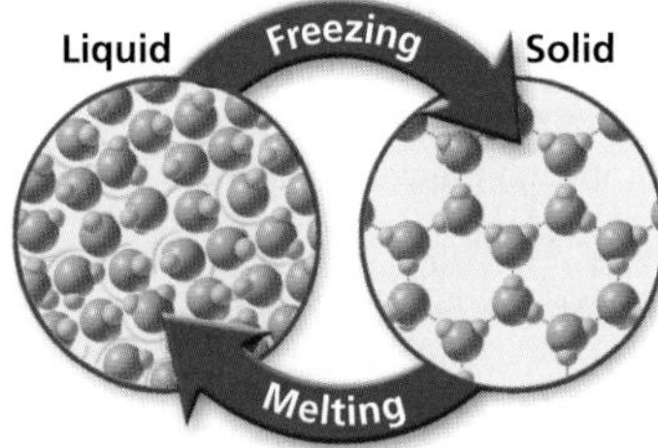

FIGURE 5
Changing State
Water moves between the liquid and gaseous states by evaporation and condensation. Water moves between the liquid and solid states by freezing and melting.

Section 1 Assessment

Target Reading Skill **Building Vocabulary** Use your definitions to help answer the questions below.

Reviewing Key Concepts

1. a. **Reviewing** What atoms make up a water molecule?
   b. **Describing** Describe the electric charge on each end of a water molecule.
   c. **Relating Cause and Effect** What causes water molecules to be attracted to one another?
2. a. **Listing** Name four unusual properties that water exhibits.
   b. **Explaining** Briefly explain why water exhibits each property.
   c. **Predicting** Oil is a nonpolar molecule. Would it dissolve in water? Why or why not?
3. a. **Identifying** What are the three states in which water exists on Earth?
   b. **Sequencing** Describe how water changes state as a patch of ice is heated by the sun.

Lab zone At-Home Activity

Observing Water's Properties Put a penny on a piece of paper. With a plastic dropper or a toothpick, have a family member place a single drop of water on the penny. Ask the person to predict how many more drops he or she can add before the water spills off the penny. Have the person add drops one at a time until the water overflows. How does the result differ from the prediction? Explain what property of water accounts for the results.

Lab zone At-Home Activity

Observing Water's Properties L1

Encourage students to challenge family members to predict how many drops can be added to the penny. Most people will predict too few drops. Have students rehearse aloud their explanations to family members about why the penny can hold so many drops. Make sure that students understand that surface tension accounts for this result.

Monitor Progress L2

Answers

Figure 4 Solid state; Gas state

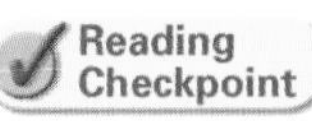

Condensation is the process by which a gas changes to a liquid.

Assess

Reviewing Key Concepts

1. a. Two atoms of hydrogen and one atom of oxygen **b.** Hydrogen atoms are positively charged, and oxygen atoms are negatively charged. **c.** The positive hydrogen ends of one water molecule attract the negative oxygen ends of nearby water molecules.

2. a. capillary action, surface tension, the ability to dissolve many substances, and high specific heat **b.** the combined force of attraction among water molecules and with the molecules of surrounding materials; tightness across the surface of water caused by polar molecules; water is polar; the strong attraction among water molecules **c.** No, oil will not dissolve in water because there are no charged ends to attract the charged molecules of water.

3. a. Water exists as a solid (ice), a liquid, and a gas (water vapor). **b.** Steady or increasing heat from the sun causes the molecules in the ice to move faster and faster, causing the solid ice to melt and form a liquid. If the liquid continues to be heated, the increase in energy causes the water molecules to move even faster and separate from one another to become a gas.

All in One Teaching Resources

- Transparency H3

Reteach L1

Use the illustrations in this section to relate the structure of water to its properties and changes of state.

Performance Assessment L2

Drawing Have students make a series of drawings showing the various ways that water changes from one state to another. Encourage them to use captions, labels, and arrows.

All in One Teaching Resources

- Section Summary: *The Properties of Water*
- Review and Reinforce: *The Properties of Water*
- Enrich: *The Properties of Water*

Section 2 Water on Earth

Objectives
After this lesson, students will be able to

H.1.2.1 State how people and other living things use water.

H.1.2.2 Describe how Earth's water is distributed.

H.1.2.3 Explain how Earth's water moves through the water cycle.

Target Reading Skill
Identifying Main Ideas Explain that identifying main ideas and details helps students sort the facts from the information into groups. Each group can have a main topic, subtopics, and details

Answers
Possible answers:

Detail: Earth's oceans in the form of salt water, in which 97 percent of Earth's water is found

Detail: Ice in the form of icebergs near the North and South Poles

Detail: Rivers and lakes, which contain the smallest amount of fresh water on Earth

Detail: Water below the surface, which fills cracks and spaces in underground soil and rock layers

All in One Teaching Resources
- Transparency H4

Preteach

Build Background Knowledge L1
Why We Need Water
Ask students to estimate how much water or other liquid they have consumed today. Ask: **Why does your body need water?** *(To replace liquid that is lost.)* Ask: **What other living things need water?** *(Possible response: All of them, including plants and animals. Some students may mention that some organisms live in water.)* Accept all answers at this time. Explain that students will learn how water is important to life.

Section 2 Water on Earth

Reading Preview
Key Concepts
- How do people and other living things use water?
- How is Earth's water distributed?
- How does Earth's water move through the water cycle?

Key Terms
- photosynthesis
- habitat
- groundwater
- water cycle
- transpiration
- precipitation

Target Reading Skill
Identifying Main Ideas As you read the Distribution of Earth's Water section, write the main idea in a graphic organizer like the one below. Then write four supporting details that further explain the main idea.

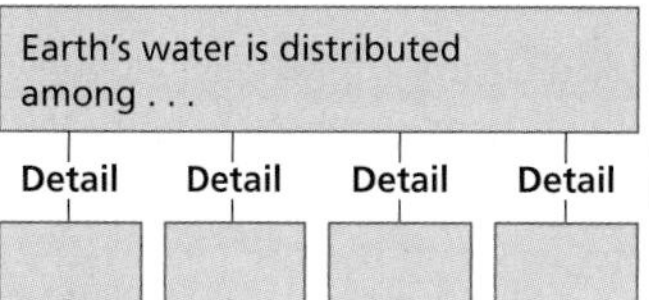

Lab zone Discover Activity
Where Does the Water Come From?
1. Fill a glass with ice cubes and water, taking care not to spill any water. Set the glass aside for 5 minutes.
2. Observe the outside of the glass. Pick up the glass and examine the surface it was sitting on.

Think It Over
Inferring Where did the water on the outside of the glass come from? How do you think it got there?

In a galaxy called the Milky Way, nine planets orbit a star known simply as the sun. Some of the planets have spectacular rings. Others have volcanoes that are larger than continents or storms that last for centuries. But only one of the planets, Earth, has a surface covered mainly by water. In fact, oceans cover about 70 percent of our planet's surface. That's why Earth is often called the "blue planet."

Earth differs from the other planets in another important way. It is the only place known thus far where you, your classmates, your pets, your plants, and every other living thing can survive. The wide variety of life on Earth could not exist without water.

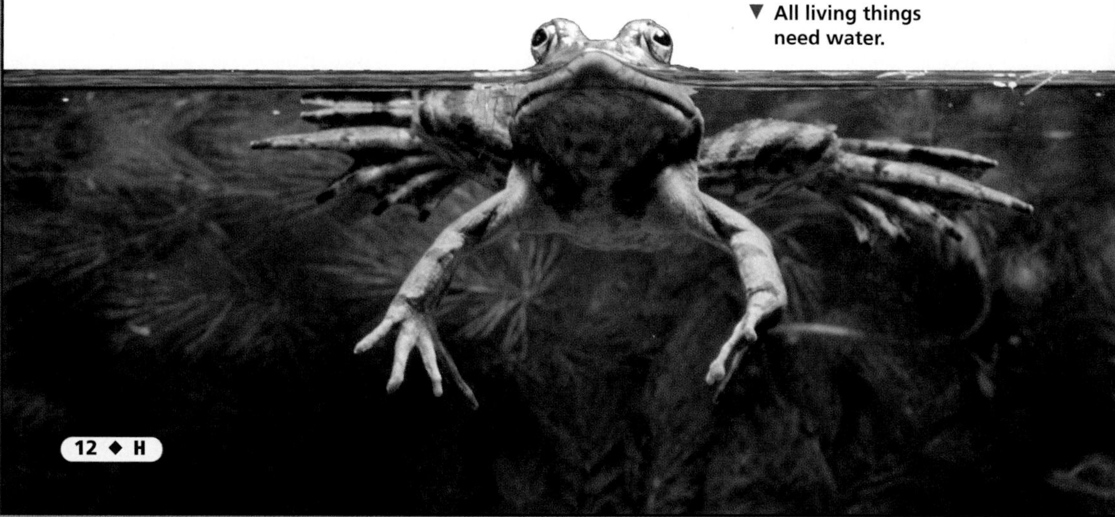
▼ All living things need water.

Lab zone Discover Activity
Skills Focus Inferring L1

Materials ice, water, pitcher, clear drinking glass

Time 10 minutes

Tips Add enough ice to the pitcher to make the water very cold, causing droplets to form quickly on the outer surface of the glass. Advise students to avoid spilling the water on the outside of the glass.

Think It Over Most students will correctly infer that the water droplets come from water vapor in the air condensing on the cold surface of the glass. Some students, however, may propose that the water somehow came from inside the glass.

All Living Things Need Water

Here's a riddle for you: What do you and an apple have in common? You both consist mostly of water! Water is a large part of every living thing. Water makes up nearly two thirds of your body's mass. That water is necessary to keep your body functioning. **All living things need water in order to carry out their body processes. In addition, many living things use water for shelter.**

Body Processes All organisms need water to carry out their body processes. Water allows organisms to obtain chemicals from their surroundings, break down food, grow, reproduce, and move substances within their bodies. Humans and other animals drink water or obtain it indirectly by eating foods that contain water. Many animals can live several weeks without food. But they cannot survive more than a few days without water.

Plants and other organisms that make their own food also need water in order to carry out their food-making processes. **Photosynthesis** (foh toh SIN thuh sis) is the process by which plants use water, along with carbon dioxide and energy from the sun, to make their own food. Animals and other organisms depend on the food made by plants during photosynthesis. Animals may eat the plants or eat organisms that eat the plants.

Shelter Bodies of water provide habitats for many living things. An organism's **habitat** is the place where it lives and obtains all the things it needs to survive. You are probably familiar with large water-dwelling organisms such as sharks. But most water-dwelling organisms are microscopic, such as amoebas. In fact, aquatic, or water, habitats contain more organisms than land habitats.

What is a habitat?

FIGURE 6
Essential for Life
As part of their daily routine, these women in Pakistan must walk to a well to get the water they need.
Interpreting Photographs *What can you infer about the availability of fresh water in the region where these women live?*

Instruct

All Living Things Need Water

Teach Key Concepts L1

The Importance of Water

Focus Have students recall that water is the universal solvent.

Teach Explain that water acts as a solvent for nutrients and other materials, such as sodium chloride, that our bodies need. Water also helps in chemical reactions in living things. Ask: **In animals, what processes require water?** *(Obtaining chemicals from their surroundings, breaking down food, growth, reproduction, and moving substances in the body)* **Why do plants need water?** *(They use water, carbon dioxide, and energy to make their food.)* **How is water important to the habitats of many organisms?** *(Many organisms live in water and get what they need to survive from water.)*

Apply Ask: **What is one reason that a plant dies if it does not get enough water?** *(The plant cannot carry out photosynthesis without water, and so cannot make food for itself.)*
learning modality: logical/mathematical

Independent Practice L2

All in One Teaching Resources

- Guided Reading and Study Worksheet: *Water on Earth*

Student Edition on Audio CD

Differentiated Instruction

Less Proficient Readers L1

Analyzing Word Parts Explain that *photo* means "light" and *synthesis* means "to put together." Ask how these two meanings relate to the process of photosynthesis. *(Plants use light, water, and carbon dioxide to make food.)*
learning modality: verbal

Gifted and Talented L3

The Role of Water in Removing Carbon Dioxide Ask students to find out what chemical reaction takes place between water and carbon dioxide to allow carbon dioxide to be moved through the bloodstream. *(Water and carbon dioxide combine to form carbonic acid, which is highly soluble: $CO_2 + H_2O \rightarrow H_2CO_3$.)*
learning modality: logical/mathematical

Monitor Progress L2

Oral Presentation Ask students to describe why water is essential for all living things.

Answers

Figure 6 Fresh water is very scarce.

Reading Checkpoint: A place where an organism lives and obtains the things it needs to survive

Distribution of Earth's Water

Teach Key Concepts L1

Where Water Is Found

Focus Refer students to Figure 8. Remind them that most of Earth's surface is water.

Teach Ask: **Where is most water on Earth found?** *(In the oceans)* Explain that salt water cannot be used for drinking and water crops. The technology for converting salt water to fresh water is expensive and impractical. Only a small percentage of water on Earth is readily available for human use. Have students examine each of the other categories featured in Figure 8. Ask: **Where are icebergs?** *(At the poles)* Explain that icebergs are fresh water, but this water is not available for people to use. **What freshwater sources are available to people?** *(Rivers and lakes, and water beneath Earth's surface)* Ask students to examine Figure 8 and determine the percentage of available fresh water. *(Approximately 23 percent)* Ask: **Where is the greatest percentage of fresh water found?** *(In icebergs; they contain 76 percent of fresh water on Earth.)*

Apply Ask: **Why can't people directly use water from the oceans for drinking?** Prompt students to think about what happens when they eat salty foods. *(The human body cannot use salt water because the salt causes the body's cells to dry out. A person who drinks only salt water will die.)* **learning modality: logical/mathematical**

Distribution of Earth's Water

Look at Figure 8. It shows how water is distributed among saltwater and freshwater sources on Earth. **Most of Earth's water—roughly 97 percent—is salt water found in oceans. Only 3 percent is fresh water.**

Of that 3 percent, about three quarters is frozen in huge masses of ice near the North and South poles. Almost a quarter of the fresh water is underground. A tiny fraction of Earth's fresh water occurs in lakes and rivers. An even tinier fraction is found in the atmosphere, most of it in the form of invisible water vapor, the gaseous form of water.

Oceans To explore Earth's waters, take an imaginary boat trip around the world. Starting in Florida, you head southeast across the Atlantic Ocean toward Africa. Swinging around the continent's southern tip, you enter the smaller but deeper Indian Ocean. Next, you travel east across the Pacific Ocean. This vast ocean covers an area greater than all the land on Earth combined. Pacific, Atlantic, Indian—these are the names used for the different parts of the ocean. But the waters are really all interconnected, making up one big ocean.

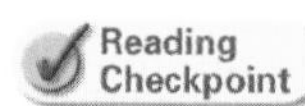

Where is most fresh water located?

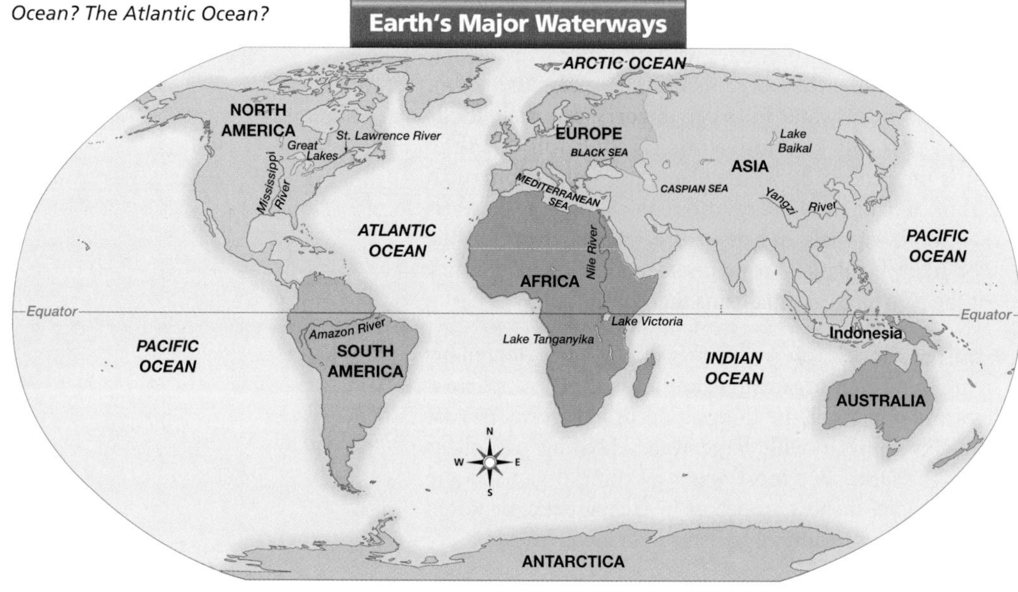

FIGURE 7
Earth's oceans are all connected, enabling a ship to sail all the way around the world. This map also shows some of the world's major rivers and lakes.
Interpreting Maps *Which continents touch the Pacific Ocean? The Atlantic Ocean?*

Lab zone Skills Activity

Skills Focus calculating L2

Materials water, 1-liter clear plastic bottle, large bowl, 5 plastic cups, graduated cylinder, calculator, dropper

Time 30 minutes

Tips Point out that the water remaining in the bottle represents only 3 percent of the total (3 mL). This 3 percent represents 100 percent of the fresh water on Earth.

Expected Outcome Ice: 76 percent of 30 mL (about 22 mL); Shallow groundwater: 12 percent of 30 mL (3.6 mL); Deep groundwater: 11 percent of 30 mL (3.3 mL); Lakes and rivers: 0.34 percent of 30 mL (about 0.1 mL); and Water vapor: 0.03 percent of 30 mL (about 0.01 mL). Water from lakes and rivers and shallow groundwater is available for human use, or a little more than 1 percent of the original one liter (about 3.6 mL).

Extend Ask students to repeat steps 3 and 4 with a full bottle of water that represents Earth's total amount of fresh water. **learning modality: kinesthetic**

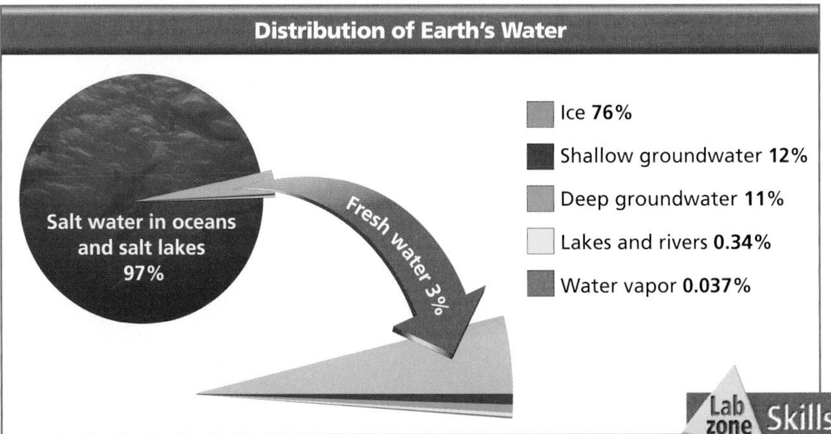

FIGURE 8
Most of Earth's water is salt water. Only 3 percent is fresh water. Of that fresh water, only a tiny fraction is available for human use.

Ice How can you get back to Florida? You could sail all the way around South America. But watch out for icebergs! These floating chunks of ice are made of fresh water. Icebergs in the southern Pacific and southern Atlantic oceans have broken off from massive sheets of ice that cover most of Antarctica. If you traveled around the North Pole, you would also find icebergs in the Arctic Ocean and in the North Atlantic.

Rivers and Lakes To see fresh water in rivers and lakes, you'll have to make a side trip inland. Sail north past Nova Scotia, Canada, to the beginning of the St. Lawrence Seaway. Navigate through the series of locks along the St. Lawrence River. Suddenly the river widens and you enter Lake Ontario, one of North America's five Great Lakes. The Great Lakes contain nearly 20 percent of all the water in the world's freshwater lakes.

Groundwater Some of the fresh water on Earth can't be seen from a sailboat. To find it, you would have to go underground. When it rains or snows, some water soaks into the ground. This water trickles down through spaces between particles of soil and rock. Eventually the water reaches a layer of rock that it cannot move through. Water that fills the cracks and spaces in underground soil and rock layers is called **groundwater.** Far more fresh water is located underground than in all of Earth's rivers and lakes. You'll learn more about groundwater in Section 5.

Lab zone **Skills Activity**

Calculating

This activity shows how Earth's water is distributed.

1. Fill a 1-liter plastic bottle with water to represent the total water on Earth.
2. Measure 97 percent, or 970 milliliters (mL), of the water and pour it into a large bowl to represent salt water on Earth.
3. Label five cups to represent Earth's freshwater sources. Figure 8 shows the percentage of water in each freshwater source. Using this graph, calculate how much of the remaining 30 mL of water should be poured into each cup.
4. Use a graduated cylinder to measure the amount of water for each cup. Use a plastic dropper for amounts that are too small to measure accurately.

Which cups contain water that is easily available to humans? How do these amounts compare to the amount in Step 1?

Use Visuals: Figure 8 L2

Distribution of Earth's Water

Focus Remind students that circle graphs show parts of a whole.

Teach Focus attention on the circle graph. Ask: **What significant fact does this circle graph tell you?** *(Salt water on Earth makes up almost all of the water on Earth.)* **How is the lower graph related to the upper graph?** *(It represents all of the water in the wedges of the upper graph.)* Explain that the freshwater sources represent those percentages of the 3 percent represented by the wedges, not the 100 percent represented by the entire circle.

Apply Show students how to calculate the percentage of Earth's total water that is made up of ice: $76 \times 0.03 = 2.28$ percent. Ask them to calculate the same for groundwater *($23 \times 0.03 = 0.69$ percent)* and lakes and rivers. *($0.34 \times 0.03 = 0.01$ percent)* **learning modality: logical/mathematical**

Lab zone Chapter **Project** L3

Interpreting Maps

Materials map of your state or county

Time 10 minutes

Focus Survey students to determine which of them can identify the source of their family's drinking water.

Teach Give each student an outline map of your state or county. Have students identify rivers and lakes and note the proximity of these sources to towns and cities. Ask students to infer which sources might be used for their town's drinking water.

Apply Ask students to confirm the source of their drinking water (if it is not from a private well) and locate the source on the map. They can consult a phone directory, or contact the local or state Environmental Protection Agency. **learning modality: visual**

Differentiated Instruction

Less Proficient Readers L1

Understanding Main Ideas For each blue heading in this passage, have students write a sentence in their own words that describes the main idea for that paragraph. Then have each student use his or her sentence and the graphics on these two pages to compose a brief paragraph supporting this statement: *Fresh water is a scarce resource.* **learning modality: verbal**

Special Needs L1

Identifying Water Sources Provide pictures from magazines or encyclopedias of the different sources of water discussed in the text. Ask students to identify and explain the relative availability of each type of source, or point out this information to them. **learning modality: visual**

Monitor Progress L2

Skills Check Have each student make a circle graph of the water available for human use. Students may use Figure 8 as a reference.

Answer

Figure 7 Asia, Australia, North America, South America

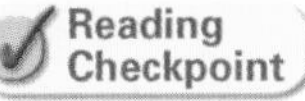
Reading Checkpoint In huge masses of ice around the North and South poles

The Water Cycle

For: Water Cycle activity
Visit: PHSchool.com
Web Code: cfp-4024

Students can interact with the art of the water cycle online.

Teach Key Concepts L1

How Water Moves

Focus Ask students to give examples of cycles. *(Possible answers: Seasons and the rock cycle)*

Teach Explain that a cycle has no beginning or end. Ask: **How does water move in a cycle?** *(Water moves from Earth's surface to the atmosphere and back to the surface.)* Refer students to Figure 9. Ask: **What are the three steps in the water cycle?** *(Evaporation, condensation, and precipitation)* **What are sources of water that evaporate?** *(Bodies of water, such as oceans and lakes, and plants)* **In which state is evaporated water?** *(Gaseous)* **How does water form clouds?** *(Water vapor in the atmosphere condenses.)* **How does water return to Earth's surface?** *(It falls as precipitation when the water droplets in clouds become larger and heavy enough to fall.)*

Apply Emphasize that transpiration by plants releases water vapor, a gas, into the air, not liquid water. Ask: **How else is water vapor released from your body besides evaporation from your skin?** *(When you breathe out, water vapor is present in your breath.)* **learning modality: logical/ mathematical**

All in One Teaching Resources

- Transparency H5

FIGURE 9
The Water Cycle
Water moves continuously through a cycle, from Earth's surface to the atmosphere and back. The sun's energy drives this process.
Interpreting Diagrams *In which step of the water cycle does water return to Earth's surface?*

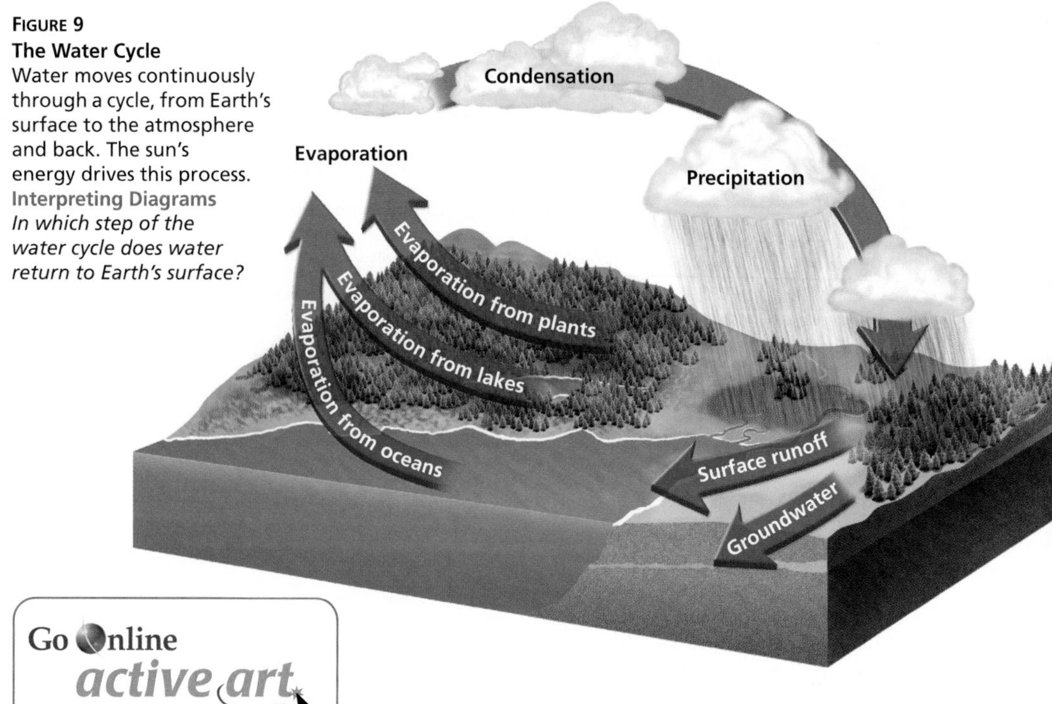

Go Online active art

For: Water Cycle activity
Visit: PHSchool.com
Web Code: cfp-4024

The Water Cycle

Earth's water is naturally recycled through the water cycle. The **water cycle** is the continuous process by which water moves from Earth's surface to the atmosphere and back. **In the water cycle, water moves from bodies of water, land, and living things on Earth's surface to the atmosphere and back to Earth's surface.** As shown in Figure 9, the water cycle has three major steps—evaporation, condensation, and precipitation. The cycle itself has no real beginning or end. But it is driven by an energy source—the sun.

Water Evaporates As you learned earlier, evaporation is the process by which molecules at the surface of a liquid absorb enough energy to change to a gaseous state. Water is constantly evaporating from the surfaces of oceans and large lakes. Smaller amounts evaporate from the soil, puddles, and even from your skin. Plants play a role, too, in this step of the water cycle. Plants draw in water from the soil through their roots. Eventually the water is given off through the leaves as water vapor in a process called **transpiration.**

Condensation Forms Clouds What happens after a water molecule evaporates? Warm air carries the water molecule upward. At higher altitudes, air tends to become much colder. Cold air cannot hold as much water vapor as warm air can. As a result, some of the water vapor cools and condenses into liquid water. Condensed droplets of water clump together around tiny dust particles in the air, forming clouds.

Water Falls As Precipitation As more water vapor condenses, the water droplets in a cloud grow larger and larger. Eventually, they become so heavy that they fall back to Earth. Water that falls to Earth as rain, snow, hail, or sleet is called **precipitation.**

Most precipitation falls directly into the ocean. The precipitation that falls on land may evaporate immediately or run off the surface into rivers and lakes. From there, it may evaporate or flow back into the ocean. In addition, some water may trickle down into the ground. After a long time, this groundwater may reach a river, lake, or ocean and continue the cycle by evaporating again.

Precipitation is the source of all fresh water on and below Earth's surface. The water cycle renews the usable supply of fresh water on Earth. For millions of years, the total amount of water on Earth has remained fairly constant—rates of evaporation and precipitation are balanced.

FIGURE 10
Precipitation
Precipitation is part of the water cycle. But you might not want it falling on your head!

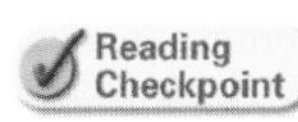
Reading Checkpoint List three sources from which water evaporates.

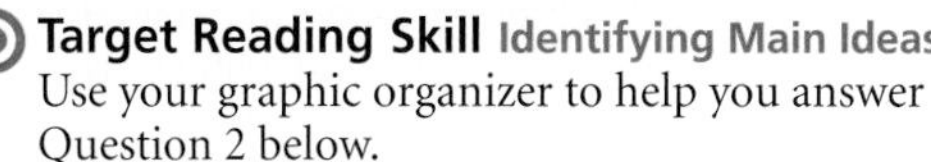
Section 2 Assessment

Target Reading Skill Identifying Main Ideas Use your graphic organizer to help you answer Question 2 below.

Reviewing Key Concepts

1. a. Describing What are two reasons that living things need water?
   b. Applying Concepts Why can't animals survive more than a few days without water?
   c. Developing Hypotheses Some desert animals live for many days without drinking water. How do you think these animals survive?
2. a. Listing What are the four main sources of water on Earth?
   b. Classifying Which of the four main water sources contain salt water? Which contain fresh water?
   c. Making Judgments Which freshwater source is most important to people? Use facts to defend your answer.
3. a. Identifying What three major steps make up the water cycle?
   b. Sequencing Starting with a puddle on a sunny day, describe how water might move through the water cycle and eventually fall back as rain.

Writing in Science

Product Label Create a product label for bottled drinking water, explaining to consumers why water is a precious resource.

Monitor Progress L2

Answers
Figure 9 Precipitation

Reading Checkpoint Any three: Oceans, lakes, puddles, soil, groundwater, surface runoff, plants, animals

Assess

Reviewing Key Concepts

1. a. All living things need water to carry out body processes. Many living things use water for shelter. **b.** Animals need water in order to obtain chemicals from their surroundings, break down food, grow, reproduce, and move substances within their bodies. **c.** Some animals may require less water for body processes. Animals in hot deserts may be active during cooler parts of the day or at night.
2. a. Oceans, ice, rivers and lakes, and groundwater **b.** Oceans and some lakes contain salt water. Rivers, icebergs, most lakes, and groundwater contain fresh water. **c.** Possible answer: Groundwater, because it contains the greatest percentage of usable fresh water
3. a. Evaporation, condensation, and precipitation **b.** Liquid water evaporates from the puddle to become water vapor. Clouds form as water vapor rises and cools. Water droplets condense and then fall back to Earth as precipitation. That water eventually evaporates again, continuing the process.

Reteach L1

Use the figures to summarize the distribution of Earth's water and how water moves through the water cycle.

Performance Assessment L2

Writing Encourage students to think about the types of precipitation and sources of water in the area where they live. Then have each student write a detailed description of the water cycle.

All in One Teaching Resources
- Section Summary: *Water on Earth*
- Review and Reinforce: *Water on Earth*
- Enrich: *Water on Earth*

Lab zone Chapter Project

Keep Students on Track Check that students have kept a daily record of water use and have listed the different uses of water in the home. Advise them to calculate the total amount of water used over one week by recording readings on a water meter or by estimating usage based on estimates for common household activities.

Writing in Science

Writing Skill Description
Scoring Rubric
4 Exceeds criteria by showing creativity and including extra details, such as art
3 Meets criteria
2 Explanation lacks imagination or is incomplete
1 Is incorrect and incomplete

Water From Trees L2

Prepare for Inquiry

Skills Objectives
Students will be able to
- observe the product of transpiration in leaves
- calculate the mass of the water transpired by leaves after 24 hours
- infer the important role that plants play in the water cycle

Class Time 20 minutes for setup; 20 minutes the next day

All in One Teaching Resources
- Lab Worksheet: *Water From Trees*

Safety
Caution students to avoid plants such as poison ivy and poison oak. Show pictures of these plants so that students will recognize them. Instruct students to carry out the activity in secure, familiar places. Review the safety guidelines in Appendix A.

Guide Inquiry

Troubleshooting the Experiment
- The bigger the leaf, the greater the difference in mass after 24 hours. Point students toward plants with large leaves.
- Advise students to twist the ties tightly so that the bags will be as airtight as possible.

Expected Outcome
After 24 hours, the bags should contain liquid water from transpiration. The water vapor given off by the leaves will have condensed because of the cooler overnight temperatures. Therefore, the bags will have more mass than before.

Analyze and Conclude
1. The difference in mass is a result of the water that collected in the bags over 24 hours.

2. Transpiration; plants absorb water from the ground and release water that evaporates into the atmosphere.

3. 260 L/day × 1,000 trees × 365 days = 94,900,000 L

4. Possible response: Trees are part of the global water cycle. If forests are destroyed, the water cycle may be affected because trees increase the amount of water vapor in the atmosphere.

Lab zone Skills Lab

Water From Trees

Problem
How much water do the leaves on a tree give off in a 24-hour period?

Skills Focus
observing, inferring, calculating

Materials
- 3 plastic sandwich bags
- balance
- 3 small pebbles
- 3 twist ties

Procedure
1. Copy the data table into your notebook.
2. Place the sandwich bags, twist ties, and pebbles on a balance. Determine their total mass to the nearest tenth of a gram.
3. Select an outdoor tree or shrub with leaves that are within your reach.
4. Put one pebble into a sandwich bag. Place the bag over one of the tree's leaves as shown. Fasten a twist tie around the bag, forming a tight seal around the stem of the leaf.
5. Repeat Step 4 on two more leaves, using the remaining plastic bags. Leave the bags in place for 24 hours.
6. The following day, examine the bags and record your observations in your notebook.
7. Carefully remove the bags from the leaves and refasten each twist tie around its bag so that the bag is closed tightly.
8. Place the three bags, including pebbles and twist ties, on the balance. Determine their total mass to the nearest tenth of a gram.
9. Subtract the original mass of the bags, ties, and pebbles that you found in Step 2 from the mass you found in Step 8.

Data Table	
Starting mass of bags, ties, and pebbles	
Mass of bags, ties, and pebbles after 24 hours	
Difference in mass	

Analyze and Conclude
1. **Observing** Use the observations you made in Step 6 to account for the difference in mass you found in Step 9.
2. **Inferring** What is the name of the process that caused the results you observed? Explain the role of that process in the water cycle.
3. **Calculating** A single birch tree may give off as much as 260 liters of water in a day. How much water would a grove of 1,000 birch trees return to the atmosphere in a year?
4. **Communicating** Based on what you learned from this lab, write a paragraph explaining why some people are concerned about the destruction of forests around the world.

Design an Experiment
Write a hypothesis about what would happen if you repeated this activity with a different type of tree. Design a plan to test your hypothesis. *Obtain your teacher's permission before carrying out your investigation.*

Extend Inquiry

Design an Experiment Students may record different results with different types of trees.

Section 3

Surface Water

Reading Preview

Key Concepts

- What is a river system?
- How do ponds and lakes form?
- What changes can occur in lakes?

Key Terms

- tributary • watershed
- divide • reservoir • nutrient
- eutrophication

Target Reading Skill

Outlining As you read, make an outline of this section. Use the red headings for the main ideas and the blue headings for the supporting ideas.

Surface Water

I. River systems
  A. Tributaries
  B.
  C.
II. Ponds and lakes
  A.

What's in Pond Water?

1. Using a hand lens, observe a sample of pond water.
2. Make a list of everything you see in the water. If you don't know the name of something, write a short description or draw a picture.
3. Your teacher has set up a microscope with a slide of pond water. Observe the slide under the microscope and add any new items to your list. Wash your hands with soap when you are done.

Think It Over

Classifying Use one of these systems to divide the items on your list into two groups: moving/still, living/nonliving, or microscopic/visible without a microscope. What does your classification system tell you about pond water?

Imagine that you are a raindrop falling from the clouds to Earth's surface. Down, down, you go and then, splash! You land in the tumbling waters of a fast-moving stream. You are in one of Earth's freshwater sources. Fresh water on Earth may be moving, as in streams and rivers, or still, as in ponds and lakes. All fresh water, however, comes from precipitation. For example, the Rio Grande—the "Big River"—begins as trickles of melting snow high in the San Juan Mountains in Colorado. But 700 kilometers downstream, the "Big River" lives up to its name as it flows past Albuquerque, New Mexico.

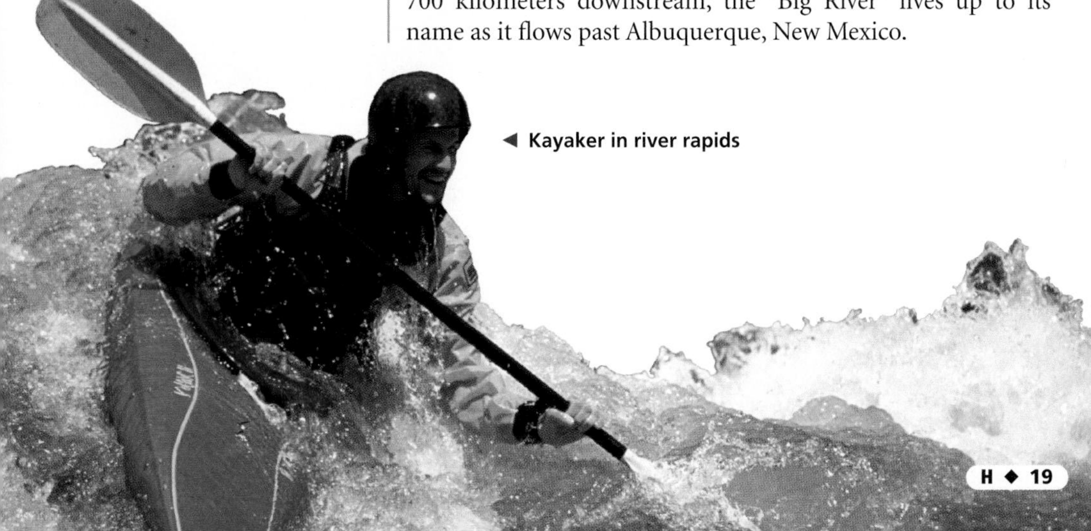

◀ Kayaker in river rapids

H ◆ 19

Discover Activity

Skills Focus Classifying L1

Materials pond water, plastic petri dish, hand lens, microscope, plastic dropper, slide, cover slip

Time 20 minutes

Tips Collect water from a local pond, being sure to obtain some bottom mud and suspended particles, or use prepared slides.

Expected Outcome Using the hand lens, students will see some larger organisms. With the microscope, they will observe an even greater variety of items.

Think It Over Students could use movement or the consumption of smaller particles as criteria for deciding whether items are alive. Pond water contains a variety of living and nonliving things.

Section 3 Surface Water

Objectives

After this lesson, students will be able to

H.1.3.1 Tell what a river system is.

H.1.3.2 Explain how lakes form.

H.1.3.3 Describe the changes that occur in ponds and lakes.

Target Reading Skill

Outlining Explain that using an outline format helps students organize information by main topic, subtopic, and details.

Answers

Surface Water
I. River Systems
  A. Tributaries
  B. Watersheds
  C. Divides
II. Ponds and Lakes
  A. Exploring a Pond
  B. Exploring a Lake
  C. Lake Formation
III. How Lakes Can Change
  A. Seasonal Changes
  B. Long-Term Changes
  C. Death of a Body of Fresh Water

All in One Teaching Resources

- Transparency H6

Preteach

Build Background Knowledge L1

Rivers, Lakes, and Ponds

Encourage students to describe rivers, lakes, and ponds they have seen. Ask questions such as these: **How big are the rivers you have seen? How fast do they flow? What is the land around a river like? How large are lakes and ponds? What types of plants and animals live around them?** List the responses on the board, and encourage students to keep them in mind as they read through the section.

Instruct

River Systems

Teach Key Concepts

L2

The Parts of a River

Focus Ask students for an example of a system. *(Possible answer: Digestive organs make up the digestive system.)*

Teach Explain that just as an organ system is made up of man parts, so a river system is made up of several parts. Refer students to Figure 11, and have them locate the headwaters. Explain that the headwaters are the point at which the river starts. Many small streams come together in the mountains to form the headwaters. **What makes up a river system?** *(A river and all of its tributaries)* **What sources of water can be tributaries?** *(Streams and smaller rivers)* Ask volunteers to trace the flow of water through a river system. Ask: **What causes the tributaries to flow downward?** *(Gravity)*

Apply Explain that streams start from precipitation that is not absorbed into the ground. The water moves over Earth's surface to form grooves that join other grooves to form a channel called a stream. Streams flow downhill and form the tributaries that make up a river. **learning modality: visual**

All in One **Teaching Resources**

- Transparency H7

Independent Practice

L2

All in One **Teaching Resources**

- Guided Reading and Study Worksheet: *Surface Water*

Student Edition on Audio CD

River Systems

If you were hiking in the mountains of Colorado, you could observe the path of the runoff from melting snow. As you followed one small stream downhill, you would notice that the stream reached another stream and joined it. These streams flow into a small river. Eventually this path would lead you to the Rio Grande itself. Figure 11 shows the parts of a typical river.

Tributaries The streams and smaller rivers that feed into a main river are called **tributaries.** Tributaries flow downward toward the main river, pulled by the force of gravity. **A river and all its tributaries together make up a river system.**

FIGURE 11
Exploring a River
Notice the changes that occur as a river flows from its origin to the ocean.

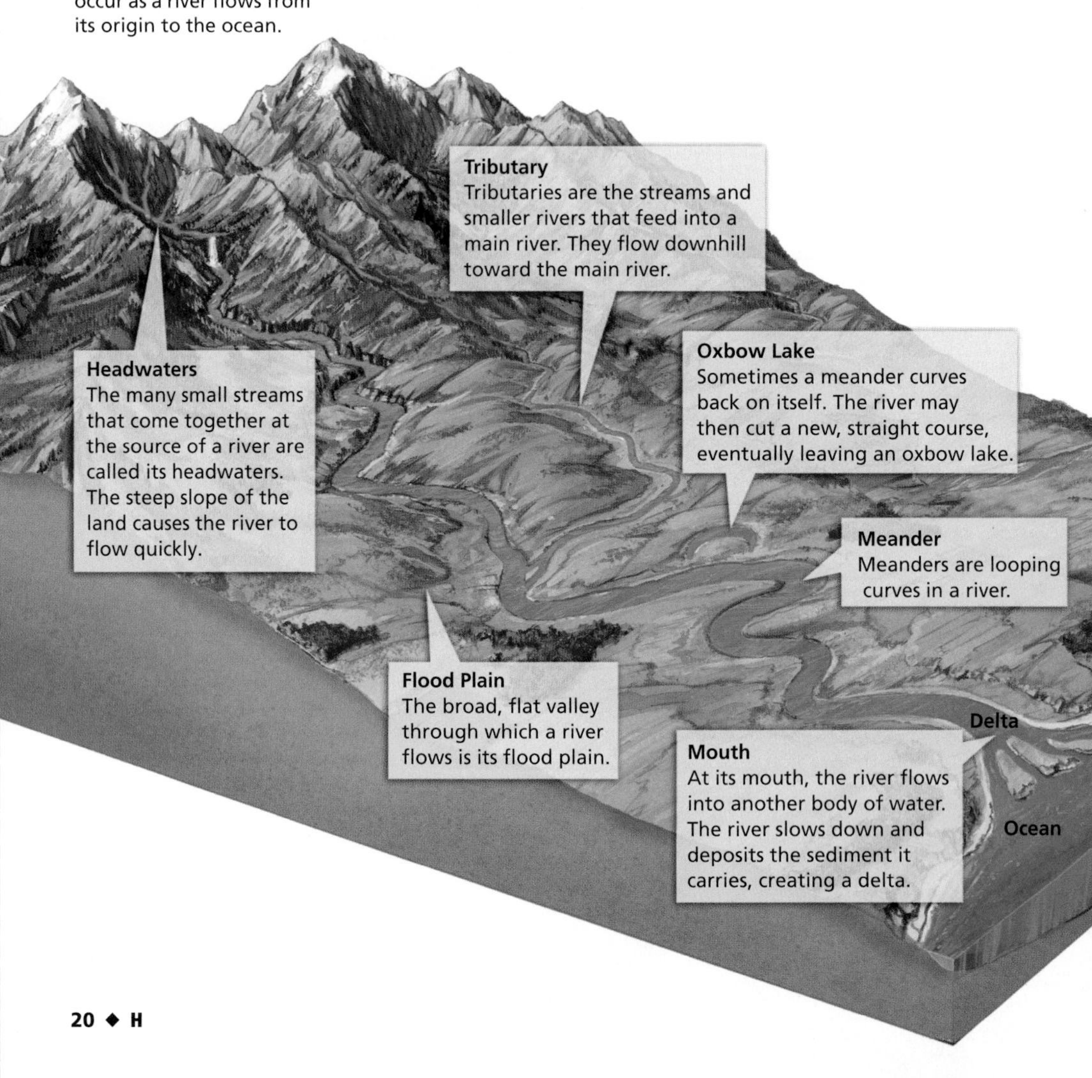

Tributary
Tributaries are the streams and smaller rivers that feed into a main river. They flow downhill toward the main river.
Headwaters
The many small streams that come together at the source of a river are called its headwaters. The steep slope of the land causes the river to flow quickly.
Oxbow Lake
Sometimes a meander curves back on itself. The river may then cut a new, straight course, eventually leaving an oxbow lake.
Meander
Meanders are looping curves in a river.
Flood Plain
The broad, flat valley through which a river flows is its flood plain.
Delta
Mouth
At its mouth, the river flows into another body of water. The river slows down and deposits the sediment it carries, creating a delta.
Ocean

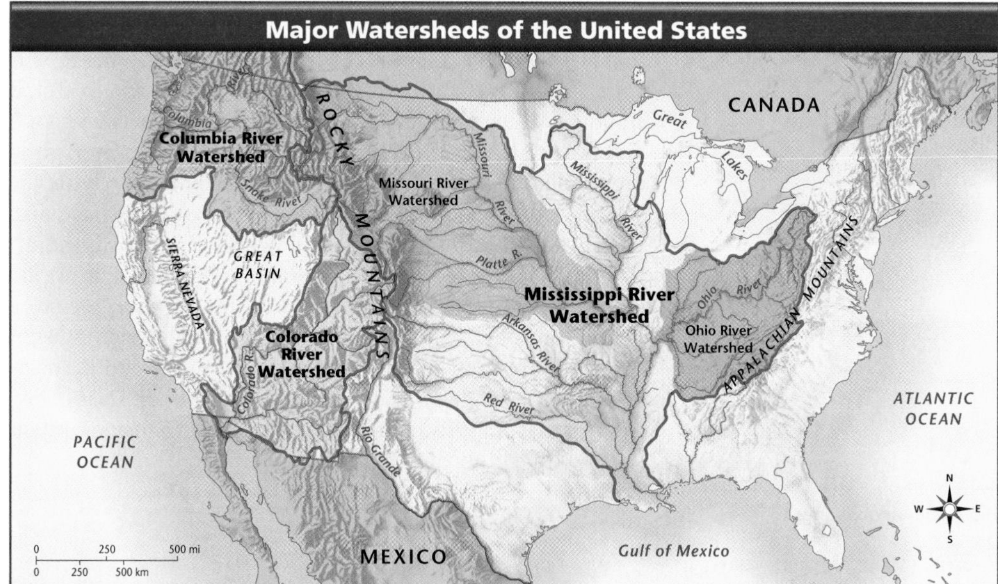

Figure 12
Major Watersheds
This map shows watersheds of several large rivers in the continental United States. Each river's watershed consists of the region drained by the river and all its tributaries. **Interpreting Maps** *What large rivers are tributaries of the Mississippi River?*

Watersheds Just as all the water in a bathtub flows toward the drain, all the water in a river system drains into a main river. The land area that supplies water to a river system is called a **watershed.** Watersheds are sometimes known as drainage basins.

As you can see in Figure 12, the Missouri and Ohio rivers are quite large. Yet they flow into the Mississippi River. So large rivers may be tributaries of still larger rivers. When rivers join another river system, the areas they drain become part of the largest river's watershed. You can identify a river's watershed on a map by drawing an imaginary line around the region drained by all its tributaries. The watershed of the Mississippi River, the largest river in the United States, covers nearly one third of the country!

Divides What keeps watersheds separate? One watershed is separated from another by a ridge of land called a **divide.** Streams on each side of the divide flow in different directions. The Continental Divide, the longest divide in North America, follows the line of the Rocky Mountains. West of the Continental Divide, water either flows toward the Pacific Ocean or into the dry Great Basin. Between the Rocky Mountains and the Appalachian Mountains, water flows toward the Mississippi River or directly into the Gulf of Mexico.

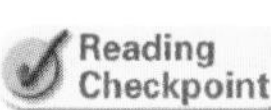 **What is a divide?**

Lab zone Skills Activity

Inferring

The Nile River in Africa flows from south to north. What can you infer about the slope of the land through which the Nile River flows? (*Hint:* Think about the factors that determine how a river system forms.)

H ◆ 21

Lab zone Skills Activity

Skills Focus Inferring L2

Time 10 minutes

Tips Have students locate the Nile River on a world map.

Expected Outcome Higher land (the divide and the Nile's headwaters) must lie to the south. The land to the north of the Nile's source must slope downward to the river's mouth.

Extend Provide world atlases so that students can compare the Nile's shape and direction of flow with the routes of other major rivers. **learning modality: visual**

Use Visuals: Figure 12 L2

Locating Watersheds

Focus Review the definition of a watershed.

Teach Display a large political map of the United States, and have students compare the two maps to see where the rivers and mountains are located within states and regions. Ask: **What role do the Rocky Mountains and the Appalachian Mountains play in the major U.S. watersheds?** *(They are the major divides that separate these watersheds.)*

Apply Encourage students to locate and identify whether your area is in any of the watersheds of the rivers shown. Ask them to identify watersheds for The Rio Grande and for other major rivers that are not labeled, for example, the Connecticut, Hudson, James, Savannah, and Sacramento. **learning modality: visual**

All in One Teaching Resources

- Transparency H8

 L2

Observing Erosion as Rivers Flow

Materials long, high-sided tray or a section of rain gutter; mix of sand, gravel, and small pebbles; water

Focus Review the effects of erosion on a river valley. Refer to Figure 11.

Teach Instruct students to fill the tray with the mix to a height of about 6 cm. Then have them create a narrow, slightly curving river channel about 4 cm deep. Holding the trough at a steep angle, students should next pour a stream of water into the upper end of their simulated river.

Apply Ask: **Where is erosion occurring along the river?** *(On the outside of each curve)* **How does this model the way that an oxbow lake is formed?** *(As water continues to erode the outer edge, the bend becomes larger, eventually curving back on itself.)* **learning modality: kinesthetic**

Monitor Progress L2

Writing Have students write a description of a river system. Tell them not to refer to Figure 11.

Answers

Figure 12 The Missouri, Red, Arkansas, and Ohio Rivers

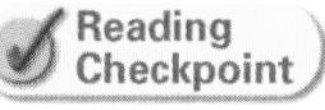 A ridge of land that separates one watershed from another

Ponds and Lakes

For: More on surface water
Visit: PHSchool.com
Web Code: cfd-3013

Students can review surface water in an online interactivity.

Teach Key Concepts L1

How Ponds and Lakes Form

Focus Remind students that water in ponds and lakes is constantly being renewed because of the water cycle.

Teach Ask: **What are some of the sources of precipitation for ponds and lakes?** *(Rainfall and melting snow and ice)* **What surface water helps form ponds and lakes?** *(Water from rivers and groundwater)* **How do ponds and lakes form?** *(Water collects in hollows and low-lying areas of land.)*

Apply Tell students that many communities, especially in cities and towns, rely on lakes for their drinking water. **learning modality: verbal**

Teacher **Demo** L2

Observing Pond Plant Life

Materials pond algae, pond plants, hand lens
Time 10 minutes

Focus Have students recall that plants grow throughout a pond.

Teach Provide specimens of common pond algae, such as *Spirogyra* or *Cladophora,* and pond plants, such as pondweeds, for students to examine. Ask: **How are the algae and plants different?** *(The plants have stems, leaves, and roots, whereas the algae have no such structures.)* **How are they alike?** *(Both are green and can carry out photosynthesis.)*

Apply Ask: **Why are plants and algae vital to pond habitats?** *(They produce food and oxygen for animals through photosynthesis.)* **learning modality: visual**

Go Online PHSchool.com
For: More on surface water
Visit: PHSchool.com
Web Code: cfd-3013

Ponds and Lakes

Ponds and lakes are bodies of fresh water. Unlike the moving water in streams and rivers, ponds and lakes contain still, or standing, water. How can you tell the difference between ponds and lakes? There is no definite rule. In general, however, ponds are smaller and shallower than lakes. Sunlight usually reaches to the bottom of all parts of a pond. Most lakes have areas where the water is too deep for sunlight to reach the bottom.

Ponds and lakes form when water collects in hollows and low-lying areas of land. Where does the water come from? Some ponds and lakes are supplied by rainfall, melting snow and ice, and runoff. Others are fed by rivers or groundwater. As a pond or lake gains water from these sources, it also loses water to natural processes. For example, water may eventually flow out of a body of fresh water into a river. Water also evaporates from the surface of a pond or lake.

FIGURE 13
Life in a Pond
From its shallow edges to its muddy bottom, a pond is rich with life.
Inferring *Why can plants grow throughout a pond?*

Some of the most important pond dwellers are the smallest. Microscopic algae are the pond's basic food producers.
The roots of water lilies cling to the pond bottom, while their leaves float on the surface. Sponges live under the leaves. Dragonflies pause on top to rest.
A slender-bodied pickerel waits among the duckweed to grab a meal of insects at the water's edge.
22 ◆ H

Exploring a Pond A pond might seem calm and peaceful at first glance. But look closer—do you notice the silvery minnows gliding beneath the surface? Plop! A frog has jumped into the water. The quiet pond is actually a thriving habitat, supporting a wide diversity of living things, as shown in Figure 13.

If you've ever waded in a pond, you know that the muddy bottom is often covered with weeds. Because the water is shallow enough for sunlight to reach the bottom, plants grow throughout a pond. Plantlike organisms called algae also live in the pond. As the plants and algae use sunlight to make food through photosynthesis, they also produce oxygen. Animals in the pond use the oxygen and food provided by plants and algae.

The shore is edged with grasses and trees that require a lot of water, such as willows and maples. These plants provide shelter and nesting places for red-winged blackbirds and other birds.
Frogs lay eggs in the shallow water near shore. They hatch in the water as tadpoles and move to the land as adults.
Sunfish and perch live in both the weedy shallows and the deeper waters of the pond.
Snails find food on the soft bottom of the pond.
Crayfish lie buried in the mud, waiting for bits of food to drift down.
H ◆ 23

Use Visuals: Figure 13 L1

Focus Review the definition of habitat.

Teach Invite student volunteers to read the captions in Figure 13. Ask: **What are some different habitats that are described?** *(The shore, the shallow water near the shore, the bottom of the pond, the surface, and the deeper waters)* Explain that not all ponds exist year-round. For example, some ponds in the northern and western United States appear only in the spring, when runoff from spring rains and melting snow collects in low areas. The ponds dry up by midsummer as the shallow water evaporates in the heat.

Apply Ask students to infer why even temporary ponds are important to wildlife. Have students use examples of organisms shown in the figure in their answers. *(Frogs, birds, flying insects, and other animals could leave the pond during dry periods and return to it when it filled again. Temporary ponds could provide habitats for organisms that require water during only part of their life cycles, such as frogs. Some plants may be able to survive the dry conditions until the pond fills again.)* **learning modality: visual**

Differentiated Instruction

English Learners/Beginning L1

Comprehension: Key Concept On the board, rewrite the boldface sentence under Ponds and Lakes. Have students construct a concept circle (cluster diagram) with this sentence in the center and words and phrases describing characteristics of ponds connected to the center by lines. **learning modality: verbal**

English Learners/Intermediate L2

Comprehension: Key Concept Read aloud the boldface sentence. Ask individual students to identify characteristics of ponds. Then pair students with students who are proficient in English, and have the partners summarize the contents of the text and visuals on these two pages. **learning modality: verbal**

Monitor Progress L2

Writing Ask students to imagine that they are organisms that live in a pond. Then have each student write a short story describing his or her habitat and activities. Remind students to keep their stories scientific. Students can place their stories in their portfolios. Portfolio

Answer

Figure 13 The water in a pond is shallow enough that sunlight can reach all areas.

Help Students Read L1

Visualizing Explain that visualizing helps readers understand the text. Ask students to read the third paragraph on this page, which describes the wildlife in a lake. Ask them to imagine what the lake looks like as they read the material. Advise them to read slowly so that they can identify the details that will help construct a mental image. When students have finished reading the paragraph, have each of them describe to a partner the mental images that he or she formed.

Integrating Life Science L1

Explain that an ecosystem is a collection of all the organisms that live in a particular place, together with their physical environment. Energy flows through an ecosystem from the sun to organisms that make their own food, such as plants and algae, to other organisms that cannot make their own food. In a food chain, organisms transfer energy by eating and being eaten. Ask: **What feeding relationships are identified in the text?** *(Loons and kingfishers eat fish. Mollusks feed on food particles that drift down from the surface. Large bony fish eat tiny bottom dwellers; they also feed on other fish and small birds at the surface.)*

Challenge students to draw a food chain that illustrates one set of feeding relationships that exists in a lake habitat. **learning modality: verbal**

FIGURE 14

Types of Lakes

A lake can be formed either by a natural process or by human efforts. **Interpreting Photographs** *What are three ways that lakes are formed?*

Volcanic Lake
Volcanic lakes such as this one in Costa Rica form when water fills the craters of old volcanoes.

Lab zone Skills Activity

Classifying

Crumple up a piece of wax paper. Straighten out the paper to model a landscape with hills and valleys. Use a permanent marker to draw lines along the highest divides of the landscape. Then draw circles where lakes and ponds will form on the landscape. Place the wax paper in a sink and sprinkle water over the landscape to simulate rain. Observe where the water collects. Which areas would you classify as ponds? Which would be lakes? Explain your reasoning.

Exploring a Lake Suppose you were shown a picture of a sandy beach. Waves are breaking on the shore. The water stretches as far as the eye can see. Gulls are screeching overhead. Where was the picture taken? Your first guess might be the ocean. But this immense body of water could actually be a lake! You could be viewing a photo of a beach in Indiana, on the shore of Lake Michigan.

Most lakes are not as large as Lake Michigan. But recall that lakes are generally deeper and bigger than ponds. A lake bottom may consist of sand, pebble, or rock, whereas the bottom of a pond is usually covered with mud and algae.

In the shallow water near shore, the wildlife of a lake is similar to that of a pond. Water beetles scurry over the slippery, moss-covered rocks. Loons and kingfishers pluck fishes from the open water. But sunlight does not reach the bottom of a deep lake, as it does in a pond. As a result, only a few organisms can live in lake's chilly, dark depths. There are no plants, but mollusks, such as clams, and worms move along the lake bottom. They feed on food particles that drift down from the surface. Deep lake waters are also home to large, bony fishes such as pike and sturgeon. These fishes eat the tiny bottom-dwellers. They also swim to the surface to feed on other fishes and even small birds.

Lab zone Skills Activity

Skills Focus Classifying

Materials wax paper, permanent marker, water L2

Time 10 minutes

Tips Caution students not to drench the wax paper with water, but to lightly sprinkle drops over the paper.

Expected Outcome Pools of water will collect in the low parts of the wax paper. Students may say that the smaller depressions in the paper are ponds, and the larger depressions are lakes.

Extend Ask students to make a wax paper model that shows how a river might form. **learning modality: kinesthetic**

Glacier-Made Lake
Lake Louise in Alberta, Canada, was formed by the movements of glaciers.

Human-Made Lake
The Lake Mead reservoir is part of the Hoover Dam complex in the southwestern United States.

Lake Formation As you read earlier, lakes and ponds form when water collects in hollows and low-lying areas of land. Let's take a closer look at some natural processes that can result in the formation of a lake. A river channel, for example, can form a lake as it changes over time. It bends and loops as it encounters obstacles in its path. Eventually, a new channel might form, cutting off a loop. The cut-off loop may become an oxbow lake.

Some other natural lakes, such as the Great Lakes, formed in depressions created by ice sheets that melted at the end of the Ice Age. Other lakes were created by movements of Earth's crust. Such movements formed the deep valleys in central Africa that lie below Lake Tanganyika and Lake Victoria. Still other lakes are the result of volcanoes. An erupting volcano can cause a flow of lava or mud that blocks a river and forms a lake. Some lakes form in the empty craters of volcanoes.

People can also create a lake by building a dam across a river. The lake may be used for supplying drinking water, for irrigating fields, and for recreation. A lake that stores water for human use is called a **reservoir.**

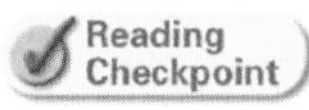 **What is a reservoir?**

L2

Modeling How a Lake Forms

Materials pan, sand, silt, water, yarn, sticks, clay, other craft materials

Time 30 minutes

Focus Review how the lakes in Figure 14 formed.

Teach After students read the text and examine the visuals, challenge them to build a model of one way in which a lake is formed. They may wish to describe the formation of a glacial lake, an oxbow lake, a volcanic lake, or a lake created by a dam. Students may design a simple model that shows the formation of an oxbow lake, perhaps by using a series of yarn loops to show the formation sequence. Students may also choose a more complex project, such as using fine sand or silt and flowing water to create a "lake in progress."

Apply Ask students to use their models to describe how changes in Earth's surface affect the formation of a lake. Ask: **Do lakes form from slow changes or events that happen over a short period of time?** *(Glacial lakes and oxbow lakes are formed over long periods of time. Volcanoes may form and movement of Earth's crust may happen over short periods, but it may take a much longer time for a lake to form as a result of these events.)* **learning modality: kinesthetic**

Differentiated Instruction

Gifted and Talented L3

Investigating Totora Reed Lakes Invite students to find out about the totora reed lakes on Lake Titicaca, which is located on the border of Peru and Bolivia in the Andes Mountains. *(Around the edges of the lake grows a hollow reed called totora. The local people weave totora reeds together to form "islands" that are strong enough to hold homes and livestock. Ropes, boats, tea, and medicine are also made from the reeds.)* Ask students to find pictures of these islands and to infer why people first started living on them centuries ago. *(Possible answers: Protection against enemies; natural resources unavailable on shore; and escape from overcrowded conditions on the lake's shore or elsewhere)* **learning modality: verbal**

Monitor Progress L2

Skills Check Have each student construct a compare-and-contrast chart that shows the similarities and differences between lakes and ponds. Charts should include the physical characteristics of ponds and lakes, significant details about how lakes and ponds are formed, and the types of plant and animal life found there.

Answers

Figure 14 Lakes may form when water fills a volcanic crater, a depression made by a glacier, or a reservoir behind a dam.

 A lake that stores water for human use

How Lakes Can Change

Teach Key Concepts L1

Types of Changes in a Lake

Focus Remind students that rivers are constantly moving, whereas lakes and ponds are still.

Teach Explain that rivers are constantly mixing nutrients and have a steady supply of oxygen year-round. The levels of nutrients in ponds and lakes vary with seasonal and long-term changes. Ask: **How do lakes change with the seasons?** *(Through lake turnover: in summer, warm water floats on top of cooler, denser water. In the fall, the top layer cools and sinks, mixing with the lower layers.)* **How does this help plants and algae grow?** *(Lake turnover refreshes the supply of nutrients.)* **What long-term change causes scum to form on the surface of lakes and ponds?** *(Eutrophication)* **How does this process lead to the death of a lake or a pond?** *(The algae block out the sunlight, so plants cannot carry out photosynthesis. Plants and other organisms die and decay, and the oxygen in the water decreases. Eventually, the lake or pond fills with decaying plants and animals, and a meadow may take the place of the water.)*

Apply Tell students that fertilizers contain nitrogen and phosphates. Ask: **How can fertilized fields affect ponds and lakes?** *(Runoff from fertilized fields can get into a pond or a lake and cause a rapid increase in algal growth.)* **learning modality: verbal**

All in One Teaching Resources

- Transparency H9

How Lakes Can Change

A maple tree in fall looks very different than it does in the summer. The green leaves change to brilliant shades of red, orange, and yellow. Lakes can change with the seasons, too. Lakes change for many reasons. **In addition to seasonal changes, a lake can undergo long-term changes that may eventually lead to its death.**

Seasonal Changes Seasonal changes in lakes are common in cool, northern areas of North America. In summer, the sun warms the upper layer of water in a lake. The warm water floats on top of the cooler, denser, lower layer. But in fall, the top layer cools off, too. As the top layer cools, it becomes denser and sinks. This causes the lake waters to mix. This mixing, also called lake turnover, causes materials to rise from the lake bottom. Lake turnover refreshes the supply of nutrients throughout the lake. **Nutrients** are substances such as nitrogen and phosphorus that enable plants and algae to grow.

Long-Term Changes The second type of change that may occur in a lake happens over a long period of time. The organisms in a lake constantly release waste products into the water. The wastes and the remains of dead organisms contain nutrients such as nitrates and phosphates. Algae feed on these nutrients. Over many years, the nutrients build up in the lake in a process called **eutrophication** (yoo troh fih KAY shun). As eutrophication causes more algae to grow, a thick, green scum forms on the surface of the water. Recall that algae are present in ponds as well as lakes. So eutrophication can also occur in ponds.

FIGURE 15
Long-Term Changes in a Lake
Lakes and ponds change gradually over time. **Relating Cause and Effect** *What effect does an increase in nutrient levels have on a lake?*

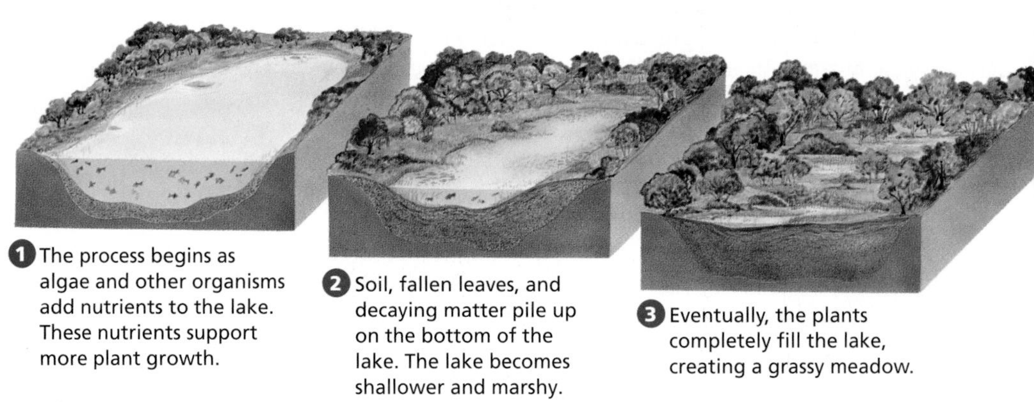

1. The process begins as algae and other organisms add nutrients to the lake. These nutrients support more plant growth.
2. Soil, fallen leaves, and decaying matter pile up on the bottom of the lake. The lake becomes shallower and marshy.
3. Eventually, the plants completely fill the lake, creating a grassy meadow.

Death of a Body of Fresh Water When the algae layer becomes so thick that it blocks out the sunlight, plants in the lake or pond can no longer carry out photosynthesis. They stop producing food and oxygen, and they die. As dead organisms in the water decay, the amount of oxygen in the water decreases. Many of the fish and other water animals no longer have enough oxygen to live. Material from decaying plants and animals piles up on the bottom, and the lake or pond becomes shallower. The sun warms the water to a higher temperature and more plants take root in the rich bottom mud. Eventually, the body of fresh water becomes completely filled with plants. The remaining water evaporates, and a grassy meadow takes the place of the former lake or pond.

Eutrophication is not the only change that can lead to the death of a lake or pond. Sometimes, water may leave a pond more rapidly than it enters it. This can happen when the source of water for a pond—a stream, for example—dries up or is cut off from the pond by natural processes such as erosion. In addition, streams and rivers carry sediments into ponds or lakes. Over a long period of time, these sediments can fill in the body of water.

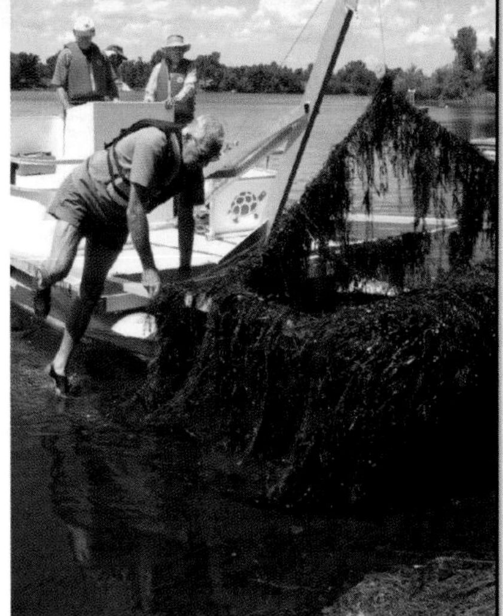

FIGURE 16
Halting Eutrophication
In some locations, a community will periodically clean out a pond or lake in order to prolong its life.

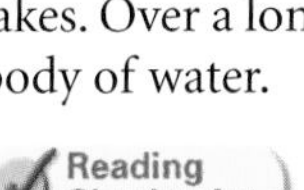

What kinds of materials can build up over time at the bottom of a lake?

Section 3 Assessment

Target Reading Skill **Outlining** Use the information in your outline to help you answer the questions below.

Reviewing Key Concepts

1. a. **Identifying** What bodies of water make up a river system?
   b. **Summarizing** How is a watershed related to a river system?
   c. **Applying Concepts** How could you determine the boundaries of a river system by studying a map of the United States?
2. a. **Reviewing** How are lakes different from ponds?
   b. **Explaining** Explain how ponds and lakes form.
   c. **Comparing and Contrasting** What is the major difference between a reservoir and most other types of lakes?
3. a. **Explaining** What causes lake turnover?
   b. **Sequencing** Describe the changes that take place at each stage of eutrophication.

Lab zone At-Home Activity

The Knuckle Divide Have a family member make a fist and put it on a paper towel, knuckles facing up. Dribble water from a spoon so that it falls onto the person's knuckles. As you both observe how the water flows over the hand, explain how the knuckles model a mountain range. Which parts of the hand represent a watershed?

Monitor Progress L2

Answers

Figure 15 When the amount of nutrients increases, the growth of algae increases, leading to eutrophication.

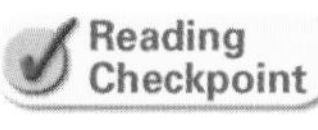

Material from decaying plants and animals and sediment from streams and rivers

Assess

Reviewing Key Concepts

1. a. Rivers and tributaries **b.** A watershed is the land area that supplies water to a river system. **c.** A topographical map of the United States shows where the watersheds are separated by ridges of land called divides.

2. a. Lakes are generally larger and deeper than ponds. Sunlight reaches the bottom of a pond, enabling plants to grow; in a lake, sunlight cannot penetrate to the bottom. **b.** Water collecting in hollows and low-lying areas of land, water filling in the craters of old volcanoes, ice melting in depressions created by ice sheets, and building a dam across a river **c.** A reservoir is constructed for human purposes. Other types of lakes formed naturally.

3. a. The top layer of water cools in the colder weather and sinks, mixing with layers underneath. **b.** During eutrophication, growth of algae increases, blocking out sunlight. Over time, plants stop producing food and die. Soon fish and other animals do not have enough oxygen to breathe, and they, too, die. Wastes and remains of dead organisms build up. Eventually, the lake fills with waste material and sediment, and it becomes a meadow.

Reteach L1

As a class, make a chart comparing and contrasting the characteristics and formation of rivers, ponds, and lakes.

All in One Teaching Resources

- Section Summary: *Surface Water*
- Review and Reinforce: *Surface Water*
- Enrich: *Surface Water*

Lab zone At-Home Activity

The Knuckle Divide L1 Advise students to pour the water slowly to be sure that it falls on top of the knuckles. The back of the hand represents one watershed, the fingers represent a second watershed, and the knuckles represent a divide between the two watersheds.

Lab zone Chapter Project

Keep Students on Track Ascertain that students have chosen a building in the community to monitor. Review students' choices, and advise them to contact a building manager or facilities manager about water use. Lead a role-play interview or phone call with students for practice. Have them write the questions they will ask.

Section 4

Wetland Environments

Objectives

After this lesson, students will be able to

H.1.4.1 Describe the common types of freshwater wetlands.

H.1.4.2 Identify human activities that threaten the Florida Everglades.

H.1.4.3 Explain important functions that wetlands serve.

Target Reading Skill

Asking Questions Explain that changing a head into a question helps students anticipate the ideas, facts, and events that they will read about in this chapter.

Answers

Possible answers:

What are the types of wetlands? *(The three types of wetlands are marshes, swamps, and bogs.)* **What is the Everglades?** *(The Everglades is a region of wetlands stretching from Lake Okeechobee south to Florida Bay.)* **How are wetlands important?** *(They provide habitats for many living things and have many functions useful to people.)*

All in One Teaching Resources

- Transparency H10

Preteach

Build Background Knowledge L1

Types of Wetlands

Write the terms *marsh, swamp,* and *bog* on the board, and ask: **What is similar about all three of these areas?** *(All are wet, and the water in them is not as deep as the water in a pond or lake.)* Then have students define each term in their own words. Encourage responses that identify differences among the three types of wet areas, but do not correct students' definitions or comment on their accuracy at this time.

Section 4

Wetland Environments

Reading Preview

Key Concepts

- What are the common types of freshwater wetlands?
- Which human activities threaten the Florida Everglades?
- What important functions do wetlands serve?

Key Term

- wetland

Target Reading Skill

Asking Questions Before you read, preview the red headings. In a graphic organizer like the one below, ask a *what* or a *how* question for each heading. As you read, write the answers to your questions.

Wetland Environments

Question	Answer
What are the types of wetlands?	Three types of wetlands are . . .

Wet or Dry?

1. Hold a kitchen sponge under water until it is soaked. Then squeeze out the water until the sponge is just damp.
2. Place the damp sponge next to a dry sponge in a pan.
3. Pour water into two paper cups until each is half full.
4. Hold a cup in each hand, about 10 centimeters above the pan. Pour the water onto both sponges at the same time.

Think It Over

Observing Which of the sponges absorbs water faster? How are your observations related to what might happen in areas of wet and dry land?

Imagine coming home from a long trip, only to find that your house is gone and has been replaced by a parking lot! Millions of migrating birds have had a similar experience. But people are beginning to understand the importance of wetlands, both to wildlife and to people. A **wetland** is a land area that is covered with a shallow layer of water during some or all of the year. These soggy regions, as you'll learn, are important in many ways.

FIGURE 17
Freshwater Wetlands
Freshwater wetlands can differ in many ways. **Predicting** *Which types of wetlands are you more likely to find in northern areas?*

Marsh Marshes, such as this one in Washington State, are grassy areas covered with shallow water.

Lab zone Discover Activity L1

Skills Focus observing

Materials 2 dry kitchen sponges, water, pan, 2 paper clips

Time 15 minutes

Tips Make sure that sponges are completely dry when students begin.

Expected Outcome The damp sponge will absorb water immediately, and water will run off the dry sponge.

Think It Over The damp sponge absorbs water faster. It models the behavior of wetlands, which soak up excess water and help prevent flooding. The dry sponge models dry land.

Types of Wetlands

Wetlands help control floods and provide habitats for many species. They form in places where water is trapped in low areas or where groundwater seeps to the surface. Wetlands may be as small as a roadside ditch or cover as much area as a city. Some wetlands fill up during spring rains, only to dry up during long, hot summers. Others are covered with water year-round.

The three common types of freshwater wetlands are marshes, swamps, and bogs. As shown in Figure 17, these wetlands are quite diverse. Marshes are usually grassy areas covered by shallow water or a stream. They teem with cattails and other tall, grasslike plants. Swamps look more like flooded forests, with trees and shrubs sprouting from the water. Many swamps are located in warm, humid climates, where trees grow quickly. Bogs are more common in cooler northern areas. They often form in depressions left by melting ice sheets thousands of years ago. The water in bogs tends to be acidic, and mosses thrive in these conditions.

Wetlands along coasts usually contain both fresh and salt water. Coastal wetlands include salt marshes and mangrove forests. Salt marshes are found along both coasts of the United States. Tall, strong grasses grow in the rich, muddy bottoms of salt marshes. Mangrove forests are found along the southeastern coast of the United States. In these forests, the mangrove trees are short and have thick, tangled roots.

For: Links on wetlands
Visit: www.SciLinks.org
Web Code: scn-0814

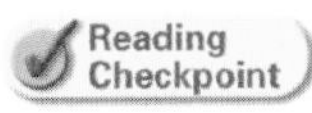

Name three types of freshwater wetlands.

Swamp Swamps look like flooded forests. Curtains of Spanish moss hang from cypress trees in this Louisiana swamp.

Bog Mosses thrive in the acidic water in bogs. Colorful flowers dot a bed of velvety moss in this bog in Montana.

Instruct

Types of Wetlands

For: Links on wetlands
Visit: www.SciLinks.org
Web Code: scn-0814

Download a worksheet that will guide students' review of Internet resources on wetlands.

Teach Key Concepts L1

Bogs, Swamps, and Marshes

Focus Refer students to the illustrations of the different types of wetlands.

Teach Ask students to describe a marsh. *(It is a grassy area covered by shallow water or a stream.)* Ask: **How does the swamp look different from the marsh?** *(The swamp is a forest with many trees.)* **What is a bog?** *(Wetlands in cooler northern areas that have acidic water and mosses)*

Apply Ask: **What criteria would you use to classify types of wetlands?** *(Possible answer: Types of plants, type of soil, and climate)* **learning modality: visual**

Independent Practice L2

All in One Teaching Resources

- Guided Reading and Study Worksheet: *Wetland Environments*

Student Edition on Audio CD

Differentiated Instruction

English Learners/Beginning L1

Comprehension: Modified Cloze Write some simple sentences on the board that require the terms *marsh, swamp, bog,* and *wetland.* For example: A grassy area covered by a shallow layer or stream of water is a ______." Model how to do the first one. As students read through the section, have them fill in the blanks. **learning modality: verbal**

English Learners/Intermediate L2

Comprehension: Modified Cloze Use the same sentences described for the *Beginning* activity, but fill in incorrect terms. Have students work in pairs to determine the correct answers. **learning modality: verbal**

Monitor Progress L2

Skills Check Have each student draw a Venn diagram to show the similarities and differences among the three types of freshwater wetlands described.

Students can place their diagrams in their portfolios. Portfolio

Answers

Figure 17 You are more likely to find marshes and bogs than swamps in northern areas.

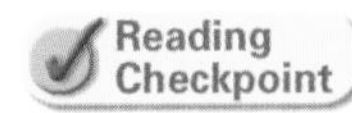

Marshes, swamps, and bogs

The Everglades: A Wetland

Help Students Read **L1**

SQ3R Have students **survey** the diagram, illustrations, and photos for this section and write a short explanation of each. Then have them write **questions, read** the the section, **recite** their questions, and give the answers in their own words. Tell students to **review** the section by writing their answers and then answer the key concepts questions on the first page of the section.

Teach Key Concepts **L2**

Threats to the Everglades

Focus Ask: **What type of wetland is shown on these pages?** *(A marsh; it is covered mostly with grass.)*

Teach Ask students to examine Figure 18. Tell students that the Everglades also has cypress swamps and mangrove forests. Have students examine the figure and identify the different plants and animals featured. Ask: **Why is preserving the Everglades important for wildlife?** *(The park provides habitats for many rare or endangered species.)* **Why is this habitat threatened?** *(Human activities are upsetting this environment. Farming has introduced chemicals that upset the balance of nutrients. Development is filling in areas for new homes and roads. New species are being introduced that compete with native organisms for food and space.)*

Apply Provide or have students investigate a list of endangered species in the Everglades, and find out what they can do to help preserve this wetland. Information can be accessed on the Web site of the National Park Service. **learning modality: verbal**

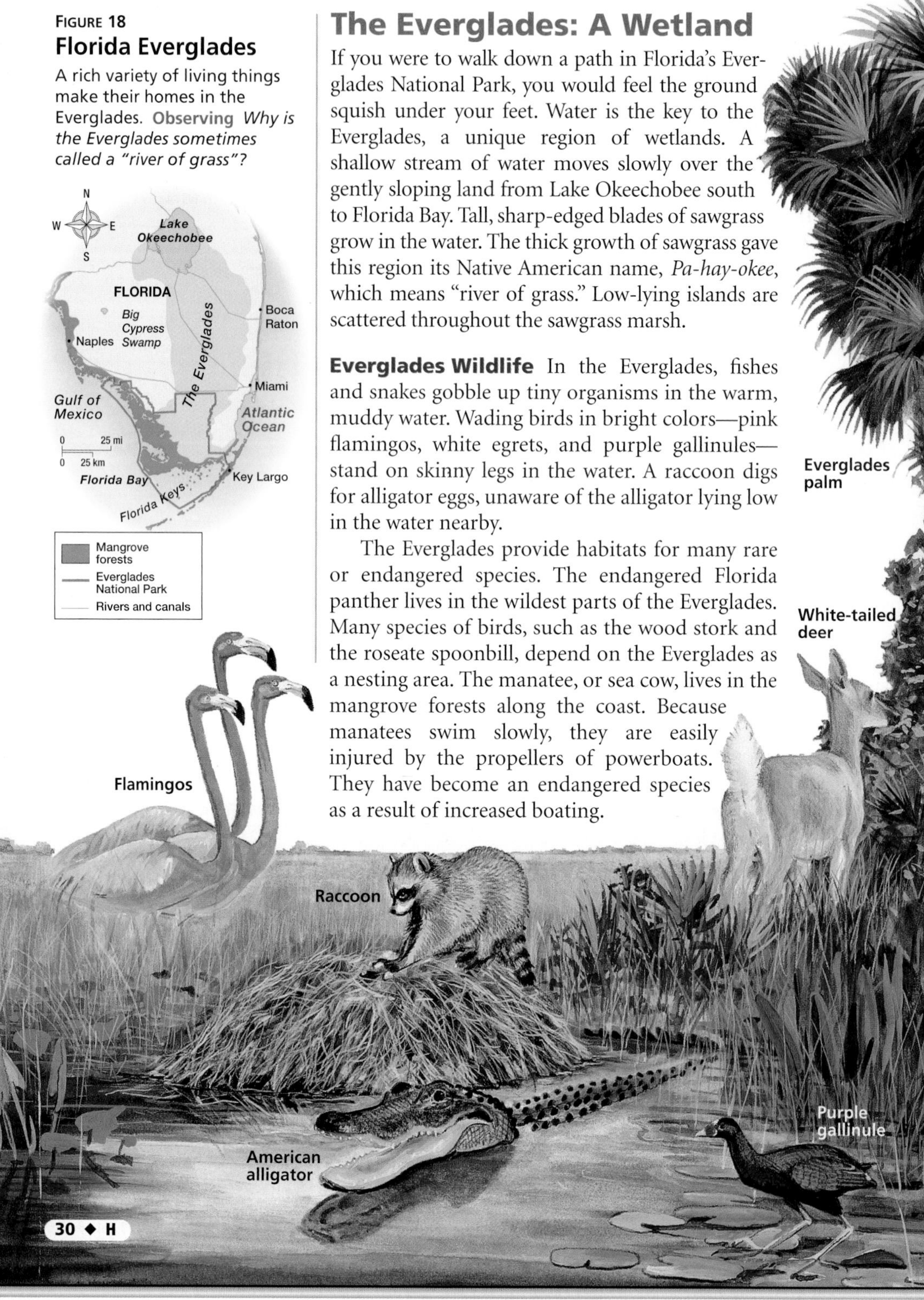

FIGURE 18
Florida Everglades
A rich variety of living things make their homes in the Everglades. Observing Why is the Everglades sometimes called a "river of grass"?
N
S
E
W
Lake Okeechobee
FLORIDA
Big Cypress Swamp
Naples
The Everglades
Boca Raton
Miami
Gulf of Mexico
Atlantic Ocean
25 mi
25 km
Florida Bay
Florida Keys
Key Largo
Mangrove forests
Everglades National Park
Rivers and canals
The Everglades: A Wetland
If you were to walk down a path in Florida's Everglades National Park, you would feel the ground squish under your feet. Water is the key to the Everglades, a unique region of wetlands. A shallow stream of water moves slowly over the gently sloping land from Lake Okeechobee south to Florida Bay. Tall, sharp-edged blades of sawgrass grow in the water. The thick growth of sawgrass gave this region its Native American name, Pa-hay-okee, which means "river of grass." Low-lying islands are scattered throughout the sawgrass marsh.
Everglades Wildlife In the Everglades, fishes and snakes gobble up tiny organisms in the warm, muddy water. Wading birds in bright colors—pink flamingos, white egrets, and purple gallinules—stand on skinny legs in the water. A raccoon digs for alligator eggs, unaware of the alligator lying low in the water nearby.
The Everglades provide habitats for many rare or endangered species. The endangered Florida panther lives in the wildest parts of the Everglades. Many species of birds, such as the wood stork and the roseate spoonbill, depend on the Everglades as a nesting area. The manatee, or sea cow, lives in the mangrove forests along the coast. Because manatees swim slowly, they are easily injured by the propellers of powerboats. They have become an endangered species as a result of increased boating.
Everglades palm
White-tailed deer
Flamingos
Raccoon
American alligator
Purple gallinule
30 ◆ H

Threats to the Everglades The Everglades are a fragile environment. Nearby farming has introduced new chemicals into the slow-moving waters of the marsh, upsetting the balance of nutrients. Outside the protected limits of the national park, developers have filled in areas of wetland to build homes and roads. New organisms brought into the area accidentally or for pest control compete with other organisms for space and food. **Agriculture, development, and the introduction of new species are some human activities that threaten the Florida Everglades.**

Water that once flowed into the Everglades from Lake Okeechobee has been diverted for farming and household use. New canals and levees built to provide drinking water and to control flooding have changed the flow of water into and out of the Everglades. Some areas are drying up, while others are flooded.

Preserving the Everglades Scientists, concerned citizens, and government officials have been trying for many years to develop a plan to preserve the Everglades and save its endangered wildlife. One plan involves building an elaborate system of pipes and canals to refill some drained areas with fresh water. The National Park Service, the state of Florida, and the U.S. Army Corps of Engineers are working together to manage the supply of water to areas around and within the Everglades.

Reading Checkpoint **What is one way that farming has affected the Everglades?**

Discovery Channel School

Earth: The Water Planet

Video Preview
▶ Video Field Trip
Video Assessment

Roseate spoonbill
Great egret
Snowy egret
Sawgrass
Little blue heron
Anhinga
Florida panther

Earth: The Water Planet

Show the Video Field Trip to let students learn more about wetlands and the unique characteristics of the Everglades. Discussion question: **What are the characteristics of a wetland?** *(It is an area covered with shallow water for all or part of the year.)*

L2

Designing an Experiment

Materials none

Time 20 minutes for design

Focus Challenge students to design an experiment to answer this question: **What effect do excess fertilizers have on the growth of algae and water plants?**

Teach Point out that the balance of nutrients affects the growth and survival of organisms in a wetlands environment. Have students recall that many fertilizers contain nitrogen and phosphates, and these can cause a rapid increase in algal growth. Have students design an experiment that will test the effect of excess fertilizers on the growth of algae and other plants. Make sure that students develop a hypothesis, describe the experimental design, control variables, record and interpret data, and draw a conclusion.

Apply Encourage students to conduct their experiments and report their results. **learning modality: logical/mathematical**

Differentiated Instruction

Gifted and Talented

L3

Advocating the Importance of Wetlands Have students work in small groups to create public service announcements, television spots, newspaper ads, transit ads, posters, or educational skits designed to increase public awareness of the importance of wetlands. Students can focus on wetlands in general or a specific wetland in your own community or in another region. Have each group present its product to the rest of the class and to the school. **learning modality: visual**

Monitor Progress

Writing Have students write a paragraph describing the wildlife found in wetlands environments, including the Everglades.

Answers

Figure 18 The region has a thick growth of sawgrass. The Native American name for sawgrass means "river of grass."

Either one: It has introduced into the waters of the marsh various chemicals that upset the balance of nutrients; water that once flowed into the Everglades has been diverted for farming.

Importance of Wetlands

Teach Key Concepts

L2

Functions That Wetlands Serve

Focus Remind students that wetlands provide a habitat for many plants and animals.

Teach Ask: **How do wetlands provide a habitat for a variety of wildlife?** *(They have sheltered waters and a rich supply of nutrients.)* **In what ways are wetlands important to people?** *(They help eliminate waste because some waste materials settle out and other wastes are absorbed by plants. Wetlands also help control floods by absorbing extra runoff from heavy rains.)*

Apply Ask: **How can people help protect the remaining wetlands in the United States?** *(People can contact local politicians and ask them to write and enact laws protecting wetland environments.)* **learning modality: verbal**

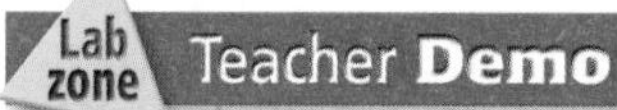

L1

Modeling Plant Roots in a Wetland

Materials clean jar with screw-top lid, soil, water, cotton batting, beaker

Time 10 minutes

Focus Ask: **How do wetland plant roots act as natural water filters?** *(They absorb waste, and they trap silt and mud.)*

Teach Prepare a muddy mixture of soil and water in the jar. Place a layer of cotton batting over the top of a large beaker or another clear container. Gently shake the jar, and ask students to describe the water. *(Very muddy and cloudy)* Wearing goggles, slowly pour the muddy water on the batting. Ask: **What does the water that collected in the bottom of the container look like?** *(A little muddy, but much clearer than the original mixture)*

Apply Ask: **What is the benefit of the roots' trapping mud and silt?** *(Water that drains from the wetlands to other bodies of water is cleaner.)* **learning modality: visual**

Lab zone Try This **Activity**

A Natural Filter

1. Cover your work surface with newspaper. In one end of a loaf pan, build a sloping hill of damp soil.
2. Add water to the other end of the pan to form a lake.
3. Use a watering can to sprinkle rain onto the hill. Observe what happens to the hill and the lake.
4. Empty the water out of the pan and rebuild the hill.

5. Now push a sponge into the soil across the bottom of the hill to model a wetland.
6. Repeat Steps 2 and 3.

Observing Based on your observations, describe how wetlands filter water.

Importance of Wetlands

If you've ever enjoyed tart cranberry sauce or tasty wild rice, you've eaten plants that grow in wetlands. The layer of water covering a wetland can range from several centimeters to a few meters deep. Dead leaves and other plant and animal materials serve as natural fertilizers. They add nitrogen, phosphates, and other nutrients to the water and soil.

Importance to Wildlife **Because of their sheltered waters and rich supply of nutrients, wetlands provide habitats for many living things.** Recall the many plants and animals that live in or near a pond—reeds, frogs, snails, dragonflies, turtles. Some of these same organisms live in freshwater wetlands year-round. Insects dart about, finding food and shelter among wetland plants. Birds nest in and around the wetlands, feeding on the plants and darting insects. In addition, some larger animals, such as manatees, live in the wetlands year-round.

Other animals spend only part of their lives in the wetlands. Have you ever seen or heard a flock of geese flying overhead? The geese may be flying south to make a temporary home in a wetland. As winter approaches, geese, ducks, and other waterfowl travel from Alaska and Canada to warmer climates. They pass millions of small, shallow marshes along their routes. The birds stop at these marshes to rest and feed. The birds then make their way to the large southern marshes where they spend the winter.

FIGURE 19
Wetlands Wildlife
Manatees depend on rich wetland habitats for food and breeding sites.

32 ◆ H

Lab zone Try This **Activity**

Skills Focus Observing

L2

Materials newspaper, loaf pan, damp soil, water, watering can, sponge

Time 20 minutes

Tips Have students start over with new soil in step 4.

Expected Outcome In both trials, water will wash soil down the hill. In the first, the soil will wash into the lake, making it muddy. In the second, the sponge will absorb some water and trap some soil, and the lake should stay clean.

Extend Suggest that students change the slope of the hill or the width of the wetland to see how these factors affect the amount of soil erosion. **learning modality: kinesthetic**

Importance to People Many people, including farmers and builders, once thought wetlands were worthless. They assumed that wetland areas could not be used unless they were drained and filled in. Thousands of square kilometers of wetlands were developed for farms, homes, and businesses. Beginning in the 1970s, however, the government passed laws to protect wetland habitats.

What prompted these laws? Scientific studies showed that wetlands serve important functions for people as well as for wildlife. For example, as water moves slowly through a wetland, some waste materials settle out. Other wastes may be absorbed by plants, such as those shown in Figure 20. The thick network of plant roots also traps silt and mud. **In this way, wetlands act as natural water filters. They also help control floods by absorbing extra runoff from heavy rains.** Wetlands are like giant sponges, storing water until it gradually drains or evaporates. When wetlands are destroyed, the floodwaters are not absorbed. Instead, the water runs off the land quickly, worsening flood problems.

What prompted wetlands protection laws?

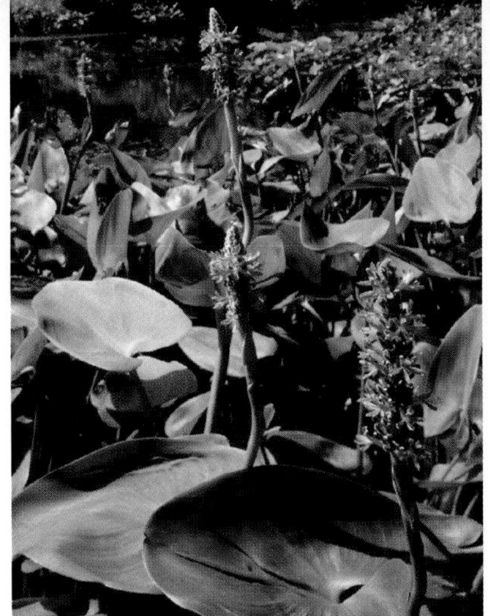

FIGURE 20
Natural Filters
Some wetland plants, such as the pickerel weed shown here, filter pollutants from water. **Inferring** *How are wetland plants like pickerel weed important to people?*

Section 4 Assessment

Target Reading Skill Asking Questions Use the answers to the questions you wrote about the headings to help you answer the questions below.

Reviewing Key Concepts

1. a. **Defining** What is a wetland?
   b. **Classifying** What are the three major types of freshwater wetlands?
   c. **Comparing and Contrasting** How are the three major types of freshwater wetlands similar? How are they different?
2. a. **Listing** List three activities that threaten the Florida Everglades.
   b. **Summarizing** What is being done to preserve the Everglades?
   c. **Making Judgments** Some of the plans to restore the Everglades will require millions of dollars and would negatively affect local farmers. What information would you consider in deciding what should be done?
3. a. **Describing** Name one way that wetlands benefit wildlife and one way that wetlands benefit people.
   b. **Explaining** How do wetlands help reduce water pollution?
   c. **Developing Hypotheses** Without plants, could a wetland still filter water? Explain.

Lab zone At-Home Activity

Runoff Take a family member outside to observe how water runs off different materials. Pour some water in the grass and watch what happens. Then pour some water on the sidewalk or driveway. What happened to the water in each case? How does this relate to the role of wetlands in controlling floods? Why would floods be more frequent if wetlands were paved over?

Lab zone At-Home Activity

Runoff L1 Advise students to use a large bucket or a hose to create runoff. Water in the grass will be absorbed, and water in a driveway will form small streams that flow over the driveway's surface. Wetlands control floods by absorbing water from heavy rainfall.

Monitor Progress L2

Answer

Figure 20 They filter pollutants from water.

Reading Checkpoint Scientific studies showed that wetlands serve important functions for people as well as for wildlife.

Assess

Reviewing Key Concepts

1. a. An area of land that is covered with a shallow layer of water during some or all of the year **b.** Bogs, marshes, and swamps **c.** Similar: All are covered with shallow layers of water during some or all of the year; Different: Bogs are found in cooler, northern areas, tend to be acidic, and contain many mosses. Marshes are usually grassy. Swamps have many trees and shrubs, and are found in the warm and humid southern United States.

2. a. Agriculture, development, and the introduction of new species **b.** Scientists and government officials have developed a plan that involves building a system of pipes to refill drained areas of the Everglades with fresh water. **c.** Answers may include the number of farmers affected and their projected losses, possible commercial uses of the restored Everglades (such as wildlife tours) and their projected revenues, and possible replacements for current agricultural practices or crops.

3. a. Wildlife: Wetlands provide habitats for many living things; People: Wetlands help control floods. **b.** Some wastes are absorbed by plants, and plant roots also trap silt and mud. **c.** No; silt and mud are trapped by the thick network of plant roots, and wastes are absorbed by the plants themselves.

Reteach L1

Use the photos and illustrations in this section to review the types of organisms that live in wetlands habitats and how these habitats are important to people.

All in One Teaching Resources

- Section Summary: *Wetland Environments*
- Review and Reinforce: *Wetland Environments*
- Enrich: *Wetland Environments*

Section 5

Water Underground

Objectives

After this lesson, students will be able to

H.1.5.1 Describe how water moves through underground layers of soil and rock.

H.1.5.2 Explain how people obtain water from an aquifer.

Target Reading Skill

Previewing Visuals Explain that looking at the visuals before they read helps students activate prior knowledge and predict what they are about to read.

Answers

Possible answers:

What is an artesian well? *(It is a well in which water rises because of pressure within an aquifer.)* **Where does the water that supplies a well come from?** *(Underground water comes from precipitation that trickles down between particles of soil and through cracks and spaces in layers of rock.)*

All in One Teaching Resources

- Transparency H11

Preteach

Build Background Knowledge L1

Sources of Water

Show the class a bottle of spring water you have purchased. Ask: **What was the original source of this water?** *(Students may mention wells, springs, or other sources.)* **Where does the water in springs come from?** *(Students may be unsure or may suggest an underground supply. Some may know the term "aquifer.")* Acknowledge responses without comment at this time.

Section 5

Water Underground

Reading Preview

Key Concepts

- How does water move through underground layers of soil and rock?
- How do people obtain water from an aquifer?

Key Terms

- permeable
- impermeable
- saturated zone
- water table
- unsaturated zone
- aquifer
- artesian well

Target Reading Skill

Previewing Visuals Before you read, preview Figure 22. Then write one question that you have about the diagram in a graphic organizer like the one below. As you read, answer your question.

Bringing Up Groundwater

Q. What is an artesian well?
A.
Q.

Lab zone Discover Activity

Where Does the Water Go?

1. Add pebbles to a jar to form a layer about 5 centimeters deep. Cover the pebbles with a layer of dry sand about 3 centimeters thick. Pour the sand in slowly to avoid moving the pebbles. These materials represent underground soil layers.
2. Sprinkle water onto the sand to simulate rainfall.
3. Looking through the side of the jar, observe the path of the water as it soaks through the layers. Wash your hands when you are finished with this activity.

Think It Over

Observing Describe what happened when the water reached the bottom of the jar.

When you were a little child, did you ever dig a hole in the ground hoping to find a buried treasure? You probably never found a trunk full of gold. But there was a certain kind of treasure hidden underground. If you had dug past the tangled grass roots and small stones, the bottom of your hole would have filled with water. You would have "struck groundwater!" In the days before public water systems, water underground was truly a hidden treasure. Today, many people still rely on the water underground to meet their water needs.

How Water Moves Underground

Where does this underground water come from? Like the water in rivers, lakes, and glaciers, it comes from precipitation. Recall that precipitation can evaporate, run off the surface, or soak into the ground. If water soaks into the ground, it trickles downward, following the pull of gravity.

If you pour water into a glass full of pebbles, the water trickles down around the pebbles until it reaches the bottom of the glass. Then the water begins to fill up the spaces between the pebbles. **In the same way, water underground trickles down between particles of soil and through cracks and spaces in layers of rock.**

Lab zone Discover Activity

Skills Focus observing L1

Materials pebbles, clear jar, ruler, dry sand, water

Time 10 minutes

Tips Using a plastic jar avoids the danger of broken glass. Advise students to add the water slowly.

Expected Outcome The water will seep through the sand and collect at the bottom of the jar.

Think It Over The water filled the spaces between the pebbles.

Effects of Different Materials Different types of rock and soil have different-sized spaces, or pores, between their particles, as shown in Figure 21. The size of the pores determines how easily water moves through rock and soil. If the pores are connected, this too affects water movement. Because they have large and connected pores, materials such as sand and gravel allow water to pass through, or permeate. They are thus known as **permeable** materials.

As water soaks down through permeable rock and soil, it eventually reaches layers of material that it cannot pass through. These materials have few or no pores or cracks. Two examples are clay and granite. Clay and granite are **impermeable,** meaning that water cannot pass through easily.

Water Zones Once water reaches an impermeable layer, it is trapped. It can't soak any deeper. Instead, the water begins to fill up the spaces above the impermeable material. The area of permeable rock or soil that is totally filled, or saturated, with water is called the **saturated zone.** The top of the saturated zone is the **water table.** If you know the depth of the water table in your area, you can tell how deep you must dig to reach groundwater.

Soil and rock layers above the water table contain some moisture, too. But here the pores contain air as well as water. They are not saturated. Therefore, the layer of rocks and soil above the water table is called the **unsaturated zone.**

Reading Checkpoint **Give an example of a permeable material.**

For: Links on water underground
Visit: www.SCiLinks.org
Web Code: scn-0815

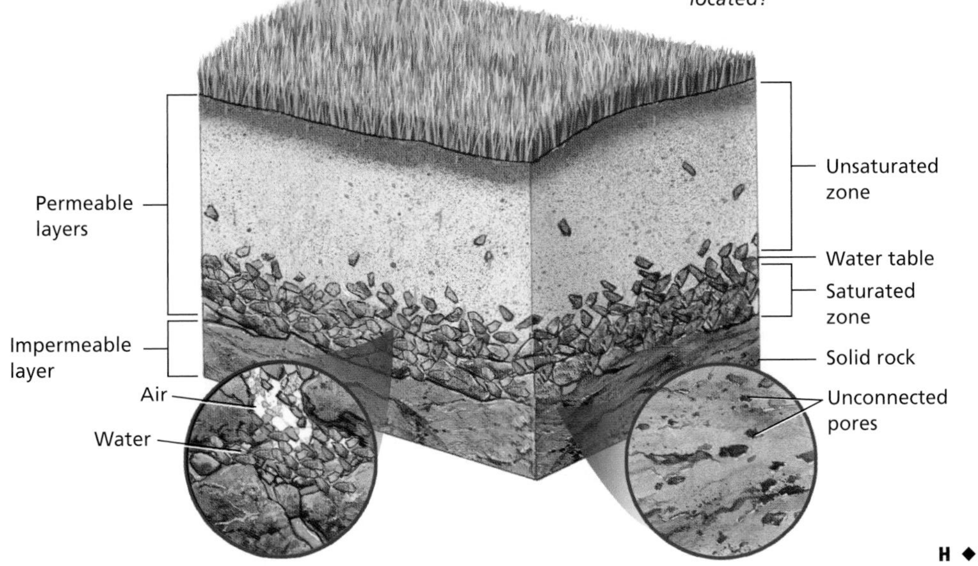

FIGURE 21
Groundwater Formation
Differences in the materials that form layers underground determine where groundwater forms. Water can move through certain layers but not others.
Interpreting Diagrams *What is the saturated zone? Where is it located?*

Instruct

How Water Moves Underground

For: Links on water underground
Visit: SciLinks.com
Web Code: scn-0815

Download a worksheet that will guide students' review of Internet resources on water underground.

Teach Key Concepts L2

Water Moves Through Soil and Rock

Focus Remind students that groundwater supplies most of the available fresh water on Earth.

Teach Refer students to Figure 21. Point out that when the water seeps into the ground and reaches an impermeable layer, the water stops sinking because the rock layer is made up of materials that have few open spaces for absorbing water. Ask: **How does water fill up spaces underground?** *(It trickles down between particles of soil and through cracks and spaces in layers of rock.)* **What is the term for the kinds of materials through which water can pass?** *(Permeable)*

Apply Ask students to find the average water table depth in your community. **learning modality: logical/mathematical**

All in One Teaching Resources

- Transparency H12

Independent Practice L2

All in One Teaching Resources

- Guided Reading and Study Worksheet: *Water Underground*

Student Edition on Audio CD

Monitor Progress L2

Drawing Have students draw a simple sketch of an underground water supply without referring to Figure 21.

Answers

Figure 21 The area of permeable rock or soil that is totally filled; between the water table and solid rock

Reading Checkpoint Possible answers: soil; porous rock, such as sandstone; materials such as foam rubber, plastic foam, and cloth

Differentiated Instruction

English Learners/Beginning L1

Vocabulary: Word Analysis Contrast the meanings of *permeable* and *impermeable.* Point out that the prefix *im-* sometimes means "not," and that words with this prefix may mean the opposite of the word without the prefix. Explore the meanings of *saturated* and *unsaturated.* **learning modality: verbal**

English Learners/Intermediate L2

Vocabulary: Word Analysis Have students find the derivation of *aquifer* in the dictionary. *(From the Latin word* aqua, *meaning "water")* Ask students to think of other English words that contain the root word *aqua. (Examples: aquarium, aquamarine, aquatic, and aqueduct.)* **learning modality: verbal**

Bringing Up Groundwater

Teach Key Concepts

L2

How People Obtain Water From an Aquifer

Focus Review with students the water zones found under Earth's surface—the saturated zone, the unsaturated zone, and the water table.

Teach Call attention to the two wells in Figure 22. Ask: **Why is one well dry?** *(The well does not reach the water table.)* **How can people obtain water from an aquifer?** *(They can use mechanical equipment to obtain groundwater from an aquifer by drilling a well below the water table.)* **Why is the water from the artesian well spurting up?** *(The water at the bottom of the aquifer is under pressure from the water at the top of the aquifer.)* Ask: **Why might the level of the water table vary?** *(The water follows the shape of the underground rock layers.)*

Apply Ask: **Why might the variations of the level of water in the water table cause people to get water in their basements?** *(During heavy rains, the water table could rise to the surface.)* **learning modality: logical/mathematical**

Math Analyzing Data

Math Skill Making and interpreting graphs

Focus Point out that a circle graph shows parts of a whole.

Teach Explain how to calculate the answer to the fifth question by converting the percentage used by power plants to a decimal and then multiplying by the total number of liters. (1,280 billion $\times$ 0.387 = 495 billion)

Answers

1. 4

2. 80.5%

3. Agriculture; industries and mining

4. The percentage for agriculture would increase, and the percentage for all of the other uses would decrease.

5. About 495 billion liters

Bringing Up Groundwater

Suppose you live far from a city, town, or body of fresh water. How could you reach groundwater to use it for your daily needs? You may be in luck: the water table in your area might be only a few meters underground. In fact, in some places the water table actually meets the surface. Springs can form as groundwater bubbles or flows out of cracks in the rock. A short distance away, the water table may be deep underground.

Aquifers Any underground layer of rock or sediment that holds water is called an **aquifer.** Aquifers can range in size from a small underground patch of permeable material to an area the size of several states. The huge Ogallala aquifer lies beneath the plains of the Midwest, from South Dakota to Texas. Millions of people obtain drinking water from this underground storehouse. The aquifer also provides water for crops and livestock.

Do you picture groundwater as a large, still pool beneath Earth's surface? In fact, the water is moving, seeping through layers of rock. The rate of movement depends largely on the slope of the aquifer and the permeability of the rocks. Groundwater in some aquifers moves only a few centimeters a day. At that rate, the water moves about 10 meters a year. Groundwater may travel hundreds of kilometers and stay in an aquifer for thousands of years before coming to the surface again.

Math Analyzing Data

Uses of Water

The graph shows water use in the United States. Each category of water use is represented by a different color. Use the graph to answer the questions below.

1. **Reading Graphs** How many categories of water use are shown on the graph?
2. **Interpreting Data** The two largest categories of water use combine to make up about what percentage of the total water used in the United States?
3. **Interpreting Data** Which of the categories of water use shown in the graph represents the largest use of water in the United States? Which represents the smallest?
4. **Predicting** How would an increase in the amount of irrigation affect this graph?

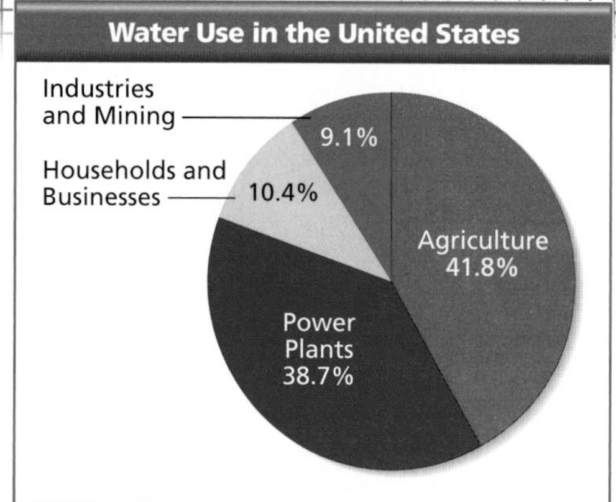

5. **Calculating** If the total daily usage of water in the United States is 1,280 billion liters, about how many liters are used each day by power plants?

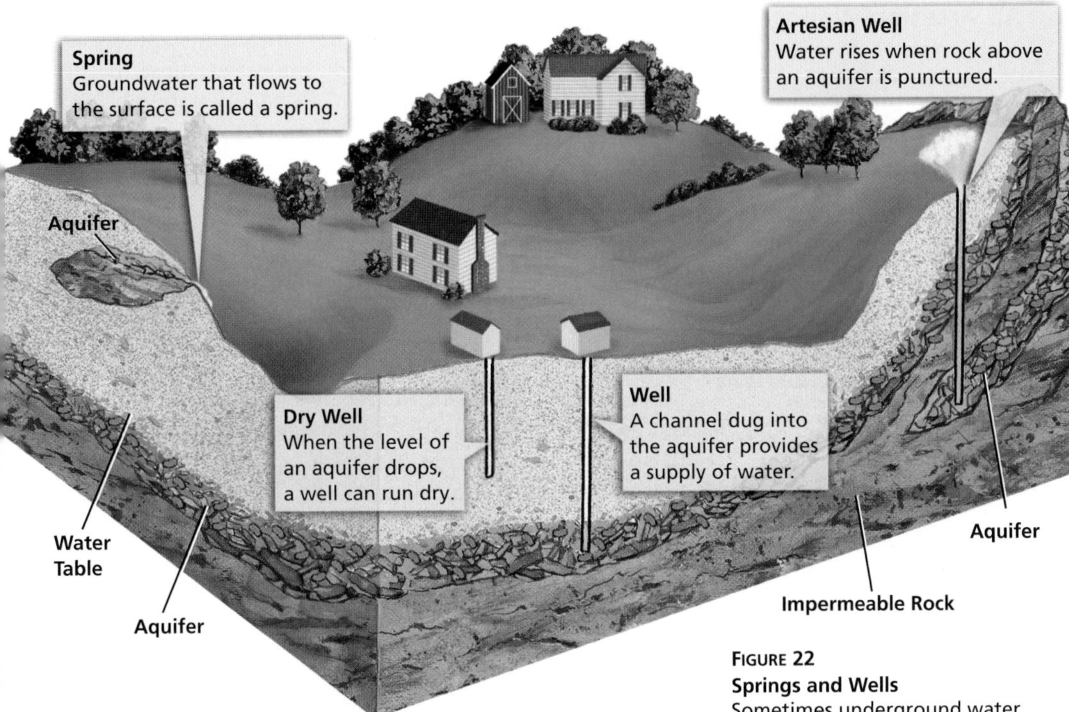

Spring
Groundwater that flows to the surface is called a spring.
Artesian Well
Water rises when rock above an aquifer is punctured.
Aquifer
Dry Well
When the level of an aquifer drops, a well can run dry.
Well
A channel dug into the aquifer provides a supply of water.
Water Table
Aquifer
Aquifer
Impermeable Rock

FIGURE 22
Springs and Wells
Sometimes underground water comes to the surface naturally. Other times, people use energy to obtain groundwater.
Comparing and Contrasting *How do the ordinary well, artesian well, and dry well differ?*

Wells The depth of a water table can vary greatly over a small area. Its level may vary as well. Generally, the level of a water table follows the shape of underground rock layers, as shown in Figure 22. But it can rise during heavy rains or snow melts, and then fall in times of dry weather. So what do you do if the depth and level of the water table in your area is far underground? How can you bring the water to the surface?

Since ancient times, people have brought groundwater to the surface for drinking and other everyday uses. **People can obtain groundwater from an aquifer by drilling a well below the water table.** Locate the well near the center of Figure 22. Because the bottom of the well is in a saturated zone, the well contains water. Notice the level of the bottom of the dry well in the diagram. Because this well does not reach below the water table, water cannot be obtained from it.

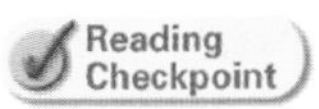 **Why might a water table rise? Why might a water table fall?**

Help Students Read 

Predicting Refer to the Content Refresher for guidelines on predicting. Tell students to examine Figure 22. Ask them to make a written prediction about how water might flow from an artesian well, based on what they know about aquifers, the flow of underground water, and water pressure. After they have finished reading the section, have them write a response to the prediction, correcting any misconceptions and adding details.

 L2

Modeling the Water Table

Focus Review with students how water moves underground.

Materials jar, sand, gravel, large rocks, water

Time 15 minutes the first day; 5 minutes the next

Teach Have students fill a jar with a mixture of sand, gravel, and rocks, and then slowly pour water into the jar and wait a few minutes. Students mark the level of the water with tape or a grease pencil. Let the jars sit for one day, and then observe the level of the water. The water level in the jars should be lower.

Apply Ask: **What is the boundary between the saturated and unsaturated zones in your jars called?** *(The water table)* **Why do you think the level of the water table changed?** *(Water evaporated from the soil.)* **learning modality: visual**

All in One Teaching Resources
- Transparency H13

Monitor Progress 

Drawing Have each student draw diagrams showing an underground dry well and a working well.

Answers

Figure 22 The ordinary well extends below the water table, so water can be pumped to the surface. The dry well does not reach the water table and cannot provide water. Pressure causes water to spurt from an artesian well without having to be pumped.

Reading Checkpoint The water table rises after rain or melting snow sink into the ground. The water table falls after a period of dry weather.

Differentiated Instruction

Less Proficient Readers L1
Understanding Water Underground
Provide students with the section on Student Edition on Audio CD and a copy of the passage Bringing Up Groundwater. Have them listen to this passage as they read along and highlight key phrases and sentences that explain the different ways that groundwater can be obtained. Then pair students with more proficient readers. Have each pair construct a concept map that includes and defines the terms *aquifer, artesian well, spring,* and *geyser.* **learning modality: verbal**

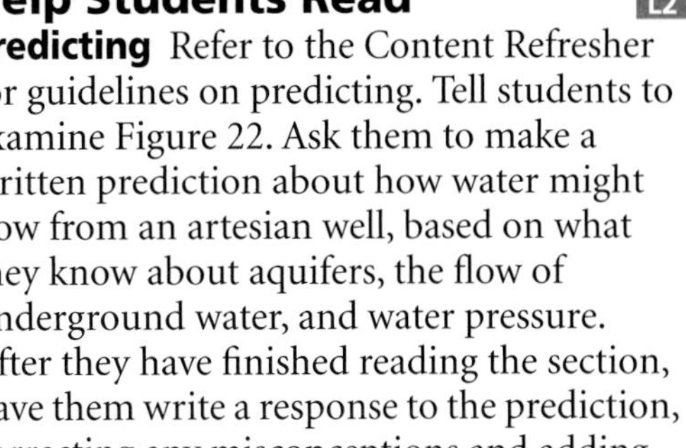

L1

Modeling a Geyser

Materials teakettle, hot plate

Time 10 minutes

Focus Review the definition of a geyser.

Teach CAUTION: *Wear goggles and heat-resistant gloves while performing this demonstration.* Heat some water in a teakettle on the hot plate. When the water boils and the kettle releases steam, ask: **What would happen if I plugged the kettle's spout?** *(The pressure of the steam would build up to a point at which it would blow the plug out of the spout.)* **CAUTION:** *Do not try this.* Emphasize that this is what happens in a geyser. Ask: **What supplied the heat to boil the water in the kettle?** *(The hot plate, electricity, electrical energy)*

Apply Ask: **What do you think heats water underground?** *(Possible answers: magma, molten rock, lava, or hot rocks.)* **learning modality: logical/mathematical**

Lab zone Try This **Activity**

An Artesian Well

For this activity, cover your desk with newspaper.

1. Cover the bottom of a loaf pan with clay. Pile the clay higher at one end. Cover the clay with about 4 cm of moist sand.
2. Cover the sand with a thin sheet of clay. Seal the edges of the clay tightly against the pan.
3. Push a funnel into the high end so the bottom of the funnel is in the sand.

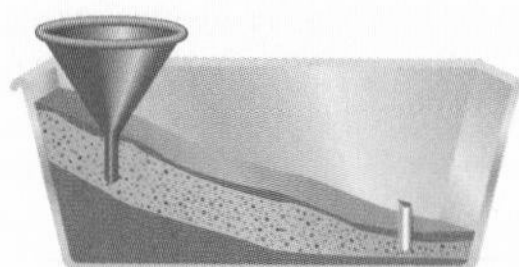

4. Insert a short piece of plastic straw through the clay and into the sand layer at the low end. Remove the straw, discard it, and then insert a new piece of straw into the same hole.
5. Slowly pour water into the funnel. Do not let the water overflow.
6. Observe the level of water in the straw.

Making Models How is your model like a real artesian well? How is it different?

Using Pumps Long ago, people dug wells by hand. They lined the sides of the well with brick and stone to keep the walls from collapsing. To bring up the water, they lowered and raised a bucket. People may also have used simple pumps, like the one shown in Figure 23. Today, however, most wells are dug with well-drilling equipment. Mechanical pumps bring up the groundwater.

Pumping water out of an aquifer lowers the water level near the well. If too much water is pumped out too fast, a well may run dry. The owners of the well will have to dig deeper to reach the lowered water table, or wait for rainfall to refill the aquifer. New water that enters the aquifer from the surface is called recharge.

Relying on Pressure Now you know how to bring groundwater to the surface. But what if that didn't work? You might not be out of luck. You might be able to drill an artesian well. In an **artesian well** (ahr TEEZH un), water rises because of pressure within an aquifer.

Look back at Figure 22 and locate the artesian well. In some aquifers, groundwater becomes trapped between two layers of impermeable rock or sediment. This water is under great pressure from the weight of the rock above. If the top layer of rock is punctured, the pressure sends water spurting up through the hole. No pump is necessary—in an artesian well, pressure does the job.

FIGURE 23
Working for Water Here a resident of Bangladesh uses a hand pump to bring groundwater to the surface.
Interpreting Photographs *What is one disadvantage of a hand pump?*

38 ◆ H

Lab zone Try This **Activity**

Skills Focus Making models

L2

Materials newspaper, loaf pan, modeling clay, moist sand, funnel, plastic straw, scissors, water

Time 20 minutes

Tips Before students begin, add a little water to the sand. Make extra clay available to stop any leaks and have paper towels available to remove water that overflows.

Expected Outcome Water will flow from the funnel into the sand layer at the high end, downhill through the sand layer, and up the straw at the low end. The clay and sand represent impermeable and permeable layers. The water represents precipitation. The flow of the water downhill represents real water movement in an aquifer. The model is like a real aquifer in that water moves through a permeable layer. It is different because water would fall as precipitation and soak through permeable material until it reached a layer of impermeable rock.

Extend Ask: **What would happen if you cut the straw below the water level of the funnel?** *(Doing so would produce a gushing artesian well.)* **learning modality: kinesthetic**

Springs and Geysers Sometimes, groundwater comes to the surface through natural processes. You read that places where groundwater bubbles or flows out of cracks in the rock are called springs. Most springs contain water at normal temperatures. Others, like those in Figure 24, contain water that is warmed by the hot rocks deep below the surface. The heated water bubbles to the surface in hot springs.

In some areas, you might see a fountain of boiling hot water and white steam burst into the air. This is a geyser, a type of hot spring from which the water periodically erupts. The word *geyser* comes from an Icelandic word, *geysir*, which means "gusher."

A geyser forms when very hot water that has been circulating deep underground begins to rise through narrow passages in the rock. Heated gases and bubbles of steam are forced up these passages by the pressure of the hot water boiling below. Just as pressure builds up in a partly blocked water pipe, the pressure within these narrow openings in the rock increases. Finally, the gases, steam, and hot water erupt high into the air.

FIGURE 24
A Hot Spring
A Japanese macaque takes advantage of the warm water that rises to the surface of a hot spring in Nagano, Japan.

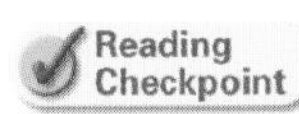
How do geysers form?

Section 5 Assessment

Target Reading Skill Previewing Visuals
Refer to your questions and answers about Figure 22 to help you answer Question 2 below.

Reviewing Key Concepts

1. a. **Reviewing** What happens to water in the ground when it reaches impermeable materials?
   b. **Explaining** What two factors determine how easily water can move through underground materials?
   c. **Inferring** Would an impermeable material have large or small pores? Would the pores be connected or unconnected? Explain.
2. a. **Describing** How can people obtain water from an aquifer?
   b. **Interpreting Diagrams** Using Figure 22 as a guide, explain why is it important to know the depth of an aquifer before drilling a well.
   c. **Problem Solving** During the winter, you draw your water from a well on your property. Every summer, the well dries up. What might be the reason for the change?

Writing in Science

Formal Letter Water usage in your town has risen in recent years due to population growth. Your town obtains its water from a nearby aquifer. You are concerned that the water level of the aquifer may be going down. Write a letter to local government officials explaining your concerns. Describe the effect of heavy water usage on the aquifer and suggest measures that can be taken to avoid a water shortage.

Writing in Science

Writing Skill Persuasion
Scoring Rubric
4 Exceeds criteria by including four or five well-thought-out measures and a convincing argument
3 Meets criteria and includes two or three measures
2 Includes only a brief explanation and one or two measures
1 Is incorrect and incomplete

Monitor Progress L2

Answers
Figure 23 Answers may vary. Sample answer: Water can be collected only when there is someone available to operate the hand pump.

Reading Checkpoint A geyser is formed by heated groundwater. The heated water, gases, and steam erupt as a result of the buildup of pressure.

Assess

Reviewing Key Concepts

1. a. It is trapped, forming a water table. **b.** The size of the pores of underground materials and whether the pores are connected **c.** Impermeable material would have small pores that would not be connected. Water could not move as easily through small pores that are not connected.
2. a. They can use mechanical equipment to drill a well below the water table. **b.** Without knowing the depth of the aquifer, drillers don't know how deep to drill the well to be below the water table. **c.** The water table must fall below the level of the well in summer and rise above it in winter. Factors such as precipitation and human water use could also affect the depth of the water table.

Reteach L1

Summarize the connection between saturated and unsaturated zones and permeable and impermeable layers of material beneath Earth's surface.

Performance Assessment

Drawing Have each student draw a simple sketch of the artesian well model that he or she made in the Try This Activity. Ask students to add labels and captions that explain how a real artesian well works.

All in One Teaching Resources
- Section Summary: *Water Underground*
- Review and Reinforce: *Water Underground*
- Enrich: *Water Underground*

Lab zone Design Your Own Lab

Soil Testing

L2

Prepare for Inquiry

Key Concept

Different soil materials have different permeabilities.

Skills Objectives

Students will be able to

- observe the flow of water through various materials
- develop a hypothesis to compare the flow of water through different materials
- design an experiment to test their hypothesis

**Class Time** 40 minutes

All in One Teaching Resources

- Lab Worksheet: *Soil Testing*

Alternative Materials

If funnels are not available, cut the tops off plastic soda bottles, or let students do this. Have them cover the rough edges with masking tape to avoid cutting themselves.

Safety

Have students wear safety goggles. Review the safety guidelines in Appendix A.

Guide Inquiry

Invitation

After distributing the sand, clay, and pebbles, have students look at and feel these items. Ask: **Which material would let water pass through most quickly? Which material do you think would hold water best?** Write the hypotheses on the board, and discuss these responses when students complete the lab.

Lab zone Design Your Own Lab

Soil Testing

Problem

How fast does water move through sand, clay, and pebbles?

Skills Focus

observing, developing hypotheses, designing experiments

Suggested Materials

- hand lens
- 100 mL of sand
- stopwatch
- 3 rubber bands
- 3 100-mL beakers
- 300 mL of water
- 100 mL of pebbles
- 100 mL of powdered potter's clay
- 3 squares of cheesecloth
- 3 large funnels or cut-off plastic bottle tops

Procedure  

PART 1 Observing the Flow of Water Through Sand

1. Copy the data table in your notebook.
2. Use a hand lens to observe the sand sample closely. Record your observations in your data table.
3. Place a piece of cheesecloth over the bottom of one funnel or bottle top and secure it with a rubber band.
4. Place the sand in the funnel. Be sure that there is about 5 cm of space above the sand in the funnel.
5. Place the funnel on top of a beaker.

Data Table		
Material	Observations	Time for Water to Stop Dripping
Sand		
Clay		
Pebbles		

6. Slowly pour 100 mL of water into the funnel. Do not let the water overflow the funnel.
7. Start the stopwatch when the water begins to flow or drip out of the funnel.
8. Stop the stopwatch when the water stops dripping out of the funnel or after 5 minutes. Record the time to the nearest second in your data table.

PART 2 Comparing the Flow of Water Through Different Soil Samples

9. Use a hand lens to observe each of the two other material samples closely. Record your observations in the data table.
10. Using the procedures you followed in Part 1, design an experiment to compare the flow of water through sand, clay, and pebbles. Be sure to write a hypothesis and to control all necessary variables.
11. Submit your experimental plan to your teacher. After making any necessary changes, carry out your experiment. Record your observations in your data table.
12. When you are finished with this activity, dispose of the materials according to your teacher's instructions. Wash your hands thoroughly with soap.

40 ◆ H

Introduce the Procedure

- Ask: **Which would be a good location for a well—in soil that lets water pass through easily, or in soil that does not let water pass through?** *(Soil that lets water pass through easily)*
- After students read through the procedure, ask: **Why should the layers of sand, clay, and pebbles be the same depth?** *(The depth is a variable that should be controlled; making the layers different depths could affect the results.)*

Analyze and Conclude

1. Observing In Part 1, how did the sand look under the hand lens? How long did it take the water to flow through the sand?
2. Developing Hypotheses What hypothesis did you test in Part 2? On what did you base your hypothesis?
3. Designing Experiments What was the manipulated variable in Part 2? What was the responding variable?
4. Drawing Conclusions Through which material did water move the fastest? The slowest? What can you conclude about the permeability of the three materials?
5. Predicting Based on the results of this lab, would you expect to get more water from a well dug in sand, pebbles, or clay? Explain.
6. Communicating You and your neighbor are discussing your gardens. You're explaining that it's important for a gardener to know the permeability of different soils. Write your conversation in dialogue form. Use quotation marks for each speaker.

More to Explore

Of the soil samples you tested, which do you think most resembles the soil on the grounds at your school? Explain your reasoning. How might you test your hypothesis?

Sample Data Table		
Materials	**Observations**	**Time for Water to Stop Dripping**
Sand	small grains, irregular shapes, whitish to brownish	9 minutes
Clay	tiny particles, regular shapes, tannish color	more than 15 minutes
Pebbles	large pieces, smooth shapes, various colors	2 minutes

Troubleshooting the Experiment

- In Step 1, suggest that students make the Observation section of their table larger than the others so that they have more room to record.
- If necessary, demonstrate how to make sure the beaker is filled exactly to the 100-mL mark in Step 6. Also remind students to stop pouring the water if it comes close to overflowing the funnel.

Expected Outcome

Times will vary. Sample data may show that it takes about 9 minutes for 100 mL of water to flow through sand, 2 minutes to flow through pebbles, and 15 minutes to flow through clay.

Analyze and Conclude

1. Possible answer: The sand was composed of small grains, had irregular shapes, and was colored white, tan, and brown; answers will vary but should be less than the time for flowing through the clay and more than the time for flowing through the pebbles.

2. Possible answer: Water will flow fastest through pebbles. It will flow more slowly through sand and slowest through clay. The hypothesis was based on the size of the particles.

3. The size of the particles was the manipulated variable. The rate of water flow was the responding variable.

4. It moved fastest through pebbles, and slowest through clay. Pebbles are the most permeable; clay is the least permeable.

5. You would get more water from a well dug in pebbles because there are larger pores that can hold more water, and the water moves quickly through the pebbles and into the well as water is pumped out.

6. Students' dialogues should include that some plants may survive and grow best in sandy soils that let water drain away from their roots, whereas other plants grow best in clay soils that hold water.

Extend Inquiry

More to Explore Students could estimate the soil's permeability by observing after a rain to see whether water is absorbed or pools on top of the soil. Each group could test an actual sample and compare results with data using sand, pebbles, and clay.

Study Guide

- Complete student edition
- Section and chapter self-assessments
- Assessment reports for teachers

Help Students Read

Building Vocabulary

Word-Part Analysis Ask students to note words that contain the suffix *-ation. (Evaporation, condensation, transpiration, precipitation, and eutrophication)* Point out that this is a Latin form that means "the act of ______ ing." To derive a definition for each word, students should use a dictionary to find each root word meaning.

Paraphrasing Help students define key terms in their own words. By paraphrasing, students can use words that are already familiar to them to define new terms. Have students find and read the text for the terms *polar molecule, capillary action, tributary, aquifer,* and *artesian well.* Then have students find the terms in a dictionary. Have them use each definition they find to help them write another definition in their own words.

Connecting Concepts

Concept Maps Help students develop one way the information in this chapter is related. All living things need water, which has unique properties because of its polar structure, moves in a cycle between Earth's surface and atmosphere, and is distributed in various ways on Earth's surface and underground. Have students brainstorm to identify the key concepts, key terms, details, and examples. Then have students write each of these on a self-stick note and attach it at random on chart paper or on the board.

Chapter 1 Study Guide

1 The Properties of Water

Key Concepts

- The positive hydrogen ends of one water molecule attract the negative oxygen ends of nearby water molecules. As a result, the water molecules tend to stick together.
- The properties of water include capillary action, surface tension, the ability to dissolve many substances, and high specific heat.
- Ice is solid water, the familiar form of water is a liquid, and water vapor is a gas.

Key Terms

polar molecule
capillary action
surface tension
solution
solvent
specific heat
evaporation
condensation

2 Water on Earth

Key Concepts

- All living things need water in order to carry out their body processes. In addition, many living things use water for shelter.
- Most of Earth's water—roughly 97 percent—is salt water found in oceans. Only 3 percent is fresh water.
- In the water cycle, water moves from bodies of water, land, and living things on Earth's surface to the atmosphere and back to Earth's surface.

Key Terms

photosynthesis
habitat
groundwater
water cycle
transpiration
precipitation

3 Surface Water

Key Concepts

- A river and all its tributaries together make up a river system.
- Ponds and lakes form when water collects in hollows and low-lying areas of land.
- In addition to seasonal changes, a lake can undergo long-term changes that may eventually lead to its death.

Key Terms

tributary
watershed
divide
reservoir
nutrient
eutrophication

4 Wetland Environments

Key Concepts

- The three common types of freshwater wetlands are marshes, swamps, and bogs.
- Agriculture, development, and the introduction of new species are some human activities that threaten the Florida Everglades.
- Wetlands provide habitats for many living things. Wetlands help people by acting as natural water filters and by helping to control floods.

Key Term

wetland

5 Water Underground

Key Concepts

- Water underground trickles down between particles of soil and through cracks and spaces in layers of rock.
- People can obtain groundwater from an aquifer by drilling a well below the water table.

Key Terms

permeable
impermeable
saturated zone
water table
unsaturated zone
aquifer
artesian well

Tell students that this concept map will be organized in hierarchical order and will begin at the top with key concepts. Ask students these questions to guide them to categorize the information on the self-stick notes: **What are the properties of water? How does water move through the water cycle? What types of water systems make up surface water and wetlands environments? What are the main types of underground water sources?**

Prompt students by using connecting words or phrases, such as "results in," "are made of," and "consists of types" to indicate the basis for the organization of the map. The phrases should form a sentence that links a set of concepts.

Answer Accept all logical presentations.

All in One Teaching Resources

- Key Terms Review: *Earth: The Water Planet*
- Connecting Concepts: *Earth: The Water Planet*

Review and Assessment

Go Online PHSchool.com
For: Self-Assessment
Visit: PHSchool.com
Web Code: cfa-3010

Organizing Information

Sequencing Copy and complete the cycle diagram to show how water moves throughout the water cycle. (For more on Sequencing, see the Skills Handbook.)

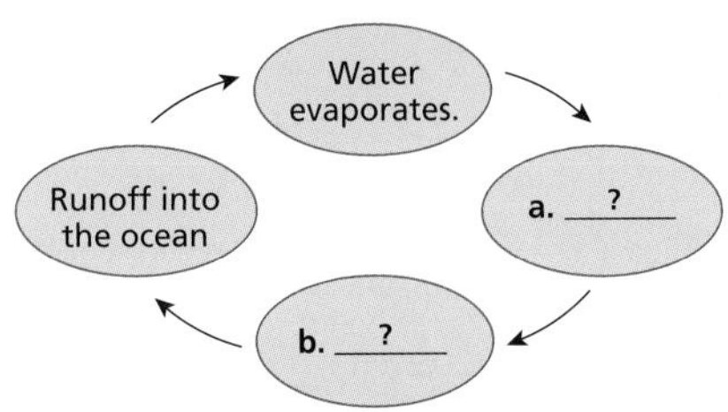

Reviewing Key Terms

Choose the letter of the best answer.

1. A molecule with electrically charged parts is a
   a. nonpolar molecule.
   b. solution.
   c. polar molecule.
   d. gas.
2. More than 97 percent of Earth's total water supply is found in
   a. ice sheets.
   b. the atmosphere.
   c. the oceans.
   d. groundwater.
3. The land area that supplies water to a river system is called a
   a. divide.
   b. watershed.
   c. wetland.
   d. tributary.
4. Wetlands help control floods by absorbing
   a. silt and mud.
   b. extra runoff.
   c. nutrients.
   d. waste materials.
5. The water table is found on top of the
   a. saturated zone.
   b. unsaturated zone.
   c. aquifer.
   d. artesian well.

If the statement is true, write *true*. If it is false, change the underlined word or words to make the statement true.

6. The property of specific heat allows some insects to walk on water.
7. In the process of condensation, water vapor is given off through the leaves of a plant.
8. One watershed is separated from another by a divide.
9. An aquifer is an area of land covered with a shallow layer of water during some or all of the year.
10. Water moves easily through permeable materials.

Writing in Science

Brochure Write a brochure describing the Florida Everglades. Be sure to include information about why so many organisms live here and why people need to protect the Everglades.

Earth: The Water Planet
Video Preview
Video Field Trip
▶ Video Assessment

Go Online PHSchool.com
For: Self-Assessment
Visit: PHSchool.com
Web Code: cfa-3010

Students can take an online practice test that is automatically scored.

All in One Teaching Resources

- Transparency H14
- Chapter Test
- Performance Assessment Teacher Notes
- Performance Assessment Student Worksheet
- Performance Assessment Scoring Rubric

ExamView® Computer Test Bank CD-ROM

Review and Assessment

Organizing Information

a. Water condenses to form clouds.
b. Water falls to Earth's surface as precipitation.

Reviewing Key Terms

1. c **2.** c **3.** b **4.** b **5.** a
6. surface tension
7. transpiration
8. true
9. wetland
10. true

Writing in Science

Writing Skill Description

Scoring Rubric

4 Exceeds criteria by including vivid, detailed descriptions of how human activities are threatening the Everglades and the importance of wetlands to people
3 Meets criteria and includes information about wildlife habitats and why the Everglades needs protection
2 Includes brief but accurate descriptions
1 Is incorrect and incomplete

Discovery Channel School Video Assessment

Earth: The Water Planet

Show the Video Assessment to review chapter content and as a prompt for the writing assignment. Discussion questions: **What makes the Everglades an important habitat to preserve?** *(In addition to providing a home to many organisms, the Everglades also act as a sponge, absorbing excess rainwater and keeping neighboring areas from flooding.)* **Why do some Everglades trees have roots above water?** *(They need to be above the water because they absorb oxygen from the air.)*

Checking Concepts

11. Students' diagrams should correctly show the structure of a water molecule, including the positive charge of the hydrogen atoms and the negative charge of the oxygen atom.

12. Examples will depend on the properties chosen. Properties that depend on water's polarity include surface tension, capillary action, the ability to dissolve many substances, and high specific heat.

13. Earth is called the "blue planet" because oceans cover nearly 71 percent of Earth's surface.

14. More than 97 percent of the total water on Earth is salt water, which is not available for human use. About three quarters of the fresh water on Earth is ice, which is mostly unavailable for human use.

15. A large river can be considered a tributary if it feeds off an even larger main river.

16. Lake turnover is a seasonal change in which the warmer water that floats on top of the lake in the summer sinks to the bottom as it cools in the fall. The sinking motion mixes the water, causing water, minerals, plant matter, and nutrients to rise from the bottom of the lake.

17. Water rises through an artesian well because of underground water pressure from an aquifer.

Review and Assessment

Checking Concepts

11. Draw a diagram of a water molecule that shows how it is polar. Be sure to label your diagram.
12. Give examples of two properties of water that are caused by the attractions between water molecules.
13. Explain why Earth is called the "blue planet."
14. Why is so little of Earth's water available for human use?
15. When can a large river be considered a tributary?
16. What is lake turnover and how does it relate to changing seasons?
17. Why doesn't an artesian well require a pump?

Thinking Critically

18. **Comparing and Contrasting** Compare the three states of water in terms of the speed and arrangement of their molecules.
19. **Relating Cause and Effect** A molecule of water is likely to evaporate more quickly from the Caribbean Sea near the equator than from the Arctic Ocean. Explain why this statement is true.
20. **Predicting** The city of Charleston, South Carolina, is located on the Atlantic coast. The city of Macon, Georgia, is located about 340 kilometers inland to the west. Predict which city is likely to be cooler in the summer. Explain your answer in terms of specific heat.

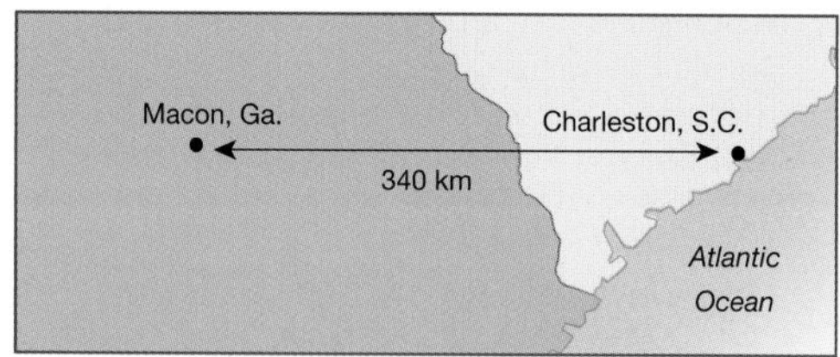

21. **Comparing and Contrasting** How would the variety of organisms in the center of a pond be different from those you would find in deep water at the center of a lake?
22. **Applying Concepts** Explain why some rivers experience severe springtime flooding as snow and ice melt along small mountain streams.
23. **Classifying** On a walk in a northern state, you come upon an area of spongy soil. It is carpeted with mosses along with some low-growing, flowering plants. What type of wetland is this likely to be? Explain.

Applying Skills

Use the diagram of underground layers to answer Questions 24–27.

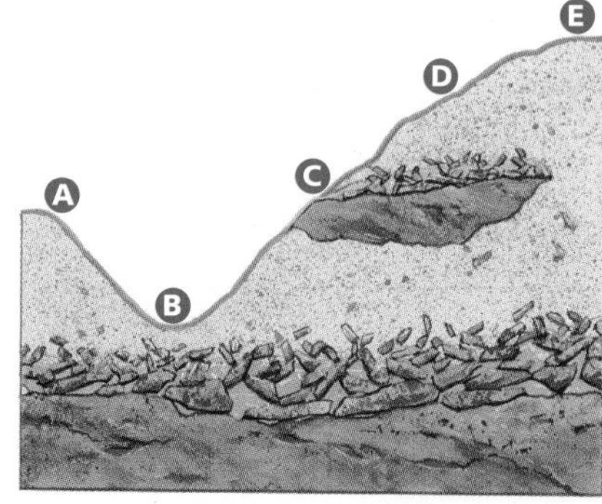

24. **Drawing Conclusions** Would point D or point E be a better location to dig a well? Explain your reasoning.
25. **Inferring** At which location could you obtain groundwater without having to use a pump? What is this location called?
26. **Interpreting Data** At which point is the water table closest to the surface?
27. **Predicting** Draw a simple diagram showing how this area might look during a very rainy season.

Lab zone Chapter Project

Performance Assessment Make graphs of your household and community water-use data. Then share your graphs with your classmates. As a class, discuss any surprising results. How do your findings compare to those of your classmates?

Lab zone Chapter Project

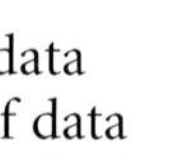

Project Wrap-Up Review students' data on household water use. Use one set of data to demonstrate how to create a bar graph. Students may make more than one graph to show all their data.

Reflect and Record Encourage students to evaluate how well they accomplished what they set out to do and to make suggestions regarding what they think would have made the project better. In the paragraph about how water is used in the community, students should include both observations about specific uses and generalizations that demonstrate an analysis of all the data collected by class members.

Standardized Test Prep

Test-Taking Tip

Reading All the Answer Choices

Always read *every* answer choice in a multiple-choice question before selecting the answer you think is correct. If you stop reading as soon as you find an answer that seems correct, you may not notice that "all of the above" is given as one of the answer choices.

Sample Question

Where on Earth is fresh water found?

A icebergs
B rivers and lakes
C groundwater
D all of the above

Answer

The correct answer is **D,** all of the above. Fresh water is found in icebergs, rivers and lakes, and groundwater.

Choose the letter of the best answer.

1. What characteristic of water explains why it has many unusual properties?
A Water is a nonpolar molecule.
B Water is a polar molecule.
C Water molecules do not have electrically charged areas.
D Water is not a molecule.

2. Why don't plants normally grow on the bottoms of deep lakes?
F The water is too salty.
G The water is too cold.
H Photosynthesis does not occur in water.
J There is not enough sunlight for photosynthesis to occur.

3. For a science project you must build a model of an aquifer. What material would be the best to use for the layer that will hold water?
A an impermeable material, such as clay
B an impermeable material, such as granite
C a permeable material, such as gravel
D a material that does not have pores

Use the diagram below and your knowledge of science to answer Questions 4–5.

4. Which of the following is a process that occurs in the water cycle?
F evaporation
G precipitation
H condensation
J all of the above

5. What is the energy source that drives the continuous process shown in the diagram?
A the sun
B the ocean
C gravity
D the tides

Constructed Response

6. Explain what a wetland is and why wetlands are important. Describe one threat to wetlands and the actions being taken to protect wetlands from this threat.

Thinking Critically

18. Water molecules in the solid state move slowly and are arranged in a rigid structure. Water molecules in the liquid state move more rapidly and spread out to take the shape of their container. Water molecules in the gas state are moving faster than those in the other two states, and they spread out to fill an enclosed space.

19. Stronger sunlight in the Caribbean provides more energy to cause the evaporation of water molecules at the ocean's surface.

20. Charleston is likely to be cooler in summer because it is nearer to a large body of water than Macon is. Because of water's high specific heat, land heats more quickly than water. The warmer land warms the air above it, while the air above water remains cool. Breezes from the ocean, then, should keep Charleston cooler in summer.

21. The variety of organisms in the center of a pond is much greater because sunlight reaches the bottom. Sunlight does not reach the deep water at the center of a lake, so plants and algae and the organisms that depend on them cannot live there.

22. Within a drainage basin, many streams filled with melted snow and ice empty into rivers. Soon, the volume of water in the rivers increases to the point that they overflow their banks and flooding occurs.

23. It is likely to be a bog because this type of wetland is found in cooler climates, and because mosses and short plants grow well in a bog.

Applying Skills

24. Accept Point D or Point E; Point D because the distance to the saturated zone is less, although Point E has a much larger water supply to draw from.

25. Point C; a spring

26. Point B

27. Students' drawings should show a higher water table and thicker saturated zone. They might show a pond at point B.

Standardized Test Prep

1. B **2.** J **3.** C **4.** J **5.** A

6. A wetland is a land area that is covered with a shallow layer of water during some or all of the year. Wetlands are important because they provide a habitat for wildlife, help control flooding, and filter out pollutants, such as waste materials, silt, and mud. One threat to wetlands is that they are often drained and filled in for development. The government has passed laws to protect wetland habitats.

Chapter at a Glance

Chapter at a Glance

PRENTICE HALL TeacherEXPRESS™ Plan • Teach • Assess

		Technology	Local Standards
Lab zone Chapter Project	*A Precious Resource* **All in One Teaching Resources** • Chapter Project Teacher Notes, pp. 112–113 • Chapter Project Student Introduction, pp. 114–115 • Chapter Project Student Worksheets, pp. 116–117 • Chapter Project Scoring Rubric, p. 118	  Discovery Channel School Video Preview	
 Section 1 3–4 periods 1–2 blocks	**Water Supply and Demand** **H.2.1.1** Identify ways that people use water. **H.2.1.2** Describe some ways to conserve available fresh water. **H.2.1.3** Discuss some possible sources of water for the future.	 Go Online PHSchool.com	
 Section 2 2–3 periods 1–1 1/2 blocks	**Water to Drink** **H.2.2.1** Identify factors that affect water quality. **H.2.2.2** Explain why drinking water is often treated before people drink it. **H.2.2.3** Describe what happens to wastewater in most communities.	 Go Online PHSchool.com	
 Section 3 2–3 periods 1–1 1/2 blocks	**Freshwater Pollution** **H.2.3.1** Explain one way that sources of pollution are classified. **H.2.3.2** Identify three sources of water pollution. **H.2.3.3** Describe the two parts of the solution to water pollution.	 Go Online NSTA SCILINKS™	
 Section 4 1–2 periods 1/2–1 block	**Droughts and Floods** **H.2.4.1** Explain what a drought is. **H.2.4.2** State what a flood is and explain how the dangers of floods can be reduced.	 Go Online PLANET DIARY	
 Section 5 1–2 periods 1/2–1 block	**Water Power** **H.2.5.1** Explain how the energy of moving water can be used to produce electricity. **H.2.5.2** Identify some advantages and disadvantages of hydroelectric power plants.	  Go Online active art   Discovery Channel School Video Field Trip	

Review and Assessment

All in One Teaching Resources
- Key Terms Review, p. 160
- Transparency H28
- Performance Assessment Teacher Notes, p. 169
- Performance Assessment Scoring Rubric, p. 170
- Performance Assessment Student Worksheet, p. 171
- Chapter Test, pp. 172–175

Discovery Channel School Video Assessment

Go Online PHSchool.com

Test Preparation

Test Preparation Blackline Masters

Chapter Activities Planner

For more activities

Student Edition	Inquiry	Time	Materials	Skills	Resources
Chapter Project, p. 47	Open-Ended	Ongoing (2 to 3 weeks)	All in One Teaching Resources See page 112.	Observing, making models	Lab zone Easy Planner All in One Teaching Resource Support pp. 112–113
Section 1					
Discover Activity, p. 48	Directed	15 minutes	Large measuring cup, water, plastic dropper, 2 small bowls, spoons, stopwatch	Predicting	Lab zone Easy Planner
Skills Lab, p. 56	Directed	Prep 30 minutes; Class 40 minutes	Hot plate, aluminum foil, 250-mL beaker, plastic spoon, 100 mL water, shallow pan, ice, plastic tube, 500-mL flask, stirring rod, rubber stopper, salt, 50 cm rubber tubing	Observing, making models	Lab zone Easy Planner Lab Activity Video All in One Teaching Resource Skills Lab: *Getting the Salt Out,* pp. 126–127
Section 2					
Discover Activity, p. 57	Guided	20 minutes	2 large trash barrels, 2 large heavy plastic trash bags, water, large plastic pitcher with lid	Calculating	Lab zone Easy Planner
Skills Activity, p. 61	Guided	10 minutes	2 clean empty jars; materials such as sand, soil, and leaves; paper towels; water	Making models	Lab zone Easy Planner
Try This Activity, p. 62	Guided	20 minutes	Books, 2 large bowls, water, pitcher, plastic tubing	Observing	Lab zone Easy Planner
Consumer Lab, pp. 66–67	Directed	Prep 30 minutes; Class 40 minutes	Hot plate, liquid soap, ruler, wax pencil, tap water, distilled water, spring water, mineral water, 4 200-mL beakers, 4 test tubes and stoppers, 4 pieces of pH paper, test tube rack, 25-mL graduated cylinder, pH indicator chart, 4 paper cups per person	Observing, inferring	Lab zone Easy Planner Lab Activity Video All in One Teaching Resource Consumer Lab: *Testing Water,* pp. 136–138
Section 3					
Discover Activity, p. 68	Directed	15 minutes	Coffee filter, food coloring, paper plate, permanent marker, plastic dropper, wet sponge	Observing	Lab zone Easy Planner
Skills Activity, p. 71	Guided	5 minutes	None	Classifying	Lab zone Easy Planner
Try This Activity, p. 74	Guided	5 minutes per day for 1 week	Liquid fertilizer, graduated cylinder, 2 wide-mouth jars with tops, masking tape, permanent marker, pond or aquarium water, tap water	Drawing conclusions	Lab zone Easy Planner
Section 4					
Discover Activity, p. 78	Guided	10 minutes setup; 10 minutes next day	Lamp, soil, stirring stick, rectangular pan, water	Observing	Lab zone Easy Planner
Skills Activity, p. 82	Guided	10 minutes	Basin, cup, funnel, water	Inferring	Lab zone Easy Planner
Section 5					
Discover Activity, p. 84	Guided	10 minutes	Various cylindrical objects, plant sprayer, large plastic trash bag, water	Observing	Lab zone Easy Planner
Try This Activity, p. 85	Directed	15 minutes	Aluminum pie plate, marker, metric ruler, running water, small foam ball, tin snips, 2 toothpicks	Developing hypotheses	Lab zone Easy Planner

Section 1 Water Supply and Demand

3–4 periods, 1–2 blocks

ABILITY LEVELS
L1 Basic to Average
L2 For All Students
L3 Average to Advanced

Objectives

H.2.1.1 Identify ways that people use water.
H.2.1.2 Describe some ways to conserve available fresh water.
H.2.1.3 Discuss some possible sources of water for the future.

Key Terms

• irrigation • conservation • desalination

Local Standards

Preteach

Build Background Knowledge

Challenge students to think of ways they directly and indirectly use water every day.

Discover Activity *Can You Find a Balance?* L1

Targeted Print and Technology Resources

All in One Teaching Resources

L2 Reading Strategy Transparency H15: Using Prior Knowledge

Presentation-Pro CD-ROM

Instruct

How People Use Water Use a map of an area where water is scarce to discuss how water is used.

Conserving Water Use the three R's to help students discuss ways to conserve water.

Fresh Water for the Future Discuss methods to obtain fresh water from ocean water and icebergs.

Skills Lab *Getting the Salt Out* L2

Targeted Print and Technology Resources

All in One Teaching Resources

L2 Guided Reading, pp. 121–123
L2 Transparency H16
L2 Skills Lab: *Getting the Salt Out,* pp. 126–127

Lab Activity Video/DVD
Skills Lab: *Getting the Salt Out*

PHSchool.com Web Code: cfd-3021

Student Edition on Audio CD

Assess

Section Assessment Questions

Have students use their graphic organizer with what they knew and learned about water conservation to answer the questions.

Reteach

As a class, list the ways that water is used and ways to conserve water.

Targeted Print and Technology Resources

All in One Teaching Resources

• Section Summary, p. 120
L1 Review and Reinforce, p. 124
L3 Enrich, p. 125

Section 2 Water to Drink

 *2–3 periods, 1–1 1/2 blocks*

ABILITY LEVELS
- L1 Basic to Average
- L2 For All Students
- L3 Average to Advanced

Local Standards

Objectives

H.2.2.1 Identify factors that affect water quality.
H.2.2.2 Explain why drinking water is often treated before people drink it.
H.2.2.3 Describe what happens to wastewater in most communities.

Key Terms

• water quality • concentration • pH • hardness • filtration • coagulation
• sewage

Preteach

Build Background Knowledge

Display a glass of water, and elicit responses on where the water came from.

 *How Hard Is It to Move Water?* L1

Targeted Print and Technology Resources

All in One Teaching Resources
- L2 Reading Strategy Transparency H17: Sequencing

Instruct

Water Quality Ask questions to help students identify factors that affect water quality.

Treating Drinking Water Use a diagram to sequence how water is treated and why each step is required.

Treating Wastewater Discuss where wastewater goes for treatment and how it is treated in a septic tank.

 *Testing Water* L2

Targeted Print and Technology Resources

All in One Teaching Resources
- L2 Guided Reading, pp. 130–133
- L2 Transparencies H18, H19
- L2 Consumer Lab: *Testing Water,* pp. 136–138

PHSchool.com Web Code: cfd-3022

Student Edition on Audio CD

Assess

Section Assessment Questions

Have students use their flowcharts sequencing the steps in drinking-water treatment to answer the questions.

Reteach

Draw a diagram to show how drinking water is treated and distributed.

Targeted Print and Technology Resources

All in One Teaching Resources
- Section Summary, p. 129
- L1 Review and Reinforce, p. 134
- L3 Enrich, p. 135

Section 3 Freshwater Pollution

 *2–3 periods, 1–1 1/2 blocks*

ABILITY LEVELS
L1 Basic to Average
L2 For All Students
L3 Average to Advanced

Local Standards

Objectives

H.2.3.1 Explain one way that sources of pollution are classified.
H.2.3.2 Identify three sources of water pollution.
H.2.3.3 Describe the two parts of the solution to water pollution.

Key Terms

• water pollution • pollutant • point source • nonpoint source • acid rain
• pesticide

Preteach

Build Background Knowledge

Invite students to define water pollution and name possible things that pollute water.

Will the Pollution Reach Your Wells? L1

Targeted Print and Technology Resources

All in One Teaching Resources
- L2 Reading Strategy Transparency H20: Outlining

Presentation-Pro CD-ROM

Instruct

What Is Pollution? Use a table to classify sources of pollution as point or nonpoint.

Human Wastes Discuss how water becomes contaminated with human and animal wastes.

Industrial Wastes Use photographs to examine sources of water pollution from industrial wastes.

Chemical Runoff Consider how chemical runoff from farms and roads gets into water sources.

Water Pollution Solutions Explain and give examples of the two parts to solving water pollution.

Targeted Print and Technology Resources

All in One Teaching Resources
- L2 Guided Reading, pp. 141–144
- L2 Transparencies H21, H22

www.SciLinks.org Web Code: scn-0823

Student Edition on Audio CD

Assess

Section Assessment Questions

Have students use their outlines of the section to answer the questions.

Reteach

Brainstorm examples of water pollution, and classify according to source and type.

Targeted Print and Technology Resources

All in One Teaching Resources
- Section Summary, p. 140
- L1 Review and Reinforce, p. 145
- L3 Enrich, p. 146

Section 4 Droughts and Floods

 *1–2 periods, 1/2–1 block*

ABILITY LEVELS
- L1 Basic to Average
- L2 For All Students
- L3 Average to Advanced

Objectives

H.2.4.1 Explain what a drought is.

H.2.4.2 State what a flood is and explain how the dangers of floods can be reduced.

Key Terms

• drought • flash flood • levee

Local Standards

Preteach

Build Background Knowledge

Ask students why conservation practices are needed during periods of low precipitation.

 *How Does Dryness Affect Soil?* L1

Targeted Print and Technology Resources

L2 Reading Strategy Transparency H23: Comparing and Contrasting

Presentation-Pro CD-ROM

Instruct

Droughts Define a drought, its effects, and how to prepare for one.

Floods Examine the causes and effects of floods.

Flood Precautions Analyze ways of reducing the dangers of floods, including warnings and actions by individuals.

Targeted Print and Technology Resources

L2 Guided Reading, pp. 149–150

L2 Transparencies H24, H25

PHSchool.com Web Code: cfd-3024

Student Edition on Audio CD

Assess

Section Assessment Questions

Have students use their graphic organizers comparing and contrasting droughts and floods to answer the questions.

Reteach

Sketch an outline of the section, and ask students to fill in the details of each subheading.

Targeted Print and Technology Resources

- Section Summary, p. 148

L1 Review and Reinforce, p. 151

L3 Enrich, p. 152

Section 5 Water Power

1–2 periods, 1/2-1 block

ABILITY LEVELS
- L1 Basic to Average
- L2 For All Students
- L3 Average to Advanced

Objectives

H.2.5.1 Explain how the energy of moving water can be used to produce electricity.

H.2.5.2 Identify some advantages and disadvantages of hydroelectric power plants.

Key Terms

• kinetic energy • potential energy • hydroelectric power

Local Standards

Preteach

Build Background Knowledge

Show a picture of Niagara Falls or water flowing over a dam, and ask students to describe the force of the water.

Discover Activity *Can Water Do Work?* L1

Targeted Print and Technology Resources

Teaching Resources

L2 Reading Strategy Transparency H26: Asking Questions

Presentation-Pro CD-ROM

Instruct

Energy and Moving Water Explain how moving water can be used to produce electricity in terms of how energy changes form.

Hydroelectric Power Plants Compare the advantages of hydroelectric power with other ways of generating electricity, and identify disadvantages of hydroelectric power.

Targeted Print and Technology Resources

All in One Teaching Resources

L2 Guided Reading, pp. 155-157

L2 Transparency H27

PHSchool.com Web Code: cfp-3025

Student Edition on Audio CD

Assess

Section Assessment Questions

Have students use their questions and answers about water power to answer the questions.

Reteach

Draw a diagram of a hydroelectric power plant, and ask students to describe the steps.

Targeted Print and Technology Resources

All in One Teaching Resources

- Section Summary, p. 154

L1 Review and Reinforce, p. 158

L3 Enrich, p. 159

Chapter 2 Content Refresher

For: Professional development support
Visit: www.SciLinks.org/PDLinks
Web Code: scf-0820

Section 1 Water Supply and Demand

Water Consumption and Management In 2000, the United States used an estimated 408 billion gallons of fresh water per day, according to the United States Geological Survey (USGS). Most fresh water used comes from surface water sources, which include rivers, lakes, and reservoirs. Irrigation and power generation accounted for the majority of the total fresh water used in 1995. Compared to 1980 estimates, total fresh water use declined by about 10 percent, partly because of improvements in technology associated with irrigation.

Much of the fresh water withdrawn for use in agriculture and industry is wasted through evaporation, runoff, and leaks, making conservation practices imperative. One way to conserve fresh water is to use treated wastewater for irrigation.

In the typical U.S. home, bathing, flushing toilets, and washing hands accounts for much of the water used. Using water-saving shower heads and low-flow toilets, and minimizing lawn watering can conserve a large amount of fresh water.

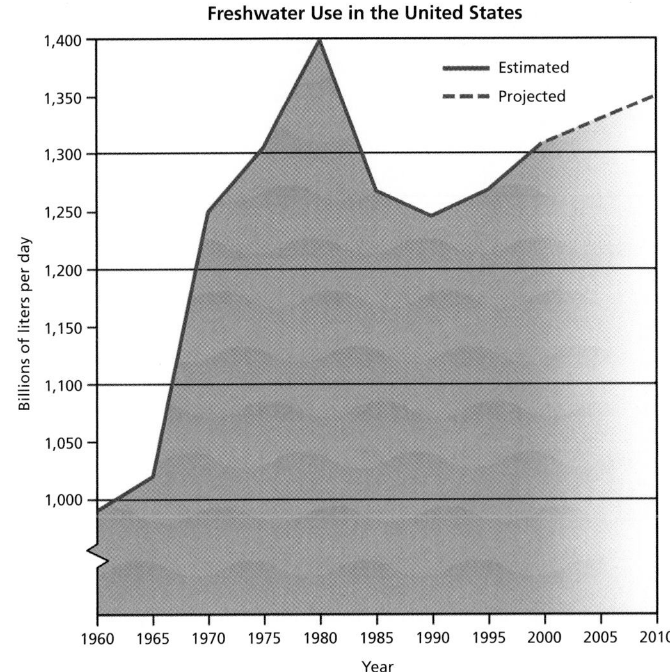

Section 2 Water to Drink

Water Quality Standards In 1998, the U.S. Environmental Protection Agency announced regulations requiring community water agencies to inform customers of basic facts regarding their drinking water, including: (1) the source of the water, (2) what contaminants were in the water and which exceeded EPA health standards, (3) what health risks were associated with those contaminants that exceeded standards, and (4) any violations and actions that had been taken against the water agency that year.

Address Misconceptions

Many students think that the term hard water *means that it is harder to the touch than soft water. However, water is called "hard" because calcium and magnesium ions are dissolved in it.* For a strategy for overcoming this misconception, see **Address Misconceptions** in "Water to Drink."

The EPA standards apply only to public water supplies serving 25 or more people. Ninety percent of U.S. residents get drinking water from public water systems. Of people getting water from community water systems, 68 percent are served by systems using surface water (lakes, reservoirs, rivers, etc.). The rest are served by systems using groundwater (such as through public wells). People who have private wells are responsible for testing and maintaining their own water supplies.

The EPA also regulates the treatment and release of wastewater. Companies and water systems that release waste into water sources must hold permits. These permits limit the contaminants that can be in the released waste. Communities and other waste producers (such as mines, farms, and factories) must also have plans to handle overflow caused by sudden storms or other events that can wash sewage and other waste into public water systems.

Section 3 Freshwater Pollution

Microorganisms and Disease For most of human history, people thought diseases were caused by a variety of agents, including swamp vapors and even poisons created by the movement of planets. Although John Snow proved that cholera was associated with sewage-contaminated drinking water, he did not know the actual cause of the disease.

The French chemist Louis Pasteur advanced the "germ theory of disease," which states that infectious diseases are caused by specific microorganisms. In 1876, a German physician, Robert Koch, proved that bacteria can cause disease. Since then, scientists have identified the agents of most infectious diseases, including diseases associated with wastewater, such as dysentery, cholera, and typhoid fever.

One way that today's scientists test a body of water for the presence of sewage is by measuring the levels of total coliform bacteria, including fecal coliforms such as E. coli, in a given waterway. Fecal coliforms are bacteria associated with human and other animal wastes. The presence of these bacteria in a waterway may indicate that the water has been polluted with sewage. Testing and monitoring the waters, however, is not the only way that waterways are kept safe. Laws and regulations have been set up by the government to help protect our waterways from pollution.

The Clean Water Act In response to public concern about water pollution, an important piece of legislation was enacted in 1972. This law was called the Federal Water Pollution Control Act Amendments of 1972. Now commonly known as the Clean Water Act, this law has been amended several times over the years and continues to evolve as different issues in water quality are addressed. The Clean Water Act protects the water quality of surface waters in the United States. It achieves this end in many different ways. For example, under the Clean Water Act, permits help regulate the point source pollution that is released into navigable waters. In addition to regulatory measures, other non-regulatory programs have been implemented through the Clean Water Act, such as a voluntary program for landowners that is aimed at reducing polluted runoff.

Section 4 Droughts and Floods

Flash Floods Flooding causes almost half of all weather fatalities, and most flood fatalities occur during flash floods. The worst flash flood in United States history was caused by a dam break in Johnstown, Pennsylvania, in May of 1889. A wall of water 12 m high washed over the city, killing 2,200 people.

It isn't dam breaks that cause most flash floods, but heavy rains. One of the worst flash floods in the United States caused by heavy rain occurred in Rapid City, South Dakota, in June of 1972. About 38 cm of rain fell in five hours, and the resulting flood killed 238 people. More recently, in June 1990, Shadyside, Ohio received 10 cm of rain in just two hours. A torrent 12 m high flooded the town, leaving 26 people dead.

Flash floods are especially dangerous because of the speed with which they can move, and because there is often little warning before they strike. The National Weather Service issues flash flood watches when weather conditions, such as heavy, slow-moving thunderstorms, may lead to flash floods. Flash flood warnings are issued when a flood is imminent or in progress.

Many flash flood deaths and injuries occur when people try to outrun the floodwaters in their cars. As little as two feet of water can float most vehicles, and the force of fast-moving water can sweep them off the road. Generally, it's safest to leave the car and climb to higher ground.

JOHNSTOWN AS LEFT BY THE FLOOD.

Section 5 Water Power

Dam Construction The largest dam construction project in the world is underway now along China's longest river, the Yangtze. It is called the Three Gorges Project, named for the scenic region in the vicinity of the dam. Estimated for completion in 2009, the dam is expected to produce enough electrical power to serve about one ninth of China's power needs. The total cost of the project is unknown, but it is expected to range in the tens to hundreds of billions in U.S. dollars.

The satellite image below, taken in 2000, shows a 60-km (37 mile) length of the Yangtze River. North is at the top of the image; the river flows to the east. The construction site of the Three Gorges Dam is the grayish area in the central part of the image. The site juts into the path of the Yangtze, which has been diverted to flow around it during construction.

Some of the expected results of constructing any dam are sediment deposits upstream of the dam as a river encounters the dam. Water slows on the upstream side of a dam, causing the river to drop part of its sediment load along the bottom of the reservoir that forms.

The Three Gorges Project has stirred controversy since it was adopted by China's government in 1954. Supporters point to benefits including flood control, power generation, and improved navigation. Opponents both in China and abroad warn of the harm the project will inflict both on the natural environment and on the human population that is being displaced. Critics also question whether the benefits promised by the project will actually be realized, arguing that the power it generates may be too expensive to compete with alternative sources, and that siltation behind the dam may actually obstruct navigation.

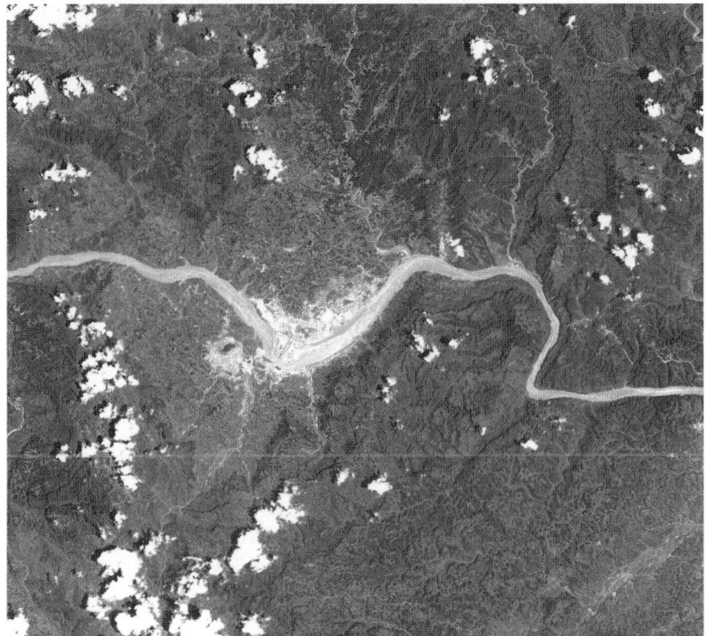

Tidal Power In addition to using rivers, another way to generate electricity from moving water is to harness the power of the tides. To generate tidal power, a long dam is built across the mouth of a bay or estuary. As the tide rises and falls, water flows in and out of tunnels which pass through the dam. The flowing water turns a turbine which generates electricity. Locks in the dam allow shipping to enter and leave the bay or estuary.

The idea of using the tides to generate power isn't new. As long ago as 1814, a dam was built across tidal flats in what is now the Back Bay neighborhood of Boston, Massachusetts. This dam was used to power a mill.

Help Students Read

Directed Reading/Thinking Activity

Predict, Read, Confirm, Revise Predictions

Strategy Help students develop their own reading and thinking processes by setting their own purposes for reading. Select a section of this chapter for students to read. Before modeling the strategy with students, divide the targeted section into approximately four equal portions. Present the steps as in the example below.

Example

1. Preview Tell students to survey the section by analyzing the titles, headings, visual elements, and boldfaced type. Have students also read the introductory and concluding paragraphs.

2. Predict/Generate Questions Ask students to hypothesize and predict what they will learn, and to formulate questions that a teacher might ask. List students' questions on the board.

3. Read/Evaluate and Refine Predictions Have students read a portion of the section. Then have students evaluate their predictions. Discuss any answers they learned to their questions and prior misconceptions that were clarified. Ask students to formulate refined predictions and questions based on the new information.

4. Repeat the process for the remaining text portions.

Interactive Textbook

- Complete student edition
- Video and audio
- Simulations and activities
- Section and chapter activities

Chapter 2 Freshwater Resources

Chapter Preview

This family is enjoying a freshwater resource—fish.

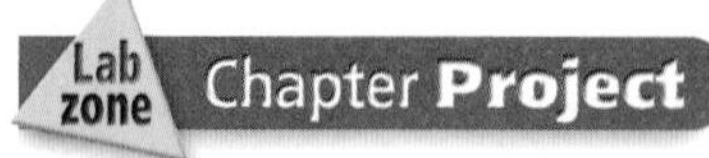

L3

Objectives

This project will help students gain a better understanding of the processes involved in water treatment. After this Chapter Project, students will be able to

- observe the characteristics of dirty water
- design and build a model water treatment system
- compare and contrast their design with those of their classmates
- communicate the features of their design to the class

Skills Focus

Observing, making models, comparing and contrasting, communicating

Project Time Line 2 to 3 weeks

All in One Teaching Resources

- Chapter Project Teacher Notes
- Chapter Project Worksheet 1
- Chapter Project Worksheet 2
- Chapter Project Scoring Rubric

Developing a Plan

During the first week, students plan a design and materials, and begin assembling their models. Students spend the second and third weeks completing, testing, and improving their models. One class period is needed for students to present their models and to have a class discussion comparing the models.

Possible Materials

- Provide dirty water by mixing 1 tablespoon of fuller's earth per cup of tap water or by using water from a local river or pond.
- Include filtration materials such as sand, gravel, charcoal or activated charcoal, window screening, various fabrics, coffee filters or other papers, and 2-L clear plastic soda bottles with the bottoms cut off.

Discovery Channel School

Freshwater Resources

▶ Video Preview
Video Field Trip
Video Assessment

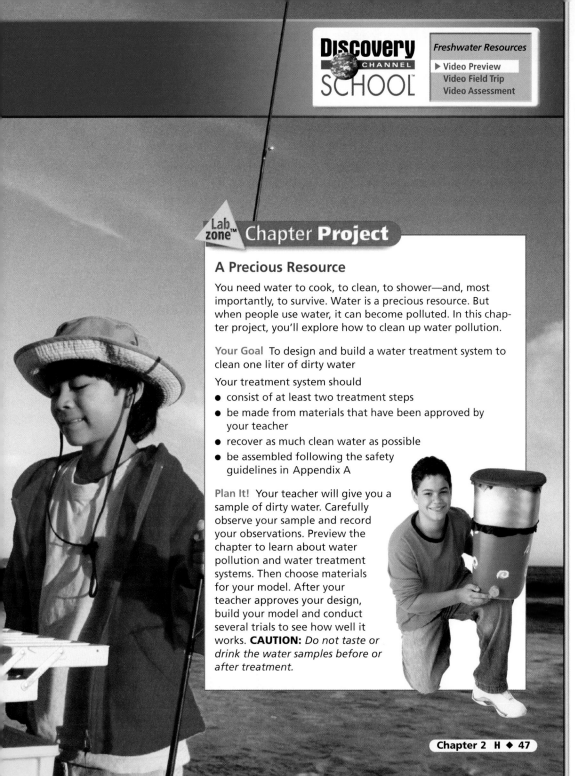

Lab zone™ Chapter **Project**

A Precious Resource

You need water to cook, to clean, to shower—and, most importantly, to survive. Water is a precious resource. But when people use water, it can become polluted. In this chapter project, you'll explore how to clean up water pollution.

Your Goal To design and build a water treatment system to clean one liter of dirty water

Your treatment system should

- consist of at least two treatment steps
- be made from materials that have been approved by your teacher
- recover as much clean water as possible
- be assembled following the safety guidelines in Appendix A

Plan It! Your teacher will give you a sample of dirty water. Carefully observe your sample and record your observations. Preview the chapter to learn about water pollution and water treatment systems. Then choose materials for your model. After your teacher approves your design, build your model and conduct several trials to see how well it works. **CAUTION:** *Do not taste or drink the water samples before or after treatment.*

Freshwater Resources

Show the Video Preview to introduce the Chapter Project and overview the chapter content. Discussion question: **What are three reasons that dams are built?** *(Most dams are built to control river flow, improve navigation, and regulate flooding. Some are also built to produce hydroelectric power.)*

Possible Shortcuts

You can simplify the project by limiting the model to filtration as the only treatment method, or have students work in small groups.

Launching the Project

Show students a container of tap water and a container of dirty water. Ask: **What are some methods you could use to make this dirty water as clean as the tap water?** *(Accept any suggestions.)* Ask: **Would adding tap water to the dirty water be a way to make the water safe to drink?** *(Most will say that simply diluting the water would not be sufficient.)* Encourage students to begin thinking of steps to make an effective water treatment system.

Performance Assessment

The Chapter Project Scoring Rubric will help you evaluate how well students complete the Chapter Project. You may want to share the rubric with your students so they know what is expected of them. Students will be assessed on

- the precision with which they design their treatment system
- how well their treatment system model works
- the organization and thoroughness of their presentation of the model to the class
- their group participation, if they worked in groups

Section 1 Water Supply and Demand

Objectives

After this lesson, students will be able to

H.2.1.1 Identify ways that people use water.

H.2.1.2 Describe some ways to conserve available fresh water.

H.2.1.3 Discuss some possible sources of water for the future.

Target Reading Skill

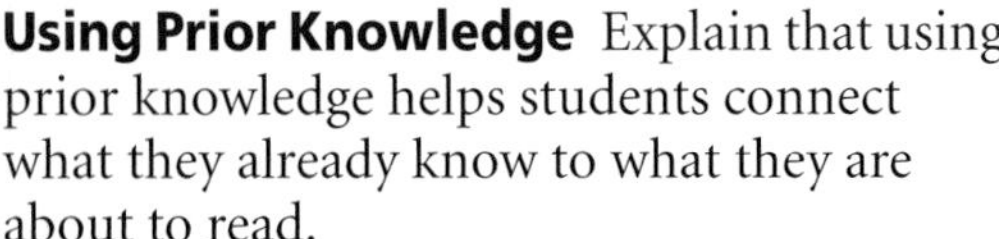

Using Prior Knowledge Explain that using prior knowledge helps students connect what they already know to what they are about to read.

Answers

Possible answers:

What You Know

1. Reducing water use helps conserve water.
2. I can conserve water by taking shorter showers.
3. People often use more water than they need.

What You Learned

1. Recycling and reusing water are two more ways to conserve water.
2. Every minute I shower I use 18 liters of water.
3. Agriculture accounts for the highest consumption of water in the United States.

All in One Teaching Resources

- Transparency H15

Preteach

Build Background Knowledge L2

How Is Water Important?

Challenge students to think of ways that they directly or indirectly use water each day. Ask: **Who can give two examples of how you have used water today?** *(Examples might include showering, brushing teeth, and drinking.)* Then hold up a piece of paper. Ask: **How is water used in the making of this object?** *(Paper is made from wood, which contains water, and water is used in the production of paper.)* Challenge students to think of more examples of direct and indirect water use.

Section 1 Water Supply and Demand

Reading Preview

Key Concepts

- How do people use water?
- What are some ways to conserve available fresh water?
- What are some possible sources of water for the future?

Key Terms

- irrigation
- conservation
- desalination

Target Reading Skill

Using Prior Knowledge Your prior knowledge is what you already know before you read about a topic. Before you read, write what you know about water conservation in a graphic organizer like the one below. As you read, continue to write in what you learn.

What You Know
1. I can conserve water by taking shorter showers. 2.

What You Learned
1. 2.

Lab zone Discover Activity

Can You Find a Balance?

1. Fill a large measuring cup with water to represent a reservoir. Record the level of the water. One partner, the water supplier, should have a plastic dropper and a small bowl of water. The other partner, the water user, should have a spoon and an empty bowl.
2. Start a stopwatch. For two minutes, the water supplier should add water to the measuring cup one dropperful at a time. Each time the water supplier adds a dropperful of water, the water user should remove one spoonful of water from the reservoir.
3. At the end of two minutes, record the level of water in the cup.
4. Now increase the rate of water use by removing two spoonfuls of water for every dropperful added.
5. After another two minutes, record the level of water in the cup again.

Think It Over

Predicting What changes will you need to make so that the water level in the reservoir stays constant?

Imagine this: you're eating dinner with your family and you ask someone to pass the rolls. As the basket makes its way around the table, each person takes a roll. By the time it gets to you, there's nothing left in the basket but crumbs!

This scenario is an example of a limited resource—the rolls—being used by many people. A similar thing can happen to a river.

For example, the Colorado River holds a resource that is precious to the Southwest—water. In this desert region, there is too little precipitation to meet people's water needs. As the river flows through five states and into Mexico, it is tapped again and again to provide water for drinking, irrigation, and other uses. Each time the river is tapped, the flow decreases. As a result, the river's mouth at the Gulf of California is often only a dry riverbed. The Colorado River often dries up before it reaches the ocean.

Lab zone Discover Activity

Skills Focus Predicting L1

Materials large measuring cup, water, plastic dropper, 2 small bowls, spoons, stopwatch

Time 15 minutes

Tips Use a small plastic dropper to accentuate the water level drop in the cup when the rate is increased in Step 4.

Expected Outcome Students will infer that the water in the reservoir will decrease unless the supply rate increases or the water demand decreases.

Think It Over The rate of water consumed must equal the rate of water supplied. One way to achieve this is to remove fewer spoonfuls of water to keep the supply constant.

How People Use Water

The deserts of Nevada and Arizona, two states along the Colorado River, are home to some of the fastest-growing cities in the country. As more people move to Las Vegas, Phoenix, and Tucson, the demand for water—already scarce in this dry region—increases.

People use water for household purposes, industry, transportation, agriculture, and recreation. As cities grow, so too does the water needed for household uses. Industries, such as mining companies, need water to cool machinery and flush out mines. Meanwhile, farmers need a large amount to water their fields. Cities, industries, and farms compete for water rights—the legal right to take water from a particular source.

The Southwest is just one of many places where water is scarce. As you know, water is constantly recycled in the water cycle. However, sometimes water is used faster than it can be replaced by precipitation. A water shortage occurs when there is too little water or too great a demand in an area—or both. A water shortage may occur because of natural processes or it can occur because of rapidly growing human water needs.

FIGURE 1
The Colorado River
The Colorado River flows through five states. The river is used by cities, mines, and farms for drinking, irrigation, and other uses.

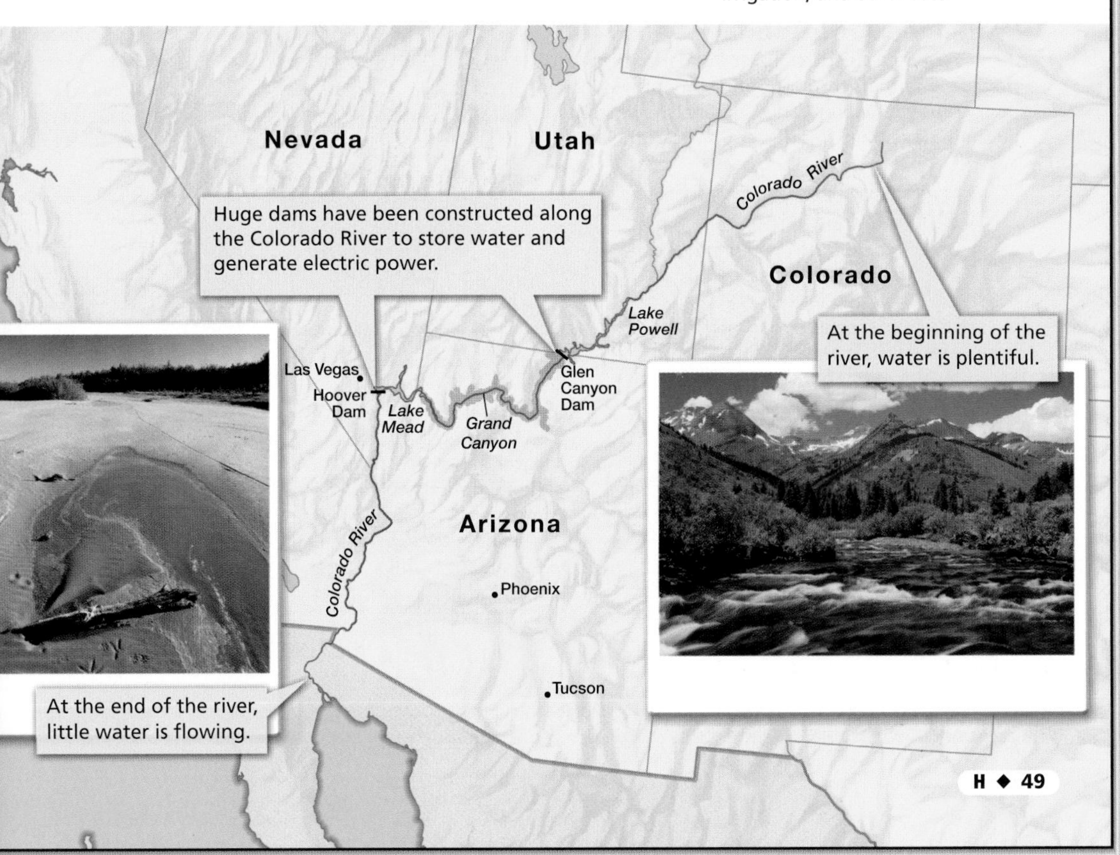
Nevada
Utah
Colorado
Arizona
Colorado River
Huge dams have been constructed along the Colorado River to store water and generate electric power.
At the beginning of the river, water is plentiful.
At the end of the river, little water is flowing.
Lake Powell
Las Vegas
Hoover Dam
Lake Mead
Grand Canyon
Glen Canyon Dam
Phoenix
Tucson

Instruct

How People Use Water

Teach Key Concepts L2

Impact of Water Use

Focus Remind students that only about 1 percent of the water on Earth is available fresh water.

Teach Tell students that overuse can lead to a strain on the water supply. Refer students to Figure 1, and have them trace the Colorado River. Ask: **Why are water shortages common in areas that obtain water from the Colorado River?** *(Demand from surrounding populated regions is high, and renewal by precipitation often is less than the amount of water withdrawn.)* **How do people in this area and elsewhere use water?** *(Household purposes, industry, agriculture, transportation, and recreation)* **What effects can an increased demand for water have on society?** *(It can lead to competition for water rights and scarcity of water as a resource, especially in arid regions.)*

Apply Explain that even though water is a renewable resource, it is a limited resource. The water we use today is the same water used by the dinosaurs. Fresh water will become scarcer as the human population continues to grow. **learning modality: verbal**

Independent Practice L2

All in One Teaching Resources

- Guided Reading and Study Worksheet: *Water Supply and Demand*

Student Edition on Audio CD

All in One Teaching Resources

- Transparency H16

Differentiated Instruction

English Learners/Beginning L1

Comprehension: Key Concept Help students understand the supply and demand of fresh water resources using the analogy of basketball shoes on sale at a sports store. If the demand from buyers is great, then the limited supply of shoes might result in a shoe shortage. **learning modality: logical/mathematical**

English Learners/Intermediate L2

Comprehension: Key Concept Students can expand on the *Beginning* activity by writing a sentence that uses another example of supply and demand of a resource. Have each student read his or her sentence aloud. **learning modality: logical/mathematical**

Monitor Progress L2

Writing Have students write a TV news reporter's script for each of the following situations: too great a demand for water results in a water shortage, too little water results in a water shortage. Students can save their scripts in their portfolios.

Portfolio

Science and **History**

Focus Emphasize that the time line shown spans 5,000 years of agricultural history.

Teach Invite student volunteers to read aloud the annotations on the time line. Have a world map available so students can locate the various sites discussed. For each method of irrigation, encourage students to draw conclusions about the environment in which it was used and how well the technology worked. Ask: **Do you think all these methods are used somewhere in the world today?** *(Students' responses will vary. Each method is still practiced today.)*

Writing in Science

Writing Skill Research

Scoring Rubric

4 Exceeds criteria by including how the method has actually worked in one or more areas of the world

3 Meets criteria and includes detailed description of method, purpose, and improvement

2 Includes only brief description of required elements

1 Is incorrect and incomplete

Help Students Read

Outlining Have students create an outline of the passages How People Use Water and Conserving Water, leaving space below each subhead. Ask them to write in the details below each subhead as they read. When they have completed their outlines, call on students to use their outlines to describe ways that water can be conserved in industry, in agriculture, and in the home.

In the Home Take a minute to list all of the ways you used water this morning. You probably washed your face, brushed your teeth, and flushed the toilet. Perhaps you drank a glass of water or used water to make oatmeal. These are some common uses of water in the home.

Industry and Transportation Think about the objects in your backpack—books, pens, folders. Even though water is not part of these things, it plays a role in making them. Industries use water in other ways, too. For example, power plants and steel mills both need huge volumes of water to cool hot machinery. Water that is used for cooling can often be recycled.

Since ancient times, water has been used to transport people and goods. If you look at a map of the United States, you will notice that many large cities are located on the coasts. Ocean travel led to the growth of these port cities. In early America, rivers also served as natural highways.

• Tech & Design in History •

Water and Agriculture

Plants require a steady supply of water to grow. How have farmers throughout history provided their crops with water? This timeline shows some methods developed in different parts of the world.

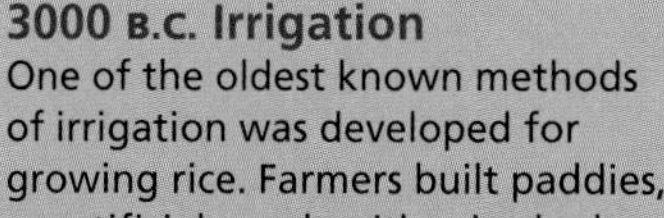

3000 B.C. Irrigation
One of the oldest known methods of irrigation was developed for growing rice. Farmers built paddies, or artificial ponds with raised edges. The farmers flooded the paddies with water from a nearby stream. This ancient technique is still widely used throughout Southeast Asia.

2000 B.C. Shadufs
Egyptian farmers invented a device to raise water from the Nile River. The shaduf acted as a lever to make lifting a bucket of water easier. The farmers then emptied the water into a network of canals to irrigate their fields. The shaduf is still in use in Egypt, India, and other countries.

700 B.C. Canals and Aqueducts
Sennacherib, king of the ancient nation Assyria, surrounded the capital city of Nineveh with fruit trees and exotic plants. To help irrigate the gardens, he built a canal and an aqueduct to transport water from the nearby hills.

3000 B.C. | 2000 B.C. | 1000 B.C.

Agriculture Has your family ever had a garden? If so, you know that growing fruits and vegetables requires water. On a large farm, a constant supply of fresh water is essential. However, some areas don't receive enough regular rainfall for agriculture. In such places, farmland must be irrigated. **Irrigation** is the process of supplying water to areas of land to make them suitable for growing crops. In the United States, more water is used for irrigation than for any other single purpose.

Recreation Do you like to swim in a neighborhood pool? Catch fish from a rowboat in the middle of a lake? Walk along a beach collecting seashells? Or maybe just sit on the edge of a dock and dangle your feet in the water? Then you know some ways that water is used for recreation. And if you brave the winter cold to ski or skate, you are enjoying water in its frozen form.

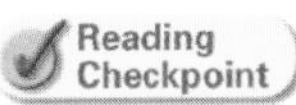

List a household use, an industrial use, and an agricultural use of water.

Writing in Science

Research and Write Find out more about one of these agricultural techniques. Imagine that you are a farmer seeing the method in action for the first time. Write a letter to a friend describing the new technique. What problem will it solve? How will it improve your farming?

A.D. 1200 *Chinampas*
To grow crops in swampy areas, the Aztecs built raised plots of farmland called *chinampas*. A grid of canals kept the crops wet and allowed the farmers to navigate boats between the *chinampas*.

A.D. 1870 Wind-Powered Pumps
When homesteaders arrived on the dry Great Plains of the central United States, they had to rely on groundwater for irrigation. Windmills provided the energy to pump the groundwater to the surface. The farmers dug ditches to transport the water to their fields.

Today Drip Irrigation
Irrigation is the key to survival in desert regions. Today, methods such as drip irrigation ensure that very little water is wasted when crops are watered. Holes in the pipe allow water to drip directly onto the soil around the roots of each plant.

A.D. 1 A.D. 1000 A.D. 2000

Lab zone Build Inquiry L2

Making Graphs on the Availability of World Water Resources

Materials calculator, art materials

Time 20 minutes

Focus Remind students that available fresh water is not evenly distributed over Earth's surface.

Teach Provide the following statistics on availability of water and percent of world population. Ask students to construct two circle graphs. One graph should show the availability of water in each area. The other graph should show the percent of the total world population in each area. Africa 11%, 13%; Asia 36%, 60%; Australia and Oceania 5%, <1%; Europe 8%, 13%; North and Central America 15%, 8%; South America 26%, 6%. Ask students to use their graphs to answer these questions: **1) Which continent appears to have about equal percentages of population and water resources? 2) Which has the greatest water supply compared to the population? 3) Which has the greatest disparity between population and water resources?** Then ask students to calculate the ratios of water availability to population for each continent to confirm their answers. *1) Africa with 0.8:1 [11 ÷ 13]); 2) Australia and Oceania with 5:1 [5 ÷ 1]); 3) (Europe and Asia, both 0.6:1 [8 ÷ 13 and 36 ÷ 60])*

Apply Tell students that Australia is a very dry continent with little rainfall. Ask students to infer why Australia has the most available water per person. *(Australia has a small population compared to the other continents.)* **learning modality: logical/mathematical**

Differentiated Instruction

Gifted and Talented L3

Making a Display Have students research irrigation practices in their local area, state, or region. Encourage them to start their research by first contacting the state department of agriculture by phone or through their Web site. Encourage students to include the major agricultural crops produced by your state or region. Have students prepare text and find illustrations that support their findings. Students can arrange their writing and illustrations in an easy-to-follow format on poster board and present their posters to the class. **learning modality: verbal**

Monitor Progress L2

Oral Presentation Call on students at random to explain a method of irrigation shown in the Science and History Feature in their own words.

Answer

Reading Checkpoint Possible answer: Water for brushing teeth (household use), making paper (industrial use), and irrigation (agricultural use)

Conserving Water

Teach Key Concepts

L2

Ways to Conserve Water

Focus Review main categories of freshwater use with students.

Teach Tell students that an easy way to remember conservation practices is to think of the three R's. Ask students to explain what those are. *(Reducing water use, recycling water, and reusing water)* Ask: **Which of the three R's can you most easily practice in your home?** *(Reducing water use)* **What is one method used by industry to conserve water?** *(Reusing water that cools machinery)* **Used by agriculture?** *(Reducing water use by using drop and sprinkler irrigation methods)*

Apply Ask students to think of ways they can reuse water. *(Possible answer: Use bath water or the water used to rinse dishes to water plants.)* **learning modality: verbal**

Use Visuals: Figure 2

L1

Conserving Water at Home

Focus Tell students that water use in the United States averages 340 liters per person per day.

Teach Ask a volunteer to read ways to conserve water in the home. Have students discuss other ways to conserve water in the home, and list these on the board.

Apply After students have answered the caption question, hypothesizing which method saves the most water, tell them that 50 to 70 percent of home water use goes to watering lawns and gardens, according to the U.S. Environmental Protection Agency. Ask them to think of ways to cut back on this particular use of water.

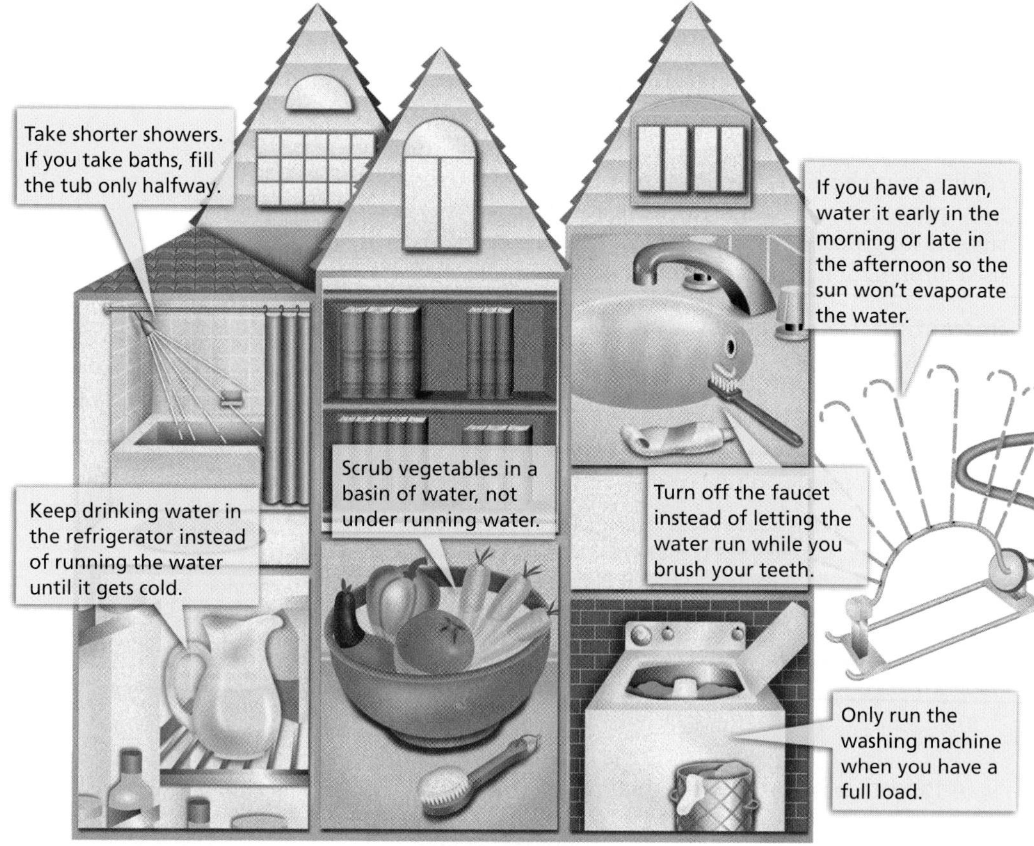

Take shorter showers. If you take baths, fill the tub only halfway.
If you have a lawn, water it early in the morning or late in the afternoon so the sun won't evaporate the water.
Scrub vegetables in a basin of water, not under running water.
Keep drinking water in the refrigerator instead of running the water until it gets cold.
Turn off the faucet instead of letting the water run while you brush your teeth.
Only run the washing machine when you have a full load.

FIGURE 2
Conserving Water at Home
There are many simple ways to conserve water at home.
Developing Hypotheses *Which of these ideas do you think would save the most water per day in your home? How could you test your hypothesis?*

Conserving Water

During a water shortage, people often try to avoid wasting water. **Conservation** is the practice of using less of a resource so that it will not be used up. **Reducing water use, recycling water, and reusing water are three ways to conserve water.**

In the Home Most people in the United States have access to as much clean, safe water as they want. As a result, we often use more water than we need without thinking much about it. But as Figure 2 shows, there are some simple things you can do to help conserve water around your home.

Can these suggestions really help? Figure it out. For every minute you shower, you use about 18 liters of water. If you shower for 10 minutes, that's about 180 liters. But if you showered for 5 minutes, you would use only 90 liters. And if each student in a class of 25 showered for 5 minutes instead of 10, they would save a total of 2,250 liters of water!

In Industry Many industries have made changes in their manufacturing processes to use less water. For example, in the 1950s it took about 227,000 liters of water to make 1,000 kilograms of writing paper. By the 1980s, paper mills needed only half that much water to make the same amount of paper.

New water-saving techniques help industries save money in water costs and meet the requirements of environmental laws. These techniques conserve water while also reducing the amount of wastewater that plants release. For example, some factories that use water to cool machinery now build cooling pools on their property. The heated water cools off in the pools and then can be used again.

In Agriculture Agriculture accounts for the highest consumption of water in the United States. In the last few decades, farmers have found new ways to use less water. When water flows into fields in open ditches, much of it is lost through evaporation. Using pipes to carry water reduces the water loss.

Sprinkler irrigation and drip irrigation both use pipes to conserve water. Sprinkler irrigation sprays water onto crops from overhead pipes. Drip irrigation distributes water through pipes with tiny holes that lie close to the ground. Water drips onto the soil near the plants' roots so that very little is wasted.

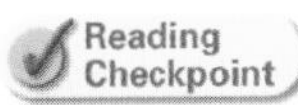
How do sprinkler irrigation and drip irrigation differ?

For: More on water conservation
Visit: PHSchool.com
Web Code: cfd-3021

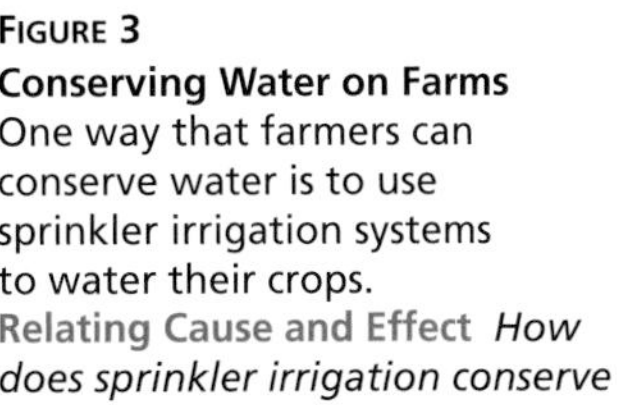

FIGURE 3
Conserving Water on Farms
One way that farmers can conserve water is to use sprinkler irrigation systems to water their crops.
Relating Cause and Effect *How does sprinkler irrigation conserve water?*

For: More on water conservation
Visit: PHSchool.com
Web Code: cfd-3021

Students can review water conservation in an online interactivity.

Build Inquiry L3

Communicating Conservation Methods

Materials discarded magazines, poster board, glue, markers, reference materials from EPA (these can be accessed online)

Time 25 minutes

Focus Review the three R's.

Teach Divide students into four groups. Assign one group to research ways to conserve water in the home kitchen, another group in the home bathroom, and a third group in the yard. Assign the fourth group to research how technology in the home can save water (such as low-flow showerheads). Have students prepare posters to highlight their findings. Arrange the posters in a school hallway.

Apply Encourage students to try one or two methods of water conservation in the home. Have them keep a log of their efforts and report to the class how successful they were. Students can share ideas for conserving water. **learning modality: visual**

Monitor Progress L2

Skills Check Have students make a concept map that includes all the suggestions mentioned in the text for how water can be conserved.

Answers

Figure 2 A typical answer is taking shorter showers. This could be tested by measuring the water saved by each idea and then comparing.

Figure 3 Most of the water is used because it is sprayed directly onto crops instead of flowing in open ditches, where it can evaporate.

Reading Checkpoint Sprinkler irrigation sprays water onto plants from overhead, while drip irrigation releases small amounts of water directly onto the soil near the roots of plants. Drip irrigation conserves water better than sprinkler irrigation.

Differentiated Instruction

Special Needs L1

Demonstrating Amount of Water To give students a sense of how much water is in a liter, provide water in several gallon containers (not liter). Ask students to pour out the amount that they think is a liter into an empty container. Then verify or adjust the amount. Ask: **Are you surprised at how much water is used in the average household?** *(Students may be surprised, for example, by the number of liters used in showering.)* Tell students that the usage rate of 340 liters per person per day is only an average. Ask: **What might make a household's water use vary from the average?** *(Number of people in the house and type of equipment)* **learning modality: kinesthetic**

Math Analyzing Data

Math Skill Making and interpreting graphs

Focus Point out that bar graphs are used to compare different categories.

Teach Remind students that vertical bar graphs are read by observing where an imaginary line from the top of each bar extends horizontally and intersects with the vertical axis.

Answers

1. Source of water use; number of liters per day;

2. Taking showers

3. 15 percent (100 ÷ 675)

4. Possible answer: People might take more showers in the summer when they are active outdoors. Water use might increase when guests visit or during holidays, when people may cook more.

5. Possible answers: Install a low-flow shower head, install a low-flow toilet, do not run the water while brushing teeth, use the washing machine only when there is a full load of clothes

Fresh Water for the Future

Teach Key Concepts

L2

Possible Water Sources

Focus Remind students that ice is a form of fresh water, even when floating as icebergs in salty ocean waters.

Teach Ask: **What are two sources of fresh water that are not commonly used?** *(The oceans and icebergs)* **How can salt water be converted to fresh water?** *(By desalination—boiling water, freezing water, or pumping water through a filter.)* **How could icebergs be used?** *(By melting them)* **What is a drawback of using icebergs as a source of fresh water?** *(Relocating and melting icebergs could change the environment.)*

Apply Ask students to infer why icebergs are not salt water using what they learned about desalination. *(When ocean water freezes, salt is not included in ice.)* **learning modality: logical/mathematical**

Math Analyzing Data

Household Water Use

A family conducted a survey of their current water use. Their average daily use is shown in the bar graph. Study the graph and answer the following questions.

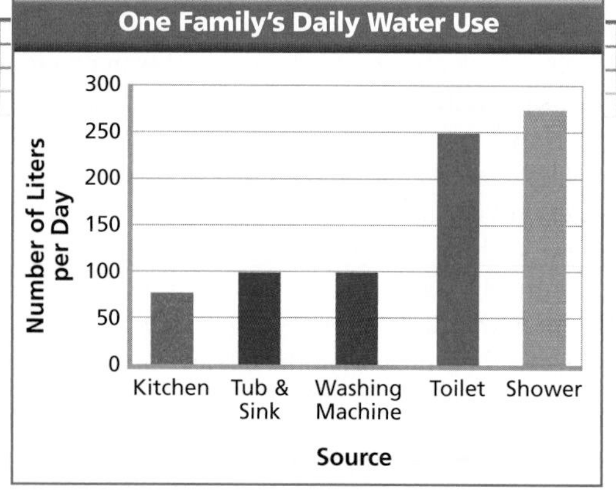

1. **Reading Graphs** What variable is shown on the horizontal axis? What variable is shown on the vertical axis?
2. **Interpreting Data** What is the source of the greatest water use for the family?
3. **Calculating** The family found that they used an average of about 675 liters of water per day. About what percentage of the water is used for laundry?
4. **Inferring** Do you think the family's water use would vary at different times of the year? Explain.
5. **Predicting** Suggest three additional ways that this family might be able to save a significant amount of water each day.

Fresh Water for the Future

As the use of water in the world increases, so does the need for water. Where can people find new sources of water for the future? One obvious place would seem to be the oceans. **Two possible methods of obtaining fresh water for the future are desalination and melting icebergs.**

Desalination For thousands of years, people have tried to make salty ocean water drinkable. One possible method of obtaining fresh water from salt water is called **desalination.**

There are several ways to desalinate water. A technique called distillation involves boiling water so that it evaporates, leaving the salt behind. The water vapor is then condensed to produce liquid fresh water. Another desalination method involves freezing the water, which also leaves the salt behind. Still another method is to pump water at high pressure through a very fine filter. The filter separates out pure water and returns salty water to the ocean.

Desalination is very expensive because of the energy and equipment it requires. In spite of the cost, however, many nations in dry Southwest Asia depend on this technology. A few cities in the United States, such as Santa Barbara, California, have also built desalination plants.

Icebergs Another possible source of fresh water is icebergs. Tugboats could tow a wrapped iceberg from Antarctica to a coastal area of Africa or South America. As the iceberg melted, it would provide millions of liters of pure water that could be piped to shore.

Such plans raise environmental questions, however. How would a huge mass of ice offshore affect the local weather? What would happen to living things in the ocean as the ice cooled the water around it? These questions must be answered before icebergs could be used to meet future water needs.

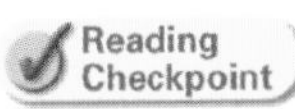
What is desalination?

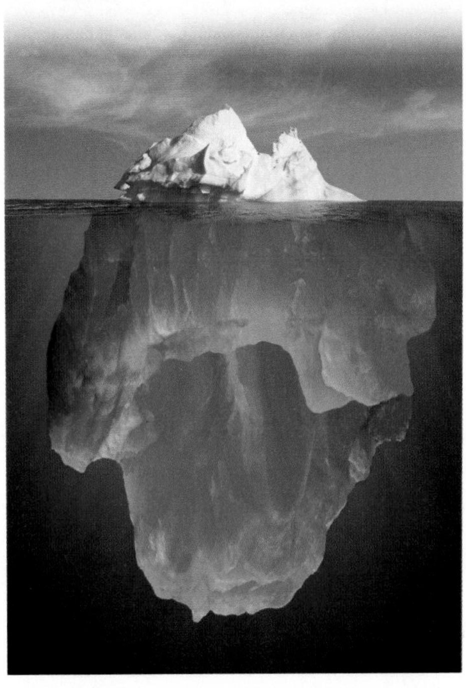

FIGURE 4
A Future Source of Drinking Water?
Icebergs are one possible source of drinking water for the future. **Applying Concepts** *How can water from icebergs reach people on shore?*

Section 1 Assessment

Target Reading Skill **Using Prior Knowledge** Revise your graphic organizer based on what you learned.

Reviewing Key Concepts

1. a. **Listing** Name five ways that people use water.
   b. **Explaining** Why are towns and cities often located near bodies of water?
   c. **Calculating** Growing wheat for one loaf of bread takes about 435 liters of water. If your family eats three loaves a week, about how much water would be used each year to make bread for your family?
2. a. **Identifying** What are three ways to conserve water?
   b. **Describing** Describe the techniques that industries can use to conserve water.
   c. **Making Judgments** To conserve water, should communities limit how often people can water their lawns or wash their cars? Why or why not?
3. a. **Reviewing** What are two possible ways to meet people's future water needs?
   b. **Inferring** What is one disadvantage of each method?

Lab zone At-Home Activity

Monitoring Water Use Place a stopper over the drain in a sink. Ask a family member to brush his or her teeth over the sink, allowing the water to run until he or she is done. Mark the level of the water in the sink with a small piece of tape. Remove the stopper and let the water drain. Replace the stopper and have the person repeat the brushing, this time turning the water on only when needed. Mark the water level with another piece of tape. Point out the difference in the amount of water used in each case.

Monitor Progress L2

Answers

Figure 4 Wrapped icebergs could be towed to populated coastal regions.

Reading Checkpoint Obtaining fresh water from salt water

Assess

Reviewing Key Concepts

1. a. Bathing, cooking, drinking, irrigation, industry **b.** Ease of transporting goods and availability for other uses **c.** 67,860 L

2. a. Reduce consumption, reuse water, and recycle water. **b.** Develop new technology in manufacturing to use less water and produce less wastewater. **c.** Possible answer: Yes because green lawns and clean cars are wants, not needs.

3. a. Desalination of ocean water and melting icebergs **b.** Desalination is very expensive because of the energy and equipment it requires. Relocating and melting icebergs could change the environment.

Reteach L1

As a class, list the ways that water is used and ways to conserve water.

Performance Assessment L2

Writing Challenge students to assume the role of a government official in a region experiencing a drought. Have students write a list of recommendations to limit water use in homes and by businesses.

All in One Teaching Resources

- Section Summary: *Water Supply and Demand*
- Review and Reinforce: *Water Supply and Demand*
- Enrich: *Water Supply and Demand*

Lab zone Chapter Project

Keep Students on Track Check that students have developed a design for their water treatment model. Make sure each design has at least two steps. Ask them to explain what each step is supposed to accomplish. Then have students begin assembly of their models.

Lab zone At-Home Activity

Monitoring Water Use L2

Encourage students to explain to family members that water is a precious resource that should not be wasted. Students might try the activity with more than one family member, making it a friendly competition about who can conserve the most water.

Getting the Salt Out L2

Prepare for Inquiry

Key Concept
Distillation is one method that can be used in desalination.

Skills Objectives
Students will be able to
- observe the distillation process
- make a model of a desalination plant

Prep Time 30 minutes
Class Time 40 minutes

All in One Teaching Resources
- Lab Worksheet: *Getting the Salt Out*

Advance Planning
Obtain bags of ice on the morning of the lab. Cut the rubber tubing into 50-cm lengths.

Alternative Materials
In place of salt, use "instant seawater," which can be purchased at pet stores.

Safety
Caution students to wear the oven mitt every time they touch the hot flask. Make sure they keep water away from electrical outlets and the hot plate plug. Do not allow the water to boil away completely. Review the safety guidelines in Appendix A.

Guide Inquiry

Troubleshooting the Experiment
- Make sure students do not add too much salt to the water; the solution should not be cloudy.
- Wet the tube or rub it with glycerin to ease insertion into the stopper.
- Warn students not to tear a large hole in the foil when they insert the tubing through its center.

Expected Outcome
The water in the flask will boil, causing it to evaporate and leave salt behind. The water vapor will move through the tubing and condense in the beaker.

Getting the Salt Out

Problem
How can distillation be used to obtain fresh water from salt water?

Skills Focus
observing, making models

Materials
- hot plate • aluminum foil • 250-mL beaker
- plastic spoon • water, 100 mL
- shallow pan • ice • plastic tube
- 500-mL flask • stirring rod • rubber stopper
- salt • rubber tubing, 50 cm

Procedure    

1. Pour 100 mL of water into the flask.
2. Add one spoonful of salt to the water in the flask and stir until it is dissolved. The solution should not be cloudy.
3. Gently insert the plastic tube through the hole of the rubber stopper. Do not force the tube into the hole; ask your teacher for help if you are having difficulty.
4. Insert one end of the plastic tube into the rubber tubing.
5. Put the rubber stopper in the flask. The bottom of the plastic tube should be above the surface of the solution.
6. Cover the beaker with aluminum foil. Press the edges of the foil against the beaker.
7. Push the free end of the rubber tubing through the center of the aluminum foil covering the top of the beaker.
8. Place the beaker into the pan, surrounded by ice.
9. Put the flask on the hot plate, keeping it away from the pan of ice. Turn the hot plate on. Bring the solution to a boil. **CAUTION:** *Do not touch the hot plate or flask. Do not allow the solution to boil completely away.*
10. Observe what happens in the flask and in the beaker. Continue heating the solution until a liquid has accumulated in the beaker.
11. Turn off the hot plate and allow the flask and the beaker to cool. What is left behind in the flask? Record your observations.

Analyze and Conclude
1. **Observing** What happened to the water in the flask during the boiling process? What happened to the salt?
2. **Making Models** What did the water in the flask represent? What did the water in the beaker represent?
3. **Drawing Conclusions** Based on your results, is distillation a useful method for obtaining fresh water from salt water? Why or why not?
4. **Communicating** Imagine building a desalination plant that uses distillation to obtain water for a city. Write a paragraph describing any difficulties you might encounter using this process on such a large scale.

Design an Experiment
How could you change the setup and procedure to recover fresh water from salt water without using the hot plate? *Obtain your teacher's permission before carrying out your investigation.*

Analyze and Conclude
1. It evaporated; it remained in the flask.
2. Ocean water; fresh water obtained by desalination
3. Possible answer: Yes, if water is urgently needed. However, it would require a lot of time and energy to boil the water.
4. Paragraphs should include that a lot of thermal energy is required to distill water on a large scale, which could be costly.

Extend Inquiry

Design an Experiment Possible design: Use the same general setup, but place the flask in direct sunlight instead of heating it on a hot plate.

Section 2

• Tech & Design •

Water to Drink

Reading Preview

Key Concepts

- What factors affect water quality?
- Why is drinking water often treated before people drink it?
- What happens to wastewater in most communities?

Key Terms

- water quality
- concentration
- pH
- hardness
- filtration
- coagulation
- sewage

Target Reading Skill

Sequencing As you read, make a flowchart that shows the steps of drinking-water treatment. Put the steps of the process in separate boxes in the flowchart in the order in which they occur.

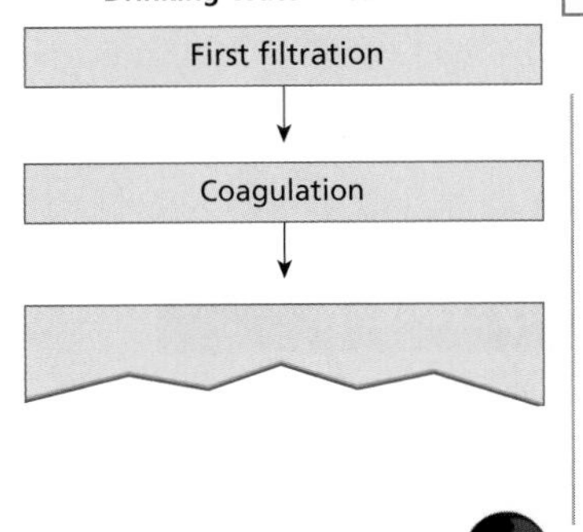

Lab zone Discover Activity

How Hard Is It to Move Water?

1. Line two large trash barrels with heavy plastic bags. Fill one barrel with 100 liters of water. This is about how much water a person uses during a five-minute shower.
2. With your classmates, form a line between the barrels. Your goal is to transfer all the water from one barrel to the other.
3. The first person in line should fill a large plastic pitcher with water, put the cover on, and hand it to the next person. **CAUTION:** *Avoid spilling the water. Be careful of slippery floors if you are indoors.*
4. Pass the pitcher to the end of the line, where the last person should empty it into the second barrel. Hand the empty pitcher back down the line to the first person.
5. Repeat Steps 3 and 4 until all the water is in the second barrel. How many times did you pass the pitcher down the line?

Think It Over

Calculating Suppose a person uses an average of 250 liters of water a day. How many times would you have to pass the pitcher to move that amount of water?

Where does the water in your kitchen faucet come from? Its source may be a lake or reservoir, or it may come from water in underground rock layers. Most people in the United States get their drinking water from one of these sources.

Your drinking water comes from either a public or private water supply. Most large communities maintain public water supplies. These communities collect, treat, and distribute water to residents. In less-populated areas, people often rely on private wells that supply water for individual families.

Lab zone Discover Activity

Skills Focus Calculating L1

Materials 2 large trash barrels, 2 large heavy plastic trash bags, water, large plastic pitcher with lid

Time 20 minutes

Tips Expect spilled water. Large pitchers will result in fewer passes. Students could pass multiple pitchers of the same volume, as long as someone keeps count.

Expected Outcome Students will observe the amount of time and effort required to move water.

Think It Over Answers will vary according to the size of the pitcher. Have students make this calculation by using the number of passes it took to transfer 100 L. For example, if it took 50 passes to transfer 100 L, then it would take 2.5 times that, or 125 passes, to transfer 250 L.

Section 2

Water to Drink

Objectives

After this lesson, students will be able to

H.2.2.1 Identify factors that affect water quality.

H.2.2.2 Explain why drinking water is often treated before people drink it.

H.2.2.3 Describe what happens to wastewater in most communities.

Target Reading Skill 

Sequencing Explain that organizing information from beginning to end helps students understand a step-by-step process.

Answers

Possible answer:

Drinking-Water Treatment

First filtration

Coagulation

Settling basins

Second filtration

Chlorination

Aeration

Additional Treatment

All in One Teaching Resources

- Transparency H17

Preteach

Build Background Knowledge 

Sources of Water

Display a glass of water, and tell students that it came from a school drinking fountain. Ask: **Where did this water come from?** *(Accept all reasonable responses. Students might mention a local river, reservoir, or well.)* Have students make a flowchart that explains a possible route for the water from the source to the school.

Instruct

Water Quality

Teach Key Concepts L2

Factors Affecting Water Quality

Focus Ask students to describe the taste or smell of different sources of water they have encountered. *(Tasteless, salty, metallic, chlorinated, rotten-egg smell)*

Teach Explain that water quality depends on the concentrations of various components in water. Ask: **Are all substances in water harmful?** *(No; iron is harmless unless present in very high levels.)* **How can disease-causing organisms be detected?** *(By measuring the number of* E. coli *bacteria; their presence indicates that water contains waste material.)* **What other factors affect water quality?** *(Acidic water can dissolve lead or other metals in the pipes through which it passes. Hard water makes it difficult to clean clothes.)*

Apply Tell students that the federal EPA standards apply to public water sources and wells that serve more than 25 people. Individual states may regulate private wells. **learning modality: verbal**

Math Skills

Math Skills Calculating a Concentration

Focus Remind students that concentrations compare the amount of one substance to the amount of another substance.

Teach Demonstrate concentration by adding 10 ml of colored water to 990 ml of clear water. Show on the board that the concentration is 10 parts per 1,000, or 10,000 ppm.

Answer
500/1,000,000, or 5/10,000

Independent Practice L2

All in One Teaching Resources

- Guided Reading and Study Worksheet: *Water to Drink*

Student Edition on Audio CD

Math Skills

Calculating a Concentration

Concentrations are often measured in parts per million (ppm). What does this unit mean? If you own one compact disc by your favorite band, and the disc sells one million copies, your disc is one of the one million sold, or one part per million. When a concentration is written in this form, you can rewrite it as a fraction. To do this, put the number of parts on top, and the "whole" on the bottom.

$$1 \text{ part per million} = \frac{1}{1{,}000{,}000}$$

Practice Problem The concentration of iron in a water sample is 500 parts per million. Write this concentration as a fraction.

Water Quality

Now you know where your water comes from. Before you raise a glass to your lips, however, you'll want to be sure the water is safe to drink. Would you be willing to take a sip if the water were rust-colored or had a funny smell? Color and odor are two factors that affect water quality.

Standards of Quality **Water quality** is a measurement of the substances in water besides water molecules. **Certain substances, such as iron, can affect the taste or color of water but are harmless unless present at very high levels. Other substances, such as certain chemicals and microorganisms, can be harmful to your health.**

In the United States, the Environmental Protection Agency (EPA) is responsible for developing water-quality standards. These standards set concentration limits for certain substances. A **concentration** is the amount of one substance in a certain volume of another substance. Figure 5 shows some water-quality standards for different substances.

Acidity The pH level of water also affects its quality. The **pH** of water is a measurement of how acidic or basic the water is, on a scale of 0 to 14. Pure water has a pH of 7—it is neutral, meaning it is neither an acid nor a base. The higher the pH, the more basic the water. The lower the pH, the more acidic the water. Acidic water can cause problems by dissolving lead or other metals from the pipes it passes through.

FIGURE 5
The EPA has set water-quality standards for drinking water. **Interpreting Data** *Based on this table, is a concentration of 0.09 ppm of arsenic in drinking water acceptable? Is a concentration of 0.05 ppm of cyanide acceptable?*

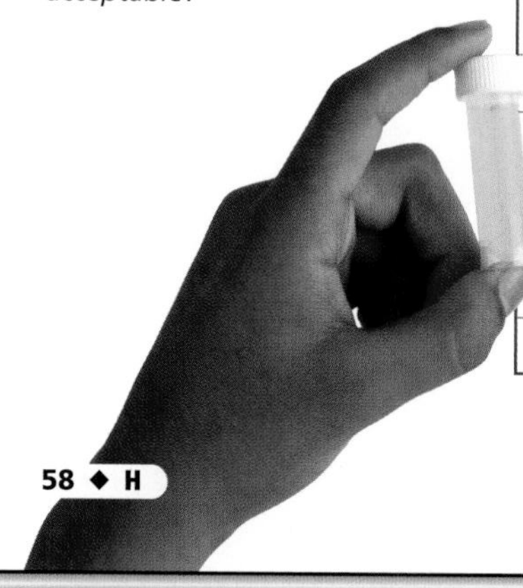

Selected Water-Quality Standards

Substance	Limit
Arsenic	0.01 parts per million (ppm)
Carbon tetrachloride	0.005 ppm
Copper	1.3 ppm
Cyanide	0.2 ppm
Lead	0.015 ppm
Coliform count	No more than 5% of samples taken in a month can be positive.
pH	6.5 – 8.5

FIGURE 6
Hardness of Water
Hard water does not form suds easily. The water being used to wash this car is probably soft water.

Hardness The combined level of two minerals—calcium and magnesium—in a sample of water is referred to as the **hardness** of that sample. Hard water contains high levels of calcium and magnesium. The minerals come from rocks, such as limestone, that water flows through underground.

For most people, the main drawback of hard water is that it does not form suds well when mixed with soap or detergent. Suds are very important to the cleaning process. So it takes more soap or detergent to get laundry clean in hard water.

The minerals in hard water can also form deposits that can clog pipes and machinery. Soft water, on the other hand, contains lower levels of calcium and magnesium. Soft water leaves fewer deposits and forms better soapsuds than hard water.

Disease-Causing Organisms The presence of disease-causing organisms affects water quality. Such organisms can be detected in water by conducting a coliform count, which measures the number of *Escherichia coli* bacteria. These bacteria are found in human and animal wastes. Thus, their presence in water shows that it contains waste material. A high coliform count is an indicator, or sign, that the water may also contain other disease-causing organisms.

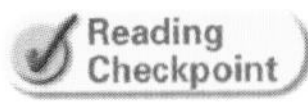
What two minerals affect a water sample's hardness?

Address Misconceptions L1

Focus Some students may think that hard water feels different than soft water.

Teach Explain to students that water is called "hard" because calcium and magnesium ions are dissolved in it. Detergents bind with the elements in hard water and cause a dull film to be left behind. Pour a sample of commercial mineral water in one beaker. In a second beaker, pour a sample of soft water from a home that has a water softener or naturally soft water. Add a small amount of soap to each beaker and stir. Students will observe more suds in the soft water.

Apply Ask: **How would hard water affect how soap acts on your skin or hair?** *(It would take more soap to produce a lather. Because hard water leaves deposits, skin and hair would be duller.)* **learning modality: visual**

L2

Interpreting Maps

Materials copies of maps obtained from the U.S. Geological Survey (Maps for particular areas showing rivers, streams, and groundwater can be accessed online.)

Time 10 minutes

Focus Ask students to name bodies of water in your area that are sources of drinking water.

Teach Have students examine the maps to locate sources of water. Students who have private wells may be able to identify aquifers near their homes.

Apply Ask students to confirm their inferences by contacting their local water department. **learning modality: visual**

Differentiated Instruction

Special Needs L1
Converting Concentrations Students may need practice in working with large numbers. Have students express the concentration of carbon tetrachloride in Figure 5 as a fraction. Explain that this would be written as 0.005/1,000,000. Show students how to move the decimal point over by the same number of places in both the numerator and the denominator to get a whole number in the numerator. This process yields 5/1,000,000,000, or 5 parts per billion. **learning modality: logical/mathematical**

Monitor Progress 

Writing Have each student write a paragraph that describes safe drinking water, including the factors that affect water quality.

Answers
Figure 5 No; yes

 Calcium and magnesium

For: More on water treatment
Visit: PHSchool.com
Web Code: cfd-3022

Students can review water treatment in an online interactivity.

Treating Drinking Water

Help Students Read L1

Predicting Before students begin reading Treating Drinking Water, tell them to use what they have just learned about water quality to make written predictions about how drinking water is treated. After students have read the passage, have them write responses to their predictions, correcting them and adding details.

Teach Key Concepts L2

Why Water Is Treated

Focus Refer students to Figure 7.

Teach Call out each step in the figure, and have volunteers describe its meaning. Ask: **Why is the coagulation step necessary before a second filtration is employed?** *(Any remaining unwanted materials are so small that they would otherwise pass through the sand and gravel. Alum creates the floc that these unwanted materials can adhere to.)* **Why must water be treated before we can drink it?** *(To get rid of particles and disease-causing organisms)*

Apply Ask: **What is the difference between the two filtration steps?** *(The first filtration uses a screen to remove large objects from the water; the second uses sand and gravel to filter out flocs of finer substances such as algae, bacteria, and some chemicals.)* **learning modality: visual**

All in One Teaching Resources

- Transparency H18

For: More on water treatment
Visit: PHSchool.com
Web Code: cfd-3022

Treating Drinking Water

Picture a huge, smooth-surfaced lake under a sky dotted with puffy, white clouds. Leaves drift upon the water's sparkling surface. Fish swim along the muddy bottom. That lake may be your source of drinking water.

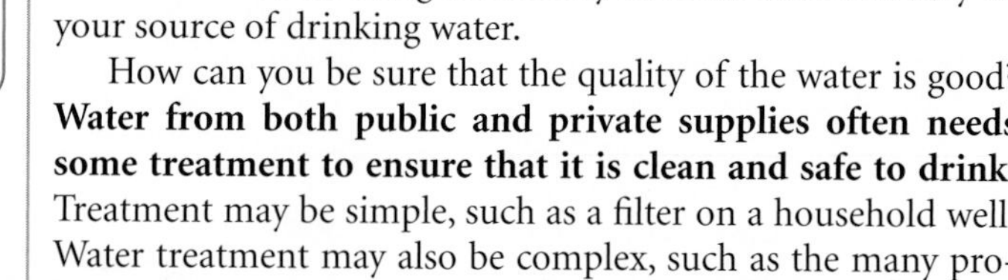

How can you be sure that the quality of the water is good? **Water from both public and private supplies often needs some treatment to ensure that it is clean and safe to drink.** Treatment may be simple, such as a filter on a household well. Water treatment may also be complex, such as the many processes water undergoes at public treatment plants. Follow the water in Figure 7 to see what happens in a typical water treatment plant.

Filtration and Coagulation The first step in treating water from a lake or river is usually filtration. **Filtration** is the process of passing water through a series of screens that allows the water through, but not larger solid particles. During this step, trash, leaves, branches, and other large objects are removed from the water.

In the second step, a chemical is added to cause sticky globs, called flocs, to form. Other particles stick to the flocs, a process known as **coagulation.** The heavy clumps then sink into the settling basins. The water is then filtered again.

FIGURE 7
Drinking-Water Treatment
A typical drinking-water treatment process includes several steps that remove unwanted substances from water.
Interpreting Diagrams *What occurs during aeration?*

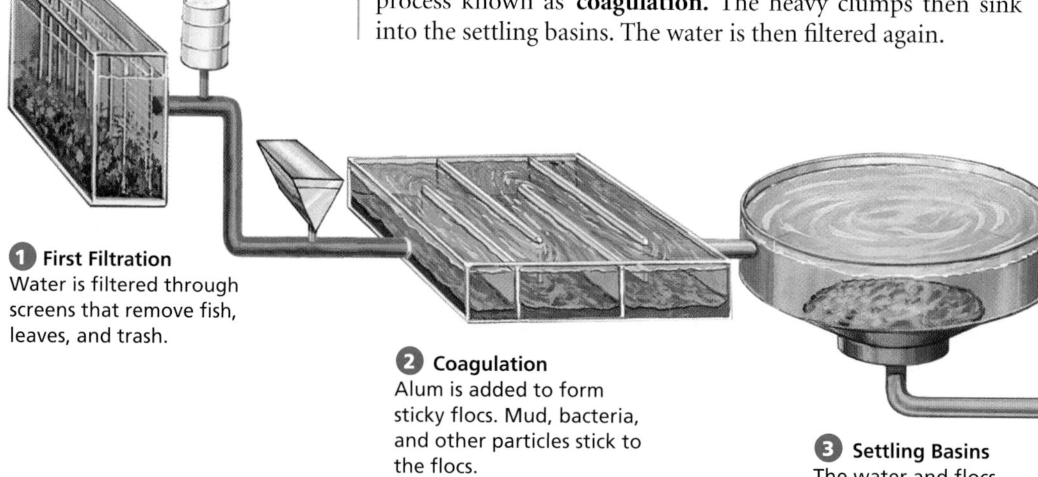

1 First Filtration
Water is filtered through screens that remove fish, leaves, and trash.
2 Coagulation
Alum is added to form sticky flocs. Mud, bacteria, and other particles stick to the flocs.
3 Settling Basins
The water and flocs then sink into settling basins.

Differentiated Instruction

Less Proficient Readers L1

Associating Vocabulary Students may have difficulty learning some of the terms used on these pages. Pair students with more proficient readers. Have them find each term in a dictionary and identify a familiar word or image to help them remember the terms. For example, they may think of set gelatin as "coagulated," or they may associate aeration with "air." Ask the paired students to use the correct terms to quiz each other on the details of the steps in water treatment. **learning modality: verbal**

Chlorination The next step is to chlorinate the water. If you have ever been to a public swimming pool, you have probably smelled chlorine. Chlorine is added to drinking water for the same reason it is added to swimming pools: to kill disease-causing microorganisms. At this point, the water is usually ready to be distributed to homes.

Water from an aquifer may require less treatment than water from a lake. Flowing through rocks or sand naturally filters and purifies the water. However, most public water supplies that use a groundwater source still add chlorine to kill disease-causing organisms.

Aeration and Additional Treatment Air is then forced through the purified water. This process reduces unpleasant odors and tastes. Minerals may then be added to soften the water or for other purposes.

Testing Samples Public health officials regularly test samples from water treatment plants to assess water quality. They test for the substances covered by the drinking-water standards, including chemicals, dissolved solids, pH, hardness, and disease-causing organisms. Private well owners should also test their water regularly to make sure no treatment is needed.

Lab zone Skills Activity

Making Models

Cover an empty jar with a paper towel; tuck the paper towel slightly into the mouth of the jar. Fill a second jar with water. Add a handful of materials to the water, such as sand, soil, and leaves. While holding the paper towel in place, slowly pour the water onto the paper towel so that it enters the empty jar. Observe what happens to the materials in the water. How does this activity relate to the process of treating drinking water?

Reading Checkpoint **What is the goal of drinking-water treatment?**

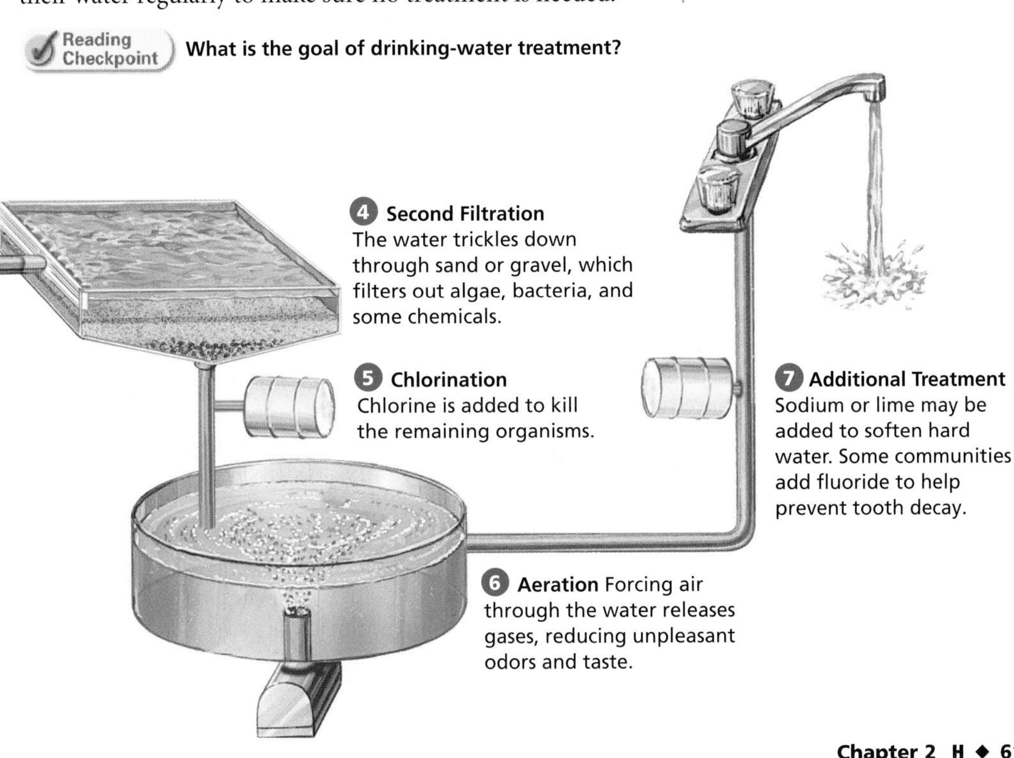

4 Second Filtration The water trickles down through sand or gravel, which filters out algae, bacteria, and some chemicals.
5 Chlorination Chlorine is added to kill the remaining organisms.
6 Aeration Forcing air through the water releases gases, reducing unpleasant odors and taste.
7 Additional Treatment Sodium or lime may be added to soften hard water. Some communities add fluoride to help prevent tooth decay.

Lab zone Build Inquiry L2

Observing Water

Materials lake or river water, microscope, plastic dropper, slide

Time 15 minutes

Focus Review the various components that can occur in natural fresh water.

Teach Have students examine, by sight and smell, samples of untreated water from a local water source and make inferences about why the water would need to be treated. Then make a slide of the water, and have students take turns observing it under the microscope. **CAUTION:** *Make sure that students do not taste the water and that they wash their hands after this activity.*

Apply Encourage students to write a short description of the water and to explain whether they think it is safe to drink. **learning modality: visual**

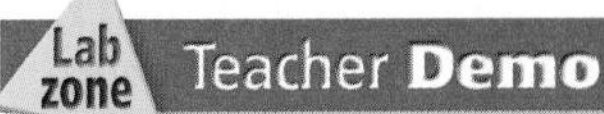

Lab zone Teacher Demo L2

Modeling Coagulation

Materials muddy water, large beaker, alum crystals, stirring rod

Time 20 minutes

Focus Review the definition of the term *coagulation.*

Teach Add one tablespoon of alum crystals to the beaker filled with muddy water, and stir slowly for 5 minutes. Students will observe that large clumps settle quickly and that smaller clumps settle later.

Apply Ask: **If this were an actual treatment plant, what would be the next step?** *(Filter the water again to get rid of the flocs.)* **Is the water safe to drink at this point?** *(No; it must be disinfected.)* **learning modality: visual**

Lab zone Skills Activity

Skills Focus Making models L2

Materials 2 clean empty jars; materials such as sand, soil, and leaves; paper towels; water

Time 10 minutes

Tips A rubber band can be used to secure the paper towel over the empty jar.

Expected Outcome Students will notice that the solid materials are trapped by the paper towel as the water is poured. This models filtration.

Extend Pour the water that was filtered by the first paper towel into another jar with a clean paper towel secured to it. **learning modality: kinesthetic**

Monitor Progress L2

Oral Presentation Call on students to name and describe the steps in treating water.

Answers

Figure 7 Air is forced through the water. Gases are released, reducing unpleasant odors and taste.

Reading Checkpoint To ensure that the water is clean and safe to drink

Integrating Physics

After students have read about water pressure and distribution, divide the class into groups of three or four. Then have each group consider this hypothesis derived from a statement in the text: *Whenever water is in an enclosed space, it exerts pressure in all directions.* Challenge groups to design an experiment that could test this hypothesis. A design should consist of a description and a drawing. When the designs are finished, groups can evaluate one another's experiments. Finally, encourage students to perform the experiments that seem most likely to test the hypothesis. **learning modality: kinesthetic**

Treating Wastewater

Teach Key Concepts L2

Focus Explain that after wastewater is treated, it often ends up as drinking water.

Teach Ask: **What are the sources of wastewater in your home that go down the drain?** *(Water from toilets, sinks, bathtubs, washing machines, and dishwashers)* **What are two places to which this wastewater goes?** *(Septic tanks and wastewater treatment plants)* Refer students to Figure 8, and have them trace how wastewater flows through a septic system. Explain that as wastes move through the soil to groundwater, a natural purification process takes place.

Apply Invite students to predict what would happen if the wastewater that goes down the drain somehow got into the underground network of water mains without going to a treatment plant. *(The drinking water would become contaminated with waste material and disease-causing organisms.)* **learning modality: verbal**

Lab zone Try This Activity

Moving Water Uphill

1. Pile a stack of books on a table. Place one bowl on top of the books and another bowl on the table. Pour water into the higher bowl until it is about half full.
2. Submerge a piece of plastic tubing in the water in the upper bowl. When the tubing is full of water, put a finger over each end.
3. Keeping one end of the tubing underwater, place the other end in the lower, empty bowl. Release both fingers and watch what happens.

Observing In what direction does the water first have to travel to get out of the higher bowl? Can you explain this movement?

Water Distribution Once it has been treated, water is ready to be distributed to homes and businesses. From a treatment plant, water goes to a central pumping station. There the water is pumped into an underground network of pipes called water mains. The water mains branch off to smaller pipes. These pipes feed into even smaller pipes that carry water into buildings.

Water pressure causes the water to move through this system of pipes. Whenever water is in an enclosed space, it exerts pressure in all directions. Pumping stations are designed to keep water pressure steady throughout the system.

Rather than use a central pumping station, some communities store their water in a water tower or tank on top of a hill. Treated water is pumped up into the water tower. When the water is needed, it is released. Then the water rushes downward, into the town's water mains and pipes.

Treating Wastewater

Finally, after a long journey, the water reaches your house. You take a shower, flush the toilet, or wash a load of laundry. What happens to the used water that goes down the drain? The wastewater and the different kinds of wastes in it are called **sewage. Two ways that communities deal with sewage are wastewater treatment plants and septic systems.**

Wastewater Treatment Plants Most communities treat their wastewater to make it safe to return to the environment. In many communities, household wastewater flows into a network of pipes called sanitary sewers. Sanitary sewers carry sewage away to wastewater treatment plants. You'll learn more about public wastewater-treatment systems in the Technology and Society feature later in this chapter.

Septic Systems Some people dispose of their sewage and treat their wastewater using a septic system. A septic system centers around a septic tank, which is an underground tank containing bacteria that treat wastewater as it passes through. Sludge and scum are materials that bacteria cannot break down or that break down very slowly. These materials must be pumped out regularly so they don't fill the tank.

The remaining water in the septic tank filters out through holes. The area around the septic tank that the water filters through is called a leach field. Over time, wastes remaining in the water break down naturally in the soil of the leach field.

What is a leach field?

Lab zone Try This Activity

Skills Focus Observing L2

Materials books, 2 large bowls, water, pitcher, plastic tubing

Time 20 minutes

Tips Cut 60-cm lengths of tubing before class. Emphasize that the finger must completely cover the end of the siphon and that no air be allowed inside the tube. Have students cover their books.

Expected Outcome Water will flow through the siphon from the higher bowl into the lower bowl, eventually emptying the higher bowl.

Extend Students can experiment with longer siphons and circuitous routes, such as holding the middle of the tubing above the higher bowl. **learning modality: kinesthetic**

FIGURE 8

A Septic System

Sewage flows into a septic tank, where bacteria break down the waste material into simpler chemicals. Cleaner water leaves the tank and flows into a leach field. **Observing** *What is the purpose of the outlet pipe?*

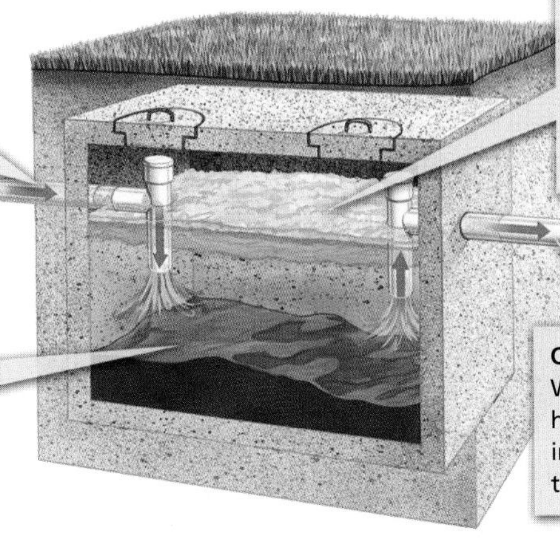
Inlet Pipe From House
Sewage enters the system through the inlet pipe. Bacteria begin to break down most of the wastes.
Sludge
Denser wastes that break down slowly sink to the bottom of the tank. Sludge must be pumped out.
Scum
Less-dense wastes that break down slowly float to the top of the tank and build up there. Scum must be pumped out regularly.
Outlet Pipe to Leach Field
Water and wastes that have broken down filter into the leach field through the outlet pipe.

Section 2 Assessment

Target Reading Skill **Sequencing** Refer to your flowchart about drinking-water treatment as you answer Question 2 below.

Reviewing Key Concepts

1. a. **Listing** Name the factors that affect water quality.
   b. **Comparing and Contrasting** How does hard water differ from soft water?
   c. **Inferring** Dissolved lead has been found in your drinking supply. What can you infer about the acidity of your water? Explain.
2. a. **Reviewing** Explain why drinking water is treated.
   b. **Sequencing** Create a flowchart showing how drinking water is delivered to homes and businesses in a community that has a central pumping station.
3. a. **Defining** What is sewage?
   b. **Sequencing** List in order the steps involved in the treatment of sewage in a septic system.
   c. **Applying Concepts** Why it is important to know the depth and location of drinking-water wells before deciding where to build a septic system?

Math Practice

4. **Calculating a Concentration** Review the EPA selected water-quality standards in Figure 5 on page 58. Note that the concentrations of the first five substances are limited to certain amounts, given in parts per million (ppm). Write the concentration of each substance as a fraction.

Monitor Progress L2

Answers

Figure 8 To allow water and wastes that have broken down to filter into the leach field

Reading Checkpoint The area around a septic tank through which the water filters

Assess

Reviewing Key Concepts

1. a. Disease-causing organisms, acidity (pH), chemicals, and hardness **b.** Hard water contains higher concentrations of calcium and magnesium. **c.** The water is acidic because acidic water can dissolve lead from pipes it passes through.

2. a. To ensure that the water is clean and safe to drink **b.** Water goes from a treatment plant to a central pumping station, then to water mains, then to smaller pipes, and then to smaller pipes that carry water into buildings.

3. a. Wastewater and the different kinds of wastes in it **b.** Sewage flows into the septic tank from the home. Bacteria break down the waste material into simpler chemicals. Sludge settles to the bottom of the tank; scum floats. Cleaner water leaves the tank through an outlet pipe to a leach field. The wastes break down naturally in the soil. **c.** Water from a septic system flows through holes into a leach field. If a septic system is built too close to a well, the wastewater from the system could mix with the water around the well and make the water unsafe to drink.

4. Math Practice Arsenic: $\frac{1}{100,000,000}$;

Carbon tetrachloride: $\frac{5}{1,000,000,000}$;

Copper: $\frac{13}{10,000,000}$; Cyanide: $\frac{2}{10,000,000}$;

Lead: $\frac{15}{1,000,000,000}$

Reteach L1

As a class, create a diagram that shows how drinking water from an aquifer or river is treated and distributed.

All in One Teaching Resources

- Section Summary: *Water to Drink*
- Review and Reinforce: *Water to Drink*
- Enrich: *Water to Drink*
- Transparency H19

Technology and Society

Treating Wastewater

Key Concept

Wastewater must be cleaned before it is released into the environment, but decisions about how much money to spend often are difficult.

Build Background Knowledge

Recalling Science Concepts

Remind students that water must meet standards of quality. Ask: **Do standards of quality apply only to drinking water?** *(No.)* **What other water must meet certain standards?** *(Wastewater)* **Are wastewater standards as strict as drinking water standards?** *(Usually not)* Tell students that laws establish the minimum standards that wastewater must meet and that these standards are achieved through wastewater treatment.

Introduce the Debate

Ask: **What are the advantages of having and maintaining efficient wastewater treatment plants?** *(Streams, lakes, and oceans are protected; the risk of waterborne disease is reduced.)* **What are the disadvantages of having and maintaining efficient wastewater treatment plants?** *(These plants can be costly to build and maintain; money might have to be taken away from other important community needs.)*

Facilitate the Debate

- Provide the class with the following scenario: Your community has an old wastewater treatment plant. During heavy rains, some contamination leaks into a nearby stream. Building a new treatment plant will eliminate leakage and provide better water treatment. However, building this plant will require that the community increase taxes or reduce other services.
- Have students read the feature and answer the Weigh the Impact questions individually as a homework assignment. The next day, organize the class in two groups. Have one group argue that a new wastewater treatment plant must be built.
- Have the other group argue that doing so would be too expensive and that construction should be delayed indefinitely. Students can use their letters to the newspaper as a basis for the debate.

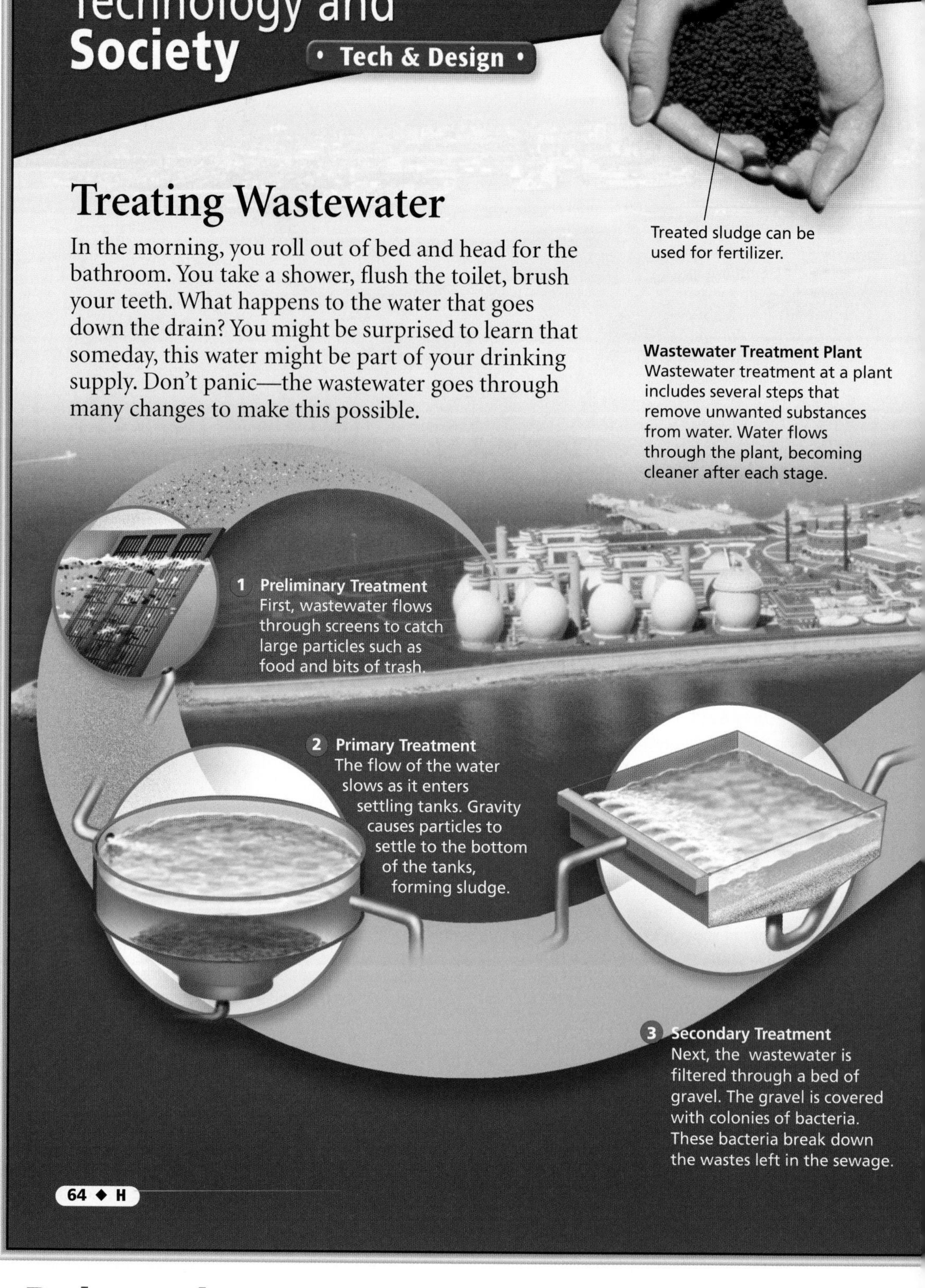

Technology and Society
• Tech & Design •
Treating Wastewater
In the morning, you roll out of bed and head for the bathroom. You take a shower, flush the toilet, brush your teeth. What happens to the water that goes down the drain? You might be surprised to learn that someday, this water might be part of your drinking supply. Don't panic—the wastewater goes through many changes to make this possible.
Treated sludge can be used for fertilizer.
Wastewater Treatment Plant
Wastewater treatment at a plant includes several steps that remove unwanted substances from water. Water flows through the plant, becoming cleaner after each stage.
1 Preliminary Treatment
First, wastewater flows through screens to catch large particles such as food and bits of trash.
2 Primary Treatment
The flow of the water slows as it enters settling tanks. Gravity causes particles to settle to the bottom of the tanks, forming sludge.
3 Secondary Treatment
Next, the wastewater is filtered through a bed of gravel. The gravel is covered with colonies of bacteria. These bacteria break down the wastes left in the sewage.
64 ◆ H

Background

Facts and Figures Some communities have begun using wastewater for essential purposes, such as irrigation and industrial use. This practice is especially common in areas where water shortages frequently occur, such as the desert southwest in the United States. Using wastewater to fulfill agricultural and industrial needs makes more of the clean water supply available for drinking, bathing, and other household and commercial needs.

Public Treatment Systems

Most communities rely on public treatment systems to clean their wastewater. Different communities often use slightly different processes. A typical wastewater treatment process, like the one shown here, involves several steps. Once treatment is complete, the water is returned to the environment. The clean water may be released back into lakes, rivers, or oceans, or pumped back into the ground. There the water rejoins the water cycle.

How Clean Is Clean?

Until about 200 years ago, wastewater was often dumped into open gutters and allowed to run directly into rivers and oceans. This practice spread disease. Cleaning wastewater before it is returned to the environment is healthier for everyone. However, treating wastewater does have some tradeoffs. By law, costly chemical tests are performed regularly to verify the water's cleanliness. Updating old systems or increasing system capacities for growing populations is expensive also. Small amounts of unwanted substances may remain in the water after treatment. The long-term effects of these substances are not known.

4 Additional Treatment
The water is pumped into open pools, where air and sunlight help purify it. Some water evaporates directly into the atmosphere. Just before releasing the treated water, chlorine may be added to kill harmful microorganisms.

Weigh the Impact

1. Identify the Need
Why is wastewater treated?

2. Research
Use the Internet to research wastewater treatment. What new technologies are being developed? Choose one of these technologies and make a list of its advantages and disadvantages.

3. Write
Your community is considering upgrading its wastewater treatment plant. Some residents believe the plan can reduce water pollution. Others are concerned about the cost. State your views in a letter to the newspaper. Back up your opinions with facts from your research.

For: More on wastewater treatment
Visit: PHSchool.com
Web Code: cfh-3020

Weigh the Impact

1. Wastewater contains microscopic organisms, solid material, and high nutrient concentrations that would be harmful to the environment if the wastewater were released untreated.
2. One new technology that students might research is the use of membrane filters to clean wastewater. Advantages include high-quality removal of small particles and affordability. Disadvantages include the fact that the membranes must be combined with more traditional treatments. Many other answers are possible.
3. Make certain that students take a firm position and argue persuasively in their letters.

For: More on wastewater treatment
Visit: PHSchool.com
Web Code: cfh-3020

Students can research this issue online.

Extend

Challenge students to design their own wastewater treatment system, using technologies of their choice. Have students make sketches that illustrate their designs.

Testing Water

L2

Prepare for Inquiry

Key Concept

Compare and contrast water quality factors among tap, distilled, spring, and mineral water samples.

Skills Objectives

Students will be able to

- observe differences among various types of water
- infer which water quality factors account for the observations
- draw conclusions about the water quality of the various samples

Prep Time 30 minutes

Class Time 40 minutes

Teaching Resources

- Lab Worksheet: *Testing Water*

Advance Planning

Make sure that the bottled water was not obtained from a municipal source; this information will appear on the label if it applies. Use a pump bottle of handwashing soap. Use narrow-range (6–8) pH paper that can detect subtle differences among similar samples.

Alternative Materials

Burners and stands can be used instead of hot plates, small jars instead of test tubes, and plastic wrap or wax paper held in place with rubber bands instead of stoppers.

Safety

Caution students to wear oven mitts when handling hot beakers and to be careful using the electric hot plates. Make sure that they pour tasting samples only from the original bottles and use a new cup each time. Review the safety guidelines in Appendix A.

Lab zone Consumer Lab

For: Data sharing
Visit: PHSchool.com
Web Code: cfd-3023

Testing Water

Problem

How do distilled water, spring water, and mineral water differ from tap water?

Skills Focus

observing, inferring, drawing conclusions

Materials

- hot plate
- liquid soap
- ruler
- wax pencil
- tap water, 200 mL
- distilled water, 200 mL
- spring water, 200 mL
- mineral water, 200 mL
- 4 200-mL beakers
- 4 test tubes and stoppers
- 4 pieces of pH paper
- test tube rack
- 25-mL graduated cylinder
- pH indicator chart
- 4 paper cups per person

Procedure    

1. Copy the data table into your notebook.
2. Label the beakers A, B, C, and D. Pour 100 mL of tap water into beaker A. Pour 100 mL of the other water samples into the correct beaker (refer to the data table).
3. Heat each water sample on a hot plate until about 20 mL remains. Do not allow the water to boil completely away. **CAUTION:** *Do not touch the hot plate or beakers with your bare hands.*
4. After the water samples have cooled, look for solids that make the water cloudy. Rank the samples from 1 to 4, where 1 has the fewest visible solids and 4 has the most visible solids. Record your rankings in the data table.
5. Label the test tubes A, B, C, and D. Pour 10 mL of each water sample from the source bottle into the correct test tube.
6. Dip a piece of pH paper into test tube A to measure its acidity. Match the color of the pH paper to a number on the pH indicator chart. Record the pH (0–14) in your data table.
7. Repeat Step 6 for the other samples.
8. Add two drops of liquid soap to test tube A. Put a stopper in the test tube and shake it 30 times. With the ruler, measure the height of the soapsuds in the test tube. Record the measurement in your data table.
9. Repeat Step 8 for the other samples.
10. Label the four cups A, B, C, and D. Write your name on each cup.
11. Pour a little tap water into cup A directly from the original source bottle. Taste the tap water. In your data table, describe the taste using one or more of these words: *salty, flat, bitter, metallic, refreshing, tasteless.* **CAUTION:** *Do not conduct the taste test in a lab room. Use a clean cup for each sample and discard it after use.*
12. Repeat Step 11 with the other samples.

Data Table

Water Sample	Visible Solids (1–4)	pH (0–14)	Soapsud Height (cm)	Taste
A – Tap Water				
B – Distilled Water				
C – Spring Water				
D – Mineral Water				

66 ◆ H

Guide Inquiry

Invitation

Ask: **Why do many people buy costly bottled water instead of using relatively inexpensive tap water?** *(Possible answers: It tastes better. It's convenient to carry. It's healthier than drinking soda.)*

Troubleshooting the Experiment

- While the water is heating or cooling in Step 3, have students continue with the rest of the procedure. After starting Step 3, they can do Steps 5–12 and then return to Step 4 at the end.
- If they are available, use wide-opening droppers to add soap to samples.

Analyze and Conclude

1. **Observing** Review your data table. Compare each of the bottled water samples to the tap water sample. What similarities and differences did you detect?
2. **Inferring** Rank the samples from the one with the fewest soapsuds to the one with the most. Compare this ranking to the one for visible solids. What pattern do you see? What do both of these tests have to do with the hardness of water?
3. **Posing Questions** What other information about the water samples might you need before deciding which one to drink regularly? Explain.
4. **Drawing Conclusions** Based on your results, which sample would you most want to use for (a) drinking, (b) boiling in a teakettle, and (c) washing laundry? Which sample would you least want to use for each purpose? Explain.
5. **Communicating** Create a brochure to educate consumers about water quality. Include information about acidity, hardness, and other factors that can affect the appearance, taste, and safety of drinking water.

More to Explore

Conduct a survey to find out what percentage of people buy bottled mineral water, distilled water, and spring water. Why do they buy each type of water, and how do they use it in their homes?

For: Data Sharing
Visit: PHSchool.com
Web Code: cfd-3023

Students can share data from this experiment online.

Expected Outcome

Water samples will differ in amounts of dissolved solids, pH value, ability to produce soapsuds, and taste. See the sample data table.

Analyze and Conclude

1. Possible answer: Distilled water has fewer visible solids, lower pH, greater soapsuds height; spring and mineral water have more visible solids, higher pH, lower soapsuds height, and a more refreshing taste.

2. See the sample data table for typical rankings. Samples with more visible solids are likely to have the least soapsuds. In general, the more dissolved solids, the harder the water.

3. Possible answer: Test results for concentrations of other potentially harmful chemicals or microorganisms

4. Possible answers to first question: a) spring water is most refreshing; b) distilled water has the fewest dissolved solids; c) distilled or tap water produces the most soapsuds. Possible answers to second question: a) distilled water is tasteless; b) mineral water leaves a residue; c) mineral water produces the lowest suds level.

5. Encourage students to research facts on how bottled water is regulated. Point out that bottled water is not necessarily "healthier" than tap water. Some tap water is better tasting and cleaner than some bottled water, which can be filtered municipal water. Check that students use reliable sources such as the EPA, rather than vendors whose goal is to sell bottled water.

Sample Data Table

r Sample	Visible Solids (1–4)	pH (0–14)	Soapsud Height (cm)	Taste
vater	2	7.0	11	metallic, refreshing
lled water	1	7.0	10	Tasteless, flat
g water	3	7.5	9	refreshing
ral water	4	8.0	8	salty, bitter

Extend Inquiry

More to Explore Students could collaborate to design a simple survey with "yes" and "no" questions as well as questions that require short answers, such as "Do you ever buy bottled water?" "If so, what kind?" "How often do you buy it, and how do you use it?" Help students make copies and decide where to do the survey.

Section 3

Freshwater Pollution

Objectives

After this lesson, students will be able to

H.2.3.1 Explain one way that sources of pollution are classified.

H.2.3.2 Identify three sources of water pollution.

H.2.3.3 Describe the two parts of the solution to water pollution.

Target Reading Skill

Outlining Explain that using an outline format helps students organize information by main topic, subtopic, and details.

Answers

Freshwater Pollution

I. What is pollution?
  A. Point and nonpoint sources
  B. Effects of pollutants
II. Human wastes
  A. Sewage in cities
  B. Sewage in rural areas
III. Industrial wastes
  A. Chemicals
  B. Smoke and exhaust
  C. Heat pollution
IV. Chemical runoff
  A. Runoff from farms
  B. Runoff from roads
V. Water pollution solutions
  A. Cleanup
  B. Prevention

All in One Teaching Resources

- Transparency H20

Preteach

Build Background Knowledge L1

Identifying Pollutants

Ask: **What is water pollution?** *(Focus on answers that relate to the addition of any substance that has a negative effect on water or living things in the water.)* Challenge students to brainstorm a list of things that could pollute water, and list their suggestions on the board. As they read the section, have students classify the list by the sources of water pollution in the text.

Section 3

Freshwater Pollution

Reading Preview

Key Concepts

- What is one way that sources of pollution are classified?
- What are three sources of water pollution?
- What are the two parts of the solution to water pollution?

Key Terms

- water pollution
- pollutant
- point source
- nonpoint source
- pesticide
- acid rain

Target Reading Skill

Outlining As you read, make an outline about freshwater pollution that you can use for review. Use the red headings for the main ideas and the blue headings for the supporting ideas.

Freshwater Pollution

I. What is pollution?
  A. Point and nonpoint sources
  B.
II. Human wastes
  A.

Lab zone Discover Activity

Will the Pollution Reach Your Wells?

1. With a permanent marker, draw three rings on a coffee filter as shown in the photo. Draw three dots and label them A, B, and C. These dots represent the locations of wells that supply drinking water.
2. Place the coffee filter on a paper plate. Moisten the coffee filter with a wet sponge. The damp coffee filter represents an aquifer.
3. Squirt five drops of food coloring onto the center of the damp coffee filter. Observe how the "pollution" travels.

Think It Over

Observing Which wells were affected by the pollution? Describe the pattern the pollution forms.

Only 50 years ago, the French Broad River in North Carolina was a river to avoid. Its color changed daily, depending on the dyes used at a nearby blanket factory. Towns dumped raw sewage into the water. Sediment and fertilizers from farms washed into the river with every rainfall. The few fish that lived in the river were unhealthy and covered with sores. Mostly, the river was home to wastes and bacteria—certainly not a place for people to play. Today, however, the river is a popular whitewater rafting spot. Fish thrive in the clear water. Factories have stopped releasing wastes into the river. The towns have sewage treatment plants. And ponds catch the runoff from farm fields before it reaches the river.

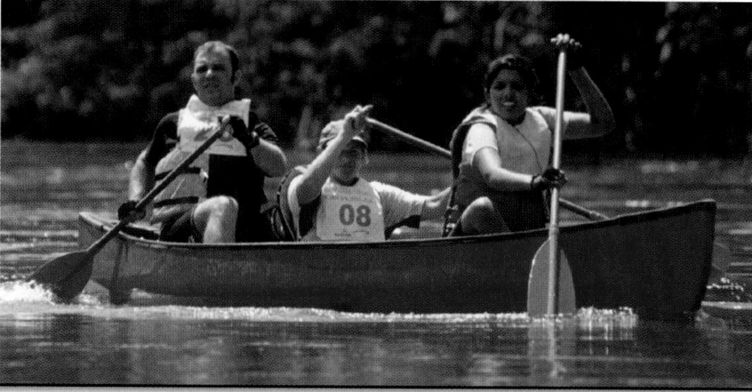

FIGURE 9
The French Broad River
Canoers can once again safely enjoy the French Broad River in North Carolina.

Discover Activity

Skills Focus Observing L1

Materials coffee filter, food coloring, paper plate, permanent marker, plastic dropper, wet sponge

Time 15 minutes

Tips Have students allow the marker ink to dry before wetting the coffee filter. Make sure that students moisten the filter thoroughly without soaking it.

Expected Outcome Students will infer that pollution can affect a water source more completely than just at the point at which it first occurs.

Think It Over The "pollution" spreads out from the center, following tiny dips and creases in the paper—very like the way that water flows in an aquifer. Wells closer to the aquifer's center are affected more than wells situated farther away.

Freshwater Pollutants		
Kind of Pollutant	Examples	Sources
Disease-causing organisms	*Giardia, Cryptosporidium,* bacteria	Human wastes, runoff from livestock pens
Pesticides and fertilizers	DDT, nitrates, phosphates	Runoff from farm fields, golf courses
Industrial chemicals	PCBs, carbon tetrachloride, dioxin	Factories, industrial waste disposal sites
Metals	Lead, mercury, copper	Factories, waste disposal sites
Radioactive wastes	Uranium, carbon-14	Medical and scientific disposal sites, nuclear power plants
Petroleum products	Oil, gasoline	Road runoff, leaking underground storage tanks

FIGURE 10
This table lists examples of different types of freshwater pollutants. Relating Cause and Effect *Why might it be helpful to know the source of a particular pollutant detected in a body of water?*

What Is Pollution?

People near the French Broad River still carry out the same activities—farming, building houses, and making blankets. But by changing how they do these things, they have reduced water pollution in the river. **Water pollution** is the addition of any substance that has a negative effect on water or the living things that depend on the water. The substances that cause water pollution are called **pollutants.** Figure 10 shows different types of pollutants.

Point and Nonpoint Sources **Sources of pollution are classified, in part, by how they enter a body of water.** For example, suppose you notice a pipe gushing brightly colored water into a river. The pipe is a **point source,** a specific source of pollution that can be identified. More often, though, the source of pollution is less obvious. Pollutants may be carried along in runoff from a farm field, a street, or a construction site. The pollutants eventually flow into a lake or river or seep into groundwater and may be carried far away. It's hard to trace the exact source of this pollution. A widely spread source of pollution that can't be tied to a specific point of origin is called a **nonpoint source.**

FIGURE 11
Point Source Pollution
The pipe gushing polluted water into a river is an example of a point source of pollution.

Instruct

What Is Pollution?

Teach Key Concepts L2

How Pollution Is Classified

Focus Remind students that fresh water is scarce in many places, and that water pollution can make the problem worse.

Teach Point out that sources of water pollution are classified by how they enter a body of water. Ask: **What are these sources called?** *(Point source and nonpoint source)* Use Figure 10 to help students classify the sources of pollution as point, nonpoint, or both. *(Possible answers: Pesticides and fertilizers are nonpoint sources because they could come from many different farm fields and golf courses. Radioactive waste is a point source from a disposal site. Industrial chemicals could be nonpoint sources if there are many industries in an area; they may be point sources if there is only one factory or one that discharges the type of chemical in question.)*

Apply Ask: **Why do some cities require vehicles carrying hazardous cargo to use outer belt freeways instead of inner belts or city streets?** *(If an accident occurred, the spill might be contained before it could enter water supplies.)* **learning modality: logical/mathematical**

Independent Practice L2

All in One Teaching Resources

- Guided Reading and Study Worksheet: *Freshwater Pollution*

Student Edition on Audio CD

Differentiated Instruction

Less Proficient Readers L1

Identifying Sources of Pollution Point out that the three main headings (beginning with Human Wastes) provide a primary list of sources of freshwater pollution. For each subhead under these main heads, have students locate and write a sentence or a phrase that explains the source of pollution. For example, for the passage Sewage in Cities, students might write *During heavy rains and floods, sanitary sewers can overflow and run into storm sewers, causing pollution of the surface water.* You may also wish to copy these sections for students to highlight. Then have students write the highlighted sentences or phrases in their own words. **learning modality: verbal**

Monitor Progress L2

Drawing Have students show the path of a pesticide used on a farm field to a lake some distance away.

Answer

Figure 10 Knowing the source could prevent further pollution.

For: Links on Water Pollution
Visit: www.SciLinks.org
Web Code: scn-0823

Download a worksheet that will guide students' review of Internet resources on water pollution.

Use Visuals: Figure 12 L2

Pesticide Levels

Focus Review with students that in a food chain, one organism eats another to obtain energy.

Teach Ask: **What can you infer from the pyramid shape of the illustration?** *(The number of organisms that make up each level decreases at each higher level of the pyramid.)* **Why does the DDT in each organism reach higher levels as you go up the food chain?** *(Each larger organism eats more of the smaller organisms.)* **How many times does the concentration of DDT increase from the fish to the birds?** *(Ten times)*

Apply Ask students to infer why people are cautioned to limit their intake of certain types of fish that may contain metals such as mercury. *(Heavy metals can build up to toxic levels in the human body.)* **learning modality: visual**

All in One Teaching Resources

- Transparency H21

Human Wastes

Teach Key Concepts L2

Human Wastes

Focus Refer students to Figure 13.

Teach Read aloud the paragraph on how Dr. Snow stopped the cholera epidemic. Then ask: **How can human waste get into our drinking water today?** *(During heavy rains or floods, sewage can overflow and enter surface water. Some disease-causing organisms resist chlorine treatment. Wastewater can leak from septic tanks into a stream or a well.)*

Apply Ask: **Why must hikers treat water from a stream before drinking it?** *(The water can contain harmful microorganisms from animal or human waste.)* **learning modality: verbal**

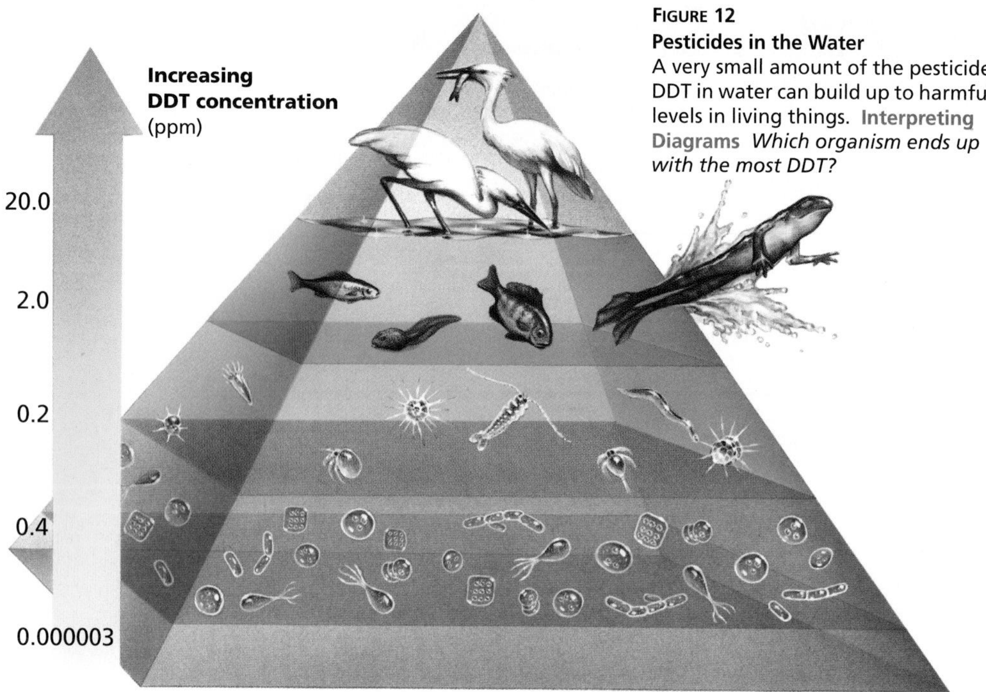

FIGURE 12
Pesticides in the Water
A very small amount of the pesticide DDT in water can build up to harmful levels in living things. **Interpreting Diagrams** *Which organism ends up with the most DDT?*

Effects of Pollutants Some pollutants, such as pesticides, can build up in the bodies of living things. **Pesticides** are chemicals intended to kill insects and other organisms that damage crops. Trace the path of one such pesticide, DDT, in Figure 12. DDT dissolves in water and is absorbed by microscopic algae. The algae, which contain only low levels of DDT, are eaten by small water animals. When frogs or fish eat these smaller animals, they also consume the chemicals from the algae these animals have eaten. The frogs and fish are in turn eaten by birds or other animals. Each larger organism consumes a greater number of the smaller organisms, and therefore more of the DDT.

When humans regularly eat contaminated fish, the toxic chemicals also build up in their bodies. Over a long time, certain pollutants can build up to levels that can cause birth defects or illnesses such as cancer. Contaminated fish and impure drinking water are not the only means by which water pollutants can affect human health. Bathing or swimming in polluted water can irritate the skin or cause more serious problems.

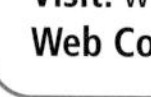

For: Links on water pollution
Visit: www.SciLinks.org
Web Code: scn-0823

 **What is a pesticide?**

For: Links on Water Pollution
Visit: www.SciLinks.org
Web Code: scn-0823

Download a worksheet that will guide students' review of Internet resources on water pollution.

Use Visuals: Figure 12 L2

Pesticide Levels

Focus Review with students that in a food chain, one organism eats another to obtain energy.

Teach Ask: **What can you infer from the pyramid shape of the illustration?** *(The number of organisms that make up each level decreases at each higher level of the pyramid.)* **Why does the DDT in each organism reach higher levels as you go up the food chain?** *(Each larger organism eats more of the smaller organisms.)* **How many times does the concentration of DDT increase from the fish to the birds?** *(Ten times)*

Apply Ask students to infer why people are cautioned to limit their intake of certain types of fish that may contain metals such as mercury. *(Heavy metals can build up to toxic levels in the human body.)* **learning modality: visual**

All in One Teaching Resources

- Transparency H21

Human Wastes

Teach Key Concepts L2

Human Wastes

Focus Refer students to Figure 13.

Teach Read aloud the paragraph on how Dr. Snow stopped the cholera epidemic. Then ask: **How can human waste get into our drinking water today?** *(During heavy rains or floods, sewage can overflow and enter surface water. Some disease-causing organisms resist chlorine treatment. Wastewater can leak from septic tanks into a stream or a well.)*

Apply Ask: **Why must hikers treat water from a stream before drinking it?** *(The water can contain harmful microorganisms from animal or human waste.)* **learning modality: verbal**

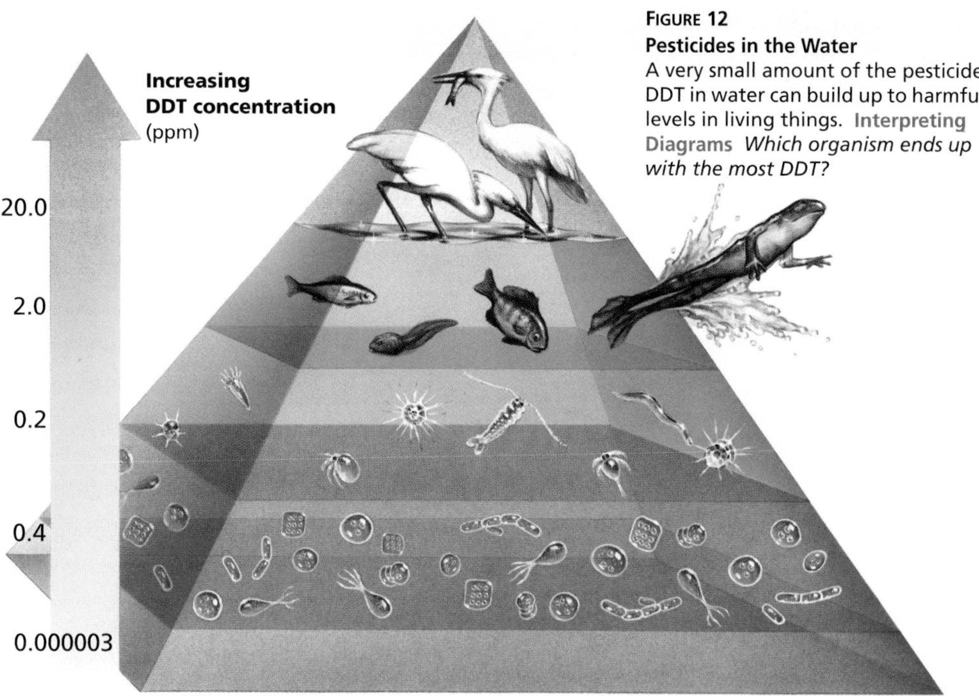

FIGURE 12
Pesticides in the Water
A very small amount of the pesticide DDT in water can build up to harmful levels in living things. **Interpreting Diagrams** *Which organism ends up with the most DDT?*

Effects of Pollutants Some pollutants, such as pesticides, can build up in the bodies of living things. **Pesticides** are chemicals intended to kill insects and other organisms that damage crops. Trace the path of one such pesticide, DDT, in Figure 12. DDT dissolves in water and is absorbed by microscopic algae. The algae, which contain only low levels of DDT, are eaten by small water animals. When frogs or fish eat these smaller animals, they also consume the chemicals from the algae these animals have eaten. The frogs and fish are in turn eaten by birds or other animals. Each larger organism consumes a greater number of the smaller organisms, and therefore more of the DDT.

When humans regularly eat contaminated fish, the toxic chemicals also build up in their bodies. Over a long time, certain pollutants can build up to levels that can cause birth defects or illnesses such as cancer. Contaminated fish and impure drinking water are not the only means by which water pollutants can affect human health. Bathing or swimming in polluted water can irritate the skin or cause more serious problems.

For: Links on water pollution
Visit: www.SciLinks.org
Web Code: scn-0823

Reading Checkpoint **What is a pesticide?**

Freshwater Pollutants		
Kind of Pollutant	**Examples**	**Sources**
Disease-causing organisms	*Giardia*, *Cryptosporidium*, bacteria	Human wastes, runoff from livestock pens
Pesticides and fertilizers	DDT, nitrates, phosphates	Runoff from farm fields, golf courses
Industrial chemicals	PCBs, carbon tetrachloride, dioxin	Factories, industrial waste disposal sites
Metals	Lead, mercury, copper	Factories, waste disposal sites
Radioactive wastes	Uranium, carbon-14	Medical and scientific disposal sites, nuclear power plants
Petroleum products	Oil, gasoline	Road runoff, leaking underground storage tanks

FIGURE 10
This table lists examples of different types of freshwater pollutants.
Relating Cause and Effect *Why might it be helpful to know the source of a particular pollutant detected in a body of water?*

What Is Pollution?

People near the French Broad River still carry out the same activities—farming, building houses, and making blankets. But by changing how they do these things, they have reduced water pollution in the river. **Water pollution** is the addition of any substance that has a negative effect on water or the living things that depend on the water. The substances that cause water pollution are called **pollutants.** Figure 10 shows different types of pollutants.

Point and Nonpoint Sources **Sources of pollution are classified, in part, by how they enter a body of water.** For example, suppose you notice a pipe gushing brightly colored water into a river. The pipe is a **point source,** a specific source of pollution that can be identified. More often, though, the source of pollution is less obvious. Pollutants may be carried along in runoff from a farm field, a street, or a construction site. The pollutants eventually flow into a lake or river or seep into groundwater and may be carried far away. It's hard to trace the exact source of this pollution. A widely spread source of pollution that can't be tied to a specific point of origin is called a **nonpoint source.**

FIGURE 11
Point Source Pollution
The pipe gushing polluted water into a river is an example of a point source of pollution.

Instruct

What Is Pollution?

Teach Key Concepts L2

How Pollution Is Classified

Focus Remind students that fresh water is scarce in many places, and that water pollution can make the problem worse.

Teach Point out that sources of water pollution are classified by how they enter a body of water. Ask: **What are these sources called?** *(Point source and nonpoint source)* Use Figure 10 to help students classify the sources of pollution as point, nonpoint, or both. *(Possible answers: Pesticides and fertilizers are nonpoint sources because they could come from many different farm fields and golf courses. Radioactive waste is a point source from a disposal site. Industrial chemicals could be nonpoint sources if there are many industries in an area; they may be point sources if there is only one factory or one that discharges the type of chemical in question.)*

Apply Ask: **Why do some cities require vehicles carrying hazardous cargo to use outer belt freeways instead of inner belts or city streets?** *(If an accident occurred, the spill might be contained before it could enter water supplies.)* **learning modality: logical/mathematical**

Independent Practice L2

All in One Teaching Resources

- Guided Reading and Study Worksheet: *Freshwater Pollution*

Student Edition on Audio CD

Differentiated Instruction

Less Proficient Readers L1

Identifying Sources of Pollution Point out that the three main headings (beginning with Human Wastes) provide a primary list of sources of freshwater pollution. For each subhead under these main heads, have students locate and write a sentence or a phrase that explains the source of pollution. For example, for the passage Sewage in Cities, students might write *During heavy rains and floods, sanitary sewers can overflow and run into storm sewers, causing pollution of the surface water.* You may also wish to copy these sections for students to highlight. Then have students write the highlighted sentences or phrases in their own words. **learning modality: verbal**

Monitor Progress L2

Drawing Have students show the path of a pesticide used on a farm field to a lake some distance away.

Answer
Figure 10 Knowing the source could prevent further pollution.

Human Wastes

One way or another, human activities cause most water pollution. **The three major sources of water pollution are human wastes, industrial wastes, and chemical runoff.** Today it seems obvious that dumping human wastes into drinking water can spread disease. But scientists have understood this connection for only the last 150 years. For example, cholera is a disease caused by bacteria that live in human wastes. It can be fatal. In 1854, an English doctor named John Snow discovered the cause of a cholera outbreak in London. In the poorer sections of the city, people carried water home in buckets from public wells. After 500 people in one neighborhood died in just ten days, Dr. Snow traced the cholera to a well near a pipe carrying sewage. He ended the epidemic by removing the pump handle so no one could get water from that source. Dr. Snow's work showed the danger of releasing untreated sewage into bodies of water that might be used for drinking.

FIGURE 13
Cholera Epidemic
This engraving from the late 1800s shows people in Hamburg, Germany, getting water from a tank during a cholera epidemic. The city wells were closed, and water was brought in from the countryside.

Sewage in Cities Today, wastewater is usually treated before being released to the environment. However, while water treatment kills most bacteria, some viruses and parasites are able to resist chlorine and other water-treatment processes. Most of these organisms come from human or animal wastes that get into the water supply.

During heavy rains and floods, sanitary sewers sometimes overflow and run into storm sewers. Because the storm sewers generally lead directly into surface water, the sewage from the sanitary sewers can pollute the water. For this reason, people are often told to boil water for drinking and cooking after a flood. The boiling kills many disease-causing organisms.

Sewage in Rural Areas Disposing of human waste is not just a problem in big cities. In rural areas, people must be careful where they locate septic tanks. If a tank is too near a stream or on a hill, wastewater can leak into the stream or flow downhill into the area of a well.

Wastes from cattle, pigs, and chickens can also be a problem in rural areas. Animal wastes can run off from pastures and barnyards and pass disease-causing bacteria and other kinds of pollution into bodies of water.

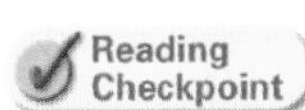

Why should drinking water and sewage be kept separate?

Lab zone Skills Activity

Classifying

Classify the following as point sources or nonpoint sources of water pollution.

- a sanitary sewer pipe with a leak
- salt used on icy roads
- an open drain in a sink at a paint factory
- fertilizer sprayed onto an orchard

Explain why you classified each source as you did.

Applying Concepts of Water Treatment

Materials reference books or online printouts from the Centers for Disease Control and Prevention or from the U.S. Food and Drug Administration

Time 25 minutes

Focus Tell students that disease outbreaks involving municipal water are uncommon in the United States, but they do occur.

Teach Assign these microorganisms to each of four groups: *Cryptosporidium, Giardia, E. coli,* and gastroenteritis viruses (such as hepatitis A and Norovirus). Have students develop information sheets describing the organisms, how they are spread, the diseases they cause, and statistics on their incidence in waterborne outbreaks.

Apply Have each group explain how water must be treated to eliminate the assigned microorganisms from drinking water. **learning modality: verbal**

Monitor Progress L2

Writing Have each student write a letter to a municipal water treatment plant, asking what processes are used to protect drinking water from disease-causing organisms. Students can place their letters in their portfolios.

Portfolio

Answers

Figure 12 The fish-eating birds

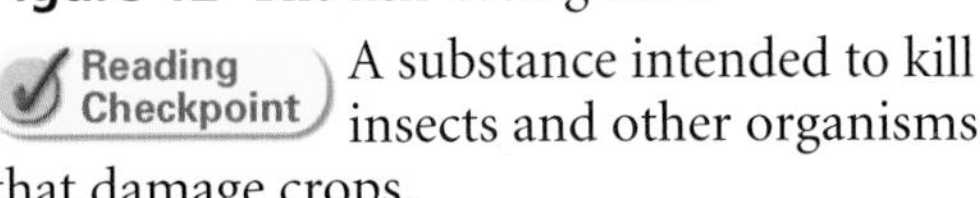

Reading Checkpoint A substance intended to kill insects and other organisms that damage crops.

Reading Checkpoint Sewage contains bacteria, viruses, and parasites that can cause disease.

Lab zone Skills Activity

Skills Focus Classifying L2

Materials none

Time 5 minutes

Tips Review the meaning of point and nonpoint sources of pollution.

Expected Outcome Road salt and fertilizer are nonpoint sources; the open drain and leaking sanitary sewer pipe are point sources.

Extend Have students explain what type of pollution would result from a leak in a sanitary sewer pipe. Then challenge them to describe how an investigator could identify the point source from a discovery of that pollution. **learning modality: logical/mathematical**

Industrial Wastes

Help Students Read

Directed Reading/Thinking Activity (DRTA) Refer to the Content Refresher for guidelines on DRTA. Have students read only the main headings for the rest of this section. Then, have them make predictions about the main ideas that will be presented in the passage. For example, they may predict that all industrial wastes consist of some type of chemical. They may also form questions about the passage, such as "What can individuals do to solve the problem of water pollution?" Record all ideas on the board. After students have finished reading the section, have them confirm which of their predictions were correct and provide answers to questions that were addressed in the passage.

Teach Key Concepts L2

Focus Point out that pollution generated by industrial wastes often can be traced to specific sources.

Teach Have students examine the photos in Figure 14 as you ask questions about them. Ask: **Why might the sources of chemical pollutants be relatively easy to identify and remedy?** *(When the chemical pollutant comes from a source such as a leaking tank or a release pipe, it is confined to a relatively small area that could be contained and remedied.)* **How can toxic chemicals stored in tanks contaminate groundwater?** *(Such tanks can break or rust, allowing the chemicals to move through soil to groundwater.)* **What are the effects of acid rain on water?** *(The water becomes so acidic that fish and other wildlife cannot survive.)* **How can heat be a source of pollution?** *(Many organisms cannot live in water that is heated by warm water released by factories.)*

Apply Ask students to infer why pollution from smoke and exhaust can affect areas far away from the sources. *(Air circulates in the atmosphere, and wind can carry the pollutants to areas far from the source.)* **learning modality: verbal**

FIGURE 14
Industrial Pollutants
Water pollution caused by industrial wastes is a serious pollution problem.

Industrial Wastes

In many cities and towns in the United States, water pollution from factories and mines is a more serious problem than pollution from sewage. This is because most areas have wastewater treatment systems that handle sewage effectively. Chemicals, smoke, and heated water are three types of pollutants produced by factories, mines, and other industries.

Chemicals Many factory processes involve toxic chemicals and strong acids. Other toxic wastes are produced as a result of manufacturing and mining processes. Although laws control many point sources of chemical pollution, some factories still release toxic chemicals directly into nearby rivers and lakes.

Another problem is pollution caused by nonpoint sources. In the past, many industries stored toxic wastes in barrels or other containers buried underground. Over the years, however, many of these containers rusted or broke. The chemicals leaked out, polluting both the soil and the groundwater.

Smoke and Exhaust Many power plants and factories burn coal or oil to fuel their processes. The engines of millions of cars, trucks, and buses burn gasoline. Smoke and exhaust from these sources pour into the air, especially around large cities.

Chemical Waste — Point Source
Some factories release chemical wastes directly into nearby rivers.

Chemical Waste — Nonpoint Source
Chemical wastes can leak out of storage containers and pollute the soil and water far away.

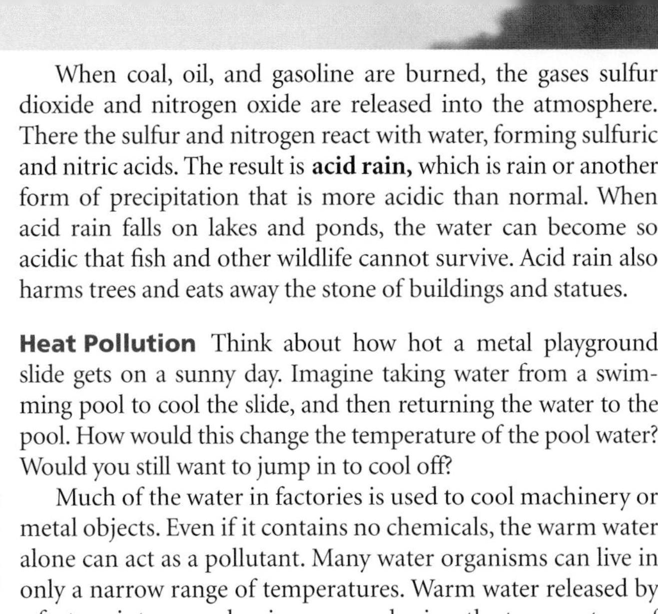

When coal, oil, and gasoline are burned, the gases sulfur dioxide and nitrogen oxide are released into the atmosphere. There the sulfur and nitrogen react with water, forming sulfuric and nitric acids. The result is **acid rain,** which is rain or another form of precipitation that is more acidic than normal. When acid rain falls on lakes and ponds, the water can become so acidic that fish and other wildlife cannot survive. Acid rain also harms trees and eats away the stone of buildings and statues.

Heat Pollution Think about how hot a metal playground slide gets on a sunny day. Imagine taking water from a swimming pool to cool the slide, and then returning the water to the pool. How would this change the temperature of the pool water? Would you still want to jump in to cool off?

Much of the water in factories is used to cool machinery or metal objects. Even if it contains no chemicals, the warm water alone can act as a pollutant. Many water organisms can live in only a narrow range of temperatures. Warm water released by a factory into a nearby river or pond raises the temperature of the water, sometimes enough to harm the living things there.

What are three types of industrial pollutants?

Smoke and Exhaust
Pollutants released from smokestacks can cause acid rain. Acid rain can kill plants and other organisms.

Heat Pollution
Heated water released by factories can harm or kill organisms in a body of water.

L2

Modeling Acid Rain

Materials distilled water, marker, pH paper, 2 small potted plants, 2 plant sprayers, tape, vinegar

Time 20 minutes; periodic attention for 1 to 2 weeks

Focus Review the pH scale. Remind students that an acid is a substance that has a pH lower than 7.0.

Teach Organize students in small groups. Have each group label one potted plant "Water" and the other plant "Acid Rain." Tell students to fill one sprayer with distilled water and label it "Water." Then have them fill the other sprayer with equal amounts of distilled water and vinegar, and label it "Acid Rain." Advise students to test the pH of each solution. Ask: **How will each solution affect its designated plant?** *(Students will probably say that the plant receiving the acidic solution will become unhealthy.)* Have students water each plant with the appropriate sprayer, wetting both the soil and the plant. Be sure that students water each plant with the same amount of liquid at the same frequency. Have them continue to observe the plants for 1 to 2 weeks.

Apply Tell students that each whole pH value below 7 is ten times more acidic than the next higher value. Normal rain has a pH of 5.5 because carbon dioxide dissolves in it. The most acidic rain in the United States has a pH of about 4.3. Ask: **How much more acidic is acid rain than normal rain?** *(About ten times)* **learning modality: kinesthetic**

Differentiated Instruction

English Learners/Beginning L1
Comprehension: Modified Cloze
Distribute sentences about the sources and types of water pollution, but omit strategic words. For example, "Water organisms that live in a narrow range of temperatures are harmed by _____." Provide students with a list of correct answers, and model how to complete one or two sentences. **learning modality: verbal**

English Learners/Intermediate L2
Comprehension: Modified Cloze
Distribute the cloze paragraph described for the *Beginning* activity, but fill in the blanks with incorrect answers. Have students work in pairs to correct the sentences. **learning modality: verbal**

Monitor Progress L2

Oral Presentation Challenge students to explain how water can be polluted by the different types of industrial wastes.

Answer

Chemicals, smoke and exhaust, and heat

Chemical Runoff

Teach Key Concepts L2

Focus Remind students that freshwater sources often are connected.

Teach Ask: **How can rainfall on a city street or farm field move into groundwater or surface water?** *(Part of the rainfall runs off into surface bodies of water or water below the ground.)* **How does this affect freshwater pollution?** *(The rain carries some of the chemicals it comes in contact with into rivers, lakes, and groundwater.)* **What are the sources of some of these pollutants?** *(Oil, gasoline, salt, and nutrients from fertilizers and pesticides)*

Apply Ask: **How can pesticides that run off into water harm organisms that do not live in water?** *(Low levels of chemicals can build up to harmful concentrations as they move through the food chain.)* **learning modality: logical/mathematical**

Modeling Groundwater Contamination L2

Materials 2-L clear plastic bottle with top cut off, gravel, sand, pump sprayer, nylon fabric, tape, water, food coloring, 2 beakers, plant sprayer

Time 30 minutes

Focus Remind students that a contaminant on land can pollute groundwater.

Teach Tape a piece of nylon fabric over the end of the pump sprayer. Fill the bottle one third full with gravel. Insert the end of the pump sprayer into the gravel. Cover the gravel with an 8-cm layer of sand. Add water until the level reaches the layer of sand. Pump water out of the sprayer to show that the water is clear. Mix food coloring with 200 mL of water, and pour it over the sand. Some colored water will seep into the sand.

Apply Ask: **What will happen when more water is sprayed onto the sand?** *(The colored water will move farther down into the sand and gravel.)* Verify that the colored "contamination' can now be pumped out with the sprayer. **learning modality: visual**

FIGURE 15
Runoff From Roads
Chemical runoff from roads can enter rivers and lakes or seep underground to pollute groundwater. **Inferring** *How might cars add to chemical runoff?*

Chemical Runoff

Have you ever "fed" a houseplant with fertilizer to make it grow? On a larger scale, farmers spread or spray fertilizing chemicals on their fields to produce better crops. When rain falls on the fields, it washes some of the chemicals away as runoff. Water used for irrigation also creates runoff. The fertilizers in the runoff are a nonpoint source of pollution.

Runoff From Farms As you know, ponds and lakes naturally change over time during eutrophication. With the addition of fertilizers, this natural process speeds up. A thick, soupy scum of algae forms on top of the water. The scum blocks sunlight and chokes the flow of water, changing the living conditions for other organisms. The rich supply of nutrients from fertilizers encourages the growth of plants and algae in and around nearby bodies of water.

Runoff and irrigation water also carry away other pollutants from farm fields. Pesticides may be sprayed on crops and then carried by runoff into streams and ponds. Sometimes they are sprayed directly on ponds to kill mosquitoes. But these chemicals can also harm insects that are not pests, as well as insect-eating animals.

Runoff From Roads Have you ever noticed an oily sheen on a puddle in a parking lot after it rains? The sheen was probably caused by gasoline and motor oil that leaked from cars. When it rains, runoff carries these oily substances into rivers and lakes, or underground and into the groundwater. During winter, runoff also picks up salt that is spread on roads and sidewalks to melt ice. Gasoline, oil, and salt are nonpoint sources that pollute rivers and lakes. They can also seep underground and pollute wells and aquifers.

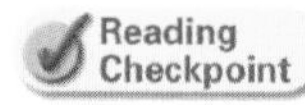

How can pesticides pollute water?

Lab zone Try This Activity

How Do Algae Grow?

1. Label two jars A and B. Pour tap water into each jar until it is half full.
2. Add water from a pond or aquarium to each jar until it is three-quarters full.

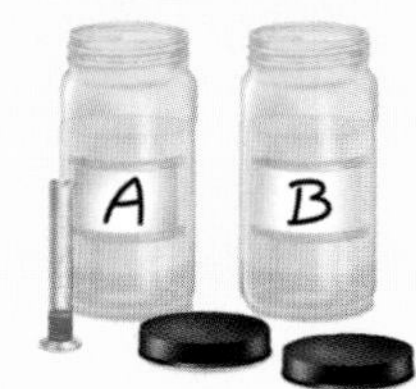

3. Add 5 mL of liquid fertilizer to jar A only.
4. Cover both jars tightly and place them on a windowsill in the sunlight. Wash your hands with soap.
5. Observe the jars every day for a week.

Drawing Conclusions How did the fertilizer affect the growth of the algae in jar A? What was the purpose of jar B in this experiment?

74 ◆ H

Lab zone Try This Activity

Skills Focus Drawing conclusions L2

Materials liquid fertilizer, graduated cylinder, 2 wide-mouth jars with tops, masking tape, permanent marker, pond or aquarium water, tap water

Time 15 minutes for setup; 5 minutes every day for 1 week

Tips Use a diluted liquid fertilizer that is marketed for home use.

Expected Outcome The water in both jars is likely to show algal growth, but Jar A will have markedly more.

Extend Have students transfer animals from one aquarium into another, and add liquid fertilizer to the original aquarium that still contains plants. The increased algal growth eventually will harm the plants, much as it would in a lake. **learning modality: kinesthetic**

Water Pollution Solutions

In the late 1960s, as people became more aware of the problems of pollution, they urged governments to create laws to clean up and reduce pollution. The goals of those laws include the cleanup of polluted lakes and rivers, better wastewater treatment, and limits on the amounts of pollutants released. Governments also monitor the health of bodies of water and enforce water-quality standards and the cleanup of waste disposal sites.

Despite some success cleaning up some water pollution, most pollutants are very difficult to remove. It is often easier to avoid causing the pollution in the first place than to clean it up. **Solving pollution problems involves cleaning up existing problems as well as preventing new ones.**

Cleanup Many pollutants are removed from fresh water through natural cleanup processes. Living things in lakes, streams, and wetlands help reduce pollution by filtering out and breaking down waste materials. For example, plant roots filter larger particles from the water. Some plants can absorb metals and chemicals. And just as certain bacteria are used in purifying wastewater, some are also useful in cleaning up toxic chemicals. Bacteria that consume oil have been used to help clean up oil spills. Waste-eating bacteria may also prove to be useful in breaking down toxic chemicals in rivers and lakes.

Pollution cleanup programs can be based on such natural treatment processes. For example, both natural and artificial wetlands can be used to clean up water pollution. Wetlands have been built near coal mines to treat acidic mining runoff before it returns to the environment.

FIGURE 16
Testing Water for Pollutants
Many lakes and rivers have been polluted by wastes from nearby industries. These environmental scientists are collecting water samples from a pond for testing.

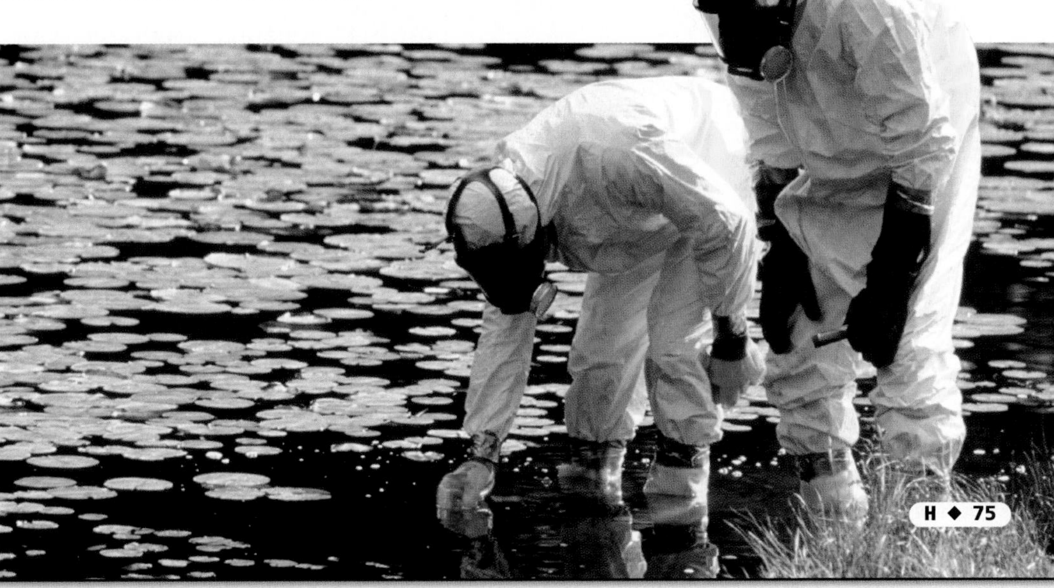

Water Pollution Solutions

Help Students Read — L1

Using Prior Knowledge Have students make a table with the head *Pollution Solutions* and two columns labeled *Prior Knowledge* and *New Knowledge*. Tell students to fill in the first column. When they have finished reading, they can complete the second column and revise information in the first column.

Teach Key Concepts — L2

Focus Remind students that individuals contribute to water pollution, just as industries do. For example, over 2 million people who change their own motor oil pour over 758 million liters of oil per year down a drain, into the ground, or into the garbage.

Teach Explain that the solution to water pollution has two parts. Ask: **What is one part?** *(Cleaning up pollution)* **How can organisms help?** *(Some plants and bacteria can filter out and break down waste materials.)* **What is the second part?** *(Preventing water pollution)* **What can industries, farms, and private citizens do to reduce water pollution?** *(Industries can cool water before releasing it, farmers can filter pollutants before they reach a water source, and citizens can dispose of toxic substances properly.)*

Apply Ask: **How does water cleaning by organisms compare with wastewater treatment?** *(Plant roots act as filters that remove larger particles, just as the filtration process operates in a wastewater treatment plant. Bacteria break down toxic chemicals and oil, just as bacteria in septic systems break down human wastes.)* **learning modality: verbal**

Differentiated Instruction

Less Proficient Readers — L1

Creating a Flowchart Pair students with more proficient readers. Have each pair create one flowchart to show how fertilizers and pesticides can flow from farm fields into a drinking water source and a second flowchart to show how gasoline, oil, and salt travel from road surfaces to a lake or an aquifer. Ask: **How could this type of pollution be controlled?** *(The best way to control a nonpoint source is to prevent it. Farmers can prevent pollution by reducing runoff from fields and avoiding overuse of applied fertilizers and pesticides.)* **learning modality: visual**

Monitor Progress — L2

Oral Presentation Have students describe how fertilizers can cause eutrophication.

Answers

Figure 15 Gasoline and motor oil leak from cars onto roads and then are carried by rain into rivers, lakes, and groundwater.

Reading Checkpoint Pesticides can be sprayed directly onto bodies of water or enter by runoff.

Use Visuals: Figure 17 L1

Focus Remind students that cleaning up water pollution involves both technological and natural solutions.

Teach Ask volunteers to read the captions and then identify and classify possible sources of pollution. *(Example: The runoff from barnyards is animal waste and is a nonpoint source.)*

Apply Have students explain how each solution shown in Figure 17 prevents or cleans up water pollution. **learning modality: visual**

Applying Concepts of Preventing Water Pollution L1

Materials batteries; containers of products that should not be disposed of in the regular trash or poured down a drain, such as paint, cleaners, motor oil, and pesticides

Time 10 minutes

Focus Remind students that homes, like industries, often are sources of chemicals that can pollute water.

Teach Before displaying the items, ask students whether they can name products that should not be disposed of in the regular trash or poured down a drain. Then display the products, and have volunteers read aloud the cautionary statements on the labels. **CAUTION:** *Instruct students not to open any container.* Tell students that 1 quart of oil can pollute 2 million gallons of drinking water.

Apply Have students use a telephone directory or the Internet to find locations of places that accept hazardous waste. Then ask volunteers to form a committee that will promote responsible hazardous waste disposal by reporting pertinent information through posters and public service announcements. **learning modality: visual**

All in One Teaching Resources

- Transparency H22

FIGURE 17

Pollution Solutions

People can prevent or clean up pollution in many ways. **Interpreting Diagrams** *How can people prevent their septic systems from polluting the environment?*

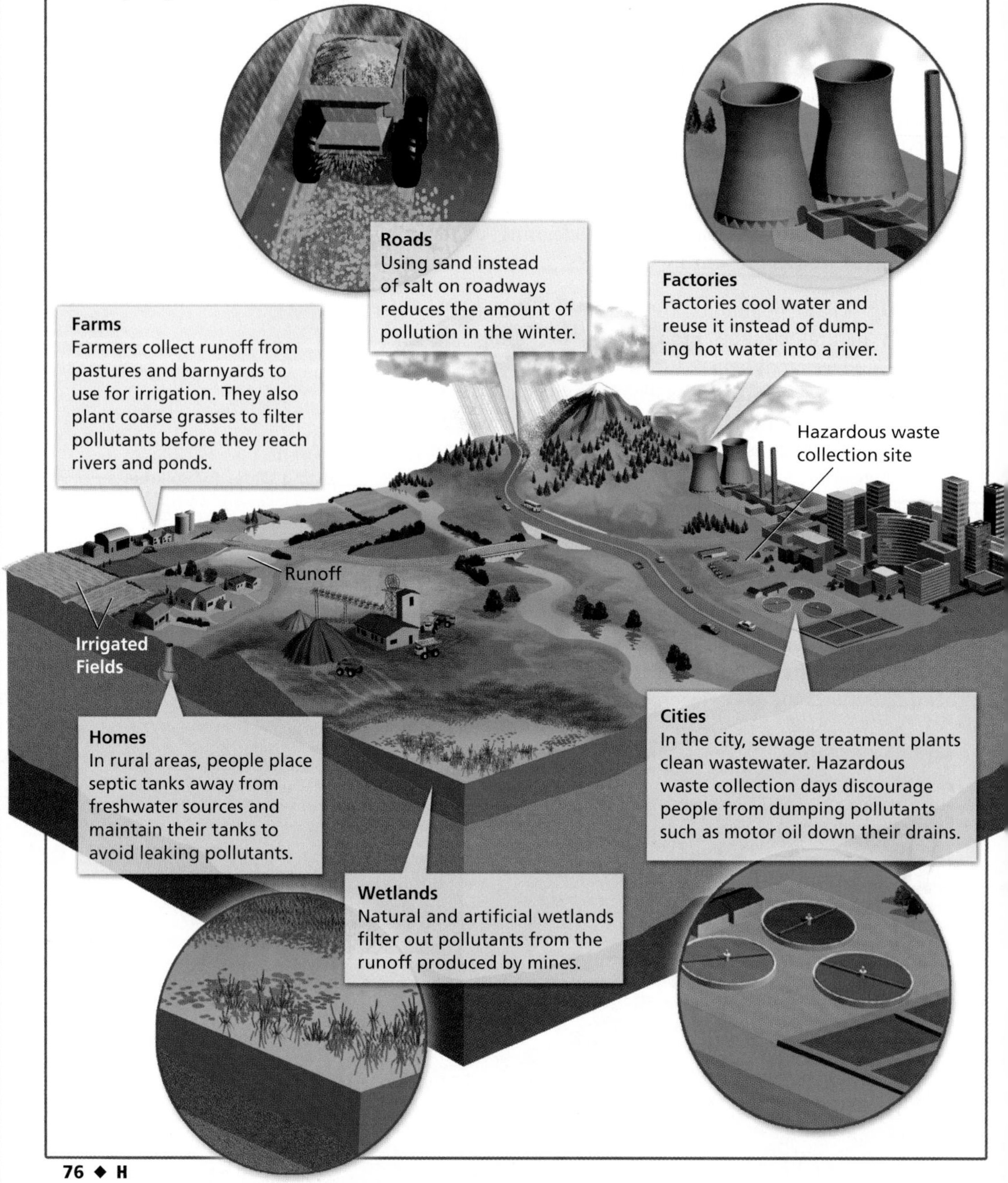

Roads
Using sand instead of salt on roadways reduces the amount of pollution in the winter.

Factories
Factories cool water and reuse it instead of dumping hot water into a river.

Farms
Farmers collect runoff from pastures and barnyards to use for irrigation. They also plant coarse grasses to filter pollutants before they reach rivers and ponds.

Hazardous waste collection site

Runoff

Irrigated Fields

Homes
In rural areas, people place septic tanks away from freshwater sources and maintain their tanks to avoid leaking pollutants.

Cities
In the city, sewage treatment plants clean wastewater. Hazardous waste collection days discourage people from dumping pollutants such as motor oil down their drains.

Wetlands
Natural and artificial wetlands filter out pollutants from the runoff produced by mines.

76 ◆ H

Prevention Many industries have found that recycling techniques that conserve water also reduce pollution. For example, factories cool the water used to cool machinery and reuse it instead of releasing it into a river. This reduces heat pollution. Industries also look for ways to use fewer toxic materials. Printing inks, for instance, can be made with water instead of chemical solvents.

Farmers are trying to reduce the pollution problem caused by the runoff of animal wastes from pastures. Some collect and reuse this water for irrigation. Other farmers plant fields of grasses that filter out pollutants before the water reaches a river or pond. These and other techniques to reduce water pollution are shown in Figure 17.

You can also help keep pollutants from entering the environment. Dispose of toxic substances properly. For example, chemicals like paint and motor oil should never be poured down the drain, but instead should be taken to sites that collect hazardous waste. Remember, water pollution can be difficult to clean up. So the most important place to stop pollution is at its source.

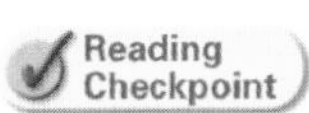
What can governments do to clean up water pollution?

FIGURE 18
Preventing Water Pollution
One way you can help prevent water pollution is to educate others about its causes. This student has stenciled a storm drain to remind people of its connection to a nearby river.

Section 3 Assessment

Target Reading Skill **Outlining** Use the information in your outline about freshwater pollution to help you answer the questions below.

Reviewing Key Concepts

1. a. **Defining** What is a point source of pollution? What is a nonpoint source?
   b. **Comparing and Contrasting** Compare and contrast point and nonpoint sources of water pollution.
   c. **Classifying** A substance added to gasoline is found in the wells of people who live miles from a gas station. Is this an example of a point source of pollution or a nonpoint source? Explain.
2. a. **Listing** List three sources of water pollution.
   b. **Developing Hypotheses** The trees in a wooded area near a factory look like burnt toothpicks. What might be causing the problem?
   c. **Making Judgments** To prevent water pollution, a factory proposes pumping its wastes into the ground instead of into a river. Would you support this change? Why or why not?
3. a. **Reviewing** What are two ways to solve a water pollution problem?
   b. **Making Generalizations** Which is easier: preventing pollution or cleaning up pollution? Give an example to support your answer.

Writing in Science

Product Label Write a "warning label" that can be pasted on a gasoline pump. In your label, include a paragraph describing how burning gasoline can cause acid rain. Be sure to explain the reaction that takes place when certain chemicals are released into the atmosphere and react with water. Also describe the effects of acid rain.

Lab zone Chapter Project

Keep Students on Track Help students with any difficulties they have in assembling their treatment systems. If the problems cannot be corrected, encourage students to think of alternative ways in which the system could be constructed.

Writing in Science

Writing Skill Description

Scoring Rubric

4 Exceeds criteria in some way, for example, by suggesting ways to reduce gasoline consumption
3 Meets criteria and includes how acid rain forms and the effects of acid rain
2 Includes only brief descriptions
1 Is incorrect and incomplete

Monitor Progress L1

Answer

Figure 17 By locating them away from water sources and by maintaining them

Reading Checkpoint Governments can make laws to control pollution and enforce water-quality standards and programs to clean up waste disposal sites.

Assess

Reviewing Key Concepts

1. a. A point source of pollution is a specific source of pollution that can be identified. A nonpoint source of pollution is a widely spread source that cannot be tied to a specific point of origin. **b.** Both are sources of pollution. A point source is a specific source close to the polluted body of water; a nonpoint source cannot be tied to a specific point of origin. **c.** It is a nonpoint source because gasoline leaking from underground tanks or spilled on the ground at the gas station has seeped into the groundwater.
2. a. Human wastes, industrial wastes, and chemical runoff **b.** Acid rain that has formed from water and sulfur dioxide or nitrogen oxide released from the factory could be killing the trees. **c.** Possible answer: This change should not be supported because the industrial wastes could potentially pollute groundwater.
3. a. Cleaning up water pollution and preventing water pollution **b.** Preventing pollution is easier because most pollutants are difficult to remove.

Reteach L1

As a class, brainstorm specific examples of water pollution. Classify each as a point or nonpoint source, and determine whether it is a human, industrial, or chemical runoff waste.

Performance Assessment L2

Writing Have students identify and explain one practice that they can implement at home to help reduce water pollution.

All in One Teaching Resources

- Section Summary: *Freshwater Pollution*
- Review and Reinforce: *Freshwater Pollution*
- Enrich: *Freshwater Pollution*

Section 4 Droughts and Floods

Objectives

After this lesson, students will be able to

H.2.4.1 Explain what a drought is.

H.2.4.2 State what a flood is and explain how the dangers of floods can be reduced.

Target Reading Skill

Comparing and Contrasting Explain that comparing and contrasting information shows how ideas, facts, and events are similar and different. The results of the comparison can be significant.

Answers

This is one possible way to complete the graphic organizer:

Droughts:
Cause: Scarce rainfall
Possible to predict? Very difficult
Preparation: Practice water and soil conservation
Major effects: Crop failure, famine, fires

Floods:
Cause: Heavy rain, melting snow, dam break
Possible to predict? Yes
Preparation: Build up levees, evacuate
Major effects: Loss of life, property damage, power outages, water pollution, landslides or mudslides

All in One Teaching Resources

- Transparency H23

Preteach

Build Background Knowledge L1

Water Conservation

Ask: **Why do the media discuss water conservation practices during periods of low precipitation?** *(People must conserve water to prevent community freshwater reservoirs from becoming too low.)*

Section 4 Droughts and Floods

Reading Preview

Key Concepts

- What is a drought?
- What is a flood, and how can the dangers of floods be reduced?

Key Terms

- drought
- flash flood
- levee

Target Reading Skill

Comparing and Contrasting As you read, compare and contrast droughts and floods by completing a table like the one below.

Droughts and Floods

Feature	Droughts	Floods
Cause	Scarce rainfall	
Possible to predict?		
Preparation		
Major effects		

Lab zone Discover Activity

How Does Dryness Affect Soil?

1. Spread a layer of soil about 3 centimeters thick in a rectangular pan.
2. Add water to the soil and stir so that it forms a thick mud.
3. Place the pan under a lamp for several hours. At the end of the day, check the soil.

Think It Over

Observing What does the soil look like? How does it feel? If the soil in your area looked similar to this soil sample, do you think it could support plants? Explain your answer.

Imagine trying to drink from a tall glass of milk through a straw no longer than a toothpick. When the level of the milk falls below the bottom of the straw, you can no longer reach the milk. In the same way, when the water table falls below the bottom of a well, the well runs dry. A water shortage may occur.

As you read in Chapter 1, water shortages can be triggered by human activities, such as overuse of an aquifer. However, natural processes also can cause areas to receive too little water—or, conversely, too much water. In this section, you'll learn what causes these conditions and how they impact people.

Droughts

A certain area might receive, on average, enough rainfall to meet its water needs. But if the area experiences a long period of scarce rainfall, a condition known as a **drought** (drowt) might occur. A drought reduces the supplies of groundwater and surface water. Without precipitation to recharge the aquifer, the amount of groundwater in the aquifer decreases. A decrease in the amount of water in the aquifer can result in a shortage of water for homes and businesses.

Causes and Effects of Droughts Droughts are weather-related events. **They are usually caused by dry weather systems that remain in one place for weeks or months at a time.**

Lab zone Discover Activity

Skills Focus Observing L1

Materials lamp, soil, stirring stick, rectangular pan, water

Time 10 minutes to set up; 10 minutes to observe after 1 day

Tips You can also place the pan outdoors in a warm, sunny spot.

Expected Outcome The soil will harden and perhaps develop cracks as it dries.

Think It Over The soil is very dry and hard and crumbles when touched. Students may say that the hard, dry soil cannot support plants.

Long-term droughts can devastate a region. Droughts can cause crop failure or even widespread famine. Streams and ponds dry up, and both people and animals suffer. During the drought that struck Florida in 1998, plants withered and died. The dry conditions set the stage for drought-related fires—more than 475,000 acres burned, causing an estimated $500 million in damage.

Predicting and Preparing for Droughts Droughts are difficult to predict. However, since the 1980s, federal and state governments have begun monitoring soil and water conditions, as well as precipitation levels. This information allows scientists to pinpoint areas that may, in the near future, experience droughts. As soon as the level of rainfall drops below normal, state agricultural officials may contact farmers to warn them of a possible drought.

Little can be done to actually control a drought. However, people can prepare for droughts in several ways. When dry conditions first occur, people can begin conserving water. Washing cars and watering lawns, for example, are two activities that can be curtailed. Farmers can grow drought-resistant plants that have been especially bred to withstand dry conditions. In general, practicing water conservation and soil conservation ensures that when droughts do occur, the effects will be as mild as possible.

Reading Checkpoint **What is a drought?**

For: More on droughts
Visit: PHSchool.com
Web Code: cfd-3024

FIGURE 19
A Drought
Europe experienced a severe drought in the summer of 2003, causing the Rhine River to dry up. The smaller photo shows Düsseldorf, Germany, during a normal summer.

For: More on droughts
Visit: PHSchool.com
Web Code: cfd-3024

Students can review droughts in an online interactivity.

Instruct

Droughts

Teach Key Concepts L2

Characteristics of Droughts

Focus Refer students to Figure 19.

Teach Ask: **What is a drought?** *(A condition in which rainfall is scarce and supplies of groundwater and surface water are reduced)* **What causes droughts?** *(Usually, dry weather systems that stay in one place for weeks or months)* **How can people prepare for droughts?** *(They can conserve water.)*

Apply Point out that warm seasons without much rain aren't the only times when an area can be stricken by drought. Drought may also occur when regions lack other forms of precipitation, such as snow. **learning modality: visual**

Independent Practice

All in One Teaching Resources

- Guided Reading and Study Worksheet: *Droughts and Floods*

Student Edition on Audio CD

Differentiated Instruction

Gifted and Talented L3
Making a Time Line Have students use print and Internet resources to research the ten worst droughts in the past 100 years. Have them provide a brief description of the weather conditions and duration of each drought, its location and effects, and the estimated casualties and loss of resources. **learning modality: visual**

Gifted and Talented L3
Researching Cloud Seeding Have students find out how cloud seeding produces rain during droughts. *(Dry ice and silver iodide are sprinkled into clouds. Water vapor condenses on the particles of silver iodide, forming rain or snow. The dry ice cools the droplets more so that they will freeze even in the absence of particles.)* **learning modality: verbal**

Monitor Progress L2

Writing Have students list ways that people can prepare for a drought. They can save their lists in their portfolios.

Answer

Reading Checkpoint A condition in which rainfall is scarce and supplies of groundwater and surface water are reduced

Floods

Teach Key Concepts

L2

Focus Tell students that flooding causes almost half of all weather fatalities and that most flood fatalities occur during flash floods.

Teach Explain that floods occur when the volume of water in a river increases so that it no longer is contained within its banks. Ask: **What can cause a flood?** *(Rain and melting snow)* **What causes flash floods?** *(Large amounts of rain, a dam breaking, and ice that has jammed a river breaking free)* **Why are flash floods so dangerous?** *(The water rises so rapidly that people have little time to reach safe ground.)*

Apply Explain that as cities have grown, the frequency and magnitude of flooding has increased. Ask students to infer why this is true. *(Much of the surface is covered with buildings and pavement that cannot absorb water. The runoff flows into drains and sewers, which cannot hold all the water.)* **learning modality: logical/mathematical**

Help Students Read

L1

Sequencing Have students sketch a river, showing how the banks overflow during a flood. Then have them construct a flowchart describing the events that lead to a flood when a river overflows its banks. The flowcharts should include as much detail as students can find from the text and the graphics.

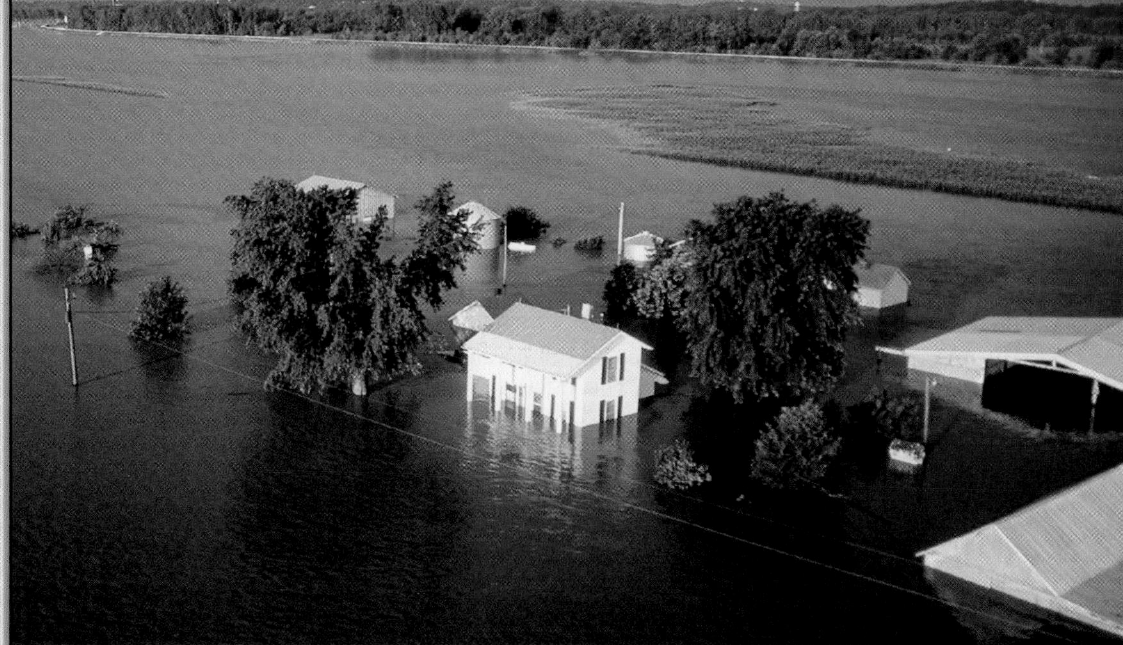

FIGURE 20
Floods
Severe flooding can leave many homes and farms under water. **Inferring** *What characteristic of the land along the river allowed floodwaters to spread out over a large area?*

Floods

The spring of 1993 was much wetter than usual in the midwestern United States. Severe rainstorms brought a great deal of rain within a short period. The Missouri and Mississippi rivers and their tributaries could not contain the huge volumes of water. The rivers soon overflowed their banks, causing some of the worst flooding on record. Along the Mississippi River at St. Louis, the flood lasted for six months! At its peak, the flood covered thousands of square kilometers of land. The flood destroyed homes, roads, and city water supplies. It also ruined valuable farmland.

Causes and Effects of Floods Not all floods are as devastating as those that struck in 1993. Some cause relatively little damage. **Small or large, however, all floods occur when the volume of water in a river increases so much that the river overflows its channel.** As rain and melting snow add more and more water, a river gains in speed and strength. When the speed of a river increases, the amount of energy it has increases, too. A flooding river can uproot trees and pluck boulders from the ground. As it overflows its banks, the powerful water can even wash away bridges and buildings.

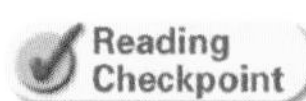

Reading Checkpoint **What happens to a river's speed and strength during a flood?**

80 ◆ H

Lab zone Skills Activity

L2

Skills Focus Inferring

Materials basin, cup, funnel, water

Time 10 minutes

Tips The funnel should be smaller than the cup so that it overflows when students fill it rapidly.

Expected Outcome In Step 1, all the water will flow through the funnel. In Step 2, some of the water will overflow the funnel. A funnel is like a river valley because both are narrow channels that collect water from much larger areas. The river might overflow its banks if a large amount of water entered the river valley over a short period of time.

Extend Challenge students to think of ways to model flood prevention. **learning modality: kinesthetic**

Flash Floods Floods are the most dangerous weather-related events in the United States. Unexpected floods, called flash floods, are the most dangerous of all because the water rises very rapidly—"in a flash"—and people have little time to reach safe ground. A **flash flood** is a sudden, violent flood that occurs within a few hours, or even minutes, of a storm. Figure 21 shows one way in which a flash flood can occur.

Most flash floods are due to large amounts of rain. For example, a line of thunderstorms may remain over an area, dropping heavy rain for several hours or days. Hurricanes or tropical storms bring downpours that quickly fill stream channels. A flash flood can also be caused by a dam breaking, releasing millions of liters of water all at once. Similarly, if ice that has jammed a river breaks free, the sudden rush of water can cause a flash flood.

Some of the most dangerous flash floods occur in the deserts of the southwestern United States. For example, in 1997, a serious flash flood struck Antelope Canyon in the northern Arizona desert. On August 12, a group of 12 hikers entered the dry, narrow canyon. That afternoon, a severe thunderstorm dropped several inches of rain on the Kaibeto Plateau, 24 kilometers away. Dry stream channels that drain into Antelope Canyon quickly filled with rainwater. The water rushed into the canyon, creating a wall of water over 3 meters high. Only one hiker survived.

Lab zone Skills Activity

Inferring

1. Fill a cup with water. Hold a funnel above a basin and pour the water very slowly into the funnel.
2. Refill the cup with the same amount of water you used in Step 1. Hold the funnel above the basin and this time pour the water rapidly into the funnel. What happens?

How is a funnel like a river valley? What do you think would happen if a large amount of water entered a river valley in a short period of time?

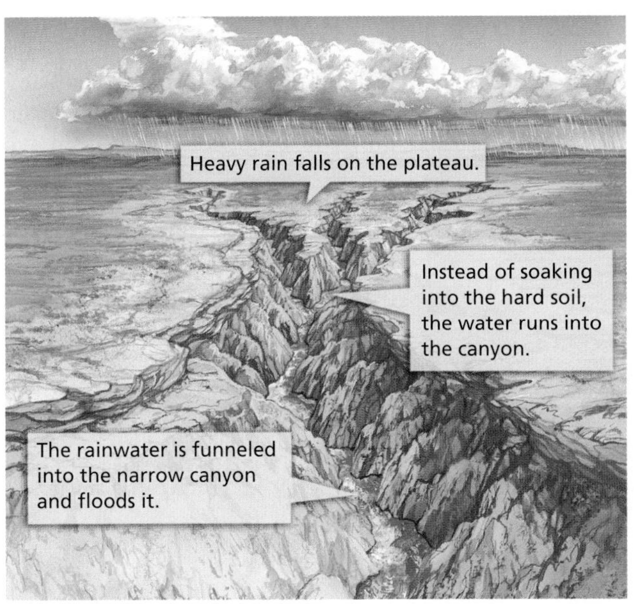

Heavy rain falls on the plateau.
Instead of soaking into the hard soil, the water runs into the canyon.
The rainwater is funneled into the narrow canyon and floods it.

FIGURE 21
Flash Floods
Flash floods (left) occur when large amounts of rain are funneled into a narrow valley. This process flooded Antelope Canyon in Arizona (right) in 1997.

H ◆ 81

Lab zone Teacher Demo L1

Modeling the Effect of Floods on Cars

Materials basin; pebbles or gravel; small, rectangular, watertight metal container; water

Time 10 minutes

Focus Ask: **How much water does it take to float a car?** *(Typical response: it takes a great deal of water to float a car.)*

Teach Point out that even though a car may have a mass of more than 1,000 kg, it can float in about 60 cm of water. Show that height between your palm and the floor. Explain that the car displaces more and more water as the water rises until it has displaced its own weight in water. When that occurs, the car floats. Weight the container with a few pieces of gravel. Place the container in a basin, and slowly add water to the basin. By the time the water level is about halfway up the side of the container, the container should start to float.

Apply Ask: **What do you think would happen if the water in the basin had a current?** *(The current would push against the container and sweep it away as soon as it floated.)* **If you are caught in a flood, should you stay in a car or leave it?** *(Leave the car immediately.)* **learning modality: visual**

All in One Teaching Resources

- Transparency H24

Differentiated Instruction

Special Needs L1

Making a Concept Map Help students construct a concept map, or provide them with copies of a blank one. As they read, students can fill in what causes floods, what can happen during a flood, and how people should respond to floods. **learning modality: verbal**

Less Proficient Readers L1

Identifying Cause and Effect Have students read Emergency Safety, then list cause-and-effect statements. Advise students to look for "if, then" pairs and the word "cause." Help them identify phrases that indicate cause-and-effect relationships, for example, *Flood waters can also saturate soil, causing landslides or mudslides.* **learning modality: verbal**

Monitor Progress L2

Oral Presentation Invite students to describe the different weather events that can lead to a flood.

Answers

Figure 20 The river's floodplain is relatively flat.

Reading Checkpoint Because of the increased volume of water, a river's speed and strength increase during a flood.

Flood Precautions

Teach Key Concepts

L2

Reducing the Dangers of Floods

Focus Review with students some of the effects of floods.

Teach Ask: **How do advance warnings help reduce the dangers of floods?** *(People have time to prepare and to evacuate an area.)* **What is a permanent way to control floods?** *(Building a dam)* **In what ways have people tried to control floods?** *(Constructing dams and levees)* **What actions can individuals take to reduce the dangers of a flood?** *(Move to higher ground, stay away from flood waters, and avoid driving on flooded roads.)*

Apply Ask: **What do you think is the difference between a flood watch and a flood warning?** *(A flood watch means that floods are possible. A flood warning means that floods are already occurring.)* **learning modality: verbal**

Build **Inquiry**

L2

Modeling Control of Floods

Materials long, high-sided tray or a section of rain gutter; mix of sand, gravel, and small pebbles; water, clay

Focus Review the definition of a levee.

Teach Instruct students to fill the tray to about 6 cm with the mix and then create a narrow, slightly curving river channel about 4 cm deep. Students will use the clay to build levees along the upper and middle sections of the "river." Holding the trough at a steep angle, pour a heavy stream of water into the upper end of the river to simulate flooding.

Apply Ask: **How can building a very high levee with sand bags have a negative effect?** *(Making a levee too high could make the channel so narrow that the flood waters would have more force, increasing the severity of the flood or re-routing it to another area.)* **learning modality: kinesthetic**

Flood Precautions

Despite efforts to control flooding, floods have killed millions of people around the world in the last century. In the United States alone, 20 million people live in places where flooding is likely. What can people do to protect themselves and their homes?

Predicting Floods Using different types of technology, scientists can often issue flood warnings. **Advance warnings help reduce flood damage and loss of life.** Weather satellites supply information about snow cover so that scientists can estimate how much water will run into rivers when the snow melts. Radar can track and measure the size of an approaching rainstorm. Scientists check river gauges that measure water levels. With this information, forecasters can predict flood heights at different points along a river. Their goal is to issue warnings in time for people to prepare and evacuate if necessary.

Controlling Floods For as long as people have lived near rivers, they have tried to control floods. **Building dams is one method of flood control.** A dam is a barrier across a river that may redirect the flow of a river to other channels. It can also be used to store water in an artificial lake. Engineers can open the dam's floodgates to release water in dry seasons. Dams work fairly well to control small floods. During severe floods, however, powerful flood waters can wash over the top of a dam or break through it.

FIGURE 22
Trying to Control a Flood
These people are working together to protect their community during a flood.

There is also a natural defense against floods—sediments. Sediments are particles of rock and soil that are picked up and carried along by forces such as flowing water. As a river overflows, it slows down, depositing its heavier sediments alongside the river channel.

Over time, these deposits build up into long ridges called **levees.** Levees that form naturally help keep the river inside its banks. People sometimes strengthen natural levees with sandbags or stone and concrete to provide further protection against floods.

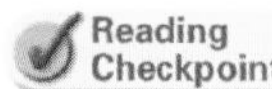

How do sediments help protect against a flood?

1 The car stalls. Moving water pushes against the car.

2 As the water rises, the car begins to float.

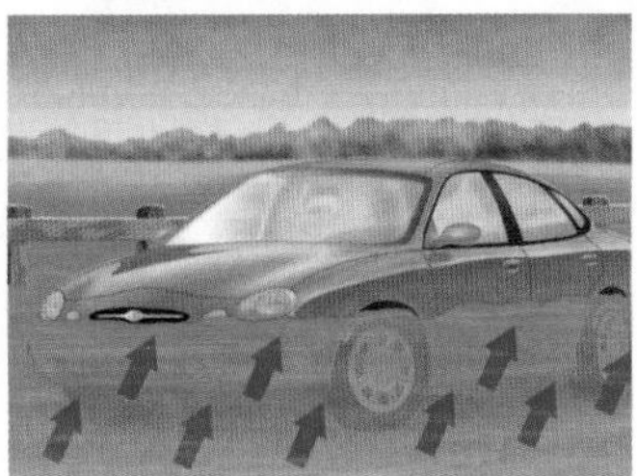

3 Sixty centimeters of water can wash a car away.

FIGURE 23
Dangers of a Flood
Flood waters can wash away cars. It is extremely dangerous to remain in a car during a flood.
Applying Concepts *Why is it dangerous to stay in a car that is caught in a flood?*

Flood Safety What should you do in the event of a flood? When the danger becomes too great or the water rises too high, people are usually evacuated. The first rule of flood safety is: Move to higher ground and stay away from flood waters. If your family is in a car, the driver shouldn't try to drive on a flooded road. Sometimes less than 60 centimeters of fast-moving water can sweep a car away.

High water is not the only hazard in a flood. Floods can knock down electrical poles and wires. Downed electrical poles can leave dangerous live wires hanging loose and cause power outages. Flood waters can also saturate soil, causing landslides or mudslides. If roads have been flooded or washed away, emergency vehicles such as fire trucks and ambulances may not be able to get through.

Flood waters can wash into wells and water treatment plants, polluting the water. Therefore, be careful with food and water that flood waters have touched. Boil drinking water after a flood if you are instructed to do so.

Section 4 Assessment

Target Reading Skill **Comparing and Contrasting** Use your table to quiz a partner about droughts and floods.

Reviewing Key Concepts

1. a. **Reviewing** What causes droughts?
   b. **Summarizing** What are some effects of droughts?
   c. **Problem Solving** What are two ways to reduce the effects of droughts?
2. a. **Describing** When do floods occur?
   b. **Explaining** What are two ways to help reduce the dangers of floods?
   c. **Making Judgments** Your community is considering building a dam and on a nearby river to reduce flooding. Would you support this proposal? Explain.

Writing in Science

Radio Announcement Write a script for a 30-second public service radio announcement in which you tell about the dangers of floods. Include safety steps to follow in case of a flood.

Writing in Science

Writing Skill Persuasion

Scoring Rubric

4 Exceeds criteria in some way, for example, by using short, vivid sentences in the style of a newscast
3 Meets criteria, but style and delivery are uninteresting
2 Includes little information
1 Is incorrect and incomplete

Monitor Progress L2

Answers

Figure 23 The car might be swept away by the floodwaters.

Reading Checkpoint Sediment deposited along a river's channel builds up and forms a natural levee.

Assess

Reviewing Key Concepts

1. a. Lengthy episodes of dry weather **b.** Plants die, streams and ponds dry up, famine occurs in devastating cases, and drought-related fires can occur. **c.** Practice water conservation and soil conservation

2. a. When water is not contained within the banks of a river **b.** Advance warnings can give people time to prepare and evacuate if necessary. Building dams can direct the flow of a river to other channels.

c. Possible answer: If your area tends to have small floods, then the dam would be a good idea because dams work well for small floods. If the floods tend to be severe, building a dam could make them worse because the water could build up behind the dam, eventually bursting out with even more force.

Reteach L1

Sketch an outline of this section on the board, and call on students to fill in details for each subheading.

Performance Assessment L2

Writing Have each student write a short (one-page) story that describes a flood, explaining both its causes and its effects.

All in One Teaching Resources

- Section Summary: *Droughts and Floods*
- Review and Reinforce: *Droughts and Floods*
- Enrich: *Droughts and Floods*
- Transparency H25

Section 5

Water Power

Objectives

After this lesson, students will be able to

H.2.5.1 Explain how the energy of moving water can be used to produce electricity.

H.2.5.2 Identify some advantages and disadvantages of hydroelectric power plants.

Target Reading Skill

Asking Questions Explain that changing a head into a question helps students anticipate the ideas, facts, and events they will read about.

Answers

Possible questions and answers:

How are energy and moving water related? *(Hydroelectric power is electricity produced by the kinetic energy of water moving over a waterfall or dam.)* **How is hydroelectric power generated?** *(The kinetic energy of moving water turns turbine blades, producing mechanical energy, which in turn is converted to electrical energy when the turbine turns the electromagnet of a generator.)*

All in One Teaching Resources

- Transparency H26

Preteach

Build Background Knowledge L1

The Force of Water

Show students a picture of Niagara Falls or water flowing over a large dam. Ask: **How would you describe the force of this falling water?** *(Students will agree that the water has great force.)* Then encourage students to suggest ways to harness the energy of water to power machinery.

Section 5

Integrating Physics

Water Power

Reading Preview

Key Concepts

- How can the energy of moving water be used to produce electricity?
- What are some advantages and disadvantages of hydroelectric power plants?

Key Terms

- kinetic energy
- potential energy
- hydroelectric power

Target Reading Skill

Asking Questions Before you read, preview the red headings. In a graphic organizer like the one below, ask a *how* or *what* question for each heading. As you read, write the answers to your questions.

Water Power

Question	Answer
How are energy and moving water related?	Hydroelectric power . . .

Lab zone Discover Activity

Can Water Do Work?

1. Spread out a large plastic trash bag on the ground. On top of the bag, place several round or cylinder-shaped objects such as corks, spools, marbles, balls, and empty cans.
2. Fill a plant sprayer with water. Then turn the nozzle to produce a fine mist of water. Try to move the objects with the spray of water. **CAUTION:** *Be careful of slippery wet floors if you are doing this activity indoors.*
3. Now turn the sprayer nozzle to produce a narrower stream of water. Try again to move the objects. Be sure to wipe up any spilled water when you are done.

Think It Over

Observing How does changing the nozzle opening affect the stream of water? At which setting did the objects move more easily? Why?

A raging river that overflows its banks can wash away homes and uproot trees. The river has power. Imagine if we could harness this power as an energy resource. Guess what? We can. Since ancient times, people have used the energy of moving water to grind corn and transport goods. Today, that energy is also used to produce electricity. One of the world's largest dams, the Itaipu, produces more electricity than 13 nuclear power plants. Straddling the border between Brazil and Paraguay, the dam took 18 years to build and contains enough iron and steel to make 380 Eiffel Towers! More than 75 percent of Paraguay's electrical needs are supplied by the dam. Paraguay is just one of many countries that rely on the energy of moving water as a source of electrical power.

▼ Itaipu Dam

Lab zone Discover Activity

Skills Focus Observing L1

Materials various cylindrical objects, plant sprayer, large plastic trash bag, water

Time 10 minutes

Tips Emphasize that students may not spray water at one another. To avoid spilled water inside, this activity is best done outdoors on a warm day.

Expected Outcome The narrower stream of water will move the objects more easily and farther than the fine mist will.

Think It Over Changing the nozzle opening narrows or widens the stream of water. The narrower stream opening moved the objects more because the force of the water was concentrated.

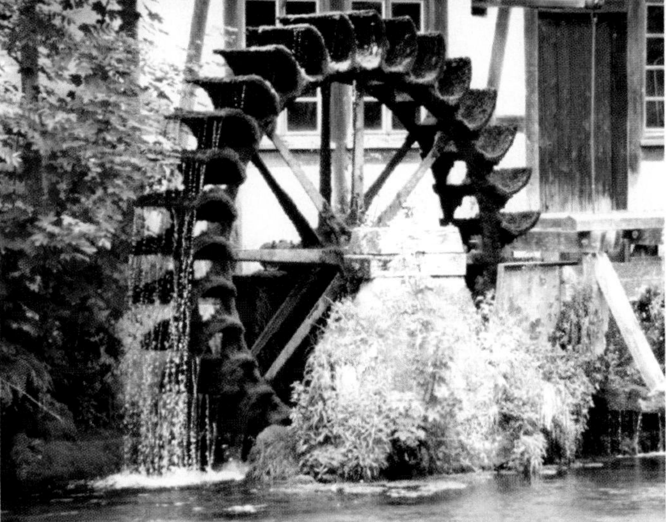

FIGURE 24
A Water Wheel
The potential energy of water is changed to kinetic energy when it hits a water wheel.

Energy and Moving Water

Have you ever seen a fast-moving river propel a kayaker along? If so, you know how much energy moving water can have. It can move boats, carve out canyons, and sweep away cars in a flood.

Kinetic and Potential Energy The energy that sends the kayak through the rapids is kinetic energy. **Kinetic energy** is the form of energy that an object has when it is moving.

Energy can change from one form to another. If the water's movement is stopped, all of its energy becomes potential energy. **Potential energy** is energy that is stored and waiting to be used. To understand how energy changes form, imagine that you're holding a baseball bat at the top of your swing. The bat at that point has potential energy. As you swing at a ball, the bat's energy becomes kinetic energy. If you hit the ball, the energy is transferred again, becoming the kinetic energy of the ball.

Energy From Moving Water Electricity produced by the kinetic energy of water moving over a waterfall or through a dam is called **hydroelectric power.** To generate hydroelectric power (or "hydropower"), engineers build a dam across a river. Water backs up behind the dam, floods the valley, and creates a reservoir. The water stored behind the dam has potential energy, which is changed to kinetic energy when the water is released. **Hydroelectric power plants capture the kinetic energy of moving water and change it into electrical energy.**

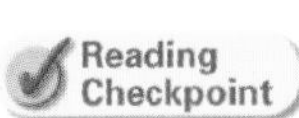
What is potential energy?

Lab zone Try This Activity

A Water Wheel

How can the kinetic energy of water do work?

1. Cut an aluminum pie plate into four squares. The sides of each square should measure 5 cm. **CAUTION:** *Be careful not to cut yourself on the sharp edges of the pie plate.*
2. Push the sides of the aluminum squares into a foam ball as shown. Insert two toothpicks into the ball.
3. Rest the toothpicks on top of your fingers and place the blades under a stream of slowly running water.

Developing Hypotheses
How would increasing the volume of water affect the speed of the water wheel? Test your hypothesis. Describe the results.

Instruct

Energy and Moving Water

Teach Key Concepts L2

How Moving Water Produces Electricity

Focus Ask students to name examples of energy. *(A typical answer will involve motion, such as a car moving or a person running.)*

Teach Remind students that energy need not involve motion. Any matter has potential energy, even if the matter is motionless. Ask: **What is potential energy?** *(The energy that is stored and waiting to be used)* **What kind of energy does an object have when it is moving?** *(Kinetic)* Refer students to Figure 24, and read the caption aloud. Explain that energy can be changed from one form to another. Ask: **How is the kinetic energy of water changed to generate electricity?** *(Hydroelectric power plants capture and change the kinetic energy of moving water into electrical energy.)*

Apply Explain that people used water wheels for centuries to grind grain and saw timber. Ask: **In what way is a water wheel like a hydroelectric dam?** *(Both use the kinetic energy of moving water.)* **learning modality: visual**

Independent Practice

All in One Teaching Resources

- Guided Reading and Study Worksheet: *Water Power*

Student Edition on Audio CD

Lab zone Try This Activity

Skills Focus Developing hypotheses L2

Materials aluminum pie plate, marker, metric ruler, running water, small foam ball, tin snips or heavy scissors, 2 toothpicks

Time 15 minutes

Tips Advise students to measure before cutting, using a marker to draw 5-cm lines. Demonstrate how and where to push the squares and toothpicks into the ball.

CAUTION: *Remind students to be careful of the sharp edges of the pie plate.*

Expected Outcome Possible hypothesis: Increasing the volume of water will increase the speed of the water wheel.

Extend Have students investigate how the number of blades on the water wheel affects its speed and motion. **learning modality: kinesthetic**

Monitor Progress L2

Skills Check Challenge students to classify the following as having kinetic energy, potential energy, or both: A rubber band stretched to its limit *(Potential);* a rock rolling down a hill *(Potential being converted into kinetic);* water in a lake *(Potential);* a moving river *(Kinetic)*

Answer

Energy that is stored and waiting to be used

Hydroelectric Power Plants

Teach Key Concepts L2

Advantages and Disadvantages of Hydroelectric Power

Focus Ask: **Is hydroelectric power a renewable or nonrenewable source of energy?** *(Renewable, because water is a renewable resource)*

Teach Ask: **What other advantages does hydroelectric power have over burning coal or oil?** *(Unlike coal or oil, hydroelectric plants do not cause air pollution.)* Point out that hydroelectric power is also safe and efficient. Ask: **What are the disadvantages of hydroelectric power?** *(The main disadvantage is that building a dam can destroy wildlife habitats as well as farms and towns. Dams must be built where there is a fast-moving river and in an area that can be flooded.)*

Apply Have students recall that a river deposits rich sediments at its mouth. Ask: **How can building a dam affect farmlands near the mouth of a river?** *(The land no longer receives the nutrients the river once brought.)* **learning modality: logical/mathematical**

All in One Teaching Resources

- Transparency H27

Teacher Demo L3

Using a Magnet to Make Electricity

Materials strong bar magnet, thin insulated wire, galvanometer, wire stripper

Time 10 minutes

Focus Invite students to read aloud the steps in Figure 25.

Teach Set up an apparatus that produces electricity from the movement of a magnet. Remove the insulation from both ends of the insulated wire. Coil the wire into at least seven loops, and connect each of the stripped ends to a galvanometer terminal. Move the bar magnet into and out of the coils of wires. The needle of the galvanometer will move, indicating an induced electric current.

Apply Ask: **What step in Figure 25 does this model?** *(A turbine shaft turning an electromagnet to produce electricity)* **learning modality: visual**

FIGURE 25

Hydroelectric Power

Hydroelectric power is generated by changing energy from one form to another. **Interpreting Diagrams** *At what point in the process is the kinetic energy of moving water converted to mechanical energy?*

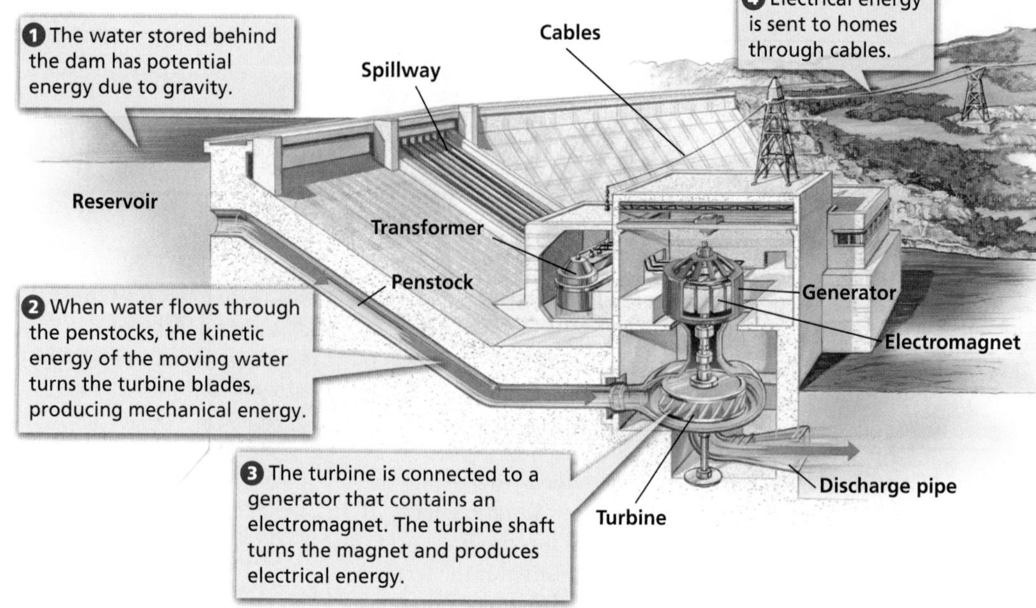
1 The water stored behind the dam has potential energy due to gravity.
Spillway
Cables
4 Electrical energy is sent to homes through cables.
Reservoir
Transformer
Penstock
Generator
Electromagnet
2 When water flows through the penstocks, the kinetic energy of the moving water turns the turbine blades, producing mechanical energy.
3 The turbine is connected to a generator that contains an electromagnet. The turbine shaft turns the magnet and produces electrical energy.
Turbine
Discharge pipe

Go Online
active art

For: Hydroelectric Power activity
Visit: PHSchool.com
Web Code: cfp-3025

Hydroelectric Power Plants

Figure 25 shows a hydroelectric power plant. In this diagram, you can see how the kinetic energy of moving water is changed into the electrical energy that lights homes and runs computers.

Advantages In some ways, hydroelectric power seems like an ideal way to produce electricity. **Hydroelectric power is clean, safe, and efficient. Building a dam is expensive, but the water is free and is naturally renewed by the water cycle.** Unlike power plants that burn coal or oil, hydroelectric plants do not contribute to air pollution.

In the United States, hydroelectric power accounts for about 9 percent of the electricity produced, while worldwide it generates about 20 percent. Some countries, such as Norway and Brazil, produce almost all of their electrical energy through hydropower.

Lab zone At-Home Activity

Modeling a Dam L1 Point out that this activity may also be carried out in a flat-bottomed sink. Advise students to use sturdy, waterproof tape, such as packing tape. Remind students that the water should completely cover the taped hole before the tape is removed.

Lab zone Chapter Project

Keep Students on Track Provide dirty water for students to use in testing their systems. Have students measure how much of the original water is recovered. Also, set up the "cleanness scale" of grades of dirty water to help groups evaluate their results. Help groups whose systems do not yield positive results evaluate their systems and make appropriate changes.

Disadvantages Hydroelectric plants do have limitations, however. Only certain locations are suitable for building a dam. A fast-moving river is necessary, as is an area that can be flooded to create a reservoir.

Dams affect all living things in the area around them. What was once a fast-moving river becomes the still, deep waters of a reservoir. Some organisms cannot survive the change. **Flooding the land behind a dam can destroy wildlife habitats as well as farms and towns. In addition, the dam forms a barrier across the river.** It may prevent fish from traveling to the parts of the river where they usually lay their eggs and hatch their young.

In some places, people have suggested building small dams to supply power to a local area. Smaller dams uproot fewer people and do less harm to the environment, while still providing energy for a region. However, since dams are expensive to build, small dams may not produce enough power to be worthwhile. Large dams, on the other hand, produce great amounts of power, but they also have a major effect on the land around them.

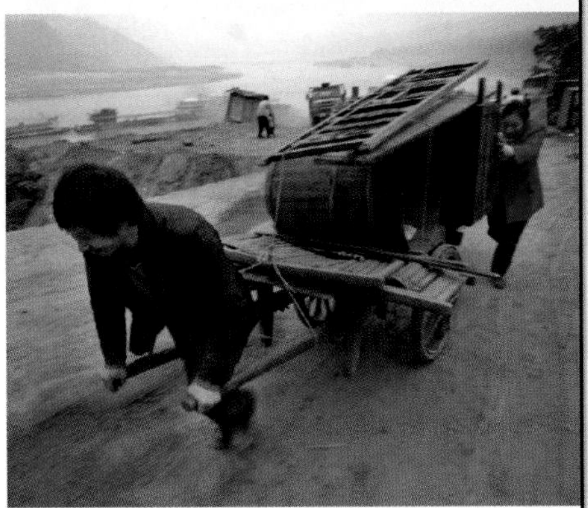

FIGURE 26
The Three Gorges Dam
The Three Gorges Dam in China has displaced more than 500,000 people. Eventually, it may displace more than 1 million. Also, historical artifacts such as the one shown here have had to be relocated.

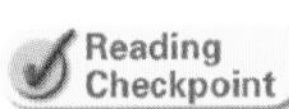

What is the main disadvantage of small dams?

Target Reading Skill Asking Questions Use your graphic organizer about the section headings to help you answer the questions below.

Reviewing Key Concepts

1. a. Reviewing What type of energy does moving water have?
   b. Comparing and Contrasting Compare and contrast the energy of moving water and the energy of water that is stored.
   c. Sequencing Make a flowchart that shows how the energy of moving water is used to produce electricity.
2. a. Defining What is a hydroelectric power plant?
   b. Listing Give two advantages and two disadvantages of hydroelectric power.
   c. Problem Solving Suppose you were hired to build a dam. What features would you look for in a site? Be sure to consider the impact on living things as well as the physical characteristics of the site.

Lab zone At-Home Activity

Modeling a Dam With the help of a family member, construct a model dam in your bathtub. Use a sturdy piece of plastic foam as wide as the tub and about 12 cm high. Cut a 3-cm square in the center of the foam, then cover the hole with tape. Place the plastic foam upright in the tub. If necessary, trim the foam so that it fits snugly against the side of the tub. Turn the water on to create a reservoir. Then carefully peel the tape off the hole and observe what happens to the water. What energy change took place?

For: Hydroelectric Power activity
Visit: PHSchool.com
Web Code: cfp-3025

Students can interact online with the art of a hydroelectric power plant.

Monitor Progress L2

Answers

Figure 25 When the moving water is turning the turbine blades

They may not produce enough power to be worthwhile.

Assess

Reviewing Key Concepts

1. a. Kinetic energy **b.** Both moving and still water contain energy that can change in form. The energy of moving water is kinetic energy; the energy of stored water is potential energy. **c.** 1) Water is released through the floodgates, and energy is converted from potential to kinetic. 2) Released water turns turbine blades, transforming kinetic energy into mechanical energy. 3) Turbine shaft turns an electromagnet, which converts mechanical energy into electrical energy.

2. a. A structure built by a dam that captures the kinetic energy of moving water and converts it to electrical energy **b.** Advantages: It does not contribute to air pollution, and the water is free. Disadvantages: Wildlife habitats can be destroyed, and the dam is a barrier across the river. **c.** Student answers might include the presence of a fast-moving river, a valley behind the proposed dam location, a limited impact on wildlife, and the need to displace as few people as possible in order to build the dam.

Reteach L2

Draw a diagram of a hydroelectric power plant. Have students identify each step of the process of converting energy and state how the energy changes form at each step as you write the data on the board.

All in One Teaching Resources

- Section Summary: *Water Power*
- Review and Reinforce: *Water Power*
- Enrich: *Water Power*

Freshwater Resources

Show the Video Field Trip to let students experience how freshwater resources are used. Discussion question: **How does the distance between the water level in the reservoir and the turbine contribute to the amount of electricity that can be generated?** *(As the water flow and distance increase, so does the amount of electricity generated.)*

Study Guide

- Complete student edition
- Section and chapter self-assessments
- Assessment reports for teachers

Help Students Read

Building Vocabulary

Word-Part Analysis Ask students what words they know that have the key word parts *hydro, kine,* and *de. (Hydroelectric power, kinetic energy, and desalination)* Have students find the definitions of these word parts in a dictionary and then provide additional examples of words with those parts. *(*Hydro *means "water";* kine *means "move"; and* de *means "away from, off, or reverse the action of")*

Word Forms Ask students to write simple definitions for the words *filter, pest,* and *conserve*. Then have students explain how these simple definitions relate to the terms *filtration, pesticide,* and *conservation*.

Connecting Concepts

Concept Maps Help students develop a way of showing how the information in this chapter is related. Emphasize that the supply of fresh water is critical as a means of human survival and as a source of clean energy, and that it must be protected from shortages and pollution. Have students brainstorm to identify key concepts, key terms, details, and examples. Then tell students to write each item on a self-stick note and attach it at random to chart paper or on the board.

Tell students that this concept map will be organized in hierarchical order and to begin at the top with key concepts. Ask students these questions to guide them to categorize the information on the stickies: **How do people use water? What are the components of water quality? How is wastewater treated? What are the main types of water pollution? How can water be harnessed for power?**

Prompt students by using connecting words or phrases, such as "consists of," "causes," and "forms," to indicate the basis for the organization of the map. The phrases should help form sentences between or among a set of concepts.

Answer

Accept logical presentations by students.

All in One Teaching Resources

- Key Terms Review: *Freshwater Resources*
- Connecting Concepts: *Freshwater Resources*

Chapter 2 Study Guide

1 Water Supply and Demand

Key Concepts

- People use water for household purposes, industry, transportation, agriculture, and recreation.
- Reducing water use, recycling water, and reusing water are three ways to conserve water.
- Two possible methods of obtaining fresh water are desalination and melting icebergs.

Key Terms

irrigation conservation desalination

2 Water to Drink

Key Concepts

- Certain substances can affect the taste or color of water but are usually harmless. Other substances, such as certain chemicals and microorganisms, can be harmful to your health.
- Water often needs some treatment to ensure that it is clean and safe to drink.
- Two ways that communities deal with sewage are wastewater treatment plants and septic systems.

Key Terms

water quality
concentration
pH
hardness
filtration
coagulation
sewage

3 Freshwater Pollution

Key Concepts

- Sources of pollution are classified, in part, by how they enter a body of water.
- The three major sources of water pollution are human wastes, industrial wastes, and chemical runoff.
- Solving pollution problems involves cleaning up existing problems and preventing new ones.

Key Terms

water pollution
pollutant
point source
nonpoint source
pesticide
acid rain

4 Droughts and Floods

Key Concepts

- Droughts are usually caused by weather systems that remain in one place for weeks or months at a time.
- Floods occur when the volume of water in a river increases so much that the river overflows its channel.
- Advance warnings help reduce flood damage and loss of life. Building dams is one method of flood control.

Key Terms

drought
flash flood
levee

5 Water Power

Key Concepts

- Hydroelectric power plants capture the kinetic energy of moving water and change it into electrical energy.
- Hydroelectric power is clean, safe, and efficient. Building a dam is expensive, but the water is free and is naturally renewed by the water cycle.
- Flooding the land behind a dam can destroy wildlife habitats as well as farms and towns. In addition, the dam is a barrier across the river.

Key Terms

kinetic energy
potential energy
hydroelectric power

Review and Assessment

Go Online PHSchool.com
For: Self-Assessment
Visit: PHSchool.com
Web Code: cfa-3020

Organizing Information

Concept Mapping Copy the concept map about freshwater pollution onto a separate sheet of paper. Then complete it and add a title. (For more on Concept Mapping, see the Skills Handbook.)

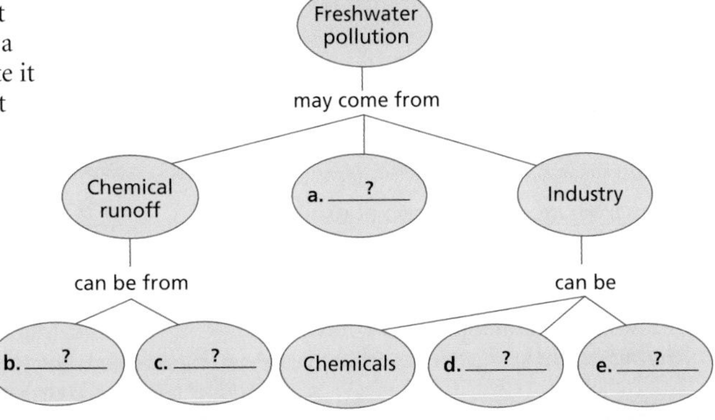

Reviewing Key Terms

Choose the letter of the best answer.

1. One process used to obtain fresh water from salt water is
   a. coagulation. **b.** filtration.
   c. recharge. **d.** desalination.
2. Chlorine is added during water treatment in order to
   a. make particles form flocs.
   b. kill disease-causing organisms.
   c. improve the taste of the water.
   d. remove objects such as fish and trash.
3. The main source of acid rain is
   a. smoke from coal-burning factories.
   b. pesticides sprayed in the air.
   c. runoff from farm fields.
   d. toxic chemicals buried underground.
4. A prolonged period of scarce rainfall is a(n)
   a. levee. **b.** reservoir.
   c. drought. **d.** aquifer.
5. Water flowing swiftly possesses
   a. mechanical energy.
   b. electrical energy.
   c. potential energy.
   d. kinetic energy.

If the statement is true, write *true*. If it is false, change the underlined word or words to make the statement true.

6. <u>Conservation</u> is the practice of using less of a resource so that it will not be used up.
7. The <u>pH</u> of water is a measurement of the amount of calcium and magnesium it contains.
8. People sometimes strengthen natural <u>levees</u> with sandbags to protect against floods.

Writing in Science

Cause and Effect Description Suppose that you were a news reporter assigned to write about a new hydroelectric power plant. Explain how the water will be harnessed to generate electricity.

Freshwater Resources
Video Preview
Video Field Trip
▶ Video Assessment

Go Online PHSchool.com
For: Self-Assessment
Visit: PHSchool.com
Web Code: cfa-3020

Students can take an online practice test that is automatically scored.

All in One Teaching Resources

- Transparency H28
- Chapter Test
- Performance Assessment Teacher Notes
- Performance Assessment Student Worksheet
- Performance Assessment Scoring Rubric

ExamView® Computer Test Bank CD-ROM

Review and Assessment

Organizing Information

a. Human wastes **b.** Farms **c.** Roads
d. Smoke and exhaust **e.** Heat

Reviewing Key Terms

1. d **2.** b **3.** a **4.** c **5.** d
6. true **7.** hardness **8.** true

Writing in Science

Writing Mode Exposition Cause and Effect

Scoring Rubric

4 Exceeds criteria in some way, for example, by providing background on potential and kinetic energy
3 Meets criteria, but does not go beyond requirements
2 Includes an accurate but brief description of the process
1 Is incorrect and incomplete

Freshwater Resources

Show the video assessment to review chapter content and as a prompt for the writing assignment. Discussion questions: **What are some of the benefits of hydroelectric power compared with other ways of generating electricity, such as nuclear power or coal?** *(Generating electricity by hydroelectric power is cleaner and cheaper than generating electricity by burning coal. Hydroelectric power can be produced at half the cost of nuclear power.)* **How is the potential energy of water in a reservoir converted into electrical energy by a hydroelectric power plant?** *(When floodgates in the dam are opened, the water flows, and its potential energy becomes kinetic energy. This energy is converted to mechanical energy when the water turns the turbines, forcing giant magnets to turn. The magnets rotate inside huge coils of copper wire, and the mechanical energy changes to electrical energy.)*

Checking Concepts

9. There is not enough water to meet all needs. Different water demands must compete for a limited supply.

10. Farmers can use pipes instead of open ditches to carry water into their fields. They can use methods that waste little water, such as drip irrigation.

11. Most of Earth's water is salty and cannot be used for drinking or irrigation. Much of Earth's freshwater is stored in ice.

12. Possible answer: Water begins in a reservoir, is treated in a water treatment plant, and then moves to a pumping station, where it is pumped through water mains to smaller pipes and finally into a single home.

13. When they are burned, coal, oil, and gasoline produce sulfur dioxide and nitrogen oxides. These gases react with water vapor in air to form sulfuric and nitric acids, which return to Earth in precipitation.

14. It might provide a clean, relatively safe, and efficient way to produce electricity. It also might force people to move.

Thinking Critically

15. It is similar in that it uses evaporation and condensation to obtain fresh water from salt water. It is different in that the water is boiled instead of evaporating naturally.

16. Pollutants build up in the bodies of larger organisms that eat many smaller organisms.

17. The diver standing on the edge of a diving board has potential energy.

18. Possible answer: The benefits of producing substantial electric power in a clean, safe manner outweigh the local loss of habitats and the displacement of structures upstream.

Review and Assessment

Checking Concepts

9. Why are water rights an important issue in dry areas?

10. Describe one way that farmers can reduce the amount of water lost during irrigation.

11. Why isn't most of the water on Earth's surface available for people to use?

12. Describe one possible path of drinking water from its source to a home.

13. How does acid rain form?

14. How might building a dam affect people living nearby?

Thinking Critically

15. Comparing and Contrasting How is the process of distillation similar to the water cycle? How is it different?

16. Relating Cause and Effect Why does the concentration of pollutants build up as shown in the diagram?

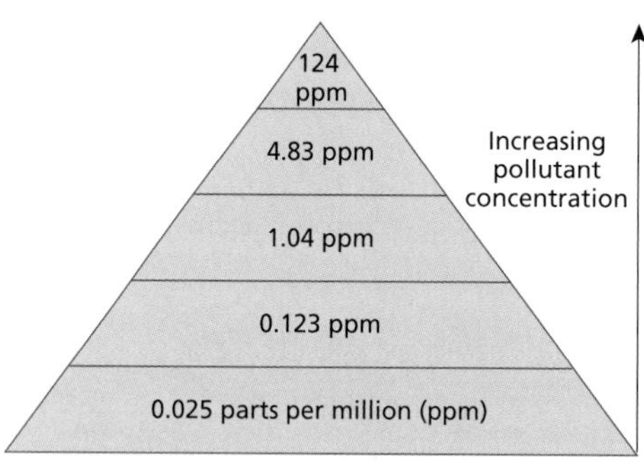

17. Applying Concepts What type of energy does a diver have while standing at the edge of a diving board?

18. Making Judgments Do you think that the benefits of hydroelectric power outweigh the disadvantages? Give reasons to support your answer.

Math Practice

19. Calculating a Concentration Look at the concentrations of lead and copper shown in the data table on this page. Write the concentrations in fraction form.

Applying Skills

Use the data in the table to answer Questions 20–22.

A family tested their drinking-water well to check the water quality. The test results are shown in the table below.

Drinking Water Sample Test Results

Lead	0.2 parts per million
Copper	0.006 parts per million
pH	5.0
Coliform count	5 out of 5 samples positive

20. Inferring The family suspects that their septic tank is polluting the well. What evidence exists to support this conclusion?

21. Designing Experiments What might be the source of the lead in the water? How could you test your answer?

22. Developing Hypotheses How might the low pH of the water be related to the lead contamination?

Lab zone Chapter Project

Performance Assessment It's time to put your treatment system to the test! Use your system to clean up the dirty water sample. Measure the volume of water recovered by your system. Share your results with your classmates. How do your results compare with theirs?

Lab zone Chapter Project L3

Project Wrap Up
As students prepare their presentations, assist them in organizing the information they need to present their models to the class. Encourage last-minute changes for students having trouble with their models, but reassure them that a good effort and clear presentation can make up for disappointing results.

Reflect and Record After all presentations, have students evaluate their own designs in light of their classmates' designs. Students can reach a consensus about what materials and procedures were most effective in cleaning water. Have all students write their reflections about the project in their journals.

Review and Assessment

Go Online PHSchool.com
For: Self-Assessment
Visit: PHSchool.com
Web Code: cfa-3020

Organizing Information

Concept Mapping Copy the concept map about freshwater pollution onto a separate sheet of paper. Then complete it and add a title. (For more on Concept Mapping, see the Skills Handbook.)

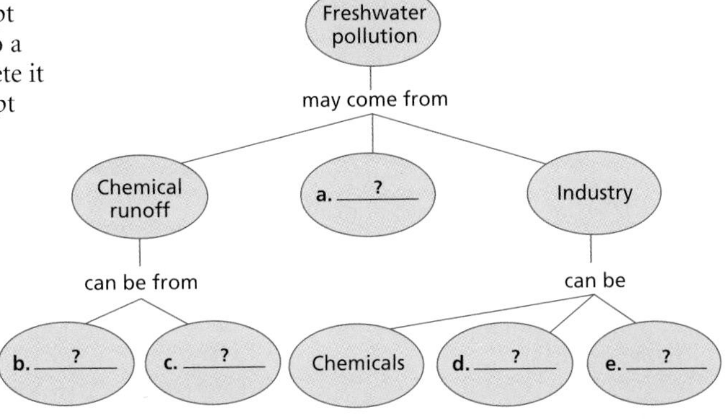

Reviewing Key Terms

Choose the letter of the best answer.

1. One process used to obtain fresh water from salt water is
   a. coagulation. **b.** filtration.
   c. recharge. **d.** desalination.
2. Chlorine is added during water treatment in order to
   a. make particles form flocs.
   b. kill disease-causing organisms.
   c. improve the taste of the water.
   d. remove objects such as fish and trash.
3. The main source of acid rain is
   a. smoke from coal-burning factories.
   b. pesticides sprayed in the air.
   c. runoff from farm fields.
   d. toxic chemicals buried underground.
4. A prolonged period of scarce rainfall is a(n)
   a. levee. **b.** reservoir.
   c. drought. **d.** aquifer.
5. Water flowing swiftly possesses
   a. mechanical energy.
   b. electrical energy.
   c. potential energy.
   d. kinetic energy.

If the statement is true, write *true*. If it is false, change the underlined word or words to make the statement true.

6. Conservation is the practice of using less of a resource so that it will not be used up.
7. The pH of water is a measurement of the amount of calcium and magnesium it contains.
8. People sometimes strengthen natural levees with sandbags to protect against floods.

Writing in Science

Cause and Effect Description Suppose that you were a news reporter assigned to write about a new hydroelectric power plant. Explain how the water will be harnessed to generate electricity.

Freshwater Resources
Video Preview
Video Field Trip
▶ Video Assessment

For: Self-Assessment
Visit: PHSchool.com
Web Code: cfa-3020

Students can take an online practice test that is automatically scored.

Teaching Resources
- Transparency H28
- Chapter Test
- Performance Assessment Teacher Notes
- Performance Assessment Student Worksheet
- Performance Assessment Scoring Rubric

ExamView® Computer Test Bank CD-ROM

Review and Assessment

Organizing Information

a. Human wastes **b.** Farms **c.** Roads **d.** Smoke and exhaust **e.** Heat

Reviewing Key Terms

1. d **2.** b **3.** a **4.** c **5.** d **6.** true **7.** hardness **8.** true

Writing in Science

Writing Mode Exposition Cause and Effect

Scoring Rubric

4 Exceeds criteria in some way, for example, by providing background on potential and kinetic energy
3 Meets criteria, but does not go beyond requirements
2 Includes an accurate but brief description of the process
1 Is incorrect and incomplete

Freshwater Resources

Show the video assessment to review chapter content and as a prompt for the writing assignment. Discussion questions: **What are some of the benefits of hydroelectric power compared with other ways of generating electricity, such as nuclear power or coal?** *(Generating electricity by hydroelectric power is cleaner and cheaper than generating electricity by burning coal. Hydroelectric power can be produced at half the cost of nuclear power.)* **How is the potential energy of water in a reservoir converted into electrical energy by a hydroelectric power plant?** *(When floodgates in the dam are opened, the water flows, and its potential energy becomes kinetic energy. This energy is converted to mechanical energy when the water turns the turbines, forcing giant magnets to turn. The magnets rotate inside huge coils of copper wire, and the mechanical energy changes to electrical energy.)*

Checking Concepts

9. There is not enough water to meet all needs. Different water demands must compete for a limited supply.

10. Farmers can use pipes instead of open ditches to carry water into their fields. They can use methods that waste little water, such as drip irrigation.

11. Most of Earth's water is salty and cannot be used for drinking or irrigation. Much of Earth's freshwater is stored in ice.

12. Possible answer: Water begins in a reservoir, is treated in a water treatment plant, and then moves to a pumping station, where it is pumped through water mains to smaller pipes and finally into a single home.

13. When they are burned, coal, oil, and gasoline produce sulfur dioxide and nitrogen oxides. These gases react with water vapor in air to form sulfuric and nitric acids, which return to Earth in precipitation.

14. It might provide a clean, relatively safe, and efficient way to produce electricity. It also might force people to move.

Thinking Critically

15. It is similar in that it uses evaporation and condensation to obtain fresh water from salt water. It is different in that the water is boiled instead of evaporating naturally.

16. Pollutants build up in the bodies of larger organisms that eat many smaller organisms.

17. The diver standing on the edge of a diving board has potential energy.

18. Possible answer: The benefits of producing substantial electric power in a clean, safe manner outweigh the local loss of habitats and the displacement of structures upstream.

Review and Assessment

Checking Concepts

9. Why are water rights an important issue in dry areas?
10. Describe one way that farmers can reduce the amount of water lost during irrigation.
11. Why isn't most of the water on Earth's surface available for people to use?
12. Describe one possible path of drinking water from its source to a home.
13. How does acid rain form?
14. How might building a dam affect people living nearby?

Thinking Critically

15. **Comparing and Contrasting** How is the process of distillation similar to the water cycle? How is it different?
16. **Relating Cause and Effect** Why does the concentration of pollutants build up as shown in the diagram?

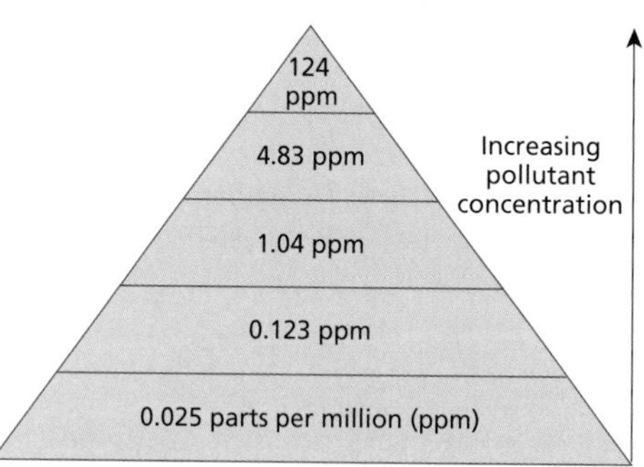

17. **Applying Concepts** What type of energy does a diver have while standing at the edge of a diving board?
18. **Making Judgments** Do you think that the benefits of hydroelectric power outweigh the disadvantages? Give reasons to support your answer.

Math Practice

19. **Calculating a Concentration** Look at the concentrations of lead and copper shown in the data table on this page. Write the concentrations in fraction form.

Applying Skills

Use the data in the table to answer Questions 20–22.

A family tested their drinking-water well to check the water quality. The test results are shown in the table below.

Drinking Water Sample Test Results

Lead	0.2 parts per million
Copper	0.006 parts per million
pH	5.0
Coliform count	5 out of 5 samples positive

20. **Inferring** The family suspects that their septic tank is polluting the well. What evidence exists to support this conclusion?
21. **Designing Experiments** What might be the source of the lead in the water? How could you test your answer?
22. **Developing Hypotheses** How might the low pH of the water be related to the lead contamination?

Lab zone Chapter Project

Performance Assessment It's time to put your treatment system to the test! Use your system to clean up the dirty water sample. Measure the volume of water recovered by your system. Share your results with your classmates. How do your results compare with theirs?

Lab zone Chapter Project

L3

Project Wrap Up
As students prepare their presentations, assist them in organizing the information they need to present their models to the class. Encourage last-minute changes for students having trouble with their models, but reassure them that a good effort and clear presentation can make up for disappointing results.

Reflect and Record After all presentations, have students evaluate their own designs in light of their classmates' designs. Students can reach a consensus about what materials and procedures were most effective in cleaning water. Have all students write their reflections about the project in their journals.

Standardized Test Prep

Test-Taking Tip

Eliminating Incorrect Answers

When answering a multiple-choice question, you can often eliminate some of the answer choices because they are clearly incorrect. By doing this, you increase your odds of choosing the correct answer.

Sample Question

A common method of water conservation in agriculture is

A desalination.
B using icebergs for fresh water.
C drip irrigation.
D coagulation.

Answer

The correct answer is **C.** You can eliminate **A** and **B** because they are not methods of water conservation. They are both possible methods of providing fresh water. **D** is also incorrect because coagulation is a process used in water treatment plants.

Choose the letter of the best answer.

1. In which step of the drinking-water treatment process are disease-causing microorganisms killed?
A chlorination
B filtration
C coagulation
D desalination

2. Which of the following is an example of a point source of water pollution?
F runoff of pesticides from wheat fields
G salt spread on roads and parking lots to melt ice
H chemicals flowing from a factory into a stream
J fertilizer from corn fields that runs off into streams

3. Two students are measuring the volume of water they use while brushing their teeth. Which of the following pieces of equipment should they use for their measurement?
A a metric ruler
B a balance
C a graduated cylinder
D a test tube

Use the data table below and your knowledge of science to answer Questions 4–5.

Hydroelectric Power in the United States

Region	Annual Power Generation (megawatt-hours)
Great Lakes	24,987,042
Upper Mississippi	3,543,100
Lower Mississippi	1,192,680
Rio Grande	441,821
Pacific Northwest	146,085,711
Lower Colorado	6,916,259
Upper Colorado	6,339,303

4. According to the data table, which region produces the most hydroelectric power?
F Upper Colorado
G Great Lakes
H Pacific Northwest
J Rio Grande

5. The Rio Grande region produces the least hydroelectric power. Why might this be?
A Dams cannot be built on the rivers in the region.
B It is a dry area, and most of the water in the rivers is used for other purposes.
C There is no need for hydroelectric power in the region.
D all of the above

Constructed Response

6. You are on a committee that is planning whether or not to build a dam on a nearby river to produce hydroelectric power. Describe some of the advantages and disadvantages you should consider before deciding to build the dam.

Math Practice

19. The concentration of lead written as a fraction is $\frac{2}{10,000,000}$. The concentration of copper written as a fraction is $\frac{6}{1,000,000,000}$.

Applying Skills

20. The coliform count result supports the suspicion because all five of the samples taken contained coliform bacteria. This is evidence that the water has been contaminated with waste material.

21. The source of lead might be the pipes through which the water passes. A way to test this hypothesis would be to measure the amount of lead in a sample of water collected before the water passes through the pipes.

22. The lower the pH is, the more acidic the water. Acidic water can dissolve lead from the pipes through which it passes.

Standardized Test Prep

1. A **2.** H **3.** C **4.** H **5.** B

6. One advantage of building a dam is that hydroelectric power can be produced cheaply by using a renewable resource. In addition, hydroelectric power is efficient and safe, and it does not pollute the air or water. A disadvantage is that wildlife habitats behind the dam will be destroyed because the land will be flooded. Fish may be prevented from entering parts of the river in which they usually lay their eggs and hatch their young.

Chapter at a Glance

PRENTICE HALL TeacherEXPRESS™ Plan • Teach • Assess

Lab zone **Chapter Project** *Design and Build an Erosion-Proof Beach*

	Technology	Local Standards
All in One Teaching Resources • Chapter Project Teacher Notes, pp. 184–185 • Chapter Project Student Introduction, pp. 186–187 • Chapter Project Student Worksheet, pp. 188–189 • Chapter Project Scoring Rubric, p. 190	 Discovery Channel School Video Preview	
 **Section 1 Wave Action** (2–3 periods, 1–1 1/2 blocks) **H.3.1.1** Explain how waves form and describe the characteristics of waves. **H.3.1.2** Describe how waves change near the shore. **H.3.1.3** Explain how waves affect shorelines and beaches.	 Go Online active art  Discovery Channel School Video Field Trip	
 **Section 2 Tides** (1–2 periods, 1/2–1 block) **H.3.2.1** Explain what causes tides. **H.3.2.2** Explain what affects the height of tides. **H.3.2.3** Describe how tides are a source of energy.	 Go Online PHSchool.com	
 **Section 3 Ocean Water Chemistry** (2–3 periods, 1–1 1/2 blocks) **H.3.3.1** Describe the salinity of ocean water. **H.3.3.2** Explain how the temperature and gas content of ocean water varies. **H.3.3.3** Describe how conditions in the ocean change with depth.	 Go Online NSTA SciLinks	
 **Section 4 Currents and Climate** (3–4 periods, 1–2 blocks) **H.3.4.1** Identify what causes surface currents and explain how surface currents affect climate. **H.3.4.2** Identify the causes of deep currents and describe the effects that the currents have. **H.3.4.3** Describe how upwelling affects the distribution of nutrients in the ocean.	 Go Online NSTA SciLinks	

Review and Assessment

	Technology	Test Preparation
All in One Teaching Resources • Key Terms Review, p. 226 • Transparency H41 • Performance Assessment Teacher Notes, p. 233 • Performance Assessment Scoring Rubric, p. 234 • Performance Assessment Student Worksheet, p. 235 • Chapter Test, pp. 236–238	 Discovery Channel School Video Assessment  Go Online PHSchool.com	**Test Preparation Blackline Masters**

Chapter Activities Planner

For more activities
LAB ZONE Easy Planner CD-ROM

Student Edition	Inquiry	Time	Materials	Skills	Resources
Chapter Project, p. 93	Open-Ended	Ongoing (2–3 weeks)	**All in One Teaching Resources** See Chapter Project in See p. 184	modeling, measuring, interpreting data, evaluating, communicating	**Lab zone Easy Planner** **All in One Teaching Resources** Chapter Project Worksheets Support pp. 184–185
Section 1					
Discover Activity, p. 94	Directed	20 minutes	Aluminum baking pan, sand, pebbles, book, ruler, water, wooden tongue depressor	Observing	**Lab zone Easy Planner**
Try This Activity, p. 97	Directed	20 minutes	Aquarium, water, several metal washers and corks, thread	Observing	**Lab zone Easy Planner**
Skills Activity, p. 99	Directed	20 minutes	Aluminum pan, beaker, book, sand, water	Making models	**Lab zone Easy Planner**
Section 2					
Discover Activity, p. 102	Directed	15 minutes	Calculator	Predicting	**Lab zone Easy Planner**
Section 3					
Discover Activity, p. 108	Directed	10 minutes	Two beakers or jars, tap water, salt, teaspoon, stirring rod, two uncooked eggs	Observing	**Lab zone Easy Planner**
Technology Lab, pp. 113–114	Open-Ended	40 minutes	Thumbtacks, 250-mL graduated cylinder, unsharpened pencil with eraser, metric ruler, fine-point permanent marker, thermometer, ice, balance, water, spoon, salt, additional materials	Building a prototype, designing a solution, troubleshooting	**Lab zone Easy Planner** **Lab Activity Video** **All in One Teaching Resources** Technology Lab: *Investigating Changes in Density,* pp. 213–215
Section 4					
Discover Activity, p. 116	Directed	15 minutes	Plastic container, warm water, cup, ice water, food coloring, plastic dropper, stirring rod	Inferring	**Lab zone Easy Planner**
Skills Activity, p. 118	Guided	5 minutes	Figure 17	Drawing conclusions	**Lab zone Easy Planner**
Skills Lab, p. 122	Directed	30 minutes	Rectangular baking tray, chalk, 3 sticks of modeling clay, ruler, permanent marker, hole puncher, newspaper, blue and red construction paper, jointed drinking straws, 400-mL of light-reflecting rheoscopic fluid or water with food coloring	Making models, observing, inferring	**Lab zone Easy Planner** **Lab Activity Video** **All in One Teaching Resources** Skills Lab: *Modeling Ocean Currents,* pp. 224–225

Section 1 Wave Action

 *2–3 periods, 1–1 1/2 blocks*

ABILITY LEVELS
L1 Basic to Average
L2 For All Students
L3 Average to Advanced

Local Standards

Objectives

H.3.1.1 Explain how waves form and describe the characteristics of waves.
H.3.1.2 Describe how waves change near the shore.
H.3.1.3 Explain how waves affect shorelines and beaches.

Key Terms

• wave • wavelength • frequency • wave height • tsunami • longshore drift • rip current • groin

Preteach

Build Background Knowledge

Recall experiences about waves at the beach.

How Do Waves Change a Beach? L1

Targeted Print and Technology Resources

All in One Teaching Resources
- L2 Reading Strategy Transparency H29: Using Prior Knowledge

Presentation-Pro CD-ROM

Instruct

What Is a Wave? Explain how wind causes waves.

How Waves Change Near Shore Describe why and how a wave changes near shore.

How Waves Affect the Shore Use the diagram in Figure 5 to explain how waves affect the shore.

Waves and Beach Erosion Explain how waves can cause beach erosion.

Targeted Print and Technology Resources

All in One Teaching Resources
- L2 Guided Reading, pp. 193–196
- L2 Transparencies H30, H31, H32

www.SciLinks.org Web Code: cfp-3031

Student Edition on Audio CD

Assess

Section Assessment Questions

Have students use their completed Using Prior Knowledge graphic organizers to answer the questions.

Reteach

Create a labeled drawing of a wave.

Targeted Print and Technology Resources

All in One Teaching Resources
- Section Summary, p. 192
- L1 Review and Reinforce, p. 197
- L3 Enrich, p. 198

Section 2 Tides

 *1–2 periods, 1/2–1 block*

ABILITY LEVELS
L1 Basic to Average
L2 For All Students
L3 Average to Advanced

Objectives

H.3.2.1 Explain what causes tides.
H.3.2.2 Explain what affects the height of tides.
H.3.2.3 Describe how tides are a source of energy.

Key Terms

• tides • spring tide • neap tide

Local Standards

Preteach

Build Background Knowledge

Share observations of tides.

 *When Is High Tide?* L2

Targeted Print and Technology Resources

L2 Reading Strategy Transparency H33: Previewing Visuals

Presentation-Pro CD-ROM

Instruct

What Causes Tides? Compare the formation of tides to a figure skater being held by her skates as she spins.

Energy From Tides Describe the energy transformations that occur when tides are used as a source of power.

Targeted Print and Technology Resources

L2 Guided Reading, pp. 201–203
L2 Transparency H34

PHSchool.com Web code: cfd-3032

Student Edition on Audio CD

Assess

Section Assessment Questions

Have students use their Previewing Visuals graphic organizers to help them answer the questions.

Reteach

Diagram the positions of the sun, Earth, and the moon during spring tide and neap tide.

Targeted Print and Technology Resources

- Section Summary, p. 200

L1 Review and Reinforce, p. 204
L3 Enrich, p. 205

Section 3 Ocean Water Chemistry

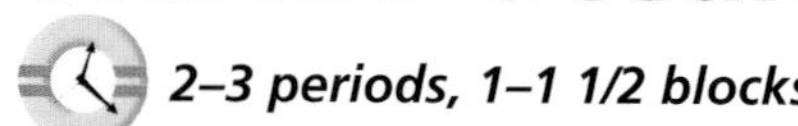

2–3 periods, 1–1 1/2 blocks

ABILITY LEVELS
- L1 Basic to Average
- L2 For All Students
- L3 Average to Advanced

Objectives

H.3.3.1 Describe the salinity of ocean water.

H.3.3.2 Explain how the temperature and gas content of ocean water varies.

H.3.3.3 Describe how conditions in the ocean change with depth.

Key Terms

• salinity • submersible

Local Standards

Preteach

Build Background Knowledge

Compare and contrast the freezing of ocean water and fresh water.

Lab zone **Discover Activity** *Will the Eggs Sink or Float?* L1

Targeted Print and Technology Resources

All in One Teaching Resources
- L2 Reading Strategy Transparency H35: Asking Questions

Presentation-Pro CD-ROM

Instruct

The Salty Ocean Describe salts in ocean water.

Other Ocean Properties Summarize the distribution of gas in ocean water.

Changes With Depth Explain how pressure changes with depth.

Lab zone **Technology Lab** *Investigating Changes in Density* L2

Targeted Print and Technology Resources

All in One Teaching Resources
- L2 Guided Reading, pp. 208–210
- L2 Transparency H36
- L2 Technology Lab: *Investigating Changes in Density,* pp. 213–215

Lab Activity Video/DVD
Technology Lab: *Investigating Changes in Density*

www.SciLinks.org: Web code: scn-0833

Student Edition on Audio CD

Assess

Section Assessment Questions

Have students use their Asking Questions graphic organizers to help them answer the questions.

Reteach

Describe how salinity, temperature, and gases in the ocean vary.

Targeted Print and Technology Resources

All in One Teaching Resources
- Section Summary, p. 207
- L1 Review and Reinforce, p. 211
- L3 Enrich, p. 212

Section 4 Currents and Climate

3–4 periods, 1–2 blocks

ABILITY LEVELS
- L1 Basic to Average
- L2 For All Students
- L3 Average to Advanced

Objectives

H.3.4.1 Identify what causes surface currents and explain how surface currents affect climate.

H.3.4.2 Identify the causes of deep currents and describe the effects that the currents have.

H.3.4.3 Describe how upwelling affects the distribution of nutrients in the ocean.

Key Terms

• current • Coriolis effect • climate • El Niño • upwelling

Local Standards

Preteach

Build Background Knowledge

Explain how a message in a bottle might get to a faraway location.

Which Is More Dense? L1

Targeted Print and Technology Resources

All in One Teaching Resources
- L2 Reading Strategy Transparency H37: Relating Cause and Effect

Presentation-Pro CD-ROM

Instruct

Surface Currents Explain how the Coriolis effect changes ocean currents.

Deep Currents Compare surface currents and deep currents.

Upwelling Explain the process by which deep ocean water is brought to the surface.

Lab zone Skills Lab *Modeling Ocean Currents* L2

Targeted Print and Technology Resources

All in One Teaching Resources
- L2 Guided Reading, pp. 218–221
- L2 Transparencies H38, H39, H40
- L2 Skills Lab: *Modeling Ocean Currents,* pp. 224–225

Lab Activity Video/DVD
Skills Lab: *Modeling Ocean Currents*

www.SciLinks.org Web Code: scn-0834

Student Edition on Audio CD

Assess

Section Assessment Questions

Have students use their Relating Cause and Effect graphic organizers to help them answer the questions.

Reteach

Define important terms related to currents.

Targeted Print and Technology Resources

All in One Teaching Resources
- Section Summary, p. 217
- L1 Review and Reinforce, p. 222
- L3 Enrich, p. 223

Chapter 3 Content Refresher

For: Professional development support
Visit: www.SciLinks.org/PDLinks
Web Code: scf-0830

Professional Development

Section 1 Wave Action

Wave Power The amount of energy in waves is tremendous. In the late 1800s, people designed a way to transform the energy of waves to usable form. A float was used to transfer kinetic energy to a piston that operated a siren. Buoys with wave-powered sirens have been used ever since. However, it was not until late in the twentieth century before a British scientist, Dr. Stephen Salter, found a way to generate electricity with waves. Now there are wave-generated power stations along the coasts of Britain, Norway, Japan, and India.

Erosion Cycles and Sand Dunes The erosion and deposition of sand that change the shape of beaches occur in cycles that correspond to the weather. During fair weather, waves generally are low, often under 1 m high, and have little energy. Under these conditions, more sand is deposited on the beach than is eroded away. During stormy weather, wave height and power increase. Under these conditions, more sand is eroded from the beach than is deposited. When the storms end, the waves return to fair-weather size and sand builds up on the beach again.

Although most sand dunes form on barrier beaches, some of the biggest dunes in the world have formed on the mainland. Dunes on the southern coast of Oregon, for example, extend up to 5 km inland from the coast, and dunes on the southwestern shore of Lake Michigan in Indiana reach a height of more than 100 m. Wetlands often occur near dunes, as shown in this photograph of Indiana Dunes National Lakeshore, Indiana.

Tsunamis Tsunamis are the biggest, strongest waves ever recorded. A 1771 tsunami that hit an island near Japan tossed a block of coral weighing more than 700 metric tons 2.5 km inland. An 1883 tsunami crashed onto the islands of Java and Sumatra. It measured more than 34 m high, or taller than a ten-story building.

Section 2 Tides

Grunion Some animals depend on tides to survive and reproduce. For example, a fish called the grunion lays its eggs on the beach during spring tide. After the tide goes out, the eggs remain safely buried in the sand to hatch into larvae. Two weeks later, just as the larvae are ready to turn into small fish, the next spring tide comes in and carries them out to sea.

Address Misconceptions

Thinking that the giant waves are caused by tides, students often refer to tsunamis as tidal waves. For a strategy for overcoming this misconception, see **Address Misconceptions** on page 104.

Measuring Sea Level Tides have been measured in many different ways. The National Oceanic and Atmospheric Administration (NOAA) measures tides at several stations around the United States. Before computers, tides were measured with a floating ball in a pipe that was open to the water. The ball was connected to a recording device that recorded the tides as the ball moved up and down with the level of the water. Today, NOAA scientists use sound waves to measure water level and predict tides. The travel times of sound waves in water are very precise, allowing scientists to make accurate measurements of water height many times a second. In deep water, scientists use pressure sensors to measure water height.

Section 3 Ocean Water Chemistry

Oxygen and Nitrogen in Ocean Water Air contains oxygen and nitrogen. At surface pressure, nitrogen is not absorbed into the blood. However, when divers are exposed to high pressure in deep water, their blood absorbs both nitrogen and oxygen. If a diver comes to the surface too quickly, the sudden pressure drop causes nitrogen dissolved in the blood to come out of solution and form bubbles. This causes a painful, even life-threatening, condition called the bends. To avoid the bends, divers going deeper than about 40 m must return to surface pressure slowly in a special decompression tank.

Ocean Water Elements Marine life plays an important role in the composition of ocean water. Clams, shrimp, and lobsters, for example, extract calcium to build their shells and bodies. Plankton use silica. Sponges and some seaweeds remove and use iodine. Some marine organisms also secrete elements that alter the composition of seawater. Snails for example, secrete lead.

Desalination The world's supply of fresh water is limited. In nature, fresh water evaporates from the ocean, forms clouds, condenses, and falls to the ground as rain. Water treatment plants remove salt from seawater and provide fresh water for drinking and other uses. There are many ways to remove salt from seawater. In reverse osmosis water is forced under pressure through a semi-permeable membrane that lets only water molecules pass and keeps salt, dirt, bacteria, heavy metals, and other contaminants out. In large-scale desalination plants, two liters of salt water must be filtered to produce one liter of drinking water. It also produces a highly concentrated brine that is dumped back into the ocean and can kill small marine organisms.

Section 4 Currents and Climate

El Niño One of the largest El Niños on record occurred during the years 1997 and 1998. Although the massive warm-water current was already shrinking by January of 1998, it was still 1.5 times the size of the continental United States. Because it was so large, the 1997–1998 El Niño brought some of the most unusual weather ever recorded in the United States. Many regions had unusually wet or dry conditions. Storms battered the coast of California. Regions outside of the United States also were affected. Torrential downpours occurred in parts of eastern and central Africa that are usually arid, and drought conditions existed in northeastern Brazil, Indonesia, and Australia, where it is usually wet. (Red and orange areas on the globe that follows indicate the areas of warmest temperatures during a recent El Niño.)

Help Students Read

SQ3R

Survey, Question, Read, Recite, and Review

Strategy Help students read material that contains technical information, diagrams, and figures. This strategy helps students focus on the main points in a section and makes it easier for them to remember what they have read. Before students begin, assign a section in the textbook for them to read such as Section 4, Currents and Climate.

Example

1. S Have students survey the entire assignment and look at the headings, words in boldface and italics, and chapter study guide. Have them write a short description of what they see in each diagram, photograph, table, or graph.

2. Q Have students write questions that they will answer later. They should turn each heading into a question and leave room below it for the answer.

3. R Have students read the section and look for the answers to their questions.

4. R When students finish reading, tell them to think about what they read. They should recite the questions they wrote and—using their own words—give the answers they found. If students can't answer a question, have them reread the material beneath the related heading and look more carefully for the answer.

5. R Have students review the section by writing the answers they recited. Finally, refer students to the key concepts questions on the first page of the section. Have students answer each of these questions.

Interactive Textbook

- Complete student edition
- Video and audio
- Simulations and activities
- Section and chapter activities

Chapter 3 Ocean Motions

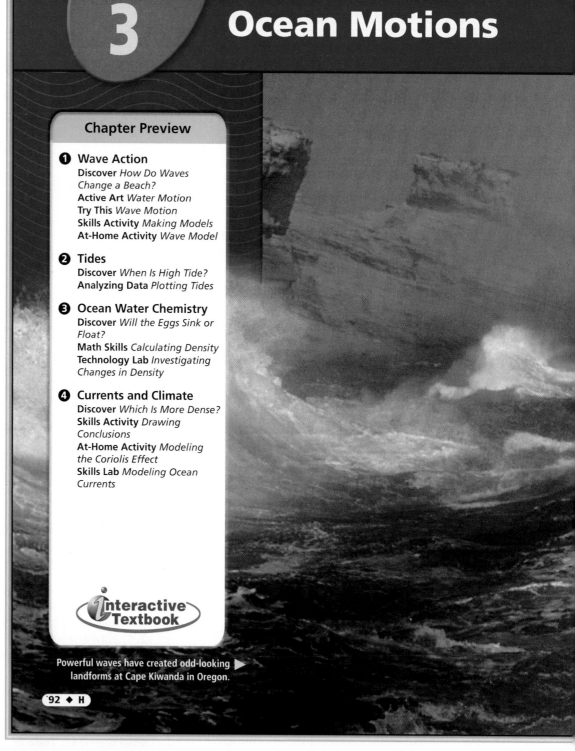

Chapter Preview

1 Wave Action
Discover *How Do Waves Change a Beach?*
Active Art *Water Motion*
Try This *Wave Motion*
Skills Activity *Making Models*
At-Home Activity *Wave Model*

2 Tides
Discover *When Is High Tide?*
Analyzing Data *Plotting Tides*

3 Ocean Water Chemistry
Discover *Will the Eggs Sink or Float?*
Math Skills *Calculating Density*
Technology Lab *Investigating Changes in Density*

4 Currents and Climate
Discover *Which Is More Dense?*
Skills Activity *Drawing Conclusions*
At-Home Activity *Modeling the Coriolis Effect*
Skills Lab *Modeling Ocean Currents*

Interactive Textbook

Powerful waves have created odd-looking landforms at Cape Kiwanda in Oregon.

L3

Objectives

This project will enhance students' understanding of how of waves cause erosion and how erosion can be controlled. After this chapter project, students will be able to

- construct a model of a beach and lighthouse and generate waves in a wave tank
- observe and measure wave erosion of the beach
- design and test methods to reduce wave erosion of the beach
- demonstrate and explain the best method to the class

Skills Focus

Modeling, measuring, interpreting data, evaluating, communicating

Project Time Line 2–3 weeks

All in One Teaching Resources

- Chapter Project Teacher Notes
- Chapter Project Worksheet 1
- Chapter Project Worksheet 2
- Chapter Project Scoring Rubric

Developing a Plan

Plan about two days for students to complete each of the following tasks: 1) Brainstorm a plan and list of materials for the wave tank and model beach and lighthouse. 2) Make a scale sketch of the tank and model and finalize the list of materials. 3) Build the wave tank, model beach, and lighthouse. 4) Generate waves and measure erosion of the beach; modify the model and method of measuring as needed. 5) Brainstorm methods and materials to prevent erosion. 6) Modify the model by introducing erosion-prevention methods and measure how well the methods prevent erosion. 7) Demonstrate and explain to the class the best method(s) of preventing erosion.

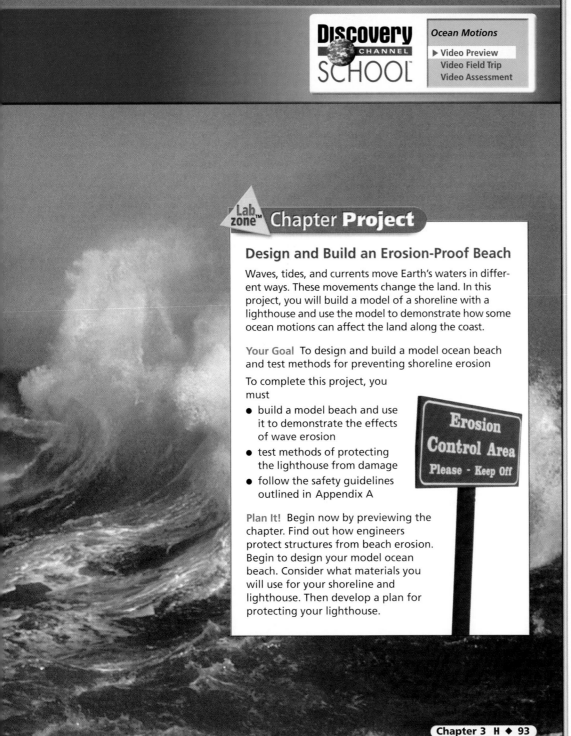

Lab zone™ Chapter Project

Design and Build an Erosion-Proof Beach

Waves, tides, and currents move Earth's waters in different ways. These movements change the land. In this project, you will build a model of a shoreline with a lighthouse and use the model to demonstrate how some ocean motions can affect the land along the coast.

Your Goal To design and build a model ocean beach and test methods for preventing shoreline erosion

To complete this project, you must

- build a model beach and use it to demonstrate the effects of wave erosion
- test methods of protecting the lighthouse from damage
- follow the safety guidelines outlined in Appendix A

Plan It! Begin now by previewing the chapter. Find out how engineers protect structures from beach erosion. Begin to design your model ocean beach. Consider what materials you will use for your shoreline and lighthouse. Then develop a plan for protecting your lighthouse.

Erosion Control Area Please - Keep Off

Ocean Motions

Show the Video Preview to introduce the Chapter Project and overview the chapter content. Discussion question: **What is the relationship between wind and waves?** *(Most ocean waves are formed when wind blows across the water's surface, transferring the wind's energy to the water.)*

Launching the Project

Challenge students to think of kinds of structures commonly built along beaches. *(Students might mention lighthouses, high-rise hotels, restaurants, homes, marinas, and amusement parks.)* Ask: **What are some limitations of building near an ocean coast?** *(Students might mention hurricanes, storms, blowing sand, and erosion.)* Emphasize that the shape of a coast is constantly being altered by wave erosion. Therefore, when structures are built on the coast, methods of controlling erosion often must be adopted to protect these structures.

Performance Assessment

The Chapter Project Scoring Rubric will help you evaluate how well students complete the Chapter Project. You may want to share the rubric with your students so they know what is expected. Students will be assessed on

- how well they plan their models and the appropriateness of their materials
- the accuracy of the models they build and how well they collect and record data
- how effectively they present their models and explain their results to the class
- how much they contribute to their groups' effort

Possible Materials

- Wave tanks can be constructed from large cardboard box tops or plastic under-bed storage boxes. Cardboard boxes must be lined with plastic. A large aluminum baking pan or a paint roller pan can be used for a smaller, simpler wave tank.
- To make the beach, students can use materials such as fine sand and small pebbles. The lighthouse can be constructed of small toy blocks, flat stones, or sugar cubes and held together with modeling clay.
- Beach protection materials might include larger stones or wooden blocks for seawalls and craft sticks or toy logs placed perpendicular to the beach for groins.
- To measure erosion, students can use toothpicks stuck into the beach and labeled with masking tape.

Section 1 Wave Action

Objectives

After completing this lesson, students will be able to

H.3.1.1 Explain how waves form and describe the characteristics of waves.

H.3.1.2 Describe how waves change near the shore.

H.3.1.3 Explain how waves affect shorelines and beaches.

Target Reading Skill

Using Prior Knowledge Explain that using prior knowledge helps students connect what they already know to what they are about to read.

Answers

Possible answers might include these:

What You Know

1. There are waves in the ocean.
2. Wind causes waves.

What You Learned

1. Waves move energy to the shore.
2. Earthquakes cause tsunamis.

All in One Teaching Resources

- Transparency H29

Preteach

Build Background Knowledge L1

Wave Action

Encourage students who have been to a beach or a wave pool to describe how it feels to stand in the waves. Ask: **What happened to your body when a wave passed by?** *(It bobbed up and down.)* **If you were at the beach, what happened to the water as it flowed onto the beach?** *(It flowed up the beach and then straight back into the ocean.)* Tell students that they will learn how waves and this up and back flow of the water change the beach.

Section 1 Wave Action

Reading Preview

Key Concepts

- How does a wave form?
- How do waves change near the shore?
- How do waves affect shorelines and beaches?

Key Terms

- wave • wavelength
- frequency • wave height
- tsunami • longshore drift
- rip current • groin

Target Reading Skill

Using Prior Knowledge Before you read, look at the section headings and visuals to see what this section is about. Then write what you know about waves in a graphic organizer like the one below. As you read, continue to write in what you learn.

What You Know
1. There are waves in the ocean. 2.

What You Learned
1. 2.

Lab zone Discover Activity

How Do Waves Change a Beach?

1. In one end of an aluminum pan, build a "beach" of sand and pebbles. Put a book under that end of the pan to raise it about 5 centimeters.
2. Pour water slowly into the other end of the pan until it covers the edge of the sand, just as water touches the edge of a beach.
3. Place a wooden tongue depressor in the water. Move it back and forth gently in a regular rhythm to make waves in the pan. Continue for about 2 minutes.
4. Once the water has stopped moving, observe what has happened to the beach. Wash your hands after completing this activity.

Think It Over

Observing How has the motion of the water changed the edge of the beach?

Hundreds of years ago, kings and queens ruled the islands of Hawaii. If you could travel back in time, you could watch the royal family engaging in the islands' favorite sport. It wasn't baseball or tennis or polo. Instead, the ancient rulers paddled into the ocean on heavy wooden boards to catch the perfect wave. They were "wave-sliding," a sport we know today as surfing.

If you've ever seen a surfer like the one in Figure 1, you know that they make this difficult sport look almost easy. But even experienced surfers can seldom predict when the next good wave will roll into shore. As you will read in this section, many different forces influence the size, shape, and timing of waves.

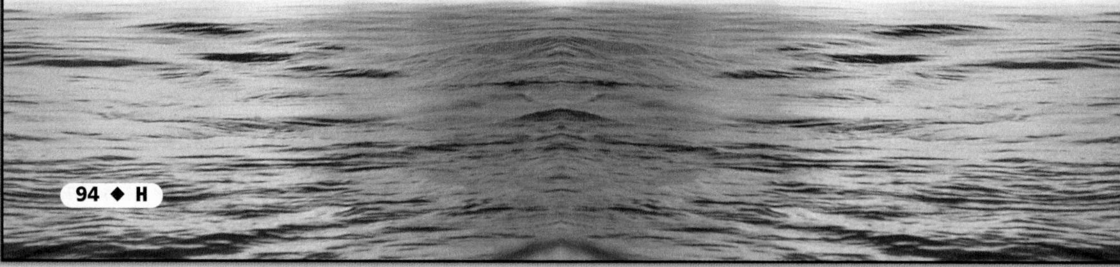

Lab zone Discover Activity

Skills Focus Observing L1

Materials aluminum baking pan, sand, pebbles, book, ruler, water, wooden tongue depressor

Time 20 minutes

Tips To save time, you can do the activity as a class demonstration.

Expected Outcome Students will observe that as water moves away from the beach, it carries sand and causes erosion of the beach.

Think It Over The flow of water away from the beach caused sand to erode it.

What Is a Wave?

When you watch a surfer's wave crash onto a beach, you are seeing the last step in the development of a wave. A **wave** is the movement of energy through a body of water. Wave development usually begins with wind. Without the energy of wind, the surface of the ocean would be as smooth as a mirror. **Most waves form when winds blowing across the water's surface transmit their energy to the water.**

Wave Size Waves start in the open ocean. The size of a wave depends on the strength of the wind and on the length of time it blows. A gentle breeze creates small ripples on the surface of the water. Stronger winds create larger waves.

The size of a wave also depends on the distance over which the wind blows. Winds blowing across longer distances build up bigger waves. Winds blowing across the Pacific Ocean can create bigger waves than winds blowing across the narrower Atlantic Ocean.

Wave Energy Although waves may appear to carry water toward shore, the water does not actually move forward in deep water. If it did, ocean water would eventually pile up on the coasts of every continent! The energy of the wave moves toward shore, but the water itself remains in place. You can test this by floating a cork in a bowl of water. Use a spoon to make a wave in the bowl. As the wave passes, the cork lurches forward a little; then it bobs backward. It ends up in almost the same spot where it started.

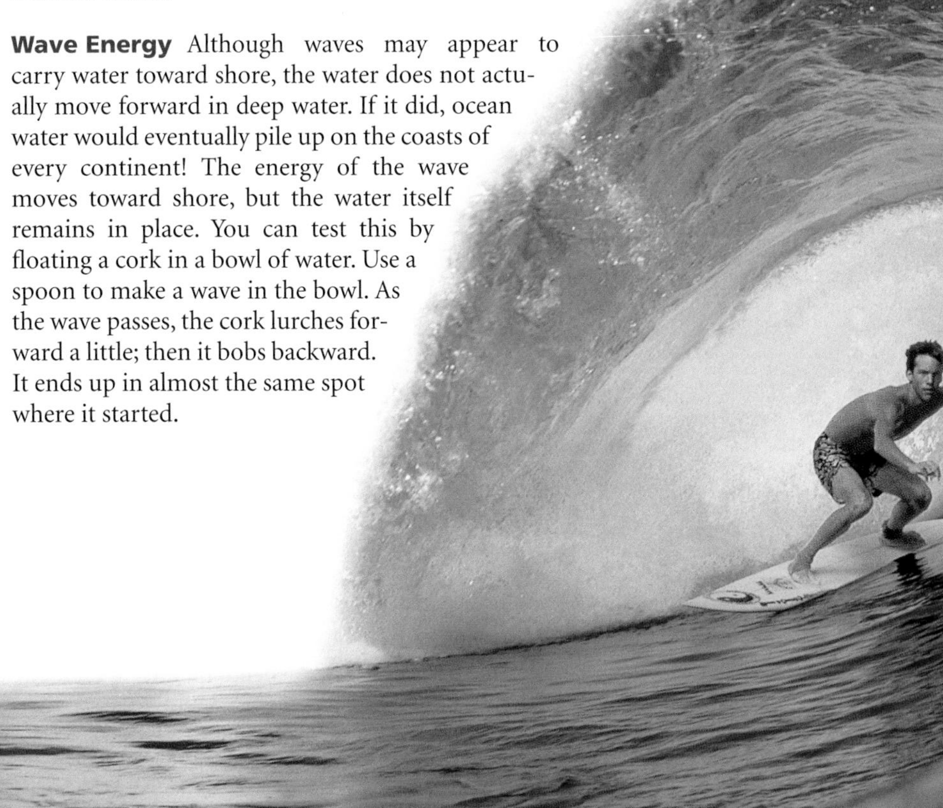

FIGURE 1
Wave Energy
A surfer cruises along a cresting wave. The wave's energy moves, but the water mostly stays in one place. **Applying Concepts** *In which direction is the energy of this wave moving?*

H ◆ 95

Differentiated Instruction

Less Proficient Readers L1

Previewing Visuals Provide students with a tape recorder. Tell them that they are to record a "play-by-play" account of what is happening in each illustration. After students have made their recordings, they should play them for the class. **learning modality: logical/mathematical**

Instruct

What Is a Wave?

Teach Key Concepts L1

Formation of Waves

Focus Ask: **Why does a sailboat move?** *(Energy from the wind transfers to the boat.)* Tell students that energy from the wind also transfers to water and moves as waves.

Teach Ask: **Which wind could give more energy to water—a strong wind or a gentle breeze?** *(A strong wind)* **A wind that blows for a long time or a wind that blows for a short time?** *(A wind that blows for a long time)* **What conditions would cause the highest waves in a body of water?** *(Strong winds that blow for a long time)*

Apply Ask: **What weather event would cause the highest waves?** *(hurricanes)* **learning modality: logical/mathematical**

Independent Practice L2

All in One Teaching Resources

- Guided Reading and Study Worksheet: *Wave Action*

Student Edition on Audio CD

Lab zone Teacher Demo L1

Energy and Waves

Focus Remind students that it is energy and not water that moves in a wave.

Materials rope

Time 5 minutes

Teach Tie one end of a rope to a stationary object. Have a volunteer move the free end of the rope up and down.

Apply Ask: **Does the rope move closer to the chair?** *(No.)* **How does this model wave energy?** *(The waves travel to the chair, but the rope does not.)* **learning modality: visual**

Monitor Progress L2

Drawing Have students draw a labeled, annotated diagram showing how wind creates waves. Students should use arrows to show the direction of the wind and the direction that energy moves. Portfolio

Answer

Figure 1 The energy of the wave is moving toward the shore.

Use Visuals: Figure 2 L2

Water Motion

Focus Remind students that the height of an object is measured in a vertical direction and that the length of an object is measured in a horizontal direction.

Teach Ask: **What is the name for the distance between the crest and trough of a wave?** *(wave height)* **What is the name for the distance from the crest of one wave to the crest of the next?** *(wavelength)* **How would you describe the movement of the buoy?** *(A circular path)*

Apply Ask students to describe the following waves: one with a long wavelength and low wave height *(A gently sloping swell)* One with a short wavelength and high wave height *(A steeply sloping wall of water)* **learning modality: visual**

All in One Teaching Resources

- Transparency H30

L2

Making Waves

Focus Remind students that waves have different shapes depending on their wavelengths and wave heights.

Materials piece of rope

Time 5 minutes

Teach Organize students into groups. Give each group a length of rope. Challenge students to make the following types of waves: high wave height, low wave height, short wavelength, long wavelength. *(To adjust wave height, students should alter how high they raise their arms while making waves. To adjust wavelength, students should alter how quickly they make waves.)*

Apply Ask: **Which waves had higher frequency—the long wavelength waves or the short wavelength waves?** *(The short wavelength waves)* **learning modality: visual**

For: Water motion activity
Visit: PHSchool.com
Web Code: cfp-3031

Students can interact with the art showing water motion online.

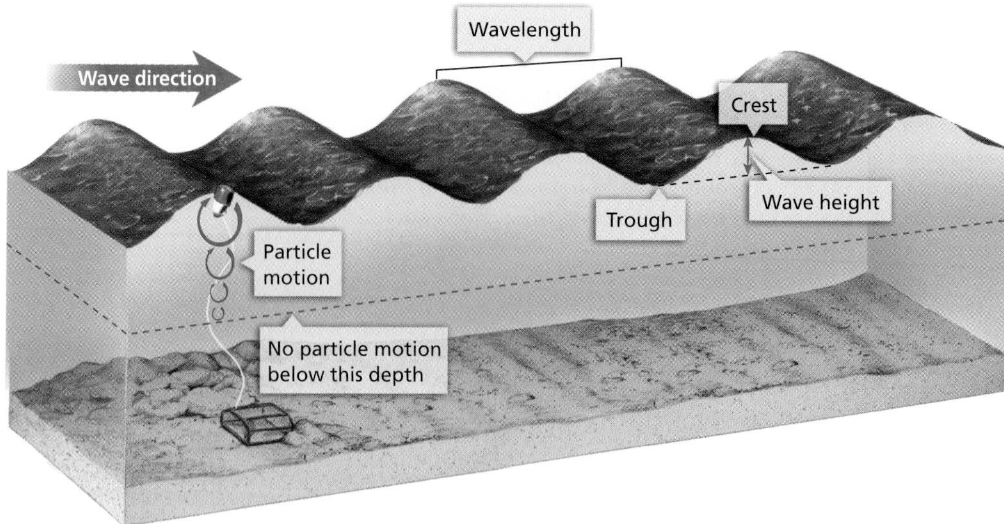

FIGURE 2
Water Motion
As a wave passes, water particles move in a circular motion. The buoy on the surface swings down into the trough of one wave, then back up to the crest of the next. Below the surface, water particles move in smaller circles. At a depth equal to about one half the wavelength, water particles are not affected by the surface wave.

For: Water Motion activity
Visit: PHSchool.com
Web Code: cfp-3031

Water Motion Figure 2 shows what happens to the water as a wave travels along. As the wave passes, water particles move in a circular path. They swing forward and down with the energy of the wave, then back up to their original position.

Notice that the deeper water particles move in smaller circles than those near the surface. The wind affects the water at the surface more than it affects the deep water. Below a certain depth, the water does not move at all as the wave passes. If you were inside a submarine in deep water, you would not be able to tell whether the water above you was rough or calm.

Other Wave Characteristics Scientists have a vocabulary of terms to describe the characteristics of waves. The name for the highest part of a wave is the crest. The horizontal distance between crests is the **wavelength.** Long, rolling waves with lots of space between crests have long wavelengths. Short, choppy waves have shorter wavelengths. Waves are also measured by their **frequency,** the number of waves that pass a point in a certain amount of time.

The lowest part of a wave is the trough. The vertical distance from the crest to the trough is the **wave height.** The energy and strength of a wave depend mainly on its wave height. In the open ocean, most waves are between 2 and 5 meters high. During storms, waves can grow much higher and more powerful.

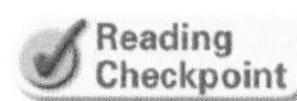

Which have longer wavelengths—waves that are close together or waves that are far apart?

How Waves Change Near Shore

Have you ever seen an area of ocean water swell, resulting in a wave? Waves begin this way out in the ocean, but as they approach the shore, they change.

Breakers The white-capped waves that crash onto shore are often called "breakers." In deep water, these waves usually travel as long, low waves called swells. As the waves approach the shore, the water becomes shallower. Follow the waves in Figure 3 as they enter the shallow water. The bottoms of the waves begin to touch the sloping ocean floor. Friction between the ocean floor and the water causes the waves to slow down. As the speed of the waves decreases, their shapes change. **Near shore, wave height increases and wavelength decreases.** When the wave reaches a certain height, the crest of the wave topples. The wave breaks onto the shore, forming surf.

As the wave breaks, it continues to move forward. At first the breaker surges up the beach. But gravity soon slows it down, eventually stopping it. The water that had rushed up the beach then flows back out to sea. Have you ever stood at the water's edge and felt the pull of the water rushing back out to the ocean? This pull, often called an undertow, carries shells, seaweed, and sand away from the beach. A strong undertow can be dangerous to swimmers.

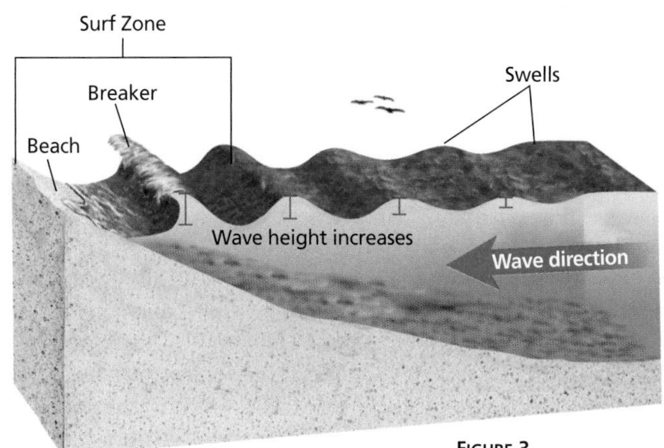

FIGURE 3
How Breakers Change Near Shore
Friction with the ocean floor causes waves to slow down in the shallow water near shore. The wave height increases until the waves break, forming surf.
Comparing and Contrasting *How do swells and breakers differ?*

Lab zone Try This Activity

Wave Motion

This activity shows how waves that form at the surface affect deeper water.

1. Fill an aquarium about three-quarters full of water.
2. Tie enough metal washers to a cork so that the cork floats about 3 cm from the bottom of the tank.

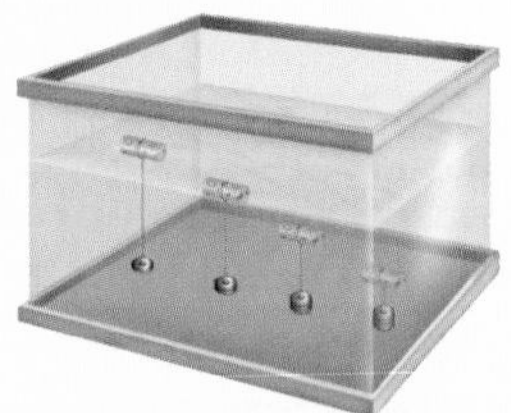

3. Repeat Step 2 with more corks so that they float 9 cm from the bottom, 15 cm from the bottom, and so on, until the last cork floats on the surface.
4. Make small, steady waves in the tank by moving your hand up and down in the water. Note what happens to each cork.
5. Repeat Step 4, increasing the height of the waves by moving your hand faster.

Observing How does increasing the wave height affect the motion of each cork?

How Waves Change Near Shore

Teach Key Concepts L1

Breaking Waves

Focus Have students imagine a line of cars traveling down the highway at the same speed. Ask: **What would happen if the cars at the front slowed down?** *(The cars would get closer together.)* Tell students that the same thing happens when waves approach shore.

Teach Ask: **Why do waves slow down close to the shore?** *(Because the waves touch the ocean floor)* **What happens to the tops of waves when the bottoms slow down?** *(The tops keep moving forward until the waves topple over.)* Point out that although the energy of a wave always moves toward shore, this is the only time that the water from a wave actually moves forward.

Apply Have students infer the meaning of the word *curl,* a common term used by surfers. *(The curl is the breaking part of the wave.)* **learning modality: logical/mathematical**

All in One Teaching Resources
- Transparency H31

Lab zone Try This Activity

Skills Focus Observing L2

Materials aquarium, water, several metal washers and corks, thread

Time 20 minutes

Tips The larger the aquarium, the greater the effect. When making waves, students should keep their hands near the surface.

Expected Outcome Students will see that corks near the surface move more in the waves than corks closer to the bottom. Increasing the wave height increases the movement of all corks.

Extend Ask: **Do you think you would be more likely to become seasick on a boat or a submarine? Explain.** *(You'd be more likely to become sick on a boat. A submarine would be below the level of water movement.)* **learning modality: visual**

Monitor Progress L2

Drawing Have students draw a diagram illustrating how a wave changes near the shore.

Answers

Figure 3 Swells are long, low waves in deep water. Swells become breakers when they reach shallow water and the waves break against the shore.

Waves that are far apart have longer wavelengths.

Use Visuals: Figure 4 L2

Tsunamis

Focus Review with students what happens during an underwater earthquake. *(Blocks of rock move on either side of a fault. Underwater landslides are sometimes triggered.)*

Teach Direct students attention to the figure. Ask: **What is the source of energy for a tsunami?** *(The energy in a tsunami is from movement related to earthquakes on the ocean floor.)* **How is this different from a regular wave?** *(The energy in a regular ocean wave is from wind blowing across the water.)*

Apply Explain that *tsunami* is a Japanese word that means "wave that overflows the land." Ask: **Why do you think that the word we use to refer to these waves is a Japanese word?** *(Tsunamis occur mainly in the Pacific Ocean, and Japan has been hit repeatedly by these waves.)* **learning modality: visual**

Help Students Read L1

Active Comprehension Have students read the first three sentences about tsunamis. Then ask, **What more would you like to know about tsunamis?** *(Possible responses might include these: How does an earthquake cause a tsunami? Where do they occur?)* Write students' responses on the board. Then have students read the remainder of the selection. After students have finished reading, ask them to respond to each question on the board. **learning modality: verbal**

Ocean Motions

Show the Video Field Trip to let students experience and understand ocean water movement. Discussion question: **In what way is a wave different from a current?** *(Waves transfer energy through water; currents actually move the water. In doing so, currents circulate heat and nutrients, affecting our global climate and enriching the ocean ecosystem.)*

FIGURE 4
Tsunamis
At sea, a tsunami travels as a long, low wave. Near shore, the wave height increases suddenly. The wall of water smashes onto land, tossing ships onto the shore and destroying buildings.

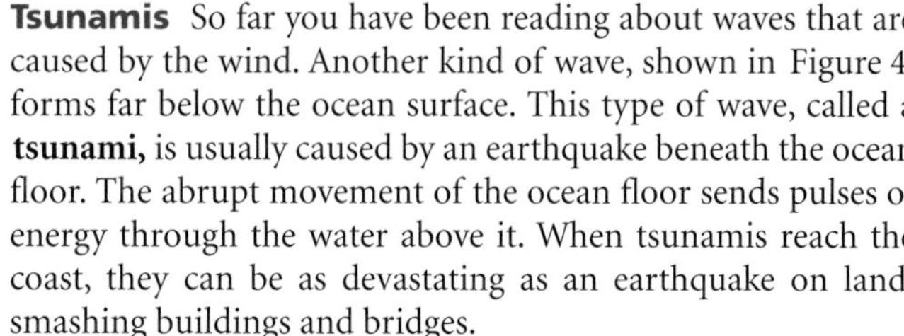

Tsunamis So far you have been reading about waves that are caused by the wind. Another kind of wave, shown in Figure 4, forms far below the ocean surface. This type of wave, called a **tsunami,** is usually caused by an earthquake beneath the ocean floor. The abrupt movement of the ocean floor sends pulses of energy through the water above it. When tsunamis reach the coast, they can be as devastating as an earthquake on land, smashing buildings and bridges.

Despite the tremendous amount of energy a tsunami carries, people on a ship at sea may not even realize a tsunami is passing. How is this possible? A tsunami in deep water may have a wavelength of 200 kilometers or more, but a wave height of less than a meter. When the tsunami reaches shallow water near the coast, friction with the ocean floor causes the long wavelength to decrease suddenly. The wave height increases as the water "piles up." The tsunami becomes a towering wall of water. Some tsunamis have reached heights of 20 meters or more—taller than a five-story building!

Tsunamis are most common in the Pacific Ocean, often striking Alaska, Hawaii, and Japan. In 1998, tsunamis in Papua New Guinea killed more than 2,000 people. Governments in areas prone to tsunamis are searching for ways to avoid such devastation. Some Japanese cities have built barriers designed to break up the waves. Scientists also monitor the ocean floor for warnings of earthquakes that may produce tsunamis.

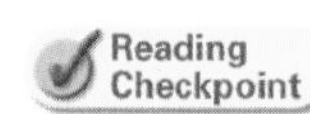

What usually causes tsunamis?

Differentiated Instruction

English Learners/Beginning L1
Comprehension: Modified Cloze
Distribute simplified sentences about the following terms: longshore drift, rip current, barrier beach, dune, and groin. For example, "Movement of sand along a beach is ______." As students read through the rest of the section, have them complete the cloze definitions. Encourage students to use the definitions as a study guide.

English Learners/Intermediate L2
Comprehension: Modified Cloze
Distribute the cloze activity described above, but do not supply a word list. As students read through the section, have them look for vocabulary words to complete the cloze sentences.

How Waves Affect the Shore

What happens on shore as waves pound the beach? Figure 5 shows some of their effects. Because wave direction at sea is determined by the wind, waves usually roll toward shore at an angle. But as they touch bottom, the shallower water slows the shoreward side of the wave first. The rows of waves gradually turn and become more nearly parallel to the shore.

Longshore Drift **As waves come into shore, water washes up the beach at an angle, carrying sand grains. The water and sand then run straight back down the beach.** This movement of sand along the beach is called **longshore drift.** As the waves slow down, they deposit the sand they are carrying on the shallow, underwater slope in a long ridge called a sandbar.

Rip Currents As a sandbar grows, it can trap the water flowing along the shore. In some places, water breaks through the sandbar and begins to flow back down the sloping ocean bottom. This process creates a **rip current,** a rush of water that flows rapidly back to sea through a narrow opening. Rip currents can carry a swimmer out into deep water. Because rip currents are narrow, a strong swimmer can usually escape by swimming across the current, parallel to the beach.

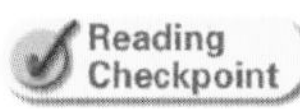
In what direction does a rip current pull a swimmer?

Lab zone Skills Activity

Making Models

Half fill an aluminum pan with water. The pan represents the ocean floor. Make the "ocean floor" slope by placing a book or other object under one long end of the pan. Add enough sand in the middle of the pan to create a sandbar. Then pour water from a beaker onto the sand to model a rip current. Use the model to explain why rip currents can be dangerous to swimmers.

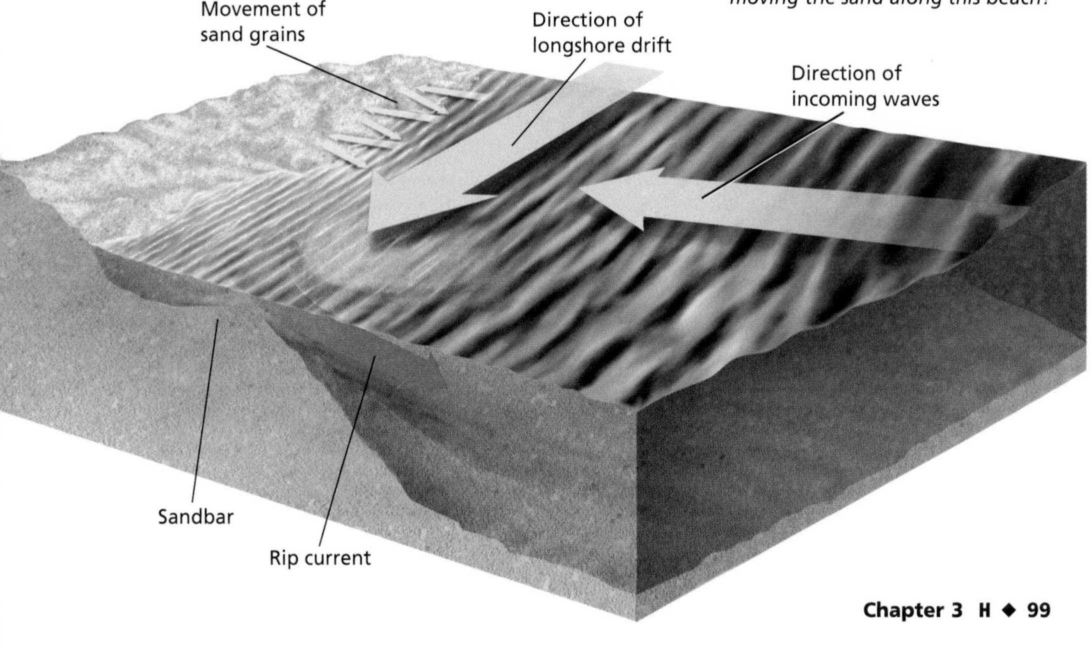

FIGURE 5
Longshore Drift
Waves approach the shore at an angle. This results in a gradual movement of sand along the beach. **Interpreting Diagrams** *In which direction is longshore drift moving the sand along this beach?*

Lab zone Skills Activity

Skills Focus Making Models L2

Materials aluminum pan, beaker, book, sand, water

Time 20 minutes

Tips Students should place the sand in the shape of a sandbar. Have them make a channel through the sandbar where the rip current will flow.

Expected Outcome Students will model the formation of a rip current.

Extend Have students investigate how the amount of water behind the sandbar affects the rip current.

How Waves Affect the Shore

Teach Key Concepts L1

Longshore Drift

Focus Remind students that wind rarely blows from a direction that is perpendicular to the shore.

Teach Ask: **If wind blows at an angle to the shore, how will the waves come in?** *(At an angle)* **Which way does gravity pull the water after a wave washes onto shore?** *(straight back down the sloping beach)* **If a sand grain were moving with the water, what path would it take?** *(A zig-zag path along the beach)*

Apply Ask: **What would happen if something blocked the sand that was moving along the beach?** *(Sand would build up on one side of the barrier.)* **learning modality: logical/mathematical**

All in One Teaching Resources

- Transparency H32

Lab zone Build Inquiry L2

Longshore Drift

Focus Remind students that beaches tilt toward the water. The angle of tilt varies.

Materials piece of plywood (about 24 inches square), marble, small wood block

Time 20 minutes

Teach Have students place a wood block under one end of a piece of plywood so that the plywood tilts at about a 10° angle. Then tell them to roll the marble up the ramp and observe as the marble rolls straight back down the incline. Have students repeat this procedure to model longshore drift.

Apply Ask: **What does the marble represent in this model?** *(A grain of sand)* **learning modality: kinesthetic**

Monitor Progress L1

Writing Have students use the following terms in a short paragraph: longshore drift, sandbar, rip current.

Answers

Figure 5 As you look out to sea from the beach, it is moving sand along the beach from left to right.

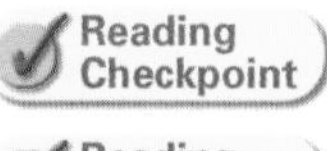
Reading Checkpoint: Earthquakes on the ocean floor usually cause tsunamis.

Reading Checkpoint: A rip current pulls a swimmer out to sea.

Waves and Beach Erosion

Teach Key Concepts

L1

Barrier Beaches, Sand Dunes, and Groins

Focus Remind students that waves and the longshore currents that the waves produce cause beach erosion.

Teach Ask: **Which natural landforms protect against erosion?** *(Barrier beaches and dunes)* **Why do these landforms protect the coastline?** *(Waves break against barrier beaches instead of the mainland; Vegetation holds dunes in place.)* **What structure do people build to reduce erosion?** *(Groins)* **How do groins work?** *(They catch sand being moved by the longshore current.)*

Apply Ask: **Why might building groins be controversial in some communities?** *(Erosion is increased down current from a groin.)* **learning modality: logical/mathematical**

L2

Modeling Barrier Beaches

Materials shallow pan, spoon, water, wood block

Time 25 minutes

Focus Review with students the meanings of the terms *barrier beach* and *lagoon*.

Teach Have students fill a shallow pan to about 1 cm depth with water. Students then should place the wood block so that it extends part of the way across the pan. Tell students that the wood block represents a barrier beach and that the water behind the barrier is the lagoon. Have students use a spoon to make waves at one end of the pan. They should compare waves along the other end of the pan and notice that the barrier beach stops most of the wave energy.

Apply Ask: **Other than groins, how could people use human-made barriers to reduce beach erosion?** *(Breakwaters could be placed offshore to absorb wave energy.)*

FIGURE 6
A Barrier Beach
Barrier beaches are sand deposits that form parallel to a shore. Sand dunes are hills of wind-blown sand that help protect the beach.
Interpreting Photographs *How does a barrier beach protect the mainland from erosion by waves?*

Waves and Beach Erosion

The boundary between land and ocean is always changing shape. If you walk on the same beach every day, you might not notice that it is changing. From day to day, waves remove sand and bring new sand at about the same rate. But if you visit a beach just once each year, you might be startled by what you see. **Waves shape a beach by eroding the shore in some places and building it up in others.**

At first, waves striking a rocky shoreline carve the rocks into tall cliffs and arches. Over many thousands of years, waves break the rocks into pebbles and grains of sand. A wide, sandy beach forms. Then the waves begin to eat away at the exposed beach. The shoreline slowly moves farther inland. Longshore drift carries the sand along the coast and deposits it elsewhere. This process of breaking up rock and carrying it away is known as erosion.

Barrier Beaches A natural landform that protects shorelines from wave action occurs along low-lying beaches. Long sand deposits called barrier beaches form parallel to the shore. Such beaches are separated from the mainland by a shallow lagoon. Waves break against the barrier beach instead of against the land inside. For this reason, people are working to preserve natural barrier beaches like those off Cape Cod, the New Jersey shore, and the Georgia and Carolina coasts.

Sand Dunes Other natural landforms also help protect beaches and reduce erosion, although they can't completely stop the movement of sand. Sand dunes, which are hills of windblown sand, can make a beach more stable and protect the shore from erosion. The strong roots of dune plants, such as beach grass and sea oats, hold the sand in place. These plants help to slow erosion caused by wind and water. But the dunes and plants can be destroyed by cars, bicycles, or even by many people walking over them. Without plants to hold the sand in place, dunes can be easily washed away by wave action.

Groins Many people like to live near the ocean. But over time, erosion can wear away the beach. This threatens the homes and other buildings near the beach. To avoid losing their property, people look for ways to reduce the effect of erosion.

One method of reducing erosion along a stretch of beach is to build a wall of rocks or concrete, called a **groin,** outward from the beach. Sand carried by the water piles up against the groins instead of moving along the shore. Figure 7 shows how groins interrupt the movement of water. However, groins increase the amount of erosion farther down the beach.

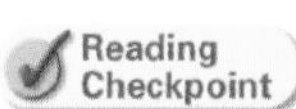
Name two natural landforms that help reduce beach erosion.

FIGURE 7
Groins
Sand piles up against a series of groins people have built along the New Jersey coast. Building groins to stop longshore drift is one way to reduce beach erosion.

Section 1 Assessment

Target Reading Skill Using Prior Knowledge Review your graphic organizer and revise it based on what you just learned in the section.

Reviewing Key Concepts

1. a. **Reviewing** How do waves form?
   b. **Explaining** Explain how both a wave's energy and the water in a wave move.
   c. **Applying Concepts** Why does an ocean buoy bob up and down as a wave passes by?
2. a. **Defining** What is the wavelength of a wave? What is wave height?
   b. **Describing** How do wavelength and wave height change as a wave enters shallow water?
   c. **Developing Hypotheses** Using what you know about the wavelength and wave height of tsunamis, propose an explanation of why tsunamis can cause so much damage when they reach the shore.
3. a. **Explaining** What is longshore drift, and how does it affect a shoreline?
   b. **Relating Cause and Effect** Explain how building a groin affects longshore drift. What happens to the beach on each side of the groin?

Lab zone At-Home Activity

Wave Model With a family member, make a construction paper model of a wave. Your model should show the wave from the time it develops in the ocean to the time it breaks on the shore. Be sure to label the features of the wave, including crests, troughs, wavelengths, wave heights, swells, and breakers.

Lab zone At-Home Activity

Wave Model L1 Encourage students to use the model to explain how energy travels through a wave and how the wave changes when it reaches the shore.

Lab zone Chapter Project

Keep Students on Track Students should have a plan about how they will construct their wave tank, model beach, and lighthouse. If plans or materials seem unworkable, suggest alternatives. Encourage students to sketch their designs before constructing their models. Stress the importance of scale for designing the beach.

Monitor Progress L2

Answers

Figure 6 A barrier beach protects the mainland because it provides a natural barrier against wave action.

Barrier beaches and sand dunes help reduce beach erosion.

Assess

Reviewing Key Concepts

1. a. Most ocean waves form as winds blowing across the ocean transmit their energy to the water. Tsunamis are usually caused by earthquakes beneath the ocean floor. **b.** Energy moves along a wave. The water does not move forward until the top of the wave breaks near the shore. **c.** Water particles move in a circular motion. As the buoy swings down into the trough of one wave and back up to the crest of the next wave, it moves in a circle.

2. a. Wavelength is the horizontal distance between the highest part of two waves. Wave height is the vertical distance from the crest to the trough. **b.** Wavelength decreases, and wave height increases. **c.** At sea, tsunamis have long wavelength and low wave height. However, when the waves reach the shore, wavelength decreases and wave height increases. A towering wave can crash onto shore.

3. a. Longshore drift is the movement of sand along a beach. Sand can be eroded at one location and deposited at another. **b.** Sand piles up on the up-current side of the groin instead of being carried down the beach, but beaches on the other side of the groin have more erosion.

Reteach L1

With the class, draw a diagram showing the characteristics of waves. Label it with the terms wavelength, wave height, crest, and trough. Use the terms to explain how breakers form.

Performance Assessment L2

Oral Presentation Call on students to identify the causes and effects of waves and to explain how each cause produces waves and how waves produce each effect.

All in One Teaching Resources

- Section Summary: *Wave Action*
- Review and Reinforcement: *Wave Action*
- Enrich: *Wave Action*

Section 2 Tides

Objectives

After this lesson, students will be able to

H.3.2.1 Explain what causes tides.

H.3.2.2 Explain what affects the height of tides.

H.3.2.3 Describe how tides are a source of energy.

Target Reading Skill

Previewing Visuals Explain that looking at the visuals before they read helps students activate prior knowledge and predict what they are about to read.

Answers

Spring and Neap Tides

When do spring tides occur? *(During the full and new moon phases)* **What is a neap tide?** *(A smaller tide that happens at the first- and third-quarter moons.)*

All in One Teaching Resources

- Transparency H33

Preteach

Build Background Knowledge L1

Ocean Tides

Encourage students who have been to the ocean to share their observations of tides. Ask: **Did the water cover more of the beach at certain times of day? Were there any signs posted about tides? Was there any other evidence of tides?** *(Students might have observed sand castles slowly covered as the tide came in, wet sand exposed when the tide went out, signs indicating times of tides or warnings about high tides, or lines of seaweed and shells marking the farthest reach of tides.)*

Tides

Reading Preview

Key Concepts

- What causes tides?
- What affects the heights of tides?
- How are tides a source of energy?

Key Terms

- tides • spring tide • neap tide

Target Reading Skill

Previewing Visuals Before you read, preview Figure 11. Then write two questions that you have about the diagram in a graphic organizer like the one below. As you read, answer your questions.

Spring and Neap Tides

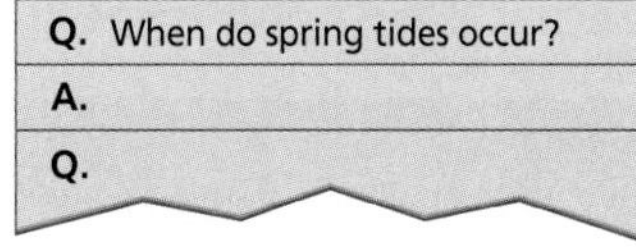

Q.	When do spring tides occur?
A.	
Q.	

Lab zone Discover Activity

When Is High Tide?

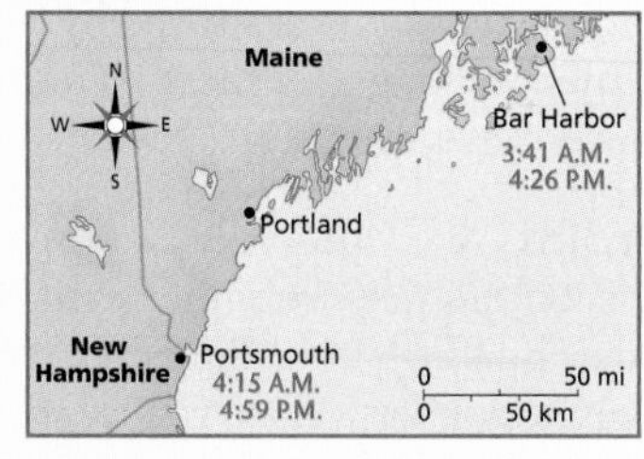

Twice a day, the ocean rises and falls on Earth's coasts. These changes in water level are called tides. The map shows the times of the two high tides in two cities on a specific day.

1. Calculate the length of time between the two high tides for each city. Remember to consider both hours and minutes.
2. Compare the times of the high tides in Bar Harbor and in Portsmouth. Do you see a pattern?

Think It Over

Predicting Based on the times of the high tides in Bar Harbor and Portsmouth, predict when the high tides will occur in Portland.

You're standing on a riverbank in the town of Saint John, New Brunswick, in Canada. In the distance there's a roaring sound. Suddenly a wall of water twice your height thunders past. The surge of water rushes up the river channel so fast that it almost looks as if the river is flowing backward!

This thundering wall of water is an everyday event at Saint John. The town is located where the Saint John River enters the Bay of Fundy, an arm of the Atlantic Ocean. The Bay of Fundy is famous for its dramatic daily tides. When the tide comes in, fishing boats float on the water near the piers. But once the tide goes out, the boats are stranded on the muddy harbor bottom!

FIGURE 8
Differences in Tides
The Bay of Fundy in Canada is noted for the great differences between its high and low tides. Near the mouth of the bay, boats float at high tide (left). At low tide, the boats are grounded (right).

Lab zone Discover Activity

Skills Focus Predicting 

Materials calculator

Time 15 minutes

Tips Remind students that when subtracting, they can change an hour into 60 minutes.

Think It Over Answers might vary slightly. Students should observe that high tides get earlier as one goes east. Therefore, high tides in Portland should occur at about 4:05 A.M. and 4:50 P.M.

Sand Dunes Other natural landforms also help protect beaches and reduce erosion, although they can't completely stop the movement of sand. Sand dunes, which are hills of windblown sand, can make a beach more stable and protect the shore from erosion. The strong roots of dune plants, such as beach grass and sea oats, hold the sand in place. These plants help to slow erosion caused by wind and water. But the dunes and plants can be destroyed by cars, bicycles, or even by many people walking over them. Without plants to hold the sand in place, dunes can be easily washed away by wave action.

Groins Many people like to live near the ocean. But over time, erosion can wear away the beach. This threatens the homes and other buildings near the beach. To avoid losing their property, people look for ways to reduce the effect of erosion.

One method of reducing erosion along a stretch of beach is to build a wall of rocks or concrete, called a **groin,** outward from the beach. Sand carried by the water piles up against the groins instead of moving along the shore. Figure 7 shows how groins interrupt the movement of water. However, groins increase the amount of erosion farther down the beach.

FIGURE 7
Groins
Sand piles up against a series of groins people have built along the New Jersey coast. Building groins to stop longshore drift is one way to reduce beach erosion.

Name two natural landforms that help reduce beach erosion.

Section 1 Assessment

Target Reading Skill Using Prior Knowledge
Review your graphic organizer and revise it based on what you just learned in the section.

Reviewing Key Concepts

1. a. Reviewing How do waves form?
   b. Explaining Explain how both a wave's energy and the water in a wave move.
   c. Applying Concepts Why does an ocean buoy bob up and down as a wave passes by?
2. a. Defining What is the wavelength of a wave? What is wave height?
   b. Describing How do wavelength and wave height change as a wave enters shallow water?
   c. Developing Hypotheses Using what you know about the wavelength and wave height of tsunamis, propose an explanation of why tsunamis can cause so much damage when they reach the shore.
3. a. Explaining What is longshore drift, and how does it affect a shoreline?
   b. Relating Cause and Effect Explain how building a groin affects longshore drift. What happens to the beach on each side of the groin?

Lab zone At-Home Activity

Wave Model With a family member, make a construction paper model of a wave. Your model should show the wave from the time it develops in the ocean to the time it breaks on the shore. Be sure to label the features of the wave, including crests, troughs, wavelengths, wave heights, swells, and breakers.

Lab zone At-Home Activity

Wave Model L1 Encourage students to use the model to explain how energy travels through a wave and how the wave changes when it reaches the shore.

Lab zone Chapter Project

Keep Students on Track Students should have a plan about how they will construct their wave tank, model beach, and lighthouse. If plans or materials seem unworkable, suggest alternatives. Encourage students to sketch their designs before constructing their models. Stress the importance of scale for designing the beach.

Monitor Progress L2

Answers
Figure 6 A barrier beach protects the mainland because it provides a natural barrier against wave action.

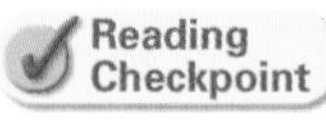
Barrier beaches and sand dunes help reduce beach erosion.

Assess

Reviewing Key Concepts

1. a. Most ocean waves form as winds blowing across the ocean transmit their energy to the water. Tsunamis are usually caused by earthquakes beneath the ocean floor. **b.** Energy moves along a wave. The water does not move forward until the top of the wave breaks near the shore. **c.** Water particles move in a circular motion. As the buoy swings down into the trough of one wave and back up to the crest of the next wave, it moves in a circle.
2. a. Wavelength is the horizontal distance between the highest part of two waves. Wave height is the vertical distance from the crest to the trough. **b.** Wavelength decreases, and wave height increases. **c.** At sea, tsunamis have long wavelength and low wave height. However, when the waves reach the shore, wavelength decreases and wave height increases. A towering wave can crash onto shore.
3. a. Longshore drift is the movement of sand along a beach. Sand can be eroded at one location and deposited at another.
b. Sand piles up on the up-current side of the groin instead of being carried down the beach, but beaches on the other side of the groin have more erosion.

Reteach L1

With the class, draw a diagram showing the characteristics of waves. Label it with the terms wavelength, wave height, crest, and trough. Use the terms to explain how breakers form.

Performance Assessment L2

Oral Presentation Call on students to identify the causes and effects of waves and to explain how each cause produces waves and how waves produce each effect.

All in One Teaching Resources
- Section Summary: *Wave Action*
- Review and Reinforcement: *Wave Action*
- Enrich: *Wave Action*

Section 2 Tides

Objectives

After this lesson, students will be able to

H.3.2.1 Explain what causes tides.

H.3.2.2 Explain what affects the height of tides.

H.3.2.3 Describe how tides are a source of energy.

Target Reading Skill

Previewing Visuals Explain that looking at the visuals before they read helps students activate prior knowledge and predict what they are about to read.

Answers

Spring and Neap Tides

When do spring tides occur? *(During the full and new moon phases)* **What is a neap tide?** *(A smaller tide that happens at the first- and third-quarter moons.)*

All in One Teaching Resources

- Transparency H33

Preteach

Build Background Knowledge L1

Ocean Tides

Encourage students who have been to the ocean to share their observations of tides. Ask: **Did the water cover more of the beach at certain times of day? Were there any signs posted about tides? Was there any other evidence of tides?** *(Students might have observed sand castles slowly covered as the tide came in, wet sand exposed when the tide went out, signs indicating times of tides or warnings about high tides, or lines of seaweed and shells marking the farthest reach of tides.)*

Section 2 Integrating Space Science

Tides

Reading Preview

Key Concepts

- What causes tides?
- What affects the heights of tides?
- How are tides a source of energy?

Key Terms

- tides
- spring tide
- neap tide

Target Reading Skill

Previewing Visuals Before you read, preview Figure 11. Then write two questions that you have about the diagram in a graphic organizer like the one below. As you read, answer your questions.

Spring and Neap Tides

Q. When do spring tides occur?
A.
Q.

Lab zone Discover Activity

When Is High Tide?

Twice a day, the ocean rises and falls on Earth's coasts. These changes in water level are called tides. The map shows the times of the two high tides in two cities on a specific day.

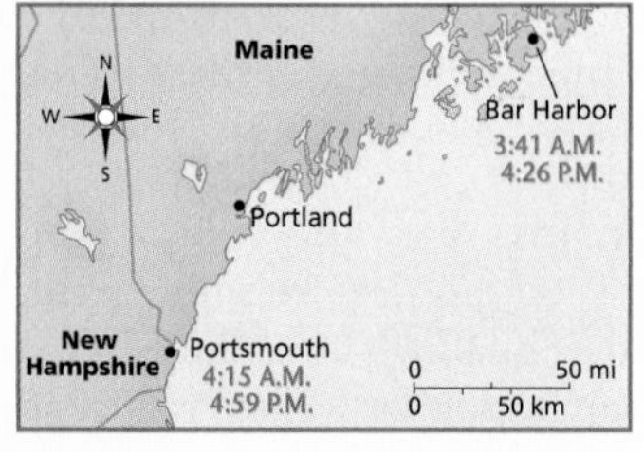

1. Calculate the length of time between the two high tides for each city. Remember to consider both hours and minutes.
2. Compare the times of the high tides in Bar Harbor and in Portsmouth. Do you see a pattern?

Think It Over

Predicting Based on the times of the high tides in Bar Harbor and Portsmouth, predict when the high tides will occur in Portland.

You're standing on a riverbank in the town of Saint John, New Brunswick, in Canada. In the distance there's a roaring sound. Suddenly a wall of water twice your height thunders past. The surge of water rushes up the river channel so fast that it almost looks as if the river is flowing backward!

This thundering wall of water is an everyday event at Saint John. The town is located where the Saint John River enters the Bay of Fundy, an arm of the Atlantic Ocean. The Bay of Fundy is famous for its dramatic daily tides. When the tide comes in, fishing boats float on the water near the piers. But once the tide goes out, the boats are stranded on the muddy harbor bottom!

FIGURE 8
Differences in Tides
The Bay of Fundy in Canada is noted for the great differences between its high and low tides. Near the mouth of the bay, boats float at high tide (left). At low tide, the boats are grounded (right).

Lab zone Discover Activity

Skills Focus Predicting L2

Materials calculator

Time 15 minutes

Tips Remind students that when subtracting, they can change an hour into 60 minutes.

Think It Over Answers might vary slightly. Students should observe that high tides get earlier as one goes east. Therefore, high tides in Portland should occur at about 4:05 A.M. and 4:50 P.M.

What Causes Tides?

The daily rise and fall of Earth's waters on its coastlines are called **tides.** As the tide comes in, the level of the water on the beach rises gradually. When the water reaches its highest point, it is high tide. Then the tide goes out, flowing back toward the sea. When the water reaches its lowest point, it is low tide. Unlike the surface waves you read about in Section 1, tides happen regularly no matter how the wind blows. Tides occur in all bodies of water, but they are most noticeable in the ocean and large lakes.

Gravity and Tides **Tides are caused by the interaction of Earth, the moon, and the sun.** How can distant objects like the moon and sun influence water on Earth? The answer is gravity. Gravity is the force exerted by an object that pulls other objects toward it. Gravity keeps you and everything around you on Earth's surface. As the distance between objects increases, however, gravity's pull grows weaker.

Figure 9 shows the effect of the moon's gravity on the water on Earth's surface. The moon pulls on the water on the side of Earth closest to it more strongly than it pulls on the center of the Earth. This pull creates a bulge of water, called a tidal bulge, on the side of Earth facing the moon. The water farthest from the moon is pulled toward the moon less strongly than are other parts of Earth. The water farthest from the moon is "left behind," forming a second bulge.

In the places where there are tidal bulges, high tide is occurring along the coastlines. In the places between the bulges, low tide is occurring. Earth's rotation through the tidal bulges causes most coastlines to experience two high tides and two low tides every 25 hours.

Moon
High tide
Low tide
North Pole
High tide
Low tide

FIGURE 9
How the Moon Causes Tides
The pull of the moon's gravity on Earth's water causes tidal bulges to form on the side closest to the moon and the side farthest from the moon. **Inferring** *Why is the water level high on the side of Earth farthest from the moon?*

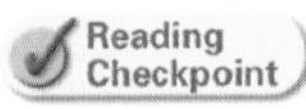

What force causes tides to occur on Earth's surface?

Instruct

What Causes Tides?

Teach Key Concepts L2

Tides

Focus Remind students how a figure skater is held by her skates as she spins. Ask: **Which part of the skater is being pulled?** *(Her feet)* **Are other parts of her body being pulled?** *(No.)* **How does the skater's body feel?** *(As if it were being stretched)*

Teach Tell students that Earth is somewhat similar to the figure skater. Because the moon's gravity decreases with distance, Earth is pulled more strongly on the side close to the moon and less strongly on the side away from the moon. This causes Earth to be slightly "stretched." Ask: **What does this difference in how hard the moon pulls result in?** *(Tides)*

Apply Ask: **Where are tides on Earth most noticeable?** *(Along the coast)* **learning modality: logical/mathematical**

Independent Practice L2

All in One Teaching Resources

- Guided Reading and Study Worksheet: *Tides*

Student Edition on Audio CD

Differentiated Instruction

Less Proficient Readers L1

Summarizing Encourage students to use the main headings of the section as a guide for study. As they read the material under each heading, they should summarize the main points with a few words. Suggest that they use their summaries to generate questions that they can use to test themselves. **learning modality: verbal**

Gifted and Talented L3

Aquatic Organisms and Tides Tell students that some aquatic organisms such as great white sharks, giant kelp, grunions, anemones, and barnacles depend on the tides to survive. Ask interested students to find out more about this subject and report to the class.

Monitor Progress L2

Drawing Have students make a simple labeled diagram to show how the moon causes tides on Earth.

Answers

Figure 9 The water on the side of Earth farthest from the moon is "left behind."

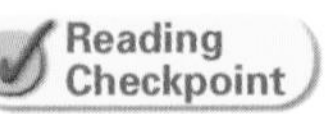

Gravity causes tides to occur on Earth.

For: More on tides
Visit: PHSchool.com
Web Code: cfd-3032

Students can review tides in an online interactivity.

L2

Tracking High Tides and Low Tides

Materials newspapers showing the times for high tides and low tides at a particular location for six consecutive days

Time 30 minutes

Focus Tell students that they will track the times for high tides and low tides and interpret data to predict tomorrow's tides.

Teach Have students consult a newspaper to write the times for high tide and low tide for five consecutive days. Then have students calculate the amount of time between low tides and high tides on each day *(Approximately 12 hours and 25 minutes)* Have students notice how the times change from day to day. Ask: **Why might the time at which tides occur change?** *(Because the moon is constantly orbiting Earth)*

Apply Ask students to use their data to predict the times of the tides on the sixth day. Present a newspaper showing the times for day 6, so students can check their predictions. *(Tides progress forward in time each day. The exact amount of time will vary somewhat.)* **learning modality: logical/mathematical**

Address Misconceptions

L1

Tidal Waves

Focus Ask: **What are tidal waves?** *(Some students may respond that tidal waves are the same as tsunamis.)*

Teach Ask: **What causes a tsunami?** *(Earthquakes on the ocean floor)* **Are these waves related to tides?** *(No.)* Tell students that the term *tidal wave* often is not a good synonym for *tsunami* because tsunamis have nothing to do with tides.

Apply Ask: **What causes the tides?** *(The gravitational pull of the moon and sun)* **What causes a tsunami?** *(Usually an earthquake on the ocean floor)* **learning modality: logical/mathematical**

For: More on tides
Visit: PHSchool.com
Web Code: cfd-3032

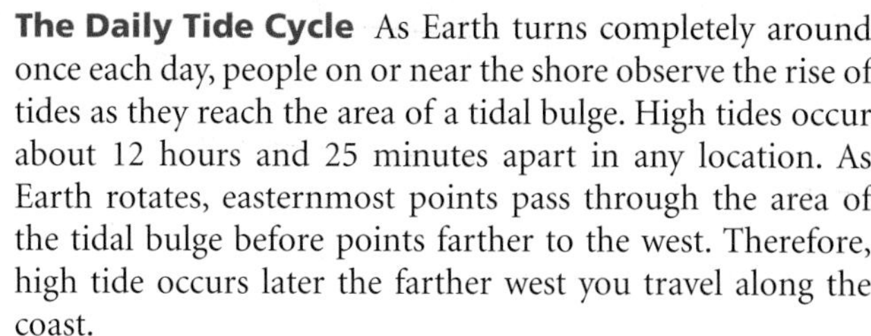

The Daily Tide Cycle As Earth turns completely around once each day, people on or near the shore observe the rise of tides as they reach the area of a tidal bulge. High tides occur about 12 hours and 25 minutes apart in any location. As Earth rotates, easternmost points pass through the area of the tidal bulge before points farther to the west. Therefore, high tide occurs later the farther west you travel along the coast.

In some places, the two high tides and two low tides are easy to observe each day. But in other places, the difference between high tide and low tide is less dramatic. One set of tides may even be so minimal that there appears to be only one high tide and one low tide per day.

Several factors affect the height of a tide in any particular location. For example, certain landforms can interrupt the water's movements. A basin at the mouth of a river can also increase the difference between high and low tide. The speed and depth of moving water increases as it flows into a narrower channel. That is what causes the dramatic tides in the mouth of the Saint John River you read about earlier.

The Monthly Tide Cycle Even though the sun is about 150 million kilometers from Earth, it is so massive that its gravity affects the tides. The sun pulls the water on Earth's surface toward it. In Figure 11, you can follow the positions of Earth, the moon, and the sun at different times during a month. **Changes in the positions of Earth, the moon, and the sun affect the heights of the tides during a month.**

Twice a month, at the new moon and the full moon, the sun and moon are lined up. Their combined gravitational pull produces the greatest difference between the heights of high and low tide, called a **spring tide.** These tides get their name from an Old English word, *springen*, which means "to jump."

At the first and third quarters of the moon, the sun and moon pull at right angles to each other. This arrangement produces a **neap tide,** a tide with the least difference between low and high tide. During a neap tide, the sun's gravity pulls some of the water away from the tidal bulge facing the moon. This acts to "even out" the water level over Earth's surface, decreasing the difference between high and low tides.

FIGURE 10
Sea Turtles and Spring Tides
Some animals are very dependent on tide cycles. Sea turtles can only come to shore to lay their eggs during certain spring tides.

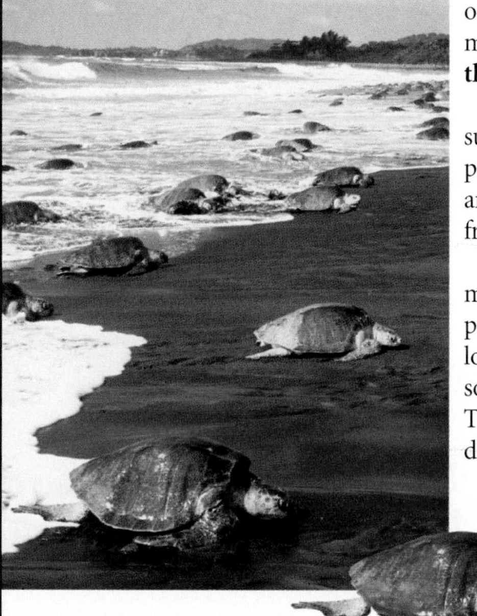

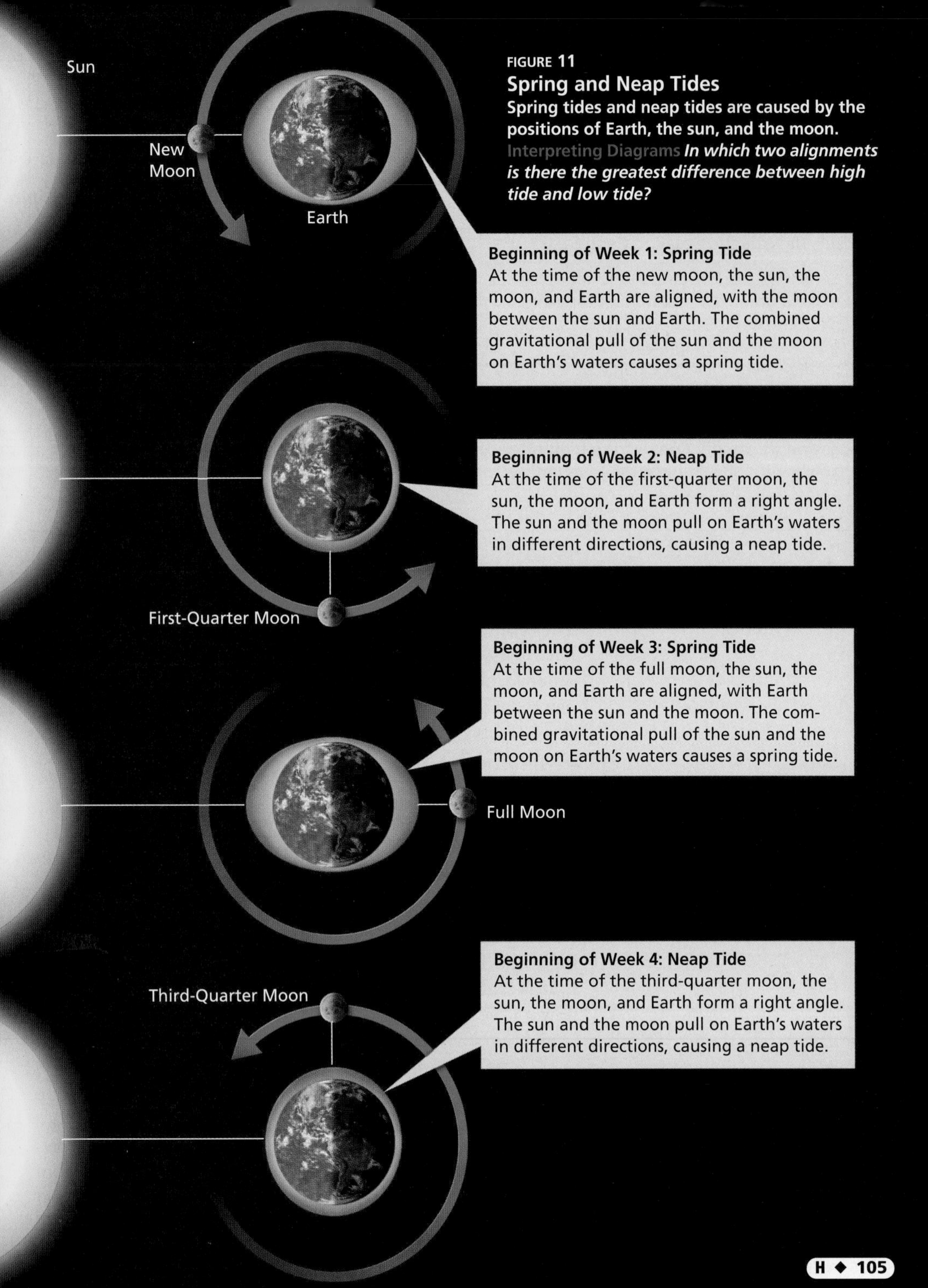

Sun
New Moon
Earth
First-Quarter Moon
Full Moon
Third-Quarter Moon
Beginning of Week 1: Spring Tide
At the time of the new moon, the sun, the moon, and Earth are aligned, with the moon between the sun and Earth. The combined gravitational pull of the sun and the moon on Earth's waters causes a spring tide.
Beginning of Week 2: Neap Tide
At the time of the first-quarter moon, the sun, the moon, and Earth form a right angle. The sun and the moon pull on Earth's waters in different directions, causing a neap tide.
Beginning of Week 3: Spring Tide
At the time of the full moon, the sun, the moon, and Earth are aligned, with Earth between the sun and the moon. The combined gravitational pull of the sun and the moon on Earth's waters causes a spring tide.
Beginning of Week 4: Neap Tide
At the time of the third-quarter moon, the sun, the moon, and Earth form a right angle. The sun and the moon pull on Earth's waters in different directions, causing a neap tide.
H ◆ 105

FIGURE 11
Spring and Neap Tides
Spring tides and neap tides are caused by the positions of Earth, the sun, and the moon. Interpreting Diagrams *In which two alignments is there the greatest difference between high tide and low tide?*

Use Visuals: Figure 11 L1

Spring Tides and Neap Tides

Focus Remind students that the moon constantly orbits Earth as Earth orbits the sun and that this causes the relative positions of the three objects to change.

Teach Ask: **When would you expect the difference between high tide and low tide to be greatest? Explain.** *(During the time of full moon and new moon because the gravity of the moon and sun adds together)* **When would you expect it to be lowest?** *(During first-quarter moon and third-quarter moon, because the gravity of the sun partly cancels the effect of the moon's gravity)*

Apply Ask: **When would the greatest amount of beach be exposed?** *(At low tide during a spring tide)* **learning modality: logical/mathematical**

Help Students Read L1

Monitor Understanding After students read about tides, ask them to stop and monitor their understanding. Ask students to quiz each other by inserting blanks into boldface sentences. If students cannot answer the questions, encourage them to review the relevant text.

All in One Teaching Resources

- Transparency H34

Differentiated Instruction

Special Needs L1

Spring Tides and Neap Tides Have students model spring tides and neap tides. Assign students to represent the sun, the moon, and Earth. Have these students demonstrate the relative positions of the bodies at the two spring tides and the two neap tides. Challenge the rest of the class to identify each type of tide as it is demonstrated. **learning modality: kinesthetic**

Less Proficient Readers L1

Earth, Sun, and Moon Paraphrase the difference between spring tides and neap tides to students. Then ask students to point out the alignments in Figure 11 that represent spring tides. Have them identify the right angles in the figure and discuss how this arrangement reduces the tidal effect.

Monitor Progress L2

Writing Have students write a concise paragraph explaining the difference between daily high and low tides and between spring and neap tides.

Answer

Figure 11 At the beginning of weeks 1 and 3, the spring tides, when the moon, the sun, and Earth are in a line at the new moon and full moon.

L1

Math Skill Making and Interpreting Graphs

Focus Review with students how tidal range changes from spring tide to neap tide.

Teach Make a sample graph on the board. Show students how both high tide values and low tide values can be plotted on the same graph.

Answers

1. Check students' progress as they make their graphs. The number −1 should occur at the base of the *y*-axis.
2. Make certain that students connect the correct points with lines.
3. During the first six days, the high tide value increases steadily while the low tide value decreases. On Day 7, the trends reverse.
4. Spring tide might be occurring on Day 6, when there is the greatest difference between high and low tides. **learning modality: logical/mathematical**

Energy From Tides

Teach Key Concepts

L2

Generating Power from Tides

Focus Remind students that water has potential energy if gravity will cause it to flow downhill.

Teach Ask: **Does trapped tidal water have potential energy?** *(Yes.)* **What happens when the water is released?** *(It flows downhill, and the potential energy changes into energy of motion.)* **How is this energy changed to electricity?** *(The flowing water turns a turbine that powers generators.)*

Apply Ask: **Where could this type of energy be used?** *(Along the coast at places that have a high tidal range)* **learning modality: verbal**

Math Analyzing Data

Plotting Tides

This table lists the highest high tides and the lowest low tides for one week at the mouth of the Savannah River, where it meets the Atlantic Ocean in Georgia.

Tide Table

Day	Highest High Tide (m)	Lowest Low Tide (m)
1	1.9	0.2
2	2.1	0.1
3	2.3	0.0
4	2.4	–0.2
5	2.5	–0.2
6	2.6	–0.3
7	1.9	0.3

1. **Graphing** Use the data in the table to make a graph. On the horizontal axis, mark the days. On the vertical axis, mark tide heights ranging from 3.0 to –1.0 meters. (*Hint:* Mark the negative numbers below the horizontal axis.)
2. **Graphing** Plot the tide heights for each day on the graph. Connect the high tide points with one line and the low tide points with another line.
3. **Interpreting Data** How do the high and low tides change during the week?
4. **Inferring** What type of tide might be occurring on Day 6? Explain.

Tide Tables Despite the complex factors affecting tides, scientists can predict tides quite accurately for many locations. They combine knowledge of the movements of the moon and Earth with information about the shape of the coastline and other local conditions. If you live near the coast, your local newspaper probably publishes a tide table. Knowing the times and heights of tides is important to sailors, marine scientists, people who fish, and coastal residents.

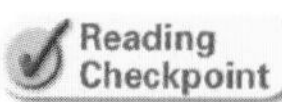

What two types of information help scientists predict the times of tides?

Energy From Tides

Look at Figure 12. Can you almost hear the roar of the rushing water? **The movement of huge amounts of water between high and low tide is a source of potential energy—energy that is stored and can be used.** Engineers have designed tidal power plants that capture some of this energy as the tide moves in and out.

The first large-scale tidal power plant was built in 1967 on the Rance River in northwestern France. As high tide swirls up the river, the plant's gates open so that the water flows into a basin. As the tide retreats, the gates shut to trap the water. Gravity pulls the water back to sea through tunnels. The energy of the water moving through the tunnels powers generators that produce electricity, just as in a hydroelectric dam on a river.

Although tidal energy is a clean, renewable source of energy, it has several limitations. Harnessing tidal power is practical only where there is a large difference between high and low tides—at least 4 or 5 meters. There are very few places in the world where such a large difference occurs. Daily tides also may not occur at the time when there is a demand for electricity. However, tidal power can be a useful part of an overall plan to generate electricity that also includes other power sources between tides.

Reading Checkpoint **Under what conditions is it practical to harness tidal power?**

FIGURE 12
Tidal Power
Pulled by the tide, water rushes through this tidal power plant in France.
Making Generalizations *Why are so few locations suitable for tidal power plants?*

Section 2 Assessment

Target Reading Skill **Previewing Visuals** Refer to your questions and answers about Figure 11 to help you answer Question 2 below.

Reviewing Key Concepts

1. a. **Defining** What is a tide? What causes tides?
   b. **Explaining** Explain why the moon causes a tidal bulge to form on the side of Earth closest to it.
   c. **Inferring** The sun is much bigger than the moon. Why doesn't the sun affect tides more than the moon does?
2. a. **Reviewing** Why do the heights of tides change during the course of a month?
   b. **Describing** Describe the positions of the sun, moon, and Earth during a spring tide and during a neap tide.
   c. **Applying Concepts** Imagine that you are the captain of a fishing boat. Why would it be helpful to consult a monthly tide table?
3. a. **Reviewing** How can tides be used to generate electricity?
   b. **Predicting** Do you think that tidal power will ever be a major source of energy worldwide? Why or why not?

Writing in Science

Firsthand Account Imagine that you are fishing on a pier on the Bay of Fundy in Canada. It was high tide when you began fishing. Now it is low tide. Write a firsthand account describing the changes that you observed as the tide went out. Use clear, descriptive language in your writing.

Monitor Progress L2

Answers

Figure 12 Few locations are suitable for tidal power plants because few locations have great enough range between high tide and low tide.

Reading Checkpoint Scientists predict tides according to knowledge of movements of the moon and Earth and knowledge of the shape of the coastline and other local conditions.

Reading Checkpoint Tidal power can best be harnessed in areas in which there is a large difference between high and low tides.

Assess

Reviewing Key Concepts

1. a. Tides are the rise and fall of water on Earth's coastlines. Tides are caused by the gravitational pull of the moon and sun. **b.** The moon's gravity pulls on the side of Earth facing it more strongly than it pulls on the center of Earth. **c.** The sun doesn't affect tides as much as the moon because the sun is much farther away from Earth.
2. a. The heights of tides change because the relative positions of Earth, the moon, and the sun change as the moon revolves around Earth and Earth revolves around the sun. **b.** The sun, moon, and Earth are in a line when spring tides occur and at right angles when neap tides occur. **c.** Low tides might be so low that it would be difficult to get boats out of their docks.
3. a. Water can be trapped at high tide. When it is released, gravity pulls it down through tunnels to power electric generators. **b.** Tidal power will probably not be a major source of energy because there are few locations that have a great enough range between high and low tides.

Reteach L1

As a class, draw a labeled diagram showing the positions of the sun, moon, and Earth during spring tide and neap tide. Use the diagram to explain the difference between spring tide and neap tide.

All in One Teaching Resources

- Section Summary: *Tides*
- Review and Reinforcement: *Tides*
- Enrich: *Tides*

Lab zone Chapter Project

Keep Students on Track By now, students should have built their wave tanks, beach, and lighthouse models. Stress the need for consistency in size and frequency of waves so that their effects on beach erosion can be compared before and after erosion-prevention methods are in place. Suggest that students measure erosion by placing numbered toothpicks labeled with masking tape at regular intervals along the beach.

Writing in Science

Writing Mode Description

Scoring Rubric

4 Exceeds criteria by writing a descriptive and concise description of the lowering water level and exposed bottom
3 Meets criteria by writing a complete description
2 Writes a partial description
1 Writes an inaccurate description

Section 3 Ocean Water Chemistry

Objectives
After this lesson, students will be able to
H.3.3.1 Describe the salinity of ocean water.
H.3.3.2 Explain how the temperature and gas content of ocean water varies.
H.3.3.3 Describe how conditions in the ocean change with depth.

Target Reading Skill 
Asking Questions Explain that changing a heading into a question helps students anticipate the ideas, facts, and events they are about to read.

Answers
One possible question and answer is the following:
How salty is the ocean? *(Ocean water has an average salt concentration of 35 parts per thousand.)* **How does the ocean change with depth?** *(As you descend, the temperature decreases and the pressure increases.)*

All in One Teaching Resources
- Transparency H35

Preteach

Build Background Knowledge L1
Ocean Water verses Fresh Water
Most students know that the ocean is salty, but they might not have thought about how this makes ocean water different from fresh water. Ask: **Why is salt often put on icy sidewalks and roads?** *(The salt melts the ice.)* **Which do you think freezes at a lower temperature—salt water or fresh water?** *(Salt water)* Guide students to conclude that the salt in ocean water interferes with the formation of ice and makes ocean water freeze at a lower temperature than fresh water would. Point out that this is one way that salty ocean water differs from fresh water.

Section 3 Ocean Water Chemistry

Reading Preview
Key Concepts
- How salty is ocean water?
- How do the temperature and gas content of ocean water vary?
- How do conditions in the ocean change with depth?

Key Terms
- salinity
- submersible

Target Reading Skill
Asking Questions Before you read, preview the red headings. In a graphic organizer like the one below, ask a *how* or *what* question for each heading. As you read, answer your questions.

Ocean Water Chemistry

Question	Answer
How salty is the ocean?	One kilogram of ocean water has . . .

Lab zone Discover Activity
Will the Eggs Sink or Float?
1. Fill two beakers or jars with tap water.
2. Add three teaspoons of salt to one beaker. Stir until it dissolves.
3. Place a whole, uncooked egg in each jar. Handle the eggs gently to avoid breakage. Observe what happens to each egg.
4. Wash your hands when you are finished with this activity.

Think It Over
Observing Compare what happens to the two eggs. What does this tell you about the difference between salt water and fresh water?

If you've ever swallowed some water while you were swimming in the ocean, you know that the ocean is salty. Why? According to an old Swedish legend, it's all because of a magic mill. This mill could grind out anything its owner wanted, such as herring, porridge, or even gold. A greedy sea captain once stole the mill and took it away on his ship, but without finding out how to use it. He asked the mill to grind some salt but then could not stop it. The mill ground more and more salt, until the captain's ship sank from its weight. According to the tale, the mill is still at the bottom of the sea, grinding out salt!

Salt storage area ▼

Lab zone Discover Activity
Skills Focus Observing 
Materials two beakers or jars, tap water, salt, teaspoon, stirring rod, two uncooked eggs
Time 10 minutes

Tips Students might need to add a little more salt for their egg to float.
Think It Over The egg sinks in fresh water, but it floats in salt water. Students might infer from their observations that salt water is denser than fresh water.

The Salty Ocean

Probably no one ever took this legend seriously, even when it was first told. The scientific explanation for the ocean's saltiness begins with the early stages of Earth's history, when the ocean covered much of the surface of the planet. Undersea volcanoes erupted, spewing chemicals into the water. Gradually, the lava from these volcanic eruptions built up areas of land. Rain fell on the bare land, washing more chemicals from the rocks into the ocean. Over time, these dissolved substances built up to the levels present in the ocean today.

Salinity Just how salty is the ocean? If you boiled a kilogram of ocean water in a pot until all the water was gone, there would be about 35 grams of salts left in the pot. **On average, one kilogram of ocean water contains about 35 grams of salts—that is, 35 parts per thousand.** The total amount of dissolved salts in a sample of water is the **salinity** of that sample.

The substance you know as table salt—sodium chloride—is the salt present in the greatest amount in ocean water. When sodium chloride dissolves in water, it separates into sodium and chloride particles called ions. Other salts, such as magnesium chloride, form ions in water in the same way. Together, chloride and sodium make up almost 86 percent of the ions dissolved in ocean water. Ocean water also contains smaller amounts of about a dozen other ions, including magnesium and calcium, and other substances that organisms need, such as nitrogen and phosphorus.

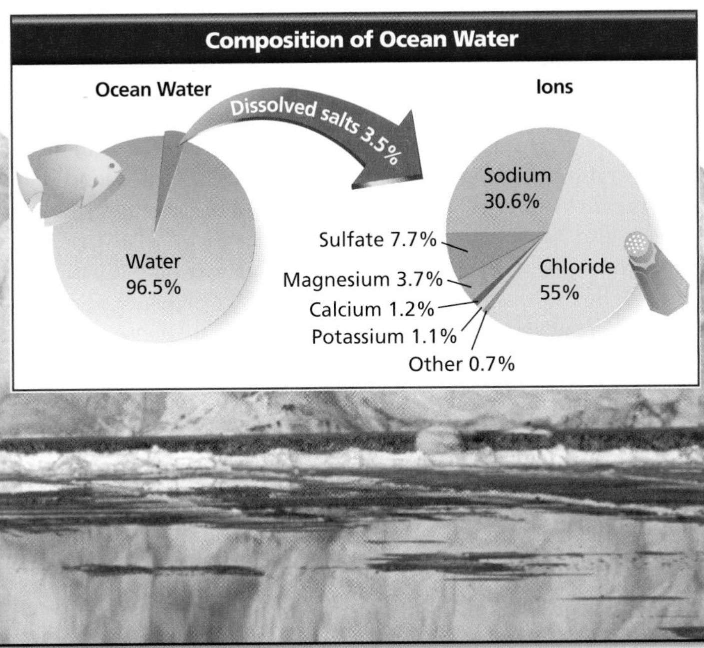

FIGURE 13
Composition of Ocean Water
Ocean water contains many different dissolved salts. When salts dissolve, they separate into particles called ions.
Reading Graphs *Which ion is most common in ocean water?*

Differentiated Instruction

Less Proficient Readers L1

Summarizing Have students work in pairs to reread and write a summary of the concepts in the subsection titled *The Salty Ocean.* When students are finished, ask whether there is anything they are still confused about and allow time for clarification. **learning modality: logical/mathematical**

Instruct

The Salty Ocean

Teach Key Concepts L2

Salinity

Focus Ask: **What happens when salt dissolves in water?** *(The charged atoms, called ions, separate and mix in the water.)* **Is it possible to see the ions in the water?** *(No.)*

Teach Tell students that an average of 35 parts per thousand of salt are dissolved in ocean water. Ask: **How many grams of salt are in 1000 grams of ocean water?** *(35 grams)* **How many grams of pure water are in 1000 grams of ocean water?** *(965 grams)* **How would salinity change if more pure water were added to the 1000 grams of ocean water?** *(Salinity would decrease.)* **How would salinity change if some ocean water were allowed to evaporate?** *(It would increase because only pure water evaporates from the mixture.)*

Apply Ask: **Where might high amounts of ocean water evaporate?** *(Where the climate is hot and dry)* **Where might high amounts of pure water be added to ocean water?** *(Where a lot of rain occurs or a lot of snow melts; where rivers enter the ocean)* **learning modality: logical/mathematical**

Independent Practice L2

All in One Teaching Resources

- Guided Reading and Study Worksheet: *Ocean Water Chemistry*

Student Edition on Audio CD

Use Visuals: Figure 13 L2

Composition of Ocean Water

Focus Direct students to the figure.

Teach Explain that each wedge of the graph on the right represents a type of ion. All of the ions contribute to the water's salinity.

Apply Ask: **What would happen to the ions if the seawater evaporated?** *(Ions would leave solid salts.)* **learning modality: visual**

Monitor Progress L2

Skills Check Have students compare and contrast fresh water and salt water.

Answer
Figure 13 Chloride

L2

Investigating Effects of Salinity

Focus Encourage students to speculate about whether salt water or fresh water will freeze first.

Materials small paper cups, salt, tablespoon measure, stirrer

Time 10 minutes; 5 minutes for each of several observations

Teach Give each student a paper cup. Have students add cold water until the cups are one-quarter full. Half of the students should mix a tablespoon of salt in their cups. Students should label their cups *Salt* or *No Salt* and place them in a freezer. At regular intervals, check the cups to determine which freeze first.

Apply Ask: **Why did the fresh water freeze first?** *(Salt interferes with the formation of ice crystals and causes salt water to have a lower freezing point.)* **learning modality: logical/ mathematical**

Help Students Read

L1

Compare and Contrast To help students understand how temperature and salinity affect the density of ocean water, have them make a compare-and-contrast chart. The chart should 1) compare the effects of warm and cold temperatures; and 2) compare the effects of high and low salinities.

FIGURE 14
Salinity and Density
These people are relaxing with the paper while floating in the water! The Dead Sea between Israel and Jordan is so salty that people float easily on its surface.
Relating Cause and Effect *How is the area's hot, dry climate related to the Dead Sea's high salinity?*

Math Skills

Calculating Density

To calculate the density of a substance, divide the mass of the substance by its volume.

$$\text{Density} = \frac{\text{Mass}}{\text{Volume}}$$

For example, 1 liter (L) of ocean water has a mass of 1.03 kilograms (kg). Therefore,

$$\text{Density} = \frac{1.03\text{ kg}}{1.00\text{ L}}$$

$$\text{Density} = 1.03\text{ kg/L}$$

Practice Problems A 5-liter sample of one type of crude oil has a mass of 4.10 kg. What is its density? If this oil spilled on the ocean's surface, would it sink or float? Explain your answer in terms of density.

Variations in Salinity In most parts of the ocean, the salinity is between 34 and 37 parts per thousand. But near the ocean's surface, rain, snow, and melting ice add fresh water, lowering the salinity. Salinity is also lower near the mouths of large rivers such as the Amazon or Mississippi. These rivers empty great amounts of fresh water into the ocean. Evaporation, on the other hand, increases salinity, since the salt is left behind as the water evaporates. For example, in the Red Sea, where the climate is hot and dry, the salinity can be as high as 41 parts per thousand. Salinity can also be higher near the poles. As the surface water freezes into ice, the salt is left behind in the remaining water.

Effects of Salinity Salinity affects several properties of ocean water. For instance, ocean water does not freeze until the temperature drops to about –1.9°C. The salt acts as a kind of antifreeze by interfering with the formation of ice crystals. Salt water also has a higher density than fresh water. That means that the mass of one liter of salt water is greater than the mass of one liter of fresh water. Because its density is greater, seawater has greater buoyancy. It lifts, or buoys up, less dense objects floating in it. This is why an egg floats higher in salt water than in fresh water, and why the people in Figure 14 float so effortlessly in the Dead Sea.

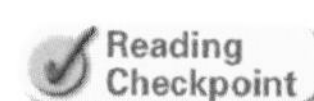
Reading Checkpoint **Why does salt water have greater buoyancy than fresh water?**

Math Skills

Skills Focus calculating

Time 10 minutes

Teach Familiarize the concept of density with the following questions: **Which is denser—lead or plastic?** *(Lead)* **Plastic or styrofoam?** *(Plastic)*

Answer The density is 0.82 kg/L (4.10 kg ÷ 5.00 L). The oil would float on top of the ocean because it is less dense than ocean water.

Other Ocean Properties

In New England, the news reports on New Year's Day often feature the shivering members of a "Polar Bear Club" taking a dip in the icy Atlantic Ocean. Yet on the same day, people enjoy the warm waters of a Puerto Rico beach. **Like temperatures on land, temperatures at the surface of the ocean vary with location and the seasons. Gases in ocean water vary as well.**

Temperature of Ocean Water Why do surface temperatures of the ocean vary from place to place? The broad surface of the ocean absorbs energy from the sun. Near the equator, surface ocean temperatures often reach 25°C, about room temperature. The temperature drops as you travel away from the equator.

Because warm water is less dense than cold water, warm water forms only a thin layer on the ocean surface. Generally, the deeper you descend into the ocean, the colder and denser the water becomes. When water temperature is lower, the water molecules stay closer together than at higher temperatures. So, a sample of cold water has more water molecules than a sample of warm water of the same volume. The sample of cold water is denser.

Gases in Ocean Water Just as land organisms use gases found in air, ocean organisms use gases found in ocean water. Two gases that ocean organisms use are carbon dioxide and oxygen.

Carbon dioxide is about 60 times as plentiful in the oceans as in the air. Algae need carbon dioxide for photosynthesis. Animals such as corals also use carbon dioxide, which provides the carbon to build their hard skeletons.

Unlike carbon dioxide, oxygen is scarcer in seawater than in air. Oxygen is most plentiful in seawater near the surface. Oxygen in seawater comes from the air and from algae in the ocean, as a product of photosynthesis. The amount of oxygen in seawater is affected by the water temperature. The cold waters in the polar regions contain more oxygen than warm, tropical waters. But there is still enough oxygen in tropical seas to support a variety of organisms.

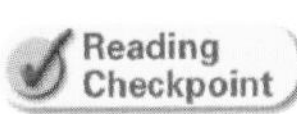
Reading Checkpoint What are two sources of oxygen in ocean water?

FIGURE 15
Organisms and Ocean Temperatures
From the warmest tropical waters to the coldest Antarctic sea, you can find organisms that are adapted to extreme ocean temperatures.

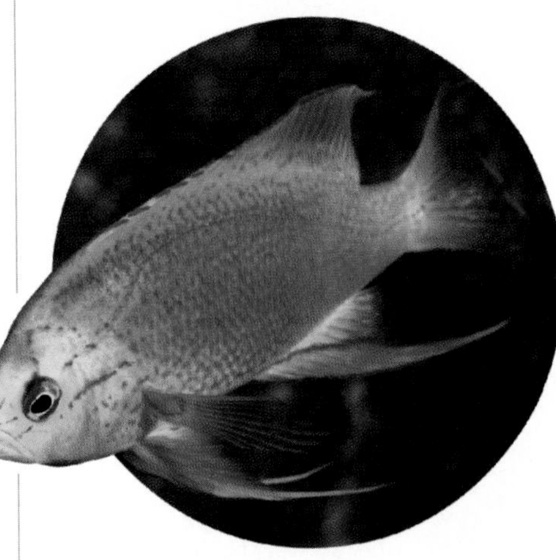

▲ This longfin anthias fish swimming near Hawaii lives in one of the warmest parts of the Pacific Ocean.

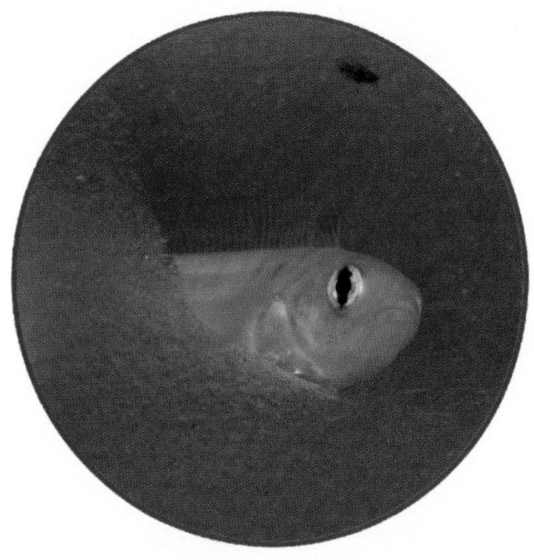

▲ This rockcod is swimming through a hole in an iceberg in near-freezing ocean water.

Other Ocean Properties

Teach Key Concepts L1

Gases in Ocean Water

Focus Help students understand that gases dissolve in water. Ask: **How do underwater plants get carbon dioxide?** *(From the water)* **How do fish get oxygen?** *(From the water)*

Teach Challenge students to explain why surface ocean water contains the most oxygen, but deeper waters contain the most carbon dioxide. *(Photosynthetic organisms, such as algae and plants, live near the surface where sunlight is available. At greater depths, respiration can occur but photosynthesis cannot. Therefore, carbon dioxide levels are higher below the depth of light penetration.)* Ask: **In what parts of the ocean can plants not live?** *(The deeper parts)* **Can you think of a reason why animals might not be able to live in such places?** *(Animals rely on plants to produce oxygen, which the animals need to live.)* **learning modality: logical/mathematical**

Differentiated Instruction

English Learners/Beginning L1
Comprehension: Key Concept Rewrite the boldfaced sentence on this page as several separate sentences such as *Temperature at the surface of the ocean varies with location. Temperature at the surface of the ocean varies with the seasons. Gases in the ocean also vary.* Read each sentence aloud. Then challenge students to explain how for each sentence. **learning modality: verbal**

English Learners/Intermediate L2
Comprehension: Key Concept After students finish the Beginning activity, have them organize the information with a concept map. **learning modality: verbal**

Monitor Progress L2

Oral Presentation Call on students to identify places in the ocean where salinity is low or high.

Answers

Figure 14 The hot, dry climate causes high amounts of evaporation, which causes high salinity in the Dead Sea.

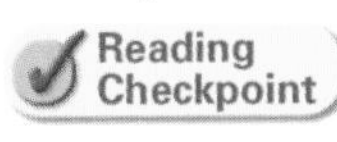
Salt water is denser than fresh water.

Oxygen comes from the atmosphere and from plants and algae in the ocean.

Changes With Depth

Teach Key Concepts L2

Water Pressure

Focus Remind students that pressure is the amount of force on a certain area. Ask: **Why does water exert force?** *(The force is the weight of the water above.)*

Teach Imagine with students a submersible vehicle descending to the depths. Have students describe how the pressure would change as the submersible descends. *(It would increase gradually.)* Ask: **What would happen if the submersible was not built well?** *(It could be crushed under the pressure.)* **What if the submersible had a hole in it and filled with water as it sank; would it still collapse?** *(No. The water pressure inside would equal the water pressure outside.)*

Apply Ask: **Where is the water pressure highest in a swimming pool?** *(At the deepest place)*

Use Visuals: Figure 16

The Water Column

Focus Direct students' attention to the figure. Have them describe the depth scale and identify the depths for the scuba diver and the two submersibles.

Teach As a class, describe how each quantity changes with depth. It might help to draw graphs on the board.

Apply Ask: **Why do the submersibles need lights?** *(Sunlight cannot penetrate to these depths.)* **Where could you find cold water in the deep equatorial ocean?** *(At the bottom)* **learning modality: visual**

All in One Teaching Resources

- Transparency H36

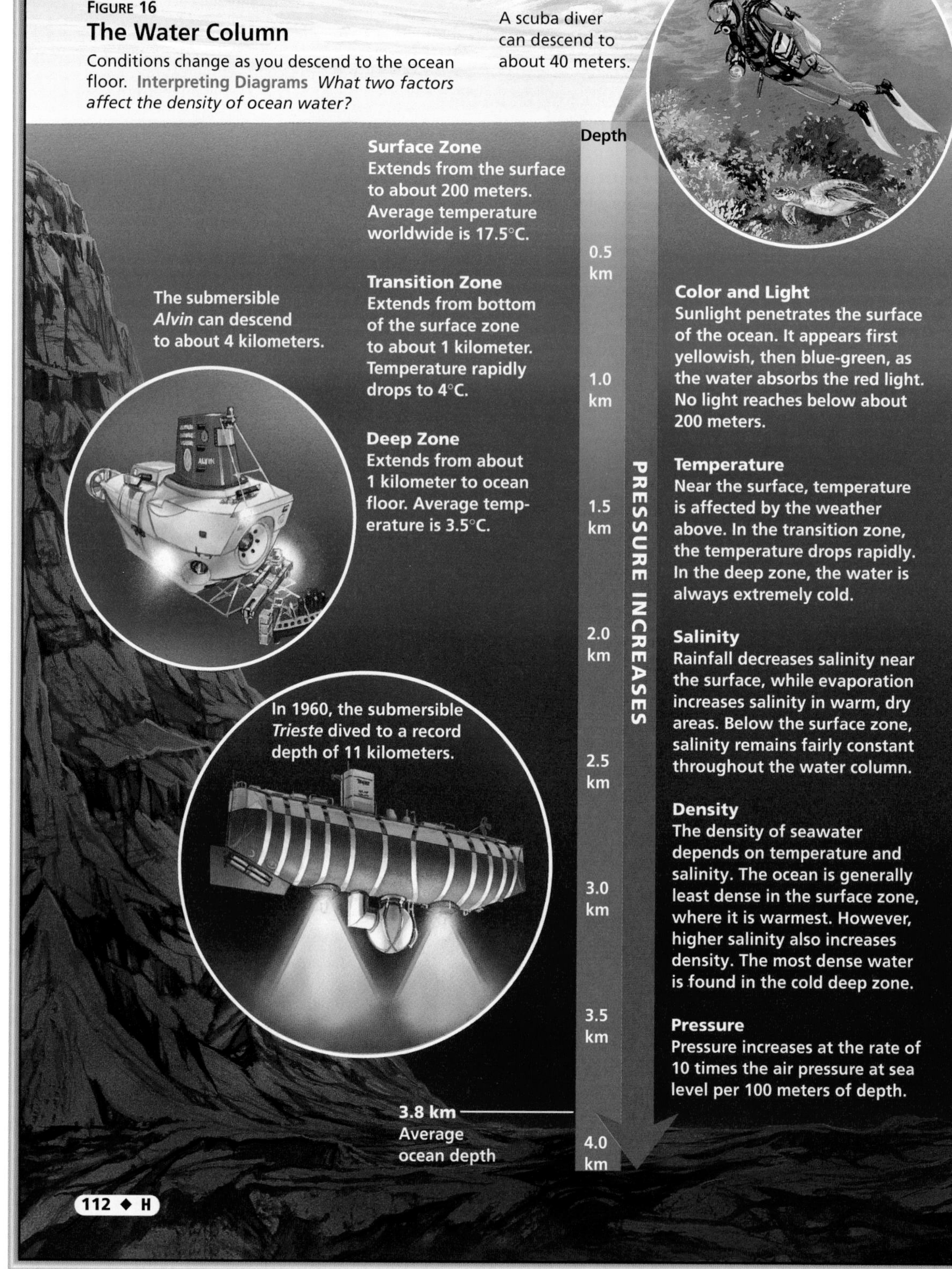

A scuba diver can descend to about 40 meters.
Depth
Surface Zone
Extends from the surface to about 200 meters. Average temperature worldwide is 17.5°C.
Transition Zone
Extends from bottom of the surface zone to about 1 kilometer. Temperature rapidly drops to 4°C.
Deep Zone
Extends from about 1 kilometer to ocean floor. Average temperature is 3.5°C.
The submersible Alvin can descend to about 4 kilometers.
In 1960, the submersible Trieste dived to a record depth of 11 kilometers.
0.5 km
1.0 km
1.5 km
2.0 km
2.5 km
3.0 km
3.5 km
4.0 km
PRESSURE INCREASES
3.8 km Average ocean depth
Color and Light
Sunlight penetrates the surface of the ocean. It appears first yellowish, then blue-green, as the water absorbs the red light. No light reaches below about 200 meters.
Temperature
Near the surface, temperature is affected by the weather above. In the transition zone, the temperature drops rapidly. In the deep zone, the water is always extremely cold.
Salinity
Rainfall decreases salinity near the surface, while evaporation increases salinity in warm, dry areas. Below the surface zone, salinity remains fairly constant throughout the water column.
Density
The density of seawater depends on temperature and salinity. The ocean is generally least dense in the surface zone, where it is warmest. However, higher salinity also increases density. The most dense water is found in the cold deep zone.
Pressure
Pressure increases at the rate of 10 times the air pressure at sea level per 100 meters of depth.
112 ◆ H

FIGURE 16
The Water Column
Conditions change as you descend to the ocean floor. **Interpreting Diagrams** *What two factors affect the density of ocean water?*

Differentiated Instruction

Special Needs L1

Making a Scale Drawing To help students visualize the ocean's depth, suggest that they make a scale drawing of the three zones. Have them use a scale of 500 m equals 1 cm. Remind students to include the ocean zones in their drawings. After students finish their drawings, have them calculate the scale height of the 442-m-high Sears Tower *(0.88 cm)*

Gifted and Talented L3

Exploring the Ocean Invite interested students to research some of the special equipment used to explore the ocean floor. In addition to the *Alvin* and *Trieste* shown in the figure, students can find out about the Jim Suit, invented in 1922, and the first bathyscaphes invented in the late 1940s and early 1950s.

Changes With Depth

If you could descend from the ocean's surface to the ocean floor, you would pass through a vertical section of the ocean referred to as the water column. Figure 16 on the previous page shows some of the dramatic changes you would observe.

Decreasing Temperature **As you descend through the ocean, the water temperature decreases.** There are three temperature zones in the water column. The surface zone is the warmest. It typically extends from the surface to between 100 and 500 meters. The transition zone extends from the bottom of the surface zone to about 1 kilometer. Temperatures drop very quickly as you descend through the transition zone, to about 4°C. Below the transition zone is the deep zone. Average temperatures there are 3.5°C in most of the ocean.

Increasing Pressure Water pressure is the force exerted by the weight of water. **Pressure increases continuously with depth in the ocean.** Because of the high pressure in the deep ocean, divers can descend safely only to about 40 meters. To observe the deep ocean, scientists must use a **submersible,** an underwater vehicle built of materials that resist pressure.

What is a submersible?

For: Links on ocean water chemistry
Visit: www.SciLinks.org
Web Code: scn-0833

Section 3 Assessment

Target Reading Skill **Asking Questions** Use the questions you wrote about the headings to help you answer the questions below.

Reviewing Key Concepts

1. a. **Defining** What is salinity? What is the average salinity of ocean water?
   b. **Describing** Describe one factor that increases the salinity of seawater and one factor that decreases its salinity.
   c. **Inferring** Would you expect the seawater just below the floating ice in the Arctic Ocean to be higher or lower in salinity than the water in the deepest part of the ocean? Explain.
2. a. **Identifying** Where would you find the warmest ocean temperatures on Earth?
   b. **Comparing and Contrasting** How do carbon dioxide and oxygen levels in the oceans compare to those in the air?
   c. **Relating Cause and Effect** How does the temperature of ocean water affect oxygen levels in the water?
3. a. **Reviewing** How do temperature and pressure change as you descend in the ocean?
   b. **Predicting** Where in the water column would you expect to find the following conditions: the highest pressure readings; the densest waters; the warmest temperatures?

Math Practice

4. **Calculating Density** Calculate the density of the following 1-L samples of ocean water. Sample A has a mass of 1.01 kg; Sample B has a mass of 1.06 kg. Which sample would likely have the higher salinity? Explain.

Math Skill Calculating

Answers Sample A, 1.01 kg/L; Sample B, 1.06 kg/L; Sample B probably has the highest salinity; salt increases the density of water.

For: Links on ocean water chemistry
Visit: SciLinks.org
Web Code: scn-0833

Download a worksheet that will guide students' review of Internet resources on ocean water chemistry.

Monitor Progress L2

Answers

Figure 16 Temperature and salinity affect the density of ocean water.

A submersible is an underwater vehicle.

Assess

Reviewing Key Concepts

1. a. Salinity is the total amount of dissolved salts in ocean water; 35 parts per thousand **b.** Evaporation or ice formation increases the salinity of seawater; rainfall, melting ice, or fresh water from rivers decreases its salinity. **c.** Higher; ice formation increases salinity. This is one region where dense water sinks to the ocean floor.
2. a. The warmest ocean temperatures are found near the equator. **b.** There is more carbon dioxide in ocean water, but less oxygen. **c.** Cold water contains more oxygen than warm water does.
3. a. Temperature decreases and pressure increases. **b.** Highest pressure readings—the deep zone; densest waters—the deep zone; warmest temperatures—the surface zone; most light—the surface zone.

Reteach L1

As a class, explain how salinity, temperature, and gases in the ocean vary.

Performance Assessment

Writing Have students write a paragraph explaining why it is easier to float in the ocean than in a freshwater lake.

All in One Teaching Resources

- Section Summary: *Ocean Water Chemistry*
- Review and Reinforcement: *Ocean Water Chemistry*
- Enrich: *Ocean Water Chemistry*

Investigating Changes in Density

L2

Prepare for Inquiry

Key Concept

The density of water increases as salinity increases or temperature decreases.

Skills Objectives

After this lab, students will be able to

- design and build a hydrometer
- measure water density using a hydrometer
- design a solution and determine how given factors affect the density of water
- troubleshoot their designs and make suggestions for improvement

Prep Time 30 minutes

Class Time 40 minutes

Alternative Materials

Plastic soda bottles can be used instead of graduated cylinders. Small test tubes with corks can be used as hydrometers in the second part of the activity.

Safety

Caution students to be careful when handling tacks and to use oven mitts to handle hot items. Review the safety guidelines in Appendix A.

All in One Teaching Resources

- Lab Worksheet: *Design and Build a Hydrometer*

Guide Inquiry

Invitation

Fill a clear soda bottle with ice-cold water and fill another with very warm water to which food coloring has been added. Invite students to touch the sides of the bottles to feel the temperature difference. Put an index card over the mouth of the warm-water bottle and carefully place it on top of the cold-water bottle. Make sure to line up the rims of the bottles. Then, as students observe, gently slide out the index card. Ask: **Why doesn't the water in the top bottle mix with water in the bottom bottle?** *(Because it is warmer, which makes it less dense)* **What would happen if the positions of the two bottles were reversed?** *(The colder water from the top bottle would sink down and mix with the warmer water in the bottom bottle.)* Reverse the positions of the bottles to demonstrate.

Investigating Changes in Density

Problem

Can you design and build an instrument that can detect differences in density?

Skills Focus

building a prototype, designing a solution, troubleshooting

Materials

- thumbtacks • 250-mL graduated cylinder
- unsharpened pencil with eraser • metric ruler
- fine-point permanent marker • thermometer
- ice • balance • water • spoon • salt
- additional materials provided by your teacher

Procedure  

PART 1 Research and Investigate

1. One way to measure the density of a liquid is with a tool called a hydrometer. You can make a simple hydrometer using an unsharpened wooden pencil.
2. Starting at the unsharpened end of a pencil, use a permanent marker to make marks every 2 mm along the side of the pencil. Make longer marks for every whole centimeter. Continue until you have marked off 5 cm.
3. Label each of the long marks, starting at the unsharpened end of the pencil.
4. Insert 3 thumbtacks as weights into the eraser end of the pencil. **CAUTION:** *Be careful not to cut yourself on the sharp points of the thumbtacks.*
5. Fill the graduated cylinder with 250 mL of water at room temperature. Place the pencil in the water, eraser end down.
6. Add or remove thumbtacks and adjust their placement until the pencil floats upright, with about 2 cm sticking up above the surface of the water.
7. In your notebook, record the temperature of the water. Next to that number, record the reading on the pencil hydrometer at the surface of the water.
8. Fill the graduated cylinder with cold water. Place the pencil hydrometer into the water, eraser end down. Then repeat Step 7.

PART 2 Design and Build

9. Using what you learned in Part 1, design and build a hydrometer that can detect density differences among different samples of water. Your hydrometer should
    - be able to measure density differences between hot water and cold water
    - be able to measure density differences between salt water and fresh water
    - be constructed of materials approved by your teacher

114 ◆ H

Introduce the Procedure

Have students read the procedure, and then describe their experimental plan. Have them state which variable, such as salinity or temperature, they want to test. Then have students explain how they will manipulate the variable. For example, if temperature is the manipulated variable, they should first specify how they will control salinity. Ask: **Which variable will you control, and how will you control it?** *(Either salinity or temperature, by using only water of the same salinity while varying the temperature or by using only water of the same temperature and varying the salinity.)* **What different temperatures or concentrations of salt will you use?** *(For best results, the temperatures or salinities should vary as much as possible.)*

10. Sketch your design in your notebook and make a list of the materials you will need. Write a plan for how you will construct your hydrometer. After you have received your teacher's approval for your design, build your hydrometer.

PART 3 Evaluate and Redesign

11. Test your hydrometer by using it to measure the density of water at different temperatures. Then test samples of water that have different salinities. Create a data table in which to record your results.

Data Table		
Temperature (°C)	Salinity $\left(\frac{\text{g salt}}{\text{L water}}\right)$	Hydrometer Reading

12. Based on your tests, decide how you could improve the design of your hydrometer. For example, how could you change your design so your hydrometer is able to detect smaller differences in density? Obtain your teacher's approval, then make the necessary changes, and test how your redesigned hydrometer functions.

Analyze and Conclude

1. **Inferring** Explain why cold water is more dense than hot water. Explain why salt water is more dense than fresh water.
2. **Building a Prototype** How well did the pencil hydrometer you built in Part 1 work? What problems did you encounter with the hydrometer?

3. **Designing a Solution** How did you incorporate what you learned in Part 1 into your hydrometer design in Part 2? For example, how did your hydrometer address the problems you encountered in Part 1?
4. **Troubleshooting** In Part 3, how well did your hydrometer perform when you measured water samples of different densities? How did you redesign your hydrometer to improve its function?
5. **Evaluating the Design** What limitations did factors such as buoyancy, materials, time, costs, or other factors place on the design and function of your hydrometer? Describe how you adapted your design to work within these limitations.

Communicate

Create an informative poster that describes how your hydrometer works. Include illustrations of your hydrometer and any important background information on density.

Troubleshooting the Experiment

- Make sure the pencils remain vertical. Students might need to adjust the tacks in the pencil's eraser.
- Students should stir salt solutions well so that as much salt dissolves as possible.

Expected Outcome

The more salt that is added to the water, or the colder the water, the greater the density and the higher the pencil hydrometer floats.

Analyze and Conclude

1. As water cools, its molecules slow down and move closer together, making the water more dense. (Some students may point out that water expands when cooled below 4°C to its freezing point.) Salt water contains dissolved salts that add to the mass of a given volume of salt water, increasing its density.

2. Answers will vary depending on how well students have built their hydrometers.

3. Answers will vary depending on the difficulties students encountered when measuring density in Part 1.

4. Hydrometers should perform well. Students might suggest marking finer measuring increments on the hydrometer.

5. Answers will vary depending on students' designs. Encourage students to explain how they were best able to measure density with the materials.

Sample Data Table 1
Manipulated Variable: Salinity

Salinity (g salt/L water)	Hydrometer Reading (cm)
0	2
30	4
60	6

Sample Data Table 2
Manipulated Variable: Temperature

Temperature (°C)	Hydrometer Reading (cm)
5	4
25	3
45	3

Section 4

Currents and Climate

Objectives

After this lesson, students will be able to

H.3.4.1 Identify what causes surface currents and explain how surface currents affect climate.

H.3.4.2 Identify the causes of deep currents and describe the effects that the currents have.

H.3.4.3 Describe how upwelling affects the distribution of nutrients in the ocean.

Target Reading Skill

Relating Cause and Effect Explain that the cause is the reason for what happens. The effect is what happens because of the cause. Relating cause and effect helps students relate the reason for what happens to what happens as a result.

Answers

Cause: Winds
Effect: Surface currents
Cause: Differences in ocean-water density
Effect: Deep currents

All in One Teaching Resources

- Transparency H37

Preteach

Build Background Knowledge L1

Ocean Currents

Ask students whether they have heard stories about someone finding a message in a bottle that was thrown into the ocean at a faraway location. Ask: **How do you think the bottle got there?** *(Some students might know that currents exist in the ocean and that a current transported the bottle.)*

Section 4

Currents and Climate

Reading Preview

Key Concepts

- What causes surface currents and how do they affect climate?
- What causes deep currents and what effects do they have?
- How does upwelling affect the distribution of nutrients in the ocean?

Key Terms

- current
- Coriolis effect
- climate
- El Niño
- upwelling

Target Reading Skill

Relating Cause and Effect As you read, identify the main factors that cause surface and deep currents in the oceans. Write the information in graphic organizers like the one below.

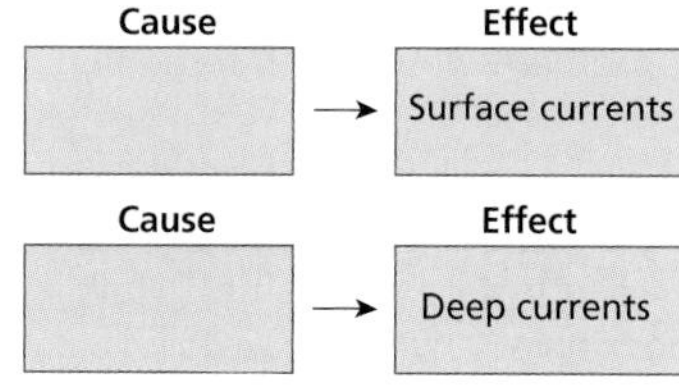

Lab zone Discover Activity

Which Is More Dense?

1. Fill a plastic container three-quarters full with warm water. Wait for the water to stop moving.
2. Add several drops of food coloring to a cup of ice water and stir.
3. Gently dribble colored water down the inside of the container. Observe.

Think It Over

Inferring Describe what happened to the cold water. Which is more dense, warm water or cold water? Explain.

One spring day, people strolling along a beach in Washington State saw an amazing sight. Hundreds of sneakers of all colors and sizes were washing ashore from the Pacific Ocean! This "sneaker spill" was eventually traced to a cargo ship accident. Containers of sneakers had fallen overboard and now the sneakers were washing ashore.

But the most amazing part of the story is this—scientists could predict where the sneakers would wash up next. And just as the scientists had predicted, sneakers washed up in Oregon, and then thousands of kilometers away in Hawaii!

How did the scientists know that the sneakers would float all the way to Hawaii? The answer lies in a type of ocean movement known as a current. A **current** is a large stream of moving water that flows through the oceans. Unlike waves, currents carry water from one place to another. Some currents move water at the surface of the ocean, while other currents move water deep in the ocean.

116 ◆ H

Lab zone Discover Activity

Skills Focus Inferring L1

Materials plastic container, warm water, cup, ice water, food coloring, plastic dropper, stirring rod

Time 15 minutes

Tips The greater the temperature difference between the warm and cold water, the more obvious the effect.

Think It Over The cold water sank to the bottom of the container. Cold water is denser than warm water.

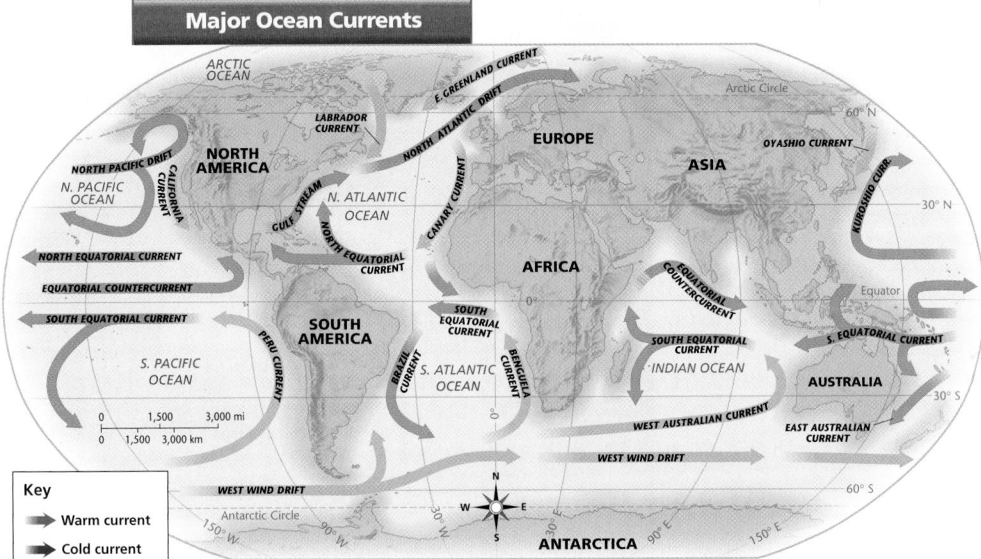

FIGURE 17
Large surface currents generally move in circular patterns in Earth's oceans. **Interpreting Maps** *Name four currents that flow along the coasts of North America. State whether each current is warm or cold.*

Surface Currents

Figure 17 shows the major surface currents in Earth's oceans. **Surface currents, which affect water to a depth of several hundred meters, are driven mainly by winds.** Following Earth's major wind patterns, surface currents move in circular patterns in the five major oceans. Most of the currents flow east or west, and then double back to complete the circle.

Coriolis Effect Why do the currents move in these circular patterns? If Earth were standing still, winds and currents would flow in straight lines between the poles and the equator. But as Earth rotates, the paths of the winds and currents curve. This effect of Earth's rotation on the direction of winds and currents is called the **Coriolis effect** (kawr ee OH lis). In the Northern Hemisphere, the Coriolis effect causes the currents to curve to the right. In the Southern Hemisphere, the Coriolis effect causes the currents to curve to the left.

The largest and most powerful surface current in the North Atlantic Ocean, the Gulf Stream, is caused by strong winds from the west. It is more than 30 kilometers wide and 300 meters deep, and carries a volume of water 100 times greater than the Mississippi River. The Gulf Stream carries warm water from the Gulf of Mexico to the Caribbean Sea, then northward along the coast of the United States. Near Cape Hatteras, North Carolina, it curves eastward across the Atlantic, as a result of the Coriolis effect.

For: Links on ocean currents
Visit: www.SciLinks.org
Web Code: scn-0834

Differentiated Instruction

Special Needs L1

Provide students with a copy of the map of ocean currents. On the copy, mark four different locations where a bottle was dropped into the water. Have students draw the path that they think the bottle would travel. Have them speculate about where it might come to shore.

Instruct

Surface Currents

For: Links on ocean currents
Visit: www.SciLinks.org
Web Code: scn-0834

Download a worksheet that will guide students' review of Internet resources on ocean currents.

Teach Key Concepts L1

Ocean Currents

Focus Ask students whether they have heard news reports about storm surges, water that blows farther inland than usual because of storm winds. Tell them that the normal winds that blow on Earth also move water from place to place in the ocean.

Teach Tell students that the Coriolis effect causes wind-formed currents to curve to the right in the northern hemisphere and to the left in the southern hemisphere. Ask: **If water currents kept curving, what path would they follow?** *(The currents would follow large circular paths.)* **How would the direction of rotation be different in the two hemispheres?** *(Rotation would be clockwise in the northern hemisphere and counterclockwise in the southern hemisphere.)*

Apply Ask: **If ocean currents rotate clockwise in the northern hemisphere, which side of a continent would have a warm current?** *(East side)* **Which side would have a cold current?** *(West side)* **learning modality: logical/mathematical**

All in One Teaching Resources

- Transparency H38

Independent Practice

All in One Teaching Resources

- Guided Reading and Study Worksheet: *Currents and Climate*

 **Student Edition on Audio CD**

Monitor Progress L2

Skills Check Have students make a table that compares and contrasts waves, tides, and surface currents.

Answer

Figure 17 The California Current and Labrador Current are cold currents; the North Pacific Drift and Gulf Stream are warm currents.

Help Students Read L1

SQ3R Refer to the Contact Refresher, which provides guidelines for Survey, Question, Read, Recite, and Review. Have students survey the headings and diagrams, and write questions that they will answer when they have completed the section.

Use Visuals: Figure 18

The Gulf Stream

Focus Have a student read the caption as the class listens. Ask: **What do the different colors represent?** *(Red and orange are warm water, and green and blue indicate cooler water.)*

Teach Ask: **Where is the coldest water?** *(In the far north Atlantic)* **Where is most of the warm water?** *(At lower latitudes)* Have students describe the path that the warm Gulf Stream water follows through the Atlantic. Point out the circular region where cold water is surrounded by warmer water. Ask: **How could this occur?** *(The warm water flow surrounded a parcel of colder North Atlantic water.)*

Apply Ask: **Why is water temperature higher on the U.S. East Coast than at similar latitudes on the U.S. West Coast?** *(The Gulf Stream is a warm current. The West Coast is affected by the cool California Current.)*

FIGURE 18
Surface Currents and Climate
This satellite image of the Atlantic Ocean has been enhanced with colors that show water temperature. Red and orange indicate warmer water, while green and blue indicate colder water.
Interpreting Maps *The Gulf Stream flows around Florida in the lower left of the map. Is the Gulf Stream a warm or cold current?*

Effects on Climate The Gulf Stream and another warm current, the North Atlantic Drift, are very important to people in the city of Trondheim, Norway. Trondheim is located along Norway's western coast. Although it is very close to the Arctic Circle, winters there are fairly mild. Snow melts soon after it falls. And fortunately for the fishing boats, the local harbors are free of ice most of the winter. The two warm currents bring this area of Norway a mild climate. **Climate** is the pattern of temperature and precipitation typical of an area over a long period of time.

Currents affect climate by moving cold and warm water around the globe. In general, currents carry warm water from the tropics toward the poles and bring cold water back toward the equator. **A surface current warms or cools the air above it, influencing the climate of the land near the coast.**

Winds pick up moisture as they blow across warm-water currents. For example, the warm Kuroshio Current brings mild, rainy weather to the southern islands of Japan. In contrast, cold-water currents cool the air above them. Since cold air holds less moisture than warm air, these currents tend to bring cool, dry weather to the land areas in their path.

Lab zone Skills Activity

Drawing Conclusions

Locate the Benguela Current in Figure 17 on the previous page. Near the southern tip of Africa, the winds blow from west to east. Using what you have learned about surface currents and climate, what can you conclude about the impact of this current on the climate of the south-western coast of Africa?

118 ◆ H

Lab zone Skills Activity

Skills Focus Drawing conclusions L3

Materials Figure 17

Time 5 minutes

Tips Make sure that students know that the Benguela Current is a cold-water current.

Expected Outcome Students should conclude that the Benguela Current brings cool, dry weather to the southwestern coast of Africa.

Extend Encourage students to speculate about the effects of the Peru Current on coastal South America. **learning modality: visual**

El Niño When changes in wind patterns and currents occur, they can have a major impact on the oceans and neighboring land. One example of such changes is **El Niño,** an abnormal climate event that occurs every two to seven years in the Pacific Ocean. El Niño begins when an unusual pattern of winds forms over the western Pacific. This causes a vast sheet of warm water to move eastward toward the South American coast. El Niño conditions can last for one to two years before the usual winds and currents return.

El Niño can have disastrous consequences. It causes shifts in weather patterns around the world, bringing unusual and often severe conditions to different areas. For example, a major El Niño occurred between 1997 and 1998 and caused an especially warm winter in the northeastern United States. However, it was also responsible for heavy rains, flooding, and mudslides in California, as well as a string of deadly tornadoes in Florida.

Although scientists do not fully understand the conditions that cause El Niño, they have been able to predict its occurrence using computer models of world climate. Knowing when El Niño will occur can reduce its impact. Scientists and public officials can plan emergency procedures and make changes to protect people and wildlife.

Reading Checkpoint **Why is it helpful to be able to predict when El Niño will occur?**

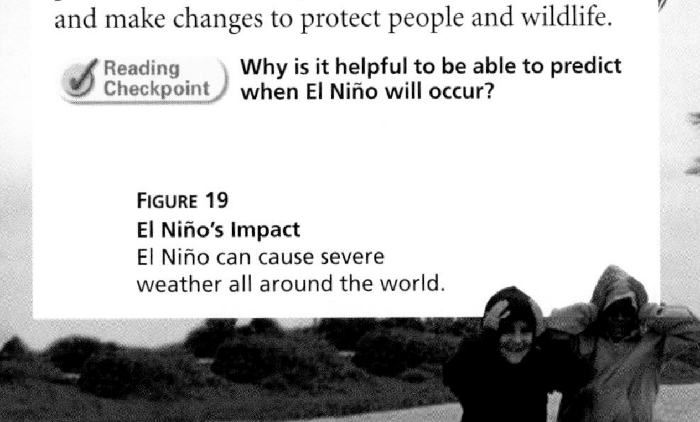

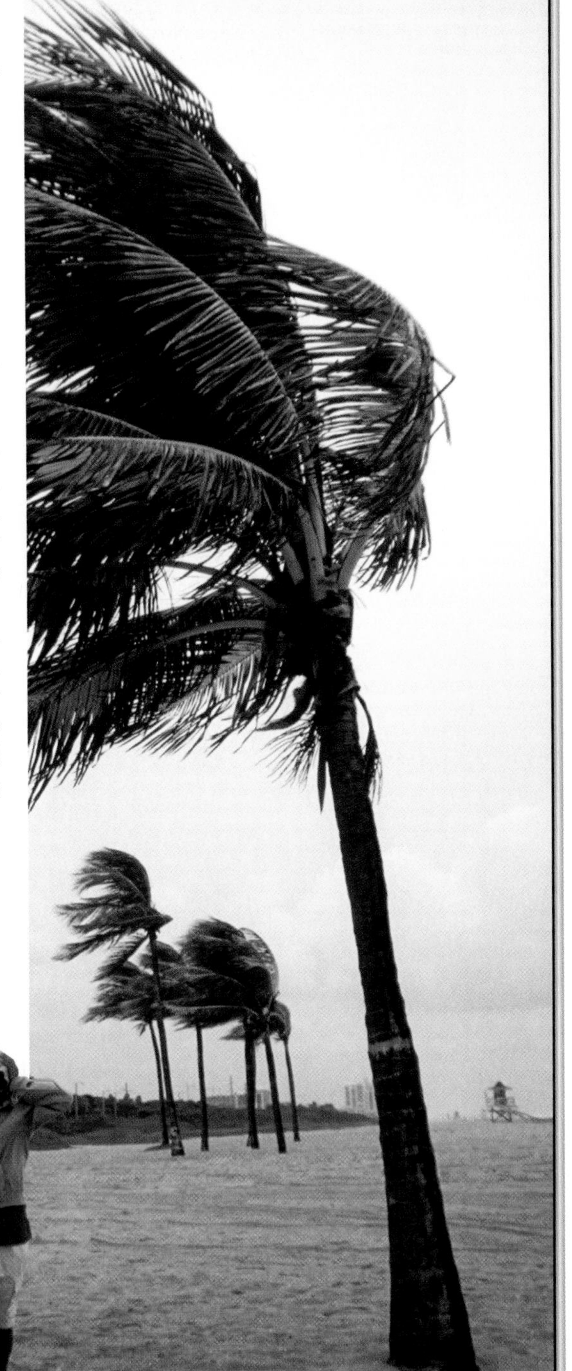

FIGURE 19
El Niño's Impact
El Niño can cause severe weather all around the world.

L3

El Niño

Focus Remind students how to identify water temperature from the colors on a satellite image.

Materials satellite image of the equatorial Pacific during an El Niño year, satellite image of the equatorial Pacific during a normal year

Time 15 minutes

Teach Show students the two satellite images. Have them describe the temperature in the eastern Pacific in both images. Students will notice that these waters are significantly warmer during an El Niño year. Tell them that during these years, warm water from the western Pacific flows to the eastern Pacific.

Apply Ask: **How might warmer water off the coast of western South America affect climate there?** *(The warmer water causes the region to have more rain.)* **learning modality: logical/mathematical**

Differentiated Instruction

English Learners/Beginning L1

Vocabulary: Prior Knowledge Write the term *current* on the board and say the word aloud. Point out that some English words have more than one meaning. *Current* can mean something that is happening in the present. Then have students define the scientific meaning of the word. **learning modality: verbal**

English Learners/Intermediate L2

Vocabulary: Prior Knowledge After students have completed the Beginning activity above, have them write sentences using both meanings of the word *current*. **learning modality: verbal**

Monitor Progress L1

Writing Have students explain how surface currents affect climate.

Answers

Figure 18 The area of the Gulf Stream is red—the color that indicates warmer water on the satellite image.

Reading Checkpoint People can prepare for El Niño and the weather events that it brings.

Deep Currents

Teach Key Concepts

L1

Deep Currents versus Surface Currents

Focus Tell students that although deep currents and surface currents can be related, the currents are very different.

Teach Ask: **Where do surface currents flow?** *(In the upper 200 m of water)* **Where do deep currents flow?** *(At greater depth)* **What causes surface currents to flow?** *(Wind)* **What causes deep currents to flow?** *(Differences in density)*

Apply Ask: **Which type of current could form in the North Atlantic Ocean, sink, and then flow south along the ocean floor?** *(A deep current)* **learning modality: logical/mathematical**

Teaching Resources

- Transparency H39

Upwelling

Teach Key Concepts

L1

Focus Remind students that plants need nutrients to grow. Tell them that the algae that live in the ocean also need nutrients. Help students understand that nutrients are compounds such as nitrates that are dissolved in the water.

Teach Ask: **If algae need nutrients to grow and reproduce, how do you think upwelling water affects algae populations in the ocean?** *(The nutrients in the water cause algae to become abundant.)* **Why might other organisms benefit from abundant algae?** *(Algae are the base of the food chain.)*

Apply Ask: **How would ocean life in this area be affected if upwelling stopped and warm water flowed in?** *(Algae and other organisms would be less abundant.)* **How would this affect the fishing industry?** *(It would hurt it; fewer fish could be caught)* **learning modality: logical/mathematical**

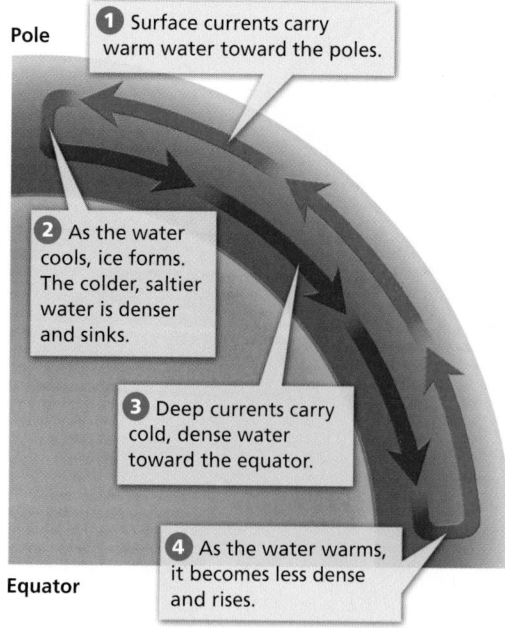

Pole
1 Surface currents carry warm water toward the poles.
2 As the water cools, ice forms. The colder, saltier water is denser and sinks.
3 Deep currents carry cold, dense water toward the equator.
4 As the water warms, it becomes less dense and rises.
Equator

FIGURE 20
Deep Currents
Deep currents are caused by differences in the density of ocean water.

Deep Currents

Deep below the ocean surface, another type of current causes chilly waters to creep slowly across the ocean floor. **These deep currents are caused by differences in the density of ocean water.**

As you read earlier, the density of water depends on its temperature and its salinity. When a warm surface current moves from the equator toward one of the poles, it gradually cools. As ice forms near the poles, the salinity of the water increases from the salt left behind during freezing. As its temperature decreases and its salinity increases, the water becomes denser and sinks. Then, the cold water flows back along the ocean floor as a deep current. Deep currents are affected by the Coriolis effect, which causes them to curve.

Deep currents move and mix water around the world. They carry cold water from the poles toward the equator. Deep currents flow slowly. They may take as long as 1,000 years to flow from the pole to the equator and back again!

Upwelling

In most parts of the ocean, surface waters do not usually mix with deep ocean waters. However, mixing sometimes occurs when winds cause upwelling. **Upwelling** is the movement of cold water upward from the deep ocean. As winds blow away the warm surface water, cold water rises to replace it.

Upwelling brings up tiny ocean organisms, minerals, and other nutrients from the deeper layers of the water. Without this motion, the surface waters of the open ocean would be very scarce in nutrients. Because nutrients are plentiful, zones of upwelling are usually home to huge schools of fish.

One major area of upwelling lies in the Pacific Ocean off the west coast of South America. Many people depend on this rich fishing area for food and jobs. The arrival of El Niño prevents upwelling from occurring. Without the nutrients brought by upwelling, fish die or go elsewhere to find food, reducing the fishing catch that season and hurting people's livelihoods.

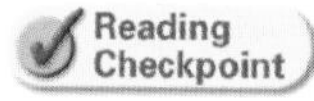
What is upwelling?

FIGURE 21
Upwelling
As cold water rises from the deep ocean, it brings a new supply of nutrients to the surface. The nutrients feed enormous schools of fish such as these anchovies.
Relating Cause and Effect *What causes cold water to rise during upwelling?*

Section 4 Assessment

Target Reading Skill **Relating Cause and Effect** Refer to your graphic organizer about the causes of ocean currents to answer Questions 1 and 2 below.

Reviewing Key Concepts

1. a. **Defining** What is a current?
   b. **Describing** What causes surface currents to occur? How do surface currents affect the climate of coastal areas?
   c. **Predicting** What type of climate might a coastal area have if nearby currents are cold?
2. a. **Explaining** Explain how deep currents form and move in the ocean.
   b. **Comparing and Contrasting** Compare the causes and effects of deep currents and surface currents.
3. a. **Reviewing** What causes upwelling?
   b. **Explaining** Why are huge schools of fish usually found in zones of upwelling?
   c. **Applying Concepts** Why would the ability to predict the occurrence of El Niño be important for the fishing industry on the western coast of South America?

Lab zone At-Home Activity

Modeling the Coriolis Effect With the help of a family member, use chalk and a globe to model the Coriolis effect. Have your family member slowly rotate the globe in an easterly direction. As the globe rotates, draw a line from the North Pole to the equator. Use your knowledge of the Coriolis effect to explain why the line is curved.

Monitor Progress 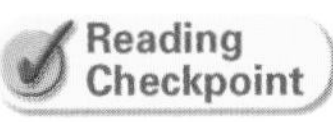 L2

Answers
Figure 21 Winds that blow away warm surface water.

Reading Checkpoint Upwelling is the upward movement of cold water from the ocean depths.

All in One Teaching Resources
- Transparency H40

Assess

Reviewing Key Concepts

1. a. A current is a large stream of water moving through the ocean. **b.** Wind causes surface currents to occur. The currents affect climate by warming or cooling air or by providing a source of moisture. **c.** The climate will likely be cool.
2. a. Deep currents form when dense ocean water near the poles sinks and flows slowly along the ocean floor toward the equator. **b.** Wind causes surface currents, but differences in water density cause deep currents. Surface currents move water relatively quickly. Deep currents move more slowly along the ocean bottom.
3. a. Upwelling occurs when wind blows surface water away from a coast and cold water rises from the ocean depths. **b.** Upwelling brings up nutrients from the ocean depths. **c.** El Niño reduces the number of fish in this region. People in the fishing industry might change their fishing patterns or fish at different locations.

Reteach L1

List *surface current, El Niño, deep current,* and *upwelling* on the board. Have students write a definition for each term.

Performance Assessment L2

Oral Presentation Have students write news articles about an effect of a strong El Niño. Students might want to include a mock interview in their article.

All in One Teaching Resources
- Section Summary: *Currents and Climate*
- Review and Reinforcement: *Currents and Climate*
- Enrich: *Currents and Climate*

Lab zone At-Home Activity

Modeling the Coriolis Effect L1
Students will observe that the line is curved toward the right. Encourage students to explain to their families that this is what happens to ocean currents as a result of Earth's rotation.

Lab zone Chapter Project

Keep Students on Track Students should make final changes to their shoreline protection structures and test their improved structures. How much additional wave action does the lighthouse withstand? To determine this, students should note how many waves it can take and how high the waves must be to topple the lighthouse.

Modeling Ocean Currents

L2

Prepare for Inquiry

Key Concept
Wind blowing across the ocean's surface creates currents that affect climate along coasts.

Skills Objectives
After this lab, students will be able to
- make a model of the Atlantic Ocean and surrounding land masses
- observe currents flowing around their model ocean
- infer how currents affect climate on nearby land masses

Prep Time 30 minutes
Class Time 40 minutes

Advance Planning
Rheoscopic fluid is a liquid that contains light-reflecting particles. It can be ordered from Novostar Innovations for Education, 317 South Main Street, Burlington, NC 27216-1382 (www.novostar.com).

Alternative Materials
Cafeteria trays can be used instead of baking trays for this lab.

All in One Teaching Resources
- Lab Worksheet: *Modeling Ocean Currents*

Guide Inquiry

Invitation
Help students focus on the key concept by asking these questions: **What causes surface currents?** *(Wind blowing across the ocean)* **What determines whether a surface current has warm water or cold water?** *(The area from which it originates; currents that start near the equator are warm and currents that start near the poles are cold.)* **How do surface currents affect climate along coasts?** *(They warm or cool the air above, which influences the climate on nearby land.)*

Lab zone Skills Lab

Modeling Ocean Currents

Problem
How can you model the movement of ocean water caused by surface currents?

Skills Focus
making models, observing, inferring

Materials
- rectangular baking tray
- chalk
- modeling clay, 3 sticks
- ruler
- permanent marker
- hole puncher
- newspaper
- construction paper, blue and red
- jointed drinking straws, one per student
- light-reflecting rheoscopic fluid, 400 mL (or water and food coloring)

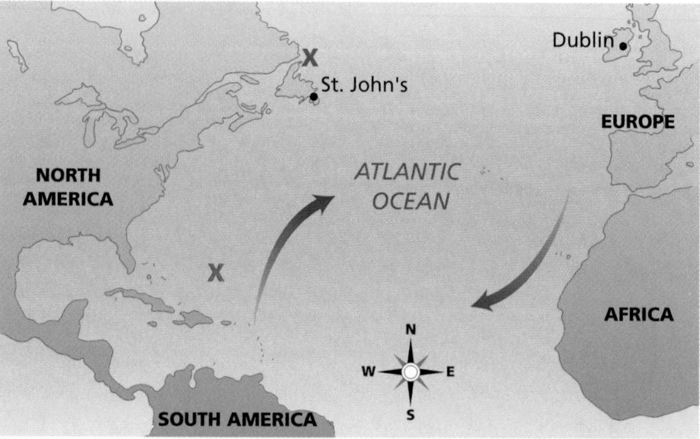

Procedure
1. Cover your work area with newspaper. Place the baking tray on top of the newspaper.
2. Using the map as a guide, draw a chalk outline of the eastern coast of North and South America on the left side of the tray. Draw the outline of the west coast of Europe and Africa on the right side of the tray.
3. Use modeling clay to create the continents, roughly following the chalk outlines you have drawn. Build the continents to a depth of about 3 cm. Press the clay tightly to the pan to form a watertight seal.
4. Fill the ocean area of your model with rheoscopic fluid (or water and food coloring) to a depth of 1 cm.
5. Place 10 blue paper punches in the ocean area marked with a blue X on the map. Place 10 red paper punches in the area marked with a red X.
6. Select a drinking straw and bend it at the joint. Write your initials on the short end of the straw with the marker.
7. With a partner, simulate the pattern of winds that blow in this region of the world. One partner should position his or her straw across the westernmost bulge of Africa and blow toward the west (see arrow on map). The other partner should position his or her straw across the northern end of South America and blow toward the northeast (see arrow on map). Make sure that the straws are bent and that the short ends are parallel to the ocean surface. Both partners should begin blowing gently through the straws at the same time. Try to blow as continuously as possible for one to two minutes.
8. Observe the motion of the fluid and paper punches over the surface of the ocean. Notice what happens when the fluid and punches flow around landmasses.

Introduce the Procedure
Allow students time to read through the procedure. Ask: **What is the purpose of the paper punches?** *(They move with the current and make it easier to see the current's direction.)* **Why does it matter in which direction you blow on the surface of the water?** *(Students are modeling specific winds.)*

Analyze and Conclude

1. **Making Models** Draw a map that shows the pattern of ocean currents that was produced in your model. Use red arrows to show the flow of warm water moving north from the equator. Use blue arrows to show the flow of cold water southward from the polar regions.
2. **Classifying** Use Figure 17 to add names to the currents you drew on your map. Which currents are warm-water currents? Which are cold-water currents?
3. **Observing** Based on what you observed with your model, describe the relationship between winds and surface currents in the ocean.
4. **Inferring** Dublin, Ireland, is located at the same latitude as St. John's in Newfoundland, Canada. However, when it's 8°C in Dublin in January, it's usually below 0°C in St. John's. Use your knowledge of ocean currents to explain why the climate in Dublin is different from the climate in St. John's.
5. **Communicating** Suppose you wanted to sail to Europe from the East Coast of the United States. Write a dialogue you might have with a crew member in which you discuss two natural factors that could help speed up the trip.

Design an Experiment

Design an investigation in which you simulate an upwelling off the coast of Africa. (*Hint:* You may use a model similar to the one used in this investigation.) *Obtain your teacher's permission before carrying out your investigation.*

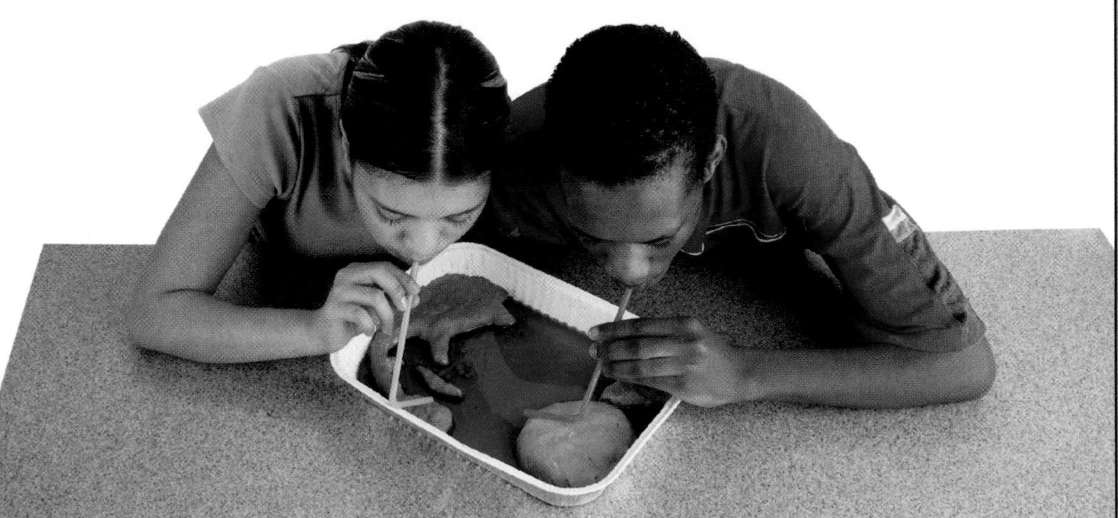

Troubleshooting the Experiment

- Check students' models of the continents before they add water so they can modify the shapes if necessary.
- Make sure students are blowing in the correct directions.

Expected Outcome

Students should observe that the paper punches travel roughly clockwise around the model ocean.

Analyze and Conclude

1. Students' maps should show that the water current moved in a circular path around the Atlantic Ocean north of the equator. Red arrows should show that warm water flowed northeast from the Gulf of Mexico toward the northern Atlantic. Blue arrows should show that cold water flowed southwest from the northern Atlantic toward the Caribbean.

2. Warm-water currents include the Gulf Stream, North Atlantic Drift, and North Equatorial Current. Cold-water currents include the Canary Current.

3. Surface currents flowed in the same direction as the winds blew in the model.

4. The warm waters of the Gulf Stream cause a warm climate in Dublin, whereas the cold waters of the Labrador Current cause a cool climate in St. John's.

5. To sail to Europe from the East Coast of the United States, the Gulf Stream and the prevailing westerlies could help speed the trip.

Extend Inquiry

Design an Experiment Students can simulate an upwelling by modeling a wind blowing off the coast of Africa onto the ocean surface.

Study Guide

- Complete student edition
- Section and chapter self-assessments
- Assessment reports for teachers

Help Students Read

Building Vocabulary

Vocabulary Knowledge Rating Chart Have students construct a chart with four columns: Term, Can Define or Use It, Have Heard or Seen It, Don't Know. Students should copy the vocabulary words for this chapter and place a checkmark under one of the other columns for each term.

Words in Context Students select key terms from the Don't Know column of their Vocabulary Knowledge Rating Chart. Have students write a sentence for each term that places the term in a correct context.

Connecting Concepts

Concept Maps Help students develop one way to show how the information in this chapter is related. Waves, surface currents, and upwellings are the result of winds blowing across the ocean, while the interaction of Earth, the moon, and the sun causes tides. Deep currents are the result of differences in density of ocean water. Have students brainstorm to identify the key concepts, key terms, details, and examples, then write each one on a sticky note and attach it at random on chart paper or on the board.

Tell students that this concept map will be organized in hierarchical order and begin at the top with key concepts. Ask students these questions to guide them to categorize the information on the sticky notes: **How are waves formed? How does the formation of waves differ from tides? How do ocean temperatures and salinity affect the formation of deep currents? How do surface currents and upwellings differ from deep currents?**

Chapter 3

Study Guide

1 Wave Action

Key Concepts

- Most waves form when winds blowing across the water's surface transmit their energy to the water.
- Near shore, wave height increases and wavelength decreases.
- As waves come ashore, water washes up the beach at an angle, carrying sand grains. The water and sand then run straight back down the beach. Waves shape a beach by eroding the shore in some places and building it up in others.

Key Terms

wave
wavelength
frequency
wave height
tsunami
longshore drift
rip current
groin

2 Tides

Key Concepts

- Tides are caused by the interaction of Earth, the moon, and the sun.
- Changes in the positions of Earth, the moon, and the sun affect the heights of the tides during a month.
- The movement of huge amounts of water between high and low tides is a source of potential energy.

Key Terms

tides
spring tide
neap tide

3 Ocean Water Chemistry

Key Concepts

- On average, one kilogram of ocean water contains about 35 grams of salts.
- Like temperatures on land, temperatures at the surface of the ocean vary with location and the seasons. Gases in ocean water vary as well.
- As you descend through the ocean, the water temperature decreases. Pressure increases continuously with depth in the ocean.

Key Terms

salinity
submersible

4 Currents and Climate

Key Concepts

- Surface currents, which affect water to a depth of several hundred meters, are driven mainly by winds. A surface current warms or cools the air above it, influencing the climate of the land near the coast.
- Deep currents are caused by differences in the density of ocean water. Deep currents move and mix water around the world. They carry cold water from the poles toward the equator.
- Upwelling brings up tiny ocean organisms, minerals, and other nutrients from the deeper layers of the water. Without this motion, the surface waters of the open ocean would be very scarce in nutrients.

Key Terms

current
Coriolis effect
climate
El Niño
upwelling

Prompt students by using connecting words or phrases, such as "results in," "is caused by," and "is affected by," to indicate the basis for the organization of the map. The phrases should form a sentence between or among a set of concepts.

Answer Accept logical presentations by students.

All in One Teaching Resources

- Key Terms Review: *Ocean Motions*
- Connecting Concepts: *Ocean Motions*

Review and Assessment

Go Online PHSchool.com
For: Self-Assessment
Visit: PHSchool.com
Web Code: cfa-3030

Organizing Information

Sequencing Copy the flowchart about the movement of a wave onto a separate sheet of paper. Then complete it by putting the following three steps in the correct sequence: wave travels as low swell; wave breaks on shore; wavelength decreases and wave height increases. (For more on Sequencing, see the Skills Handbook.)

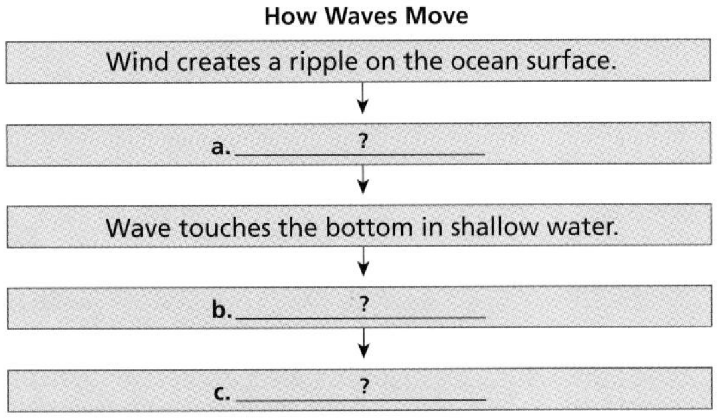

How Waves Move
Wind creates a ripple on the ocean surface.
a. ?
Wave touches the bottom in shallow water.
b. ?
c. ?

Reviewing Key Terms

Choose the letter of the best answer.

1. Rolling waves with a large horizontal distance between crests have a long
   - **a.** wave height.
   - **b.** wavelength.
   - **c.** frequency.
   - **d.** trough.
2. Groins are built to reduce the effect of
   - **a.** tsunamis.
   - **b.** longshore drift.
   - **c.** rip currents.
   - **d.** deep currents.
3. At the full moon, the combined gravitational pulls of the sun and moon produce the biggest difference between low and high tide, called a
   - **a.** surface current.
   - **b.** neap tide.
   - **c.** spring tide.
   - **d.** rip current.
4. Ocean water is more dense than fresh water at the same temperature because of
   - **a.** pressure.
   - **b.** the Coriolis effect.
   - **c.** upwelling.
   - **d.** salinity.
5. Winds and currents move in curved paths because of
   - **a.** the Coriolis effect.
   - **b.** longshore drift.
   - **c.** wave height.
   - **d.** tides.
6. Cold and warm ocean water is carried around the world by
   - **a.** spring tides.
   - **b.** neap tides.
   - **c.** currents.
   - **d.** tsunamis.

Writing in Science

Essay Suppose you were planning to take part in an around-the-world sailing race. Write a short essay about the knowledge of currents that you will need to prepare for the race.

Ocean Motions
Video Preview
Video Field Trip
▶ Video Assessment

Go Online PHSchool.com
For: Self-assessment
Visit: PHSchool.com
Web Code: cfa-3030

Students can take a practice test online that is automatically scored.

All in One Teaching Resources

- Transparency H41
- Chapter Test
- Performance Assessment Teacher Notes
- Performance Assessment Student Worksheet
- Performance Assessment Scoring Rubric

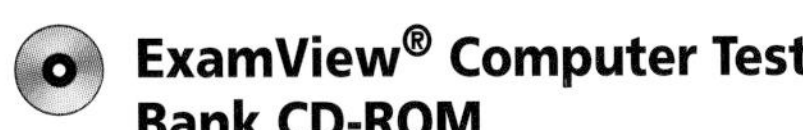

ExamView® Computer Test Bank CD-ROM

Review and Assessment

Organizing Information

a. Wave travels as a low swell
b. Wavelength decreases and wave height increases
c. Wave breaks on shore

Reviewing Key Terms

1. b **2.** b **3.** c **4.** d **5.** a **6.** c

Writing in Science

Writing Mode Descriptive

Scoring Rubric

4 Exceeds criteria by including a complete description about how currents could be used to race around the world
3 Meets criteria by including a description of currents and general knowledge about how they can be used in the race
2 Demonstrates knowledge of currents but does not explain how currents could be used in the race
1 Demonstrates inaccurate knowledge

Ocean Motions

Show the Video Assessment to review chapter content and as a prompt for the writing assignment. Discussion question: **What causes tides?** *(Tides are the response to the gravitational pull of the moon and sun.)* **How do currents affect Earth?** *(Currents circulate the warmer water away from the equator and bring cooler water toward the equator from the poles. A surface current can warm or cool the air above it and, as a result, influence the climate of coastal regions.)*

Checking Concepts

7. The strength of the wind and length of time and distance over which the wind blows all influence the size of a wave.

8. As a wave approaches the shore, its bottom begins to make contact with the sloping ocean floor. The friction that results slows down the wave and changes its shape.

9. A rip current forms when water trapped behind a sandbar rushes away from the shore through a narrow opening.

10. There are two high tides a day in most places because, as Earth rotates on its axis once every 24 hours, each place on Earth passes through a tidal bulge two times.

11. A spring tide has the largest difference between high and low tide. It occurs twice a month, when the sun, Earth, and moon are all aligned. A neap tide has the smallest difference between high and low tide. It occurs when the sun, Earth, and moon form a right angle.

12. Salinity increases the density and lowers the freezing point of ocean water.

13. The Coriolis effect is the apparent deflection of winds and currents caused by Earth's rotation. In the Northern Hemisphere, it causes currents to curve to the right.

14. Warm-water currents make the climate milder and wetter because the air acquires heat and moisture.

15. El Niño is an unusual climate event that occurs every two to seven years in the Pacific Ocean. It can have many effects, such as preventing the upwelling of nutrients off the western coast of South America and causing shifts in weather patterns around the world.

16. Upwelling occurs when wind blows warm surface water away from the coast, allowing cold water to rise up to replace it. Upwelling brings tiny organisms, minerals, and nutrients from the deeper layers of water, and this attracts large numbers of fish.

Review and Assessment

Checking Concepts

7. What factors influence the size of a wave?
8. Why does the height of a wave change as it approaches shore?
9. How does a rip current form?
10. Why are there two high tides a day in most places?
11. What is a spring tide? How does it differ from a neap tide?
12. Name two properties of ocean water affected by salinity. How does salinity affect each?
13. What is the Coriolis effect? How does it influence ocean currents?
14. How do warm-water currents influence climate?
15. What is El Niño? What are some of its effects?
16. Describe the cause and effects of upwelling.

Thinking Critically

17. **Predicting** How will the duck's location change as the wave moves? Explain your answer.

18. **Applying Concepts** Would you expect the salinity of the ocean to be high or low in a rainy region near the mouth of a river? Why?
19. **Comparing and Contrasting** In what ways is the ocean at 1,000 meters deep different from the ocean at the surface in the same location?
20. **Relating Cause and Effect** How does the movement of ocean currents explain the fact that much of western Europe has a mild, wet climate?
21. **Classifying** Classify the following movements of ocean water by stating whether or not each is caused by winds: waves, tides, surface currents, deep currents, upwelling.

Math Practice

22. **Calculating Density** Two 1-liter samples of water were taken from the ocean, one during the winter, and one during the summer. Sample A has a mass of 1.02 kg. Sample B has a mass of 1.05 kg. Which sample was taken during the winter? Explain your answer.

Applying Skills

Use the data to answer Questions 23–25.

The temperature readings in the table were obtained in the Atlantic Ocean near Bermuda.

Ocean Temperatures

Depth (m)	Temp. (°C)	Depth (m)	Temp. (°C)
0	19	1,000	9
200	18	1,200	5
400	18	1,400	5
600	16	1,600	4
800	12	1,800	4

23. **Graphing** Construct a line graph using the data in the table. Plot depth readings on the horizontal axis and temperature readings on the vertical axis.
24. **Drawing Conclusions** Use your graph to identify the temperature range in the transition zone.
25. **Predicting** Predict how the ocean temperature at depths of 0 meters and at 1,400 meters would change with the seasons in this location. Explain your reasoning.

Lab zone Chapter Project

Performance Assessment Using your model, present your method of shoreline protection to the class. Show your classmates how the method you chose protects the lighthouse from ocean waves and the beach erosion that can result.

Lab zone Chapter Project

L3

Performance Assessment

As students demonstrate their best methods of erosion control, assess how well the method prevents beach erosion and protects the lighthouse. Students can explain other methods they tried and why they were less successful. Students can compare their methods with those of other students. If the methods differ, they should reflect on how these differences affected the results. Students should also consider how their models differ from real beaches.

Standardized Test Prep

Test-Taking Tip

Interpreting Diagrams

When answering questions about a diagram, examine the diagram carefully, including all the labels. For example, the labels on the diagram below identify the shoreline, a series of groins, and the longshore drift. The arrow labeled *Longshore Drift* shows the direction of the drift. The diagram also has an arrow indicating which way is north on the diagram. Study the diagram and answer the sample question below it.

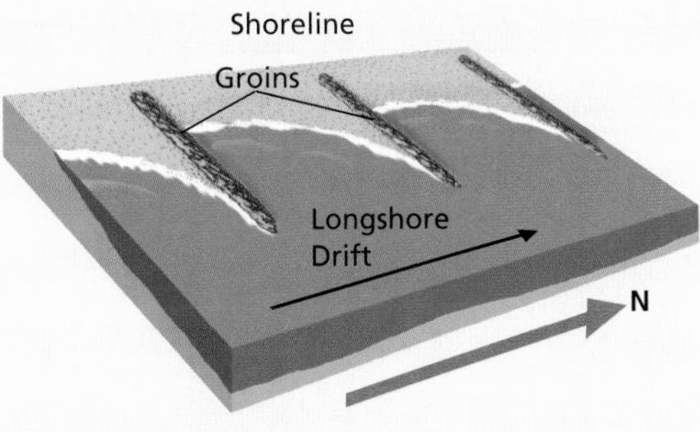

Sample Question

Where will sand pile up against the groins shown in the diagram?

A on the north side of the groins
B on the west side of the groins
C on the south side of the groins
D No sand will pile up against the groins.

Answer

The correct answer is **C**. By looking at the direction of the longshore drift and the north arrow, you can see that sand has begun to pile up on the south side of the groins.

Choose the letter of the best answer.

1. A scientist plans to test the effect temperature has on the density of ocean water. What will the manipulated variable be in her experiment?

A density
B salinity
C temperature
D water depth

2. In which of the following areas would the salinity of the ocean water be the highest?

F in a hot, dry area
G near a rainy coastal area close to the equator
H at the mouth of a large river
J in cold, deep water, near the ocean bottom

3. A major warm ocean surface current flows along a coastal area. What type of climate would you most likely find in the area influenced by the current?

A extremely hot and dry
B cool and dry
C extremely cool and wet
D mild and wet

Use the wave diagram below and your knowledge of science to answer Questions 4–5.

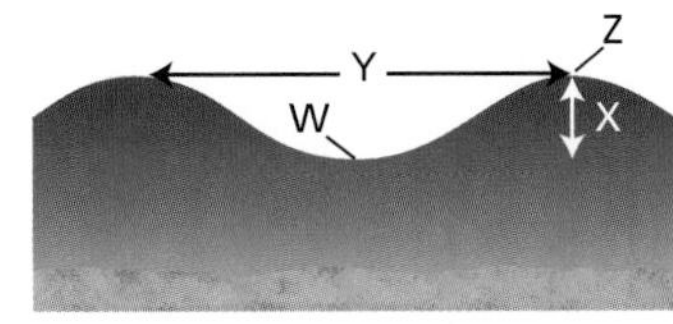

4. What is the wave feature labeled **W** in the diagram?

F wave crest
G wave trough
H wavelength
J wave height

5. What is the wave feature labeled **Y** in the diagram?

A wave crest
B wave trough
C wavelength
D wave height

Constructed Response

6. Some people refer to a tsunami as a tidal wave. Explain why this is incorrect. In your answer, describe what a tsunami is and how it forms.

Standardized Test Prep

1. C **2.** F **3.** D **4.** G **5.** C

6. A tsunami is incorrectly called a tidal wave because some people think it is caused by tides. Earthquakes at the bottom of the ocean cause tsunamis. Tsunamis travel as very long waves. As they near the shore, the length of the wave decreases and the height of the wave increases, causing a high wall of water to crash onto shore.

Thinking Critically

17. As the wave passes, the duck bobs up and then down again. Water particles move in a circular motion, which causes the duck to move in a circular motion.

18. You would expect the salinity to be low because rain and river water are both fresh.

19. Compared to the surface, ocean water at 1,000 meters is colder, darker, denser, and at higher pressure. Water at 1,000 meters might also be more or less salty than water at the surface.

20. Much of western Europe has a mild, wet climate because the Gulf Stream brings warm water from the Gulf of Mexico northeast across the Atlantic to the coast of Europe. Winds blowing inland across this warm current make the climate warmer and wetter on the mainland.

21. Waves, yes; tides, no; surface currents, yes; deep currents, no; upwelling, yes

Math Practice

22. Sample B was taken during the winter because it has a higher density. Cold water is denser than warm water. The water might also have a higher salinity because of reduced winter precipitation.

Applying Skills

23. Students' graphs should be properly labeled with depth on the *x*-axis and temperature on the *y*-axis. The curve should be highest at 0 meters, fall to the right as depth increases, and then level out at about 1,200 meters.

24. The transition zone occurs between about 400 meters and 1,200 meters. Between these depths, the temperature drops from about 18°C to 5°C. The range is 13°C.

25. Answers will vary. Students might predict that temperature at the surface fluctuates from season to season because the water is warmed by the sun more in summer than in winter. Temperature at 1,400 meters will not change with the seasons because it is too deep for sunlight to penetrate.

Chapter at a Glance

PRENTICE HALL

 Chapter Project *At Home in the Sea*

Technology | **Local Standards**

All in One Teaching Resources

- Chapter Project Teacher Notes, pp. 248–249
- Chapter Project Student Introduction, pp. 250–251
- Chapter Project Student Worksheets, pp. 252–253
- Chapter Project Scoring Rubric, p. 254

Video Preview

Section 1

Exploring the Ocean

3–4 periods
1–2 blocks

H.4.1.1 Discuss the reasons that people have studied the ocean.
H.4.1.2 Identify the features and main sections of the ocean floor.
H.4.1.3 Describe the processes that have shaped the ocean floor.

Video Field Trip

Ocean Habitats

1–2 periods
1/2–1 block

H.4.2.1 Identify the zones into which scientists divide the ocean.
H.4.2.2 Describe how marine organisms are classified.

Intertidal Zone

1–2 periods
1/2–1 block

H.4.3.1 Identify the conditions that organisms in the rocky intertidal zone must tolerate.
H.4.3.2 List and describe the major types of coastal wetlands.

Neritic Zone and Open Ocean

2–3 periods
1–1 1/2 blocks

H.4.4.1 Describe the conditions in the neritic zone.
H.4.4.2 Describe two neritic zone habitats—coral reefs and kelp forests.
H.4.4.3 Describe the conditions in the open ocean.

Resources From the Ocean

3–4 periods
1–2 blocks

H.4.5.1 Explain how people use living resources from the ocean.
H.4.5.2 Identify the ocean's nonliving resources.
H.4.5.3 Identify sources of ocean pollution.

Review and Assessment

All in One Teaching Resources

- Key Terms Review, p. 297
- Transparency H56
- Performance Assessment Teacher Notes, p. 304
- Performance Assessment Scoring Rubric, p. 305
- Performance Assessment Student Worksheet, p. 306
- Chapter Test, pp. 307–310

Video Assessment

Test Preparation

Test Preparation Blackline Masters

Chapter Activities Planner

For more activities
LAB ZONE Easy Planner CD-ROM

Student Edition	Inquiry	Time	Materials	Skills	Resources
Chapter Project, p. 129	Open-Ended	Ongoing (2–3 weeks)	See Chapter Project in All in One **Teaching Resources** See p. 24	modeling, interpreting data, communicating	**Lab zone Easy Planner** All in One **Teaching Resources** Support pp. 248–254
Section 1					
Discover Activity, p. 130	Guided	10 minutes	10 plastic drinking straws, covered box with mystery object	Inferring	**Lab zone Easy Planner**
Skills Lab, p. 140	Guided	30 minutes	Pencil, graph paper	Graphing, predicting, inferring	**Lab zone Easy Planner** **Lab Activity Video** All in One **Teaching Resources** Skills Lab: *The Shape of the Ocean Floor,* pp. 263–264
Section 2					
Discover Activity, p. 141	Guided	10 minutes	String, index cards	Inferring	**Lab zone Easy Planner**
Try This Activity, p. 142	Directed	10 minutes	Ball-point pen, milk carton, water	Making Models	**Lab zone Easy Planner**
Section 3					
Discover Activity, p. 146	Inferring	15 minutes	Ping-pong ball, rock, box of common materials (such as suction cups, glue, tape, string, rubber bands, plastic wrap, hooks, clay) sink or deep pan, water	Inferring	**Lab zone Easy Planner**
Section 4					
Discover Activity, p. 150	Directed	20 minutes	Permanent marker, white plastic lid, scissors, string, paper clip, tape, meterstick, bucket, tap water, flour, plastic spoon, stirring rod	Observing	**Lab zone Easy Planner**
Skills Activity, p. 155	Directed	10 minutes	None	Inferring	**Lab zone Easy Planner**
Section 5					
Discover Activity, p. 158	Directed	15 minutes	Labels from household products such as cooking thickeners, foods, abrasives, polishes, shampoos, and spice mixes containing sea salt	Classifying	**Lab zone Easy Planner**
Try This Activity, p. 160	Directed	20 minutes, then several hours	0.5-ounce package of agar, 1 cup sugar, 4 cups guava juice or other fruit juice, food coloring, water, saucepan, shallow pan, kitchen spatula	Inferring	**Lab zone Easy Planner**
Skills Lab, p. 165	Guided	40 minutes	water, feather, marking pen, shallow pan, paper towels, paper cup, cotton balls, vegetable oil, plastic dropper, wooden sticks, 100-mL graduated cylinder	Making models, observing	**Lab zone Easy Planner** **Lab Activity Video** All in One **Teaching Resources** Skills Lab: *Cleaning Up an Oil Spill,* pp. 294–296

Section 1 Exploring the Ocean

ABILITY LEVELS
L1 Basic to Average
L2 For All Students
L3 Average to Advanced

 *3–4 periods, 1–2 blocks*

Objectives

H.4.1.1 Discuss the reasons that people have studied the ocean.
H.4.1.2 Identify the features and main sections of the ocean floor.
H.4.1.3 Describe the processes that have shaped the ocean floor.

Local Standards

Key Terms

• sonar • continental shelf • continental slope • abyssal plain • mid-ocean ridge
• trench • plate • seafloor spreading

Preteach

Build Background Knowledge

Describe the ocean floor.

 *What Can You Learn Without Seeing?* L1

Targeted Print and Technology Resources

All in One Teaching Resources

L2 Reading Strategy Transparency: Building Vocabulary

Presentation-Pro CD-ROM

Instruct

Learning About the Ocean Compare how ancient and modern people have studied the ocean.

Features of the Ocean Floor Describe ocean floor features and compare the features to those on the continents.

Movements of the Ocean Floor Contrast plate movements.

 *The Shape of the Ocean Floor* L2

Targeted Print and Technology Resources

All in One Teaching Resources

L2 Guided Reading, pp. 257–260
L2 Transparencies H42, H43, H44, H45
L2 Skills Lab: *The Shape of the Ocean Floor,* pp. 263–264

Lab Activity Video/DVD
Skills Lab: *The Shape of the Ocean Floor*

www.SciLinks.org Web Code: scn-0841

Student Edition on Audio CD

Assess

Section Assessment Questions

Have students use their definitions of key terms to answer the questions.

Reteach

Diagram the ocean floor.

Targeted Print and Technology Resources

All in One Teaching Resources

• Section Summary, p. 256
L1 Review and Reinforce, p. 261
L3 Enrich, p. 262

Section 2 Ocean Habitats

 *1–2 periods, 1/2–1 block*

ABILITY LEVELS
- L1 Basic to Average
- L2 For All Students
- L3 Average to Advanced

Objectives

H.4.2.1 Identify the zones into which scientists divide the ocean.
H.4.2.2 Describe how marine organisms are classified.

Key Terms

• intertidal zone • neritic zone • open-ocean zone • plankton • nekton • benthos • food web

Local Standards

Preteach

Build Background Knowledge

Describe marine organisms.

How Complex Are Ocean Feeding Relationships? L1

Targeted Print and Technology Resources

Teaching Resources

L2 Reading Strategy Transparency H46: Using Prior Knowledge

Presentation-Pro CD-ROM

Instruct

Ocean Zones and Conditions Infer conditions within ocean zones.

Life in the Ocean Describe nekton, benthos, and plankton.

Targeted Print and Technology Resources

Teaching Resources

L2 Guided Reading, pp. 267–269
L2 Transparencies H47, H48, H49

PHSchool.com Web code: cfp-3042

Student Edition on Audio CD

Assess

Section Assessment Questions

Have students use their using prior knowledge graphic organizers to help them answer the questions.

Reteach

Make a chart that includes the three ocean zones and typical organisms.

Targeted Print and Technology Resources

Teaching Resources

• Section Summary, p. 266
L1 Review and Reinforce, p. 270
L3 Enrich, p. 271

Section 3 Intertidal Zone

 *1–2 periods, 1/2–1 block*

ABILITY LEVELS
L1 Basic to Average
L2 For All Students
L3 Average to Advanced

Objectives

H.4.3.1 Identify the conditions that organisms in the rocky intertidal zone must tolerate.

H.4.3.2 List and describe the major types of coastal wetlands.

Local Standards

Key Terms

- estuary

Preteach

Build Background Knowledge

Students describe the region between the tides.

Can Your Animal Hold On? L1

Targeted Print and Technology Resources

Teaching Resources

L2 Reading Strategy Transparency H50: Outlining

Presentation-Pro CD-ROM

Instruct

Rocky Shores Explain how organisms survive the intertidal zone.

Where River Meets Ocean Discuss brackish water plants.

Targeted Print and Technology Resources

All in One **Teaching Resources**

L2 Guided Reading, pp. 274–276
L2 Transparency H51

PHSchool.com Web code: cfd-3043

Student Edition on Audio CD

Assess

Section Assessment Questions

Have students use their outlining graphic organizers to help them answer the questions.

Reteach

Describe conditions in a tide pool.

Targeted Print and Technology Resources

All in One **Teaching Resources**

- Section Summary, p. 273

L1 Review and Reinforce, p. 277
L3 Enrich, p. 278

Section 4 Neritic Zone and Open Ocean

ABILITY LEVELS
- L1 Basic to Average
- L2 For All Students
- L3 Average to Advanced

 *2–3 periods, 1–1 1/2 blocks*

Objectives

H.4.4.1 Describe the conditions in the neritic zone.
H.4.4.2 Describe two neritic zone habitats—coral reefs and kelp forests.
H.4.4.3 Describe the conditions in the open ocean.

Local Standards

Key Terms

• atoll • bioluminescence • hydrothermal vent

Preteach

Build Background Knowledge

Describe the the ocean beyond the intertidal zone.

 *How Deep Can You See?* L1

Targeted Print and Technology Resources

All in One **Teaching Resources**

L2 Reading Strategy Transparency H52: Relating Cause and Effect

Presentation-Pro CD-ROM

Instruct

Conditions in the Neritic Zone Explain why life is abundant in the neritic zone.

Coral Reefs Describe the environment in which coral reefs grow.

Life in a Kelp Forest Learn about kelp forest habitats.

Conditions in the Open Ocean Describe conditions for life in the open ocean.

Targeted Print and Technology Resources

All in One **Teaching Resources**

L2 Guided Reading, pp. 281–283
L2 Transparency H53

www.SciLinks.org Web Code: scn-0844

Student Edition on Audio CD

Assess

Section Assessment Questions

Have students use their Relating Cause and Effect graphic organizers to help them answer the questions.

Reteach

Diagram the ocean zones.

Targeted Print and Technology Resources

All in One **Teaching Resources**

- Section Summary, p. 280

L1 Review and Reinforce, p. 284
L3 Enrich, p. 285

Section 5 Resources From the Ocean

3–4 periods, 1–2 blocks

ABILITY LEVELS
L1 Basic to Average
L2 For All Students
L3 Average to Advanced

Objectives

H.4.5.1 Explain how people use living resources from the ocean.
H.4.5.2 Identify the ocean's nonliving resources.
H.4.5.3 Identify sources of ocean pollution.

Key Terms

• aquaculture • nodule

Local Standards

Preteach

Build Background Knowledge

Describe familiar resources from the ocean.

Is It From the Ocean? L1

Targeted Print and Technology Resources

Teaching Resources

L2 Reading Strategy Transparency H54: Identifying Main Ideas

Presentation-Pro CD-ROM

Instruct

Living Resources Describe living resources in the sea.

Nonliving Resources Explain why nonliving resources are extracted from the ocean.

Ocean Pollution Use visuals to engage students in a discussion of the sources of ocean pollution.

Cleaning Up an Oil Spill L2

Targeted Print and Technology Resources

All in One Teaching Resources

L2 Guided Reading, pp. 288–291
L2 Transparency H55
L2 Skills Lab: *Cleaning Up an Oil Spill*, pp. 294–296

Lab Activity Video/DVD
Skills Lab: *Cleaning Up an Oil Spill*

www.SciLinks.org Web Code: scn-0845

Student Edition on Audio CD

Assess

Section Assessment Questions

Have students use their Identifying Main Ideas graphic organizers to help them answer the questions.

Reteach

Compare and contrast living and nonliving resources from the sea.

Targeted Print and Technology Resources

All in One Teaching Resources

• Section Summary, p. 287
L1 Review and Reinforce, p. 292
L3 Enrich, p. 293

Chapter 4 Content Refresher

For: Professional Development Support
Visit: www.SciLinks.org/PDLinks
Web Code: scf-0840

Professional Development

Section 1 Exploring the Ocean

The JIM Suit A significant development for deep-sea diving is the JIM suit, named for Jim Jarret, its inventor. This diving suit has joints that allow divers to bend their arms and legs. The JIM suit can protect a diver at depths of up to 450 m. Some JIM suits have thrusters that enable the diver to hover in the water. Most importantly, the suit maintains atmospheric pressure so the diver does not need to undergo decompression when resurfacing.

Originally used for work on oil rigs, the JIM suit was first used for scientific research by Sylvia Earle, a marine biologist who has earned international recognition for her deep-sea explorations. Earle's experiences are described in *Window on the Deep* by Andrea Conley (New York: Franklin Watts, 1991). The image below shows a diver preparing to dive in a JIM suit.

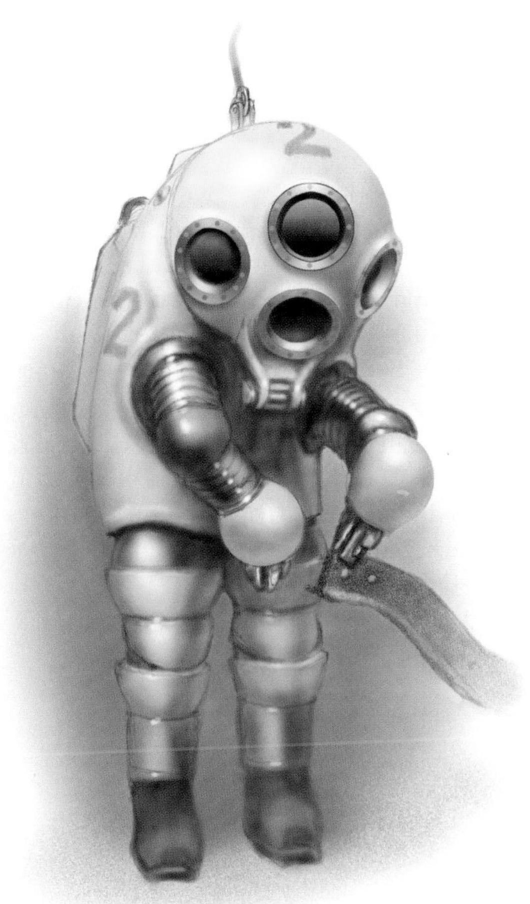

The Ring of Fire Much of the Pacific Ocean is encircled by a series of oceanic trenches and volcanoes known as the Ring of Fire. The volcanic and seismic activity that occurs along the length of the Ring of Fire is caused by the plate tectonics of the Pacific basin. As the ocean floor spreads away from the mid-ocean ridge, it collides with and slides beneath the surrounding continental plates in a process known as subduction. As the plate subducts, rock above the plate melts and forms magma. The magma rises to the surface, creating a volcano.

Over 75 percent of the world's active volcanoes are located in the Ring of Fire. Washington's Mount St. Helens, which erupted catastrophically in 1980, is one of these.

Ocean Sediment Sediment on the ocean floor is of two types. One type forms from the shells and remains of organisms that live in the ocean's waters. The other type consists of material that was eroded from the land. Most of the eroded material is deposited on the continental shelves and at the foot of continental slopes. Many parts of the deep ocean floor are covered with ooze, or sediment, of which at least one third is microscopic shells and the remains of ocean organisms. Sediment thickness varies throughout the ocean. Near the mid-ocean ridge, the newly formed crust has little or no sediment covering it. Away from the ridge, the depth increases to hundreds of meters.

Alfred Wegener In 1915, the German geophysicist and meteorologist Alfred Wegener first published his hypothesis of continental drift. He argued that the continents were once joined together in a single supercontinent, called Pangaea, that broke apart 200–180 million years ago. The continents then drifted to their present locations. As evidence to support his theory, Wegener cited similar types of fossils and ages of geological formations on separate continents.

Wegener's hypothesis was not widely accepted until the 1950s and 1960s, when scientists found evidence of Earth's alternating magnetic poles in bands of rock along the mid-ocean ridge. Interpreting this evidence, geologist Harry Hess proposed that new ocean floor is created at the ridge through the process of sea-floor spreading.

Professional Development

Section 2 Ocean Habitats

The Benthos Benthic organisms are most abundant on the continental shelf, where nutrients and light provide ideal conditions for life. These organisms live on or below the ocean floor. Many species of clams, for example, burrow into the sediment. The animals extend a siphon above the sediment-water boundary and draw in water from which food is filtered. Wastes are ejected through a second siphon. Some benthic organisms are capable of movement and others, called sessile organisms, are anchored to the bottom. Sea anemones and sea lilies are examples of the sessile benthos.

Kinds of Fish There are at least 20,000 species of fish, more than all other kinds of water and land vertebrates put together. Additional species of fish are identified at a rate of more than 100 per year.

Fish are classified in two main groups: fishes without jaws and fishes with jaws. Jawless fishes, such as lampreys and hagfish, are the most primitive fish. Jawed fishes are further divided into two groups: cartilaginous fish, such as sharks and rays, whose skeletons are made of cartilage; and bony fish, such as flounder and cod.

Fish have evolved to live in all kinds of marine habitats, from surface waters to deep within ocean trenches. The most common fish in the ocean is the Cyclothone or "bristlemouth." About the size of a small minnow, it lives at depths of 500 meters or deeper.

Section 3 Intertidal Zone

Organisms in the Intertidal Zone Having regular exposure to waves, air, and sunlight, the intertidal zone is a stressful habitat for the organisms that live there. Many organisms in the rocky shore habitat have some way of sealing in moisture—a slimy coating, for example, or a shell that can be closed. Unlike the organisms that inhabit the rocky shore, organisms that live on a sandy beach generally do not have adaptations to protect them from drying out. Because the sand is constantly shifting and provides little protection from wave action, most beach animals are active burrowers. Rather than staying in one place, many of these animals follow the changing tide line up and down the beach.

Estuary Productivity Estuaries are extremely productive ecosystems. Productivity is a measure of how quickly carbon and nutrients cycle through an ecosystem. Several factors contribute to the high productivity of estuaries. Rivers provide nutrients washed from the land. Ocean tides circulate the nutrients and remove waste products. The numerous plants that grow in the fertile mud of estuaries provide shelter and food for other organisms.

Salt Marshes and Humans In addition to acting as nurseries for many species, salt marshes benefit humans in other ways. They protect the coastline from erosion by acting as a barrier to the force of waves and storm surges. They help to counteract pollutants by filtering, absorbing, and breaking down toxins and wastes. They also conserve open space and provide a habitat for many kinds of migratory birds.

More than half of the salt marshes in the United States have been lost since 1950, mainly through the filling of marshes to create land for development. Others have been ditched for mosquito control. In recent years, salt marshes have begun to be perceived not as wasteland, but as having intrinsic value. This is reflected in federal and state laws designed to protect salt marshes and other wetlands. In April 2004, the federal government established a national goal to achieve an overall increase of America's wetlands each year. The program's goal is to restore, improve, and protect at least three million additional acres of wetlands by 2010.

Section 4 Neritic Zone and Open Ocean

Corals In addition to obtaining food from algae that live inside them, coral polyps capture prey with stinging tentacles. In fact, some coral species do not contain symbiotic algae. However, only those with algae build reefs. During recent years, many tropical reefs have been affected by a mysterious aliment known as "bleaching." Affected corals expel the algae from their tissues and eventually die. Scientists hypothesize that bleaching is triggered by environmental stresses, such as elevated ocean temperatures and higher levels of ultraviolet radiation. Ultraviolet radiation exposure depends on water clarity, which might change during certain climatic events, such as El Niño. The corals pictured below grow in the waters off the Gili Isles of Indonesia.

The Deep Zone The deep zone of the ocean represents most of the water column. This zone is also called the aphotic zone, meaning, "without light." Most deep-ocean species have dark color and have few stripes or other markings. Many deep-zone organisms have small, poorly developed eyes or are completely blind.

Section 5 Resources from the Ocean

Methods of Commercial Fishing Most of the world's commercial fish harvest is caught with huge nets, of which there are three main types. Seines are used to surround schools of large fish. One end of a seine is attached to a large vessel, and the other end is towed by a small, high-powered boat. After the school is surrounded, the bottom of the net is pulled tight, trapping the fish. As you see in the figure below, trawls are funnel-shaped nets with a large, open mouth and a small closed tail. Fish are caught as the trawl is pulled through the water. Gill nets are long, rectangular nets used to form a wall of webbing that entangles fish that swim into it. A fourth type of net, called a drift net, is about 5.5 km long and used mainly in open waters. Its use is controversial because whales, dolphins, marine birds, sea turtles, and other animals are sometimes caught.

Address Misconceptions

Some students think that the ocean has an unlimited supply of resources. For a strategy for overcoming this misconception, see **Address Misconceptions** on page 160.

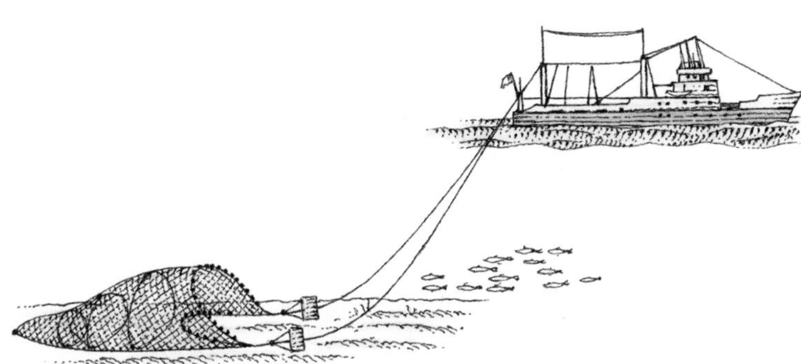

The Impact of Overfishing The world's fisheries are being overfished at an accelerating rate. A United Nations study has concluded that most of the world's fisheries are either already being exploited or have begun to be depleted. In addition to threatening the biodiversity of fish, overfishing impacts the well-being of hundreds of millions of people. Approximately 200 million people, mostly in developing nations, depend on fishing for their livelihood, while 20 percent of the world's population relies on fish as their primary source of protein.

Methane Hydrate In addition to petroleum reserves, the ocean floor contains methane hydrate, another resource that may be used for fuel. Methane hydrate is a form of water ice that contains a large amount of methane. Vast amounts have been discovered buried beneath sediment on the floor of the deep ocean. Researchers believe that these deposits are formed when methane gas seeps from reservoirs far beneath the seabed and comes in contact with water. The combination of the very low temperatures and very high pressures in the deep ocean causes the methane and water to crystallize.

Methane hydrate deposits on the ocean floor are estimated to amount to many times the known reserves of natural gas. Because of its potential as an energy source, Congress passed the Methane Hydrate Research and Development Act of 2000. Before the ocean's methane hydrate deposits can be used, researchers must develop a practical and environmentally safe way of locating and recovering them.

Help Students Read

Directed Reading/Thinking Activity (DRTA)

Predict, Read, Evaluate, Revise Predictions

Strategy Help students develop their reading and thinking skills by establishing their own purposes for reading. Select a section of this chapter for students to read, such as Section 3, pages 146–149. Before modeling the strategy with students, divide the targeted section into approximately four equal portions. Present the steps shown in the example below.

Example

1. Preview Tell students to survey the section by analyzing the title, headings, visual elements, and boldfaced type. Have students read the introductory and concluding paragraphs.

2. Predict/Generate Questions Ask students to predict what they will learn and to formulate their own "teacher-type" questions to be answered. List students' responses on the board.

3. Read/Evaluate and Revise Predictions Have students read a portion of the section. Pause afterward for students to evaluate their predictions. Discuss any answers to their questions that they learned and any prior misconceptions that were clarified. Ask students to revise their predictions and questions based on their new understanding.

4. Repeat the process for the remaining text portions.

Interactive Textbook

- Complete student edition
- Video and audio
- Simulations and activities
- Section and chapter activities

Chapter 4

Ocean Zones

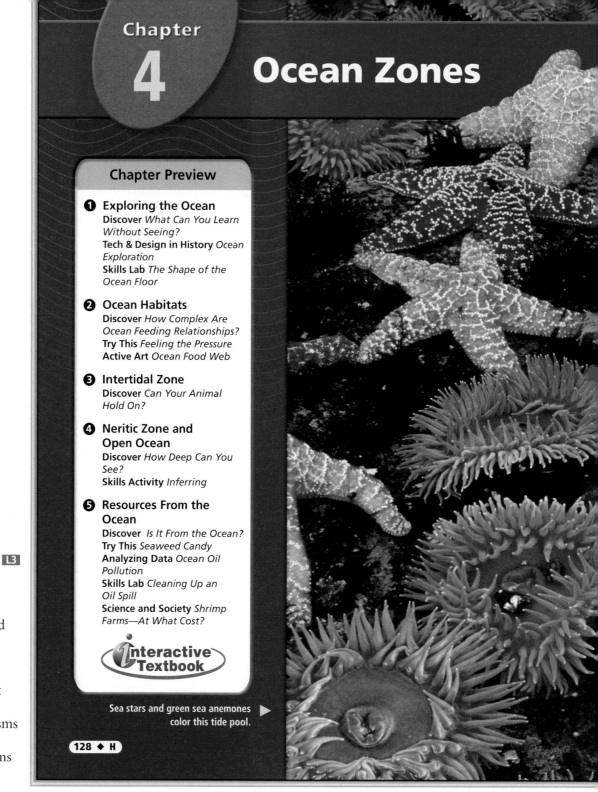

Chapter Preview

1. **Exploring the Ocean**
   Discover *What Can You Learn Without Seeing?*
   Tech & Design in History *Ocean Exploration*
   Skills Lab *The Shape of the Ocean Floor*
2. **Ocean Habitats**
   Discover *How Complex Are Ocean Feeding Relationships?*
   Try This *Feeling the Pressure*
   Active Art *Ocean Food Web*
3. **Intertidal Zone**
   Discover *Can Your Animal Hold On?*
4. **Neritic Zone and Open Ocean**
   Discover *How Deep Can You See?*
   Skills Activity *Inferring*
5. **Resources From the Ocean**
   Discover *Is It From the Ocean?*
   Try This *Seaweed Candy*
   Analyzing Data *Ocean Oil Pollution*
   Skills Lab *Cleaning Up an Oil Spill*
   Science and Society *Shrimp Farms—At What Cost?*

Interactive Textbook

Sea stars and green sea anemones color this tide pool.

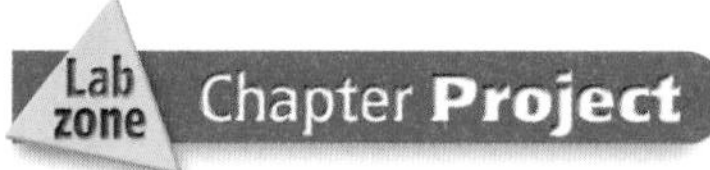

L3

Objectives

This project will enhance students' knowledge of specific marine habitats and the organisms that live there. After this chapter project, students will be able to

- create three-dimensional models of marine habitats and the organisms that live within the habitats
- identify adaptations that enable organisms to survive
- illustrate interactions between organisms and their physical environment

Skills Focus

Interpreting data, evaluating, inferring, communicating

Project Time Line 2–3 weeks

All in One Teaching Resources

- Chapter Project Teacher Notes
- Chapter Project Worksheet 1
- Chapter Project Worksheet 2
- Chapter Project Scoring Rubric

Developing a Plan

During the first week, each group should measure the space available for the habitat model, choose a habitat, research and list its physical features, sketch the planned model for your review, and choose materials for building the model. During the second week, each group should begin building its model habitat. Each group member should choose one organism to model, research its characteristics, and present a plan for your review. During the third week, group members should complete their model organisms, place them in the habitat, and prepare the presentation.

Possible Materials

Provide a wide variety of materials from which students can choose. Encourage students to suggest and use additional materials.

- *To form the habitat enclosure:* cardboard box, sheets of cardboard or posterboard, chicken wire

Discovery Channel School

Ocean Zones

▶ Video Preview

Video Field Trip

Video Assessment

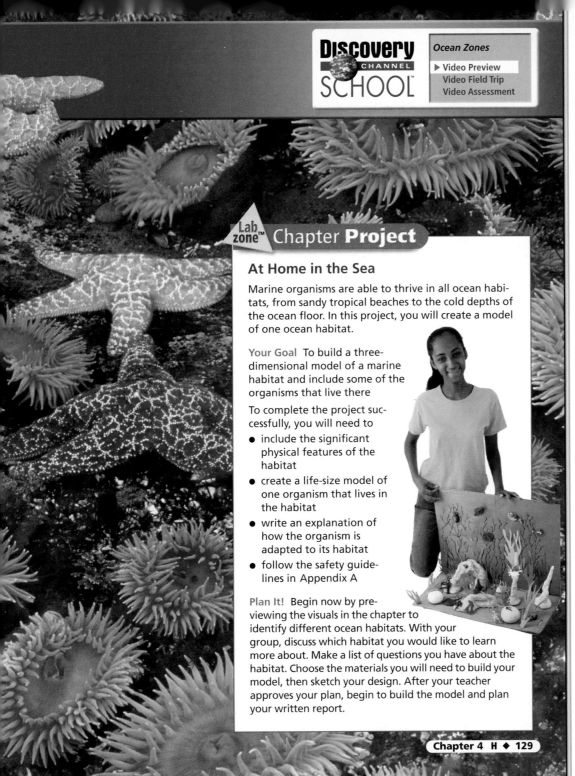

Lab zone™ Chapter Project

At Home in the Sea

Marine organisms are able to thrive in all ocean habitats, from sandy tropical beaches to the cold depths of the ocean floor. In this project, you will create a model of one ocean habitat.

Your Goal To build a three-dimensional model of a marine habitat and include some of the organisms that live there

To complete the project successfully, you will need to

- include the significant physical features of the habitat
- create a life-size model of one organism that lives in the habitat
- write an explanation of how the organism is adapted to its habitat
- follow the safety guidelines in Appendix A

Plan It! Begin now by previewing the visuals in the chapter to identify different ocean habitats. With your group, discuss which habitat you would like to learn more about. Make a list of questions you have about the habitat. Choose the materials you will need to build your model, then sketch your design. After your teacher approves your plan, begin to build the model and plan your written report.

Ocean Zones

Show the Video Preview to introduce the Chapter Project and overview the chapter content. Discussion question: **Where is the deepest part of the ocean and how deep is it?** *("Challenger Deep," at the bottom of the Mariana Trench, southwest of Guam in the Pacific Ocean, is 11 kilometers deep.)*

- *To shape and form the ocean floor:* brown paper, modeling clay, salt dough or paper mâché, plaster of paris, glue, and sand to add texture
- *To make the organisms:* fabric, rolls of brown or white paper, cotton batting or tissue paper, construction paper, foam rubber, styrofoam, household sponges, paints or colored markers, pipe cleaners, toothpicks
- *To show a food web:* colored yarn to connect organisms

Launching the Project

To interest students, show photographs, a video, or CD-ROM of different marine organisms. Encourage students to ask questions and offer comments about the environments and organisms they see, but do not preteach chapter content. Encourage discussion of the various habitats and organisms that could be modeled, materials that could be used, and any initial questions students might have. Have students work in cooperative groups of no more than four to ensure that every student will have ample opportunity to participate. Emphasize that each student is responsible for building his or her own model organism.

Performance Assessment

The Chapter Project Scoring Rubric will help you evaluate how well students complete the Chapter Project. You might want to share the rubric with your students so they know what is expected. Students will be assessed on

- planning their models, including the completeness and accurateness of their final habitat sketches and the thoroughness of their research about their marine organism
- how accurately and neatly they make their models
- how well they present their models to the class
- how well they work in their groups

Section 1 Exploring the Ocean

Objectives

After this lesson, students will be able to

H.4.1.1 Discuss the reasons that people have studied the ocean.

H.4.1.2 Identify the features and main sections of the ocean floor.

H.4.1.3 Describe the processes that have shaped the ocean floor.

Target Reading Skill

Building Vocabulary Explain that knowing the definitions of key-concept words helps students understand what they read.

Answers As students read each paragraph that contains a key term, remind them to write a sentence in their own words. Encourage students to write one or two descriptive phrases to help them remember the key term. Call on students to share their definitions.

Preteach

Build Background Knowledge L1

The Ocean Floor

Ask students to explain what they think the ocean floor is like. Many students will envision a featureless plain. Tell them that large, flat regions do exist on the ocean floor, but that they will be surprised to learn what else exists at the ocean's bottom.

Help Students Read L1

Use Context Clues As students read through the section, have them look for unfamiliar words. Encourage them to use surrounding sentences to help them understand the word. Demonstrate this process with the word *oceanography.*

Section 1 Exploring the Ocean

Reading Preview

Key Concepts

- For what reasons have people studied the ocean?
- What are the main sections of the ocean floor?
- What processes have shaped the ocean floor?

Key Terms

- sonar • continental shelf
- continental slope
- abyssal plain
- mid-ocean ridge • trench
- plate • seafloor spreading

Target Reading Skill

Building Vocabulary A definition states the meaning of a word or phrase by telling about its most important feature or function. After you read the section, reread the paragraphs that contain definitions of Key Terms. Use all the information you have learned to write a definition of each Key Term in your own words.

Lab zone Discover Activity

What Can You Learn Without Seeing?

1. Your teacher will provide your group with ten plastic drinking straws and a covered box containing a mystery object. The top of the box has several holes punched in it. Using the straws as probes, try to determine the size, shape, and location of the object inside the box.
2. Based on the information you gathered, describe your object. What can you say about its length, shape, and position? Write down your hypothesis about the identity of the object.
3. Remove the box top to reveal the object.

Think It Over

Inferring Explain how you used the method of indirect observation to learn about the object.

Imagine going on a voyage around the world that will last three and a half years. Your assignment: to investigate everything about the sea. Your vessel: a ship powered by sails and a steam engine. On board there are thermometers for measuring the temperature of ocean water and cable for lowering dredges beneath the surface. With the dredges, you scrape sand, muck, and rock from the ocean floor. You drag nets behind the ship to collect ocean organisms.

The crew of a British ship, HMS *Challenger*, began such a voyage in 1872. By the end of the journey, scientists on the ship had gathered enough data to fill 50 volumes and had collected more than 4,000 new organisms! The scientists learned about ocean-water chemistry, currents, ocean life, and the shape of the ocean floor. The voyage of the *Challenger* was so successful that it became the model for many later ocean expeditions.

◀ HMS *Challenger*

130 ◆ H

Lab zone Discover Activity

Skills Focus Inferring

Materials 10 plastic drinking straws, covered box with mystery object L2

Time 10 minutes

Tips Obtain in advance small cardboard boxes with lids. Glue or tape an object that can be identified easily to the bottom of each box. Use a different object in each box, and make sure that it clears the lid by at least 2 cm. Poke 10 to 15 holes in the lid at various locations.

Expected Outcome Students should be able to infer the shape of the object and hypothesize about the object's identity.

Think It Over The depths of the straws indicated the object's location, size, and shape.

Learning About the Ocean

People have explored the ocean for thousands of years. Knowledge of the ocean has always been important to the people living along its coasts. **People have studied the ocean since ancient times, because the ocean provides food and serves as a route for trade and travel. Modern scientists have studied the characteristics of the ocean's waters and the ocean floor.**

Trading Routes The Phoenicians, who lived along the Mediterranean Sea, were one of the earliest cultures to explore the oceans. By about 1200 B.C., they had established sea routes for trade with other nations around the Mediterranean. After the Phoenicians, people of many European, African, and Asian cultures sailed along the coasts to trade with distant lands.

In the Pacific Ocean around 2,000 years ago, the Polynesians left the safety of their islands and boldly sailed into the open ocean. Their knowledge of winds and currents enabled the Polynesians to settle the widely scattered islands of Hawaii, Tahiti, and New Zealand. To navigate the ocean, they used devices such as the one shown in Figure 1.

Scientific Discoveries As modern science developed and trade increased, ocean exploration changed. Nations needed accurate maps of the oceans and lands bordering them. Governments also wanted their countries to be known for new scientific discoveries. For example, in the late 1700s, the British government hired Captain James Cook to lead three voyages of exploration. Cook's crew included scientists who studied the stars and those who collected new species of plants and animals.

Within a century of Cook's voyages, almost all of Earth's coastlines had been mapped. Scientists then turned to the study of the ocean's waters. The *Challenger* expedition marked the beginning of the modern science of oceanography.

FIGURE 1
Polynesian Explorers
Around 2,000 years ago, Polynesians explored the Pacific Ocean in boats such as the one above. They used stick charts (above right) to navigate.
Inferring *Why is careful navigation important to explorers?*

Instruct

Learning About the Ocean

Teach Key Concepts L1

Knowledge of the Ocean

Focus As a class, list reasons why it is important to understand the oceans. *(Trade, travel, food, science, recreation, resources)*

Teach Ask: **How did ancient people study the oceans?** *(Travel in sail boats, make maps of the coastline, obtain fish and other resources)* **In what additional ways are the oceans studied today?** *(Submersible vehicles, sonar, scuba diving, gathering data about the water)*

Apply Ask: **What do people know about the ocean today that ancient people did not know?** *(Features of the ocean floor, deep life forms, affect on climate, chemistry of ocean water)* **learning modality: verbal**

Independent Practice L2

All in One Teaching Resources

- Guided Reading and Study Worksheet: *Exploring the Ocean*

Student Edition on Audio CD

Differentiated Instruction

Gifted and Talented L3

The Voyage of *Challenger* Invite interested students to research the journey of the British ship, *HMS Challenger.* Students can draw the route of the voyage on a world map and include dates and captions that describe important events.

Monitor Progress L2

Oral Presentation Have students identify some early ocean explorers and describe their voyages.

Answer

Figure 1 Navigation allows explorers to know precise locations and enables them to travel safely.

L2

Modeling Sonar

Materials rubber ball, stopwatch

Time 10 minutes

Focus Ask whether students have heard their own echo. Tell them that sonar also emits and receives sound waves and that these waves are used to determine the depth of the ocean floor.

Teach Organize the class into groups of three students. Have two students repeatedly bounce a rubber ball back and forth while the third student records the average amount of time for a round trip. Then, have students repeat the procedure three more times at progressively greater distance. Ask: **How did the amount of time for a round trip change as distance was increased?** *(The amount of time increased.)*

Apply Ask: **How could scientists determine the depth of the ocean bottom by bouncing sound waves off of it?** *(They record the time that it takes for the echo to return. The longer the time, the deeper the ocean is.)* **learning modality: kinesthetic**

Exploring the Ocean Floor Until recently, the ocean floor was unexplored. Why did it take so long to reach the ocean floor? Studying the ocean floor is difficult because the ocean is so deep—3.8 kilometers deep on average, more than twice as deep as the Grand Canyon. At such depths, conditions are very harsh. First, because sunlight does not penetrate far below the surface, the deep ocean is in total darkness. Second, the water is very cold. Finally, deep ocean water exerts tremendous pressure due to the mass of water pushing down from above.

Humans cannot survive the darkness, cold temperatures, and extreme pressure of the deep ocean. So scientists have had to develop technology to study the ocean floor. Many of the inventions have involved indirect methods of gathering information.

• Tech & Design in History •

Ocean Exploration

The timeline includes several inventions that have helped scientists overcome the challenges of studying the oceans.

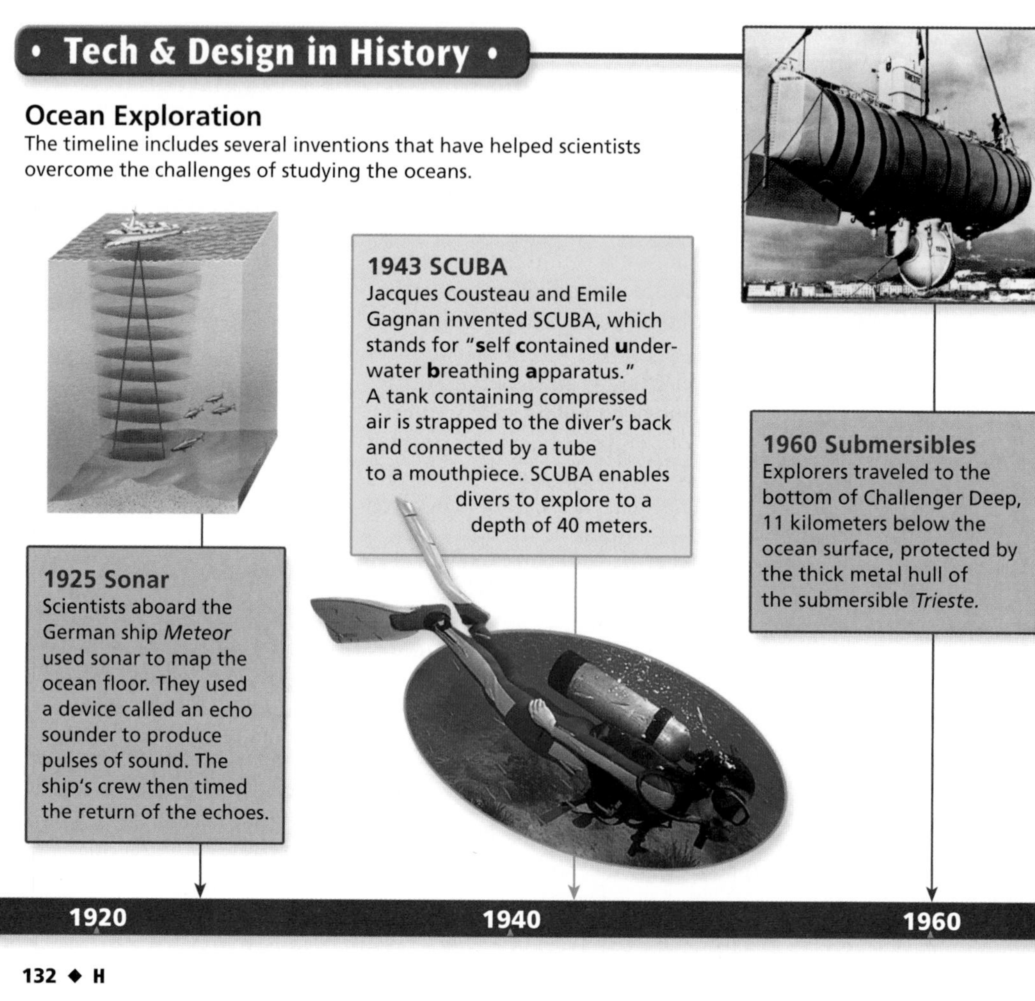

1925 Sonar
Scientists aboard the German ship *Meteor* used sonar to map the ocean floor. They used a device called an echo sounder to produce pulses of sound. The ship's crew then timed the return of the echoes.

1943 SCUBA
Jacques Cousteau and Emile Gagnan invented SCUBA, which stands for "**s**elf **c**ontained **u**nderwater **b**reathing **a**pparatus." A tank containing compressed air is strapped to the diver's back and connected by a tube to a mouthpiece. SCUBA enables divers to explore to a depth of 40 meters.

1960 Submersibles
Explorers traveled to the bottom of Challenger Deep, 11 kilometers below the ocean surface, protected by the thick metal hull of the submersible *Trieste.*

One of the simplest methods, used by the *Challenger*'s crew, was to lower a weight on a long line into the water until the weight touched the bottom. The length of line that got wet was approximately equal to the water's depth. However, this method was slow and often inaccurate.

A major advance in ocean-floor mapping was **sonar,** which stands for **so**und **na**vigation and **r**anging. Sonar is a system that uses sound waves to calculate the distance to an object. The sonar equipment on a ship sends out pulses of sound that bounce off the ocean floor. The equipment then measures how quickly the sound waves return to the ship. Sound waves return quickly if the ocean floor is close. Sound waves take longer to return if the ocean floor is farther away.

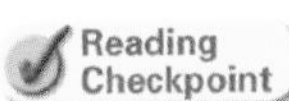
What conditions exist in the depths of the ocean?

Writing in Science

Research and Write Each of the inventions shown in this timeline helped solve a challenge of ocean exploration. Find out more about one of these inventions. Write a short newspaper article telling the story of its development. Include details about the people who invented it and how it added to people's knowledge of the oceans.

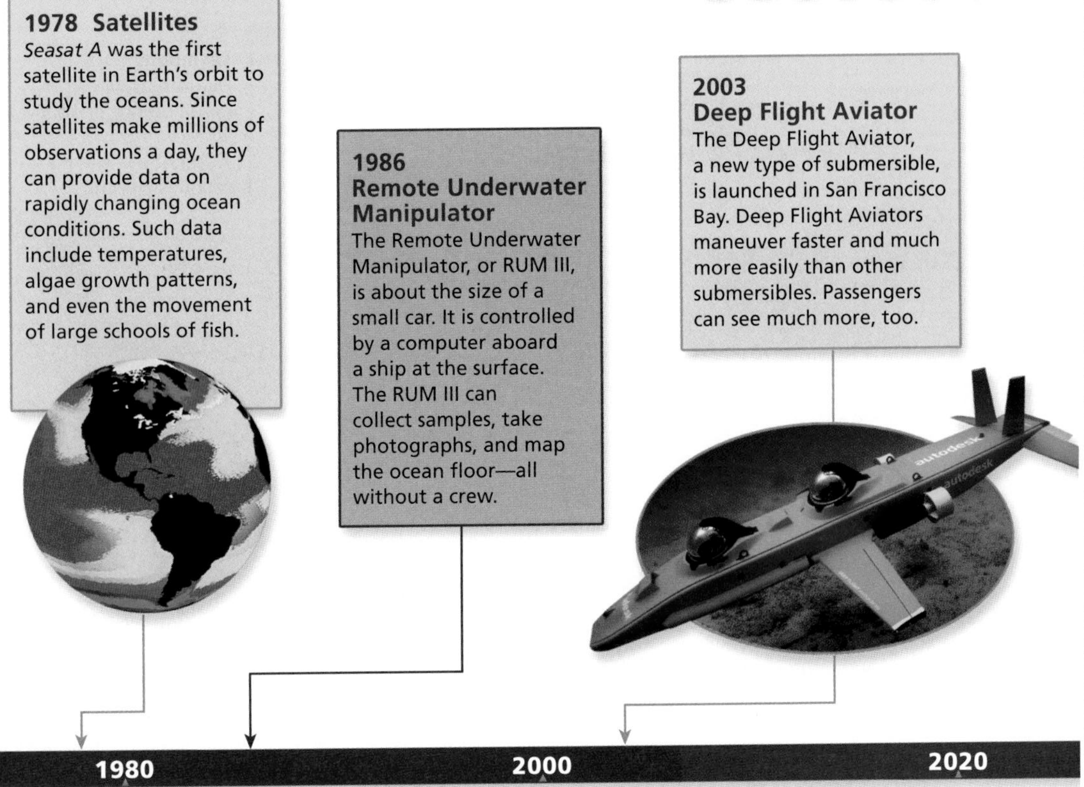

1978 Satellites
Seasat A was the first satellite in Earth's orbit to study the oceans. Since satellites make millions of observations a day, they can provide data on rapidly changing ocean conditions. Such data include temperatures, algae growth patterns, and even the movement of large schools of fish.
1986 Remote Underwater Manipulator
The Remote Underwater Manipulator, or RUM III, is about the size of a small car. It is controlled by a computer aboard a ship at the surface. The RUM III can collect samples, take photographs, and map the ocean floor—all without a crew.
2003 Deep Flight Aviator
The Deep Flight Aviator, a new type of submersible, is launched in San Francisco Bay. Deep Flight Aviators maneuver faster and much more easily than other submersibles. Passengers can see much more, too.
autodesk
1980
2000
2020

• Tech & Design in History •

Focus Direct attention to the timeline and have students note the time span shown. Ask: **How long does an average U.S. citizen live?** *(About 77 or 78 years)* Point out that all of these inventions occurred during this same amount of time.

Teach Ask: **How does new technology benefit ocean science?** *(It allows scientists to study more of the ocean in new ways.)* Guide students through the sequence of technological developments. Ask: **What is the advantage of using a submersible?** *(People can explore the ocean at great depths.)* **How do satellites improve our ability to study the oceans?** *(Data are obtained quickly from large regions.)*

Writing in Science

Writing Mode Research

Scoring Rubric

4 Exceeds criteria by writing a well-researched newspaper article that describes the development of one invention, includes details about the people who invented it, and explains how it has furthered people's knowledge of the ocean

3 Meets criteria by writing a newspaper article that includes the requested information

2 Writes a newspaper article that omits one or two of the requested types of information

1 Writes an article that contains errors or omits most of the requested information

Differentiated Instruction

Less Proficient Readers L1

Have students draw a blueprint for their own submersible vehicle. Students should consider the conditions in the ocean depths and explain how their submersible will function under these conditions. Encourage students to also consider the needs of any people who might be onboard, such as air, adequate space, and lighting. After students have finished, have them compare designs and make modifications to their blueprints. **learning modality: logical/mathematical**

Monitor Progress L1

Skills Check Have students compare and contrast the benefits and limitations of scuba and submersibles.

Answer

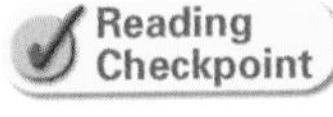
Possible answers: darkness, high pressure, low temperature

Features of the Ocean Floor

Teach Key Concepts L1

Exploring the Ocean Floor

Focus Have students imagine a journey across the Great Plains, over the Rocky Mountains, past the Cascade volcanoes, and ending at the Grand Canyon. Tell them that the ocean floor has features that are even more spectacular.

Teach Work with students to develop a list of descriptive adjectives for each of the following terms: *abyssal plain, volcanic island, mid-ocean ridge,* and *trench.* Have students compare these features to similar features on the continents.

Apply Ask: **How are ocean floor features more spectacular than those on the continents?** *(Ocean floor features generally are longer, wider, taller, or deeper than features on the continents.)* **learning modality: visual**

All in One Teaching Resources

- Transparency H42

Help Students Read L1

Relating Text and Figures As students read the text on these pages, have them refer to Figure 2. Tell students to compare the written descriptions with the corresponding features in the visual.

Features of the Ocean Floor

Once scientists were able to map the ocean floor, they discovered something surprising. The ocean floor was not a flat, sandy plain. The deep waters hid mountain ranges bigger than any on land, as well as deep canyons reaching into Earth's interior. If you could take a submarine voyage along the ocean floor, what would you see? **If you could travel along the ocean floor, you would see the continental shelf, the continental slope, the abyssal plain, and the mid-ocean ridge.** Trace your journey from the edge of one continent to the edge of another in Figure 2.

Shallow Water As you leave the harbor, your submarine first passes over the **continental shelf,** a gently sloping, shallow area of the ocean floor that extends outward from the edge of a continent. At a depth of about 130 meters, the slope of the ocean floor gets steeper. The steep edge of the continental shelf is called the **continental slope.** The continental slope marks the true edge of a continent, where the rock that makes up the continent stops and the rock of the ocean floor begins.

FIGURE 2

The Ocean Floor

The floor of the ocean has mountains, slopes, and other features. To show the major features of the ocean floor, thousands of kilometers have been "squeezed" into one illustration.

Interpreting Diagrams *Which is steeper, the continental slope or the continental shelf?*

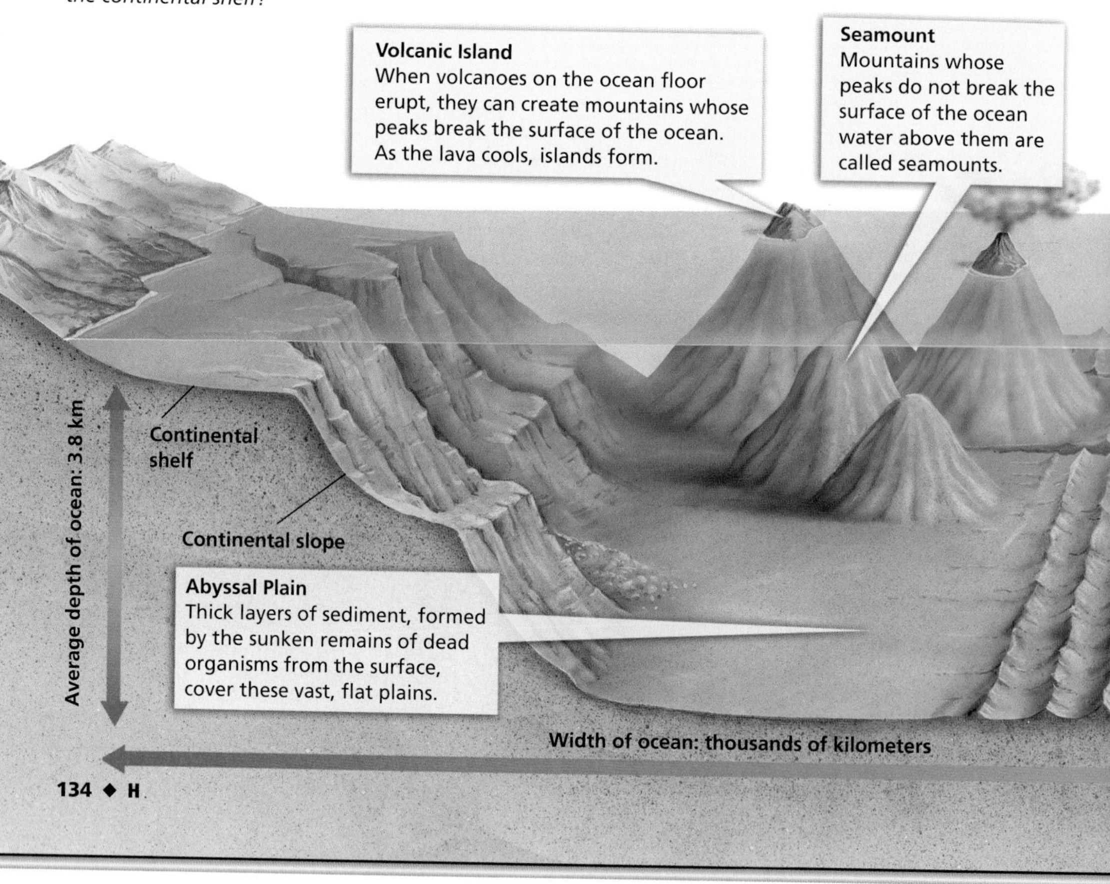
Volcanic Island
When volcanoes on the ocean floor erupt, they can create mountains whose peaks break the surface of the ocean. As the lava cools, islands form.
Seamount
Mountains whose peaks do not break the surface of the ocean water above them are called seamounts.
Continental shelf
Continental slope
Abyssal Plain
Thick layers of sediment, formed by the sunken remains of dead organisms from the surface, cover these vast, flat plains.
Average depth of ocean: 3.8 km
Width of ocean: thousands of kilometers
134 ◆ H

Open Ocean Your submarine descends more gradually now, following the ocean floor as it slopes toward the deep ocean. After some distance, you encounter a group of mountains. Some are tall enough to break the ocean's surface, forming islands. Others, called seamounts, are mountains that are completely underwater. Some seamounts have flat tops because their peaks have eroded away.

Next you cross a broad area covered with thick layers of mud and silt. This smooth, nearly flat region of the ocean floor is called the **abyssal plain** (uh BIHS ul). After gliding over the abyssal plain for many kilometers, you need to steer the submarine sharply upward to avoid a mountain range ahead. The **mid-ocean ridge** is a continuous range of mountains that winds around Earth, much as the line of stitches winds around a baseball. The mid-ocean ridge passes through all of Earth's oceans. Nearly 80,000 kilometers long, it is the longest mountain range on Earth.

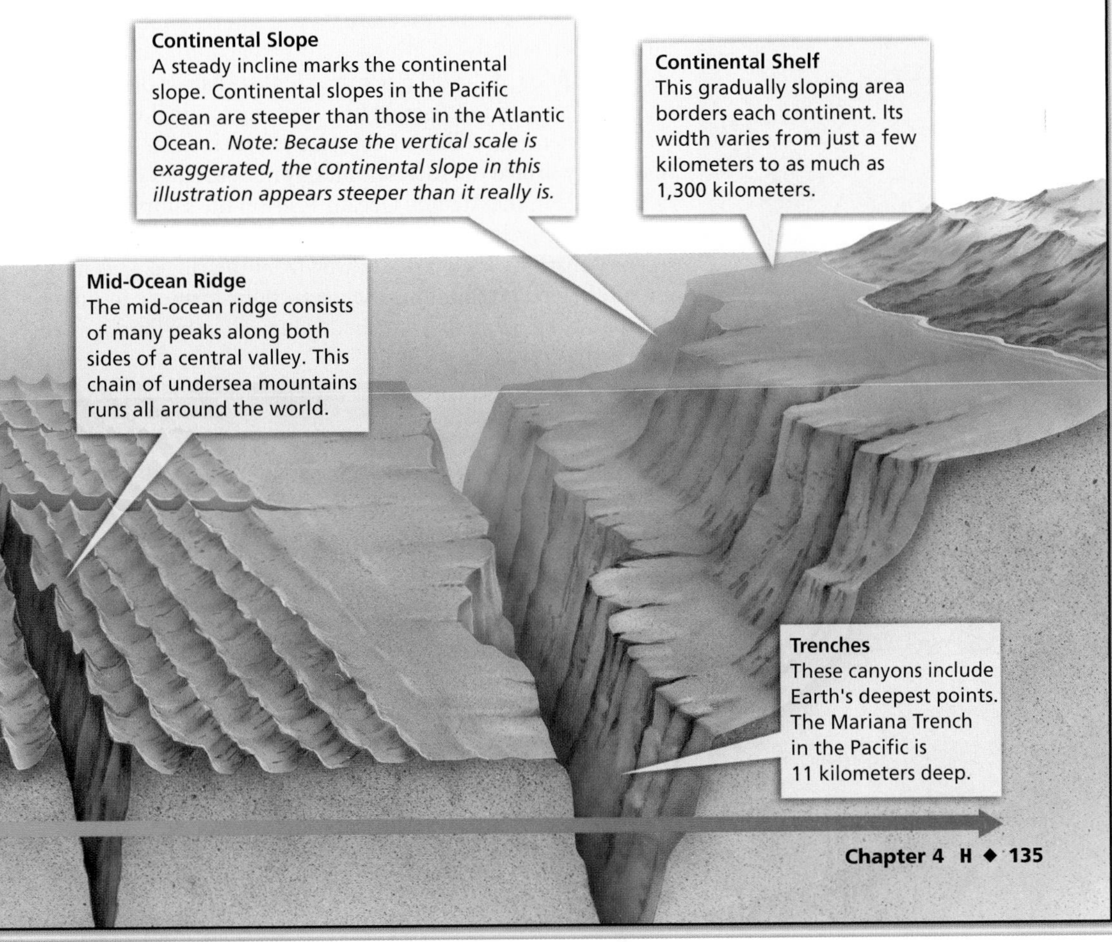

Continental Slope
A steady incline marks the continental slope. Continental slopes in the Pacific Ocean are steeper than those in the Atlantic Ocean. Note: Because the vertical scale is exaggerated, the continental slope in this illustration appears steeper than it really is.
Continental Shelf
This gradually sloping area borders each continent. Its width varies from just a few kilometers to as much as 1,300 kilometers.
Mid-Ocean Ridge
The mid-ocean ridge consists of many peaks along both sides of a central valley. This chain of undersea mountains runs all around the world.
Trenches
These canyons include Earth's deepest points. The Mariana Trench in the Pacific is 11 kilometers deep.

Ocean Zones

Show the Video Field Trip to let students experience ocean zones. Discussion question: **How have fish adapted to the harsh environment of the transition zone?** *(Some have enormous eyes, some have sharp fangs. Some are transparent, others have colors that blend in with water. Some are bioluminescent.)*

L3

Graphing the Ocean Floor

Materials graph paper, metric ruler

Time 20 minutes

Focus Review with students about what a scale is and how to make a scale drawing.

Teach Challenge students to make a scale drawing that includes the continental shelf, continental slope, abyssal plain, mid-ocean ridge, and deep-sea trench. Give them the following typical depths for each feature: shelf, 0 to 200 m; slope, 200 m to 3.8 km; abyssal plain 3.8 km; mid-ocean ridge, about 2.5 km; trench, about 9 km

Apply Ask: **How many times deeper is a trench than a continental shelf?** *(About 45 times deeper)* **How much deeper is a trench than an abyssal plain?** *(From 2 to 3 times deeper)* **learning modality: visual**

Differentiated Instruction

Special Needs L1

Refer students to the volcanic islands shown in the figure on these pages. Then provide students with a map of the Pacific Ocean. Have them identify as many volcanic islands as they can. *(Some notable examples include the Hawaiian Islands, Marshall Islands, and Galapagos Islands)*

Gifted and Talented L3

Have students research the formation of guyots and report their findings to the class. *(Guyots are flat-topped volcanic islands that are now below sea level. The islands went below sea level as the ocean floor gradually spread away from a mid-ocean ridge and sank. The flat tops on guyots formed as a result of wave action that occurred when the island tops were near sea level.)*

Monitor Progress L1

Writing Have students imagine that they are traveling along the ocean floor in a submersible. Have them write about what they see.

Answer

Figure 2 The continental slope

Movements of the Ocean Floor

Teach Key Concepts

L2

Seafloor Spreading

Focus To help students remember Earth's layers, ask them to visualize a hard-boiled egg. Tell students that the shell represents the crust, the white represents the mantle, and the yolk represents the core.

Teach Remind students that plates are pieces of Earth's crust. Ask: **In which ways could two plates move relative to each other?** *(Toward each other, away from each other, or past each other)* **Which of these movements would make space between the plates that could be filled by lava to form new ocean floor?** *(Plates moving away from each other)* **Which movement would cause plates to overlap and reduce the amount of ocean floor?** *(Plates moving together)* **Which movement neither makes nor destroys ocean floor?** *(Plates sliding past each other)*

Apply Compare the process of seafloor spreading to two end-to-end conveyor belts. Tell students that the same process occurs in the Pacific Ocean—two plates meet at a mid-ocean ridge where new ocean crust forms, ocean crust moves to each edge of the ocean, where it sinks into a trench. **learning modality: logical/mathematical**

L2

Movement of Earth's Plates

Materials several meters of paper towel, 2 desks or tables

Time 5 minutes

Focus Tell students that they will model plate movement in the Pacific Ocean in this activity.

Teach Have students lower the middle of the length of paper towel into the crack between the two desks or tables. After most of the towel has been lowered, have students pull each end in opposite directions over the table or desk surface until the towel falls off the desk or table toward the floor.

Apply Ask: **Which part of the model represents a mid-ocean ridge?** *(The crack between the desks or tables)* **Which part represents a trench?** *(The edges of the tables or desks where the towel sinks to the floor)* **learning modality: kinesthetic**

FIGURE 3
The Ocean Depths
On the dark ocean floor, huge masses of shrimp feed near a black smoker—a vent in the ocean floor that releases very hot, mineral-rich water.

Deepest Depths At the top of the mid-ocean ridge, your submarine is about two kilometers above the abyssal plain, but you are still at least one kilometer below the surface. From this vantage you can see that the mid-ocean ridge actually consists of two parallel chains of mountains separated by a central valley.

You cross the ocean floor from the mid-ocean ridge toward the abyssal plain. Soon your submarine's lights reveal a dark gash in the ocean floor ahead of you. As you pass over it, you look down into a canyon in the ocean floor called a **trench.** The trench is so deep you cannot see the bottom.

Your journey is nearly over as your submarine slowly climbs the continental slope. Finally you cross the continental shelf and maneuver the submarine into harbor.

Reading Checkpoint **Which ocean-floor feature makes up the deepest parts of the ocean?**

Movements of the Ocean Floor

As oceanographers mapped the ocean floor, their measurements told them about the features you saw on your imaginary journey between the continents. To gather more information about the floor of the deep ocean, scientists used a drilling ship named *Glomar Challenger*, in honor of the original *Challenger*.

The scientists collected samples of rock from the ocean floor. They drilled the rock samples from both sides of the mid-ocean ridge in the Atlantic Ocean. Tests on the samples showed that the rock closest to the ridge had formed much more recently than the rock farther away from the ridge. This information helped explain how the ocean floor formed. To understand how the ocean floor formed, you need to be familiar with Earth's structure.

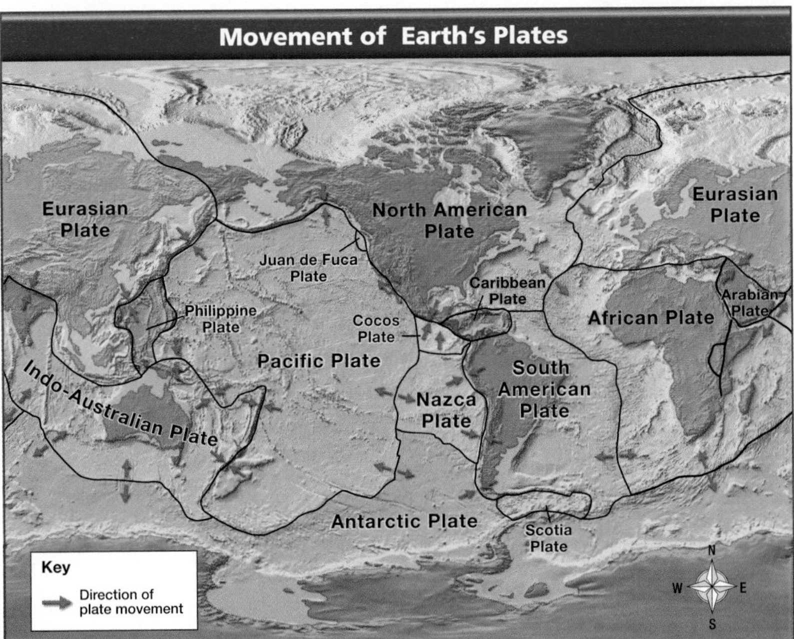

Layers Inside Earth Earth consists of layers that cover the planet's center, or core. The thin, rocky, outer layer of Earth is called the crust. The thick layer between the crust and the core is the mantle. The high temperature inside Earth causes some of the material in the mantle to form a hot liquid called magma. Magma flows very slowly. It can escape upward through cracks in the crust and erupting volcanoes. Magma that reaches the surface is called lava. As lava cools, it forms new crust.

Earth's Plates Earth's crust is solid rock that is broken into irregularly shaped pieces like the shell of a cracked, hard-boiled egg. The pieces of Earth's crust, along with parts of the upper mantle, are called **plates.** Such plates move slowly on the underlying portion of the mantle.

About 14 major plates make up Earth's crust, as shown in Figure 4. They lie beneath the continents as well as the oceans. The plates move at an average speed of several centimeters per year—barely faster than your fingernails grow! Where two plates come together or spread apart, they create features such as mountains and trenches. **Plate movements have shaped many of the most dramatic features of Earth, both on land and under the ocean.** The sea floor, trenches, underwater volcanoes, and the mountain ranges of the mid-ocean ridges have all been formed by the interactions of Earth's plates.

FIGURE 4
Earth's Plates
Earth's crust and upper mantle are divided into 14 major plates.
Interpreting Maps *Name the plates that lie beneath parts of the continent of North America.*

For: Links on plate tectonics
Visit: www.SciLinks.org
Web Code: scn-0841

For: Links on Plate Tectonics
Visit: www.SciLinks.org
Web Code: scn-0841

Download a worksheet that will guide students' review of Internet resources on plate tectonics.

Use Visuals: Figure 4 L2

Earth's Plates

Focus Direct attention to the key in the figure. Ask: **What do the arrows on the map show?** *(The direction of relative plate movement)*

Teach Have students study the arrows and identify the three types of arrow pairs *(Arrows pointing away from each other, arrows pointing toward each other, and arrows pointing past each other)* Ask: **What is happening along the west coast of South America?** *(Plates are moving together.)* **What is happening where the Nazca Plate and the Pacific Plate meet?** *(Plates are moving apart.)* **Where do plates slide past each other?** *(Along the San Andreas Fault at the western edge of North America)*

Apply Ask: **Which ocean is getting larger—the Atlantic or the Pacific?** *(The Atlantic)* **How do you know?** *(It does not have any trenches.)* **learning modality: visual**

All in One Teaching Resources

- Transparency H43

Differentiated Instruction

English Learners/Beginning L1
Vocabulary: Science Glossary Have students compile a Science Glossary that includes the words *mid-ocean ridge, trench, plate, and seafloor spreading.* **learning modality: verbal**

English Learners/Intermediate L2
Vocabulary: Science Glossary Students can expand on the activity in Beginning by using each word in a sentence and drawing a picture to illustrate their meanings. **learning modality: verbal**

Monitor Progress L1

Writing Have each student select a tectonic plate and describe what is happening along its edges.

Answers

Figure 4 The North American, Caribbean, and Pacific Plates

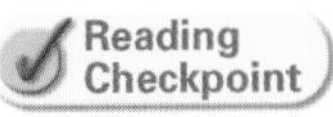

Trenches are the deepest parts of the ocean floor.

Lab zone
Teacher Demo

L1

Plate Divergence

Materials 1 m length of paper towel, 2 desks or tables

Time 15 minutes

Focus Remind students that new ocean floor forms at mid-ocean ridges

Teach Drop the middle of a length of paper towel between the desks or tables. Pull up 2 cm of paper towel on each side and mark a line at the "mid-ocean ridge." Tell students that this represents the amount of ocean crust produced during a 1-million-year time period. Repeat the procedure until all of the towel is pulled up. Count with students the number of million-year increments on each side of the ridge.

Apply Ask: **Where is the youngest crust?** *(At the ridge)* **Where is the oldest crust?** *(Farthest away from the ridge)* **How does the age of ocean crust change away from the mid-ocean ridge?** *(It gets progressively older.)* **learning modality: visual**

All in One Teaching Resources

- Transparencies H44, H45

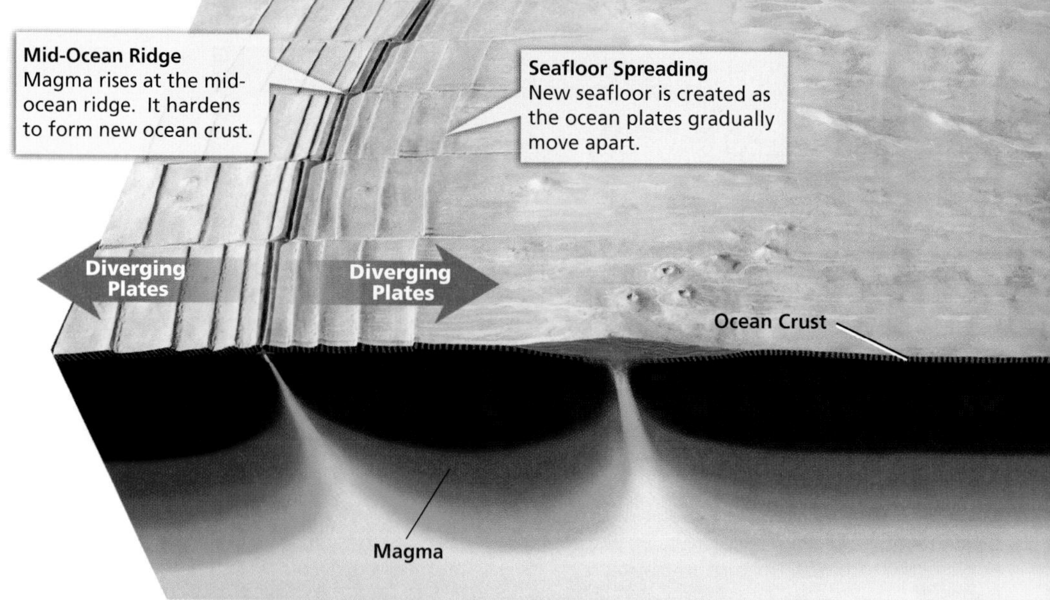
Mid-Ocean Ridge
Magma rises at the mid-ocean ridge. It hardens to form new ocean crust.
Seafloor Spreading
New seafloor is created as the ocean plates gradually move apart.
Diverging Plates
Diverging Plates
Ocean Crust
Magma

FIGURE 5
Moving Plates Beneath the Ocean
Where two plates diverge, magma from Earth's mantle rises up through the crack. Where two plates converge at a trench, one plate sinks under the other.
Interpreting Diagrams *What happens when magma rises to the surface of the ocean floor?*

Plates Moving Apart The mid-ocean ridge is located along the boundaries between plates that are moving apart, or diverging. Along the ridge, magma squeezes up through the cracks between the diverging plates. As the magma hardens along the ridge, it adds a new strip of rock to the ocean floor. Over millions of years, this process, called **seafloor spreading,** has produced the ocean floor.

The rock samples collected by the *Glomar Challenger* helped confirm the theory of seafloor spreading. Scientific analysis showed that the rocks closer to the ridge had been produced more recently than those farther away.

Plates Moving Together When the new ocean floor grows along the mid-ocean ridge, where does the old ocean floor farther away from the ridge go? Why doesn't Earth keep getting bigger? The answers to these questions lie in the deep ocean trenches you read about earlier. Where plates come together, or converge, one plate sinks under the other, as shown in Figure 5. As new rock is added along the mid-ocean ridge, old rock farther away from the mid-ocean ridge sinks into the trenches. The sinking rock is pushed back into Earth's interior. This process allows the ocean floor to spread while Earth itself remains the same size.

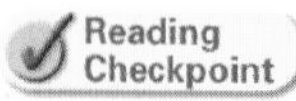
Reading Checkpoint
What happens to magma during seafloor spreading?

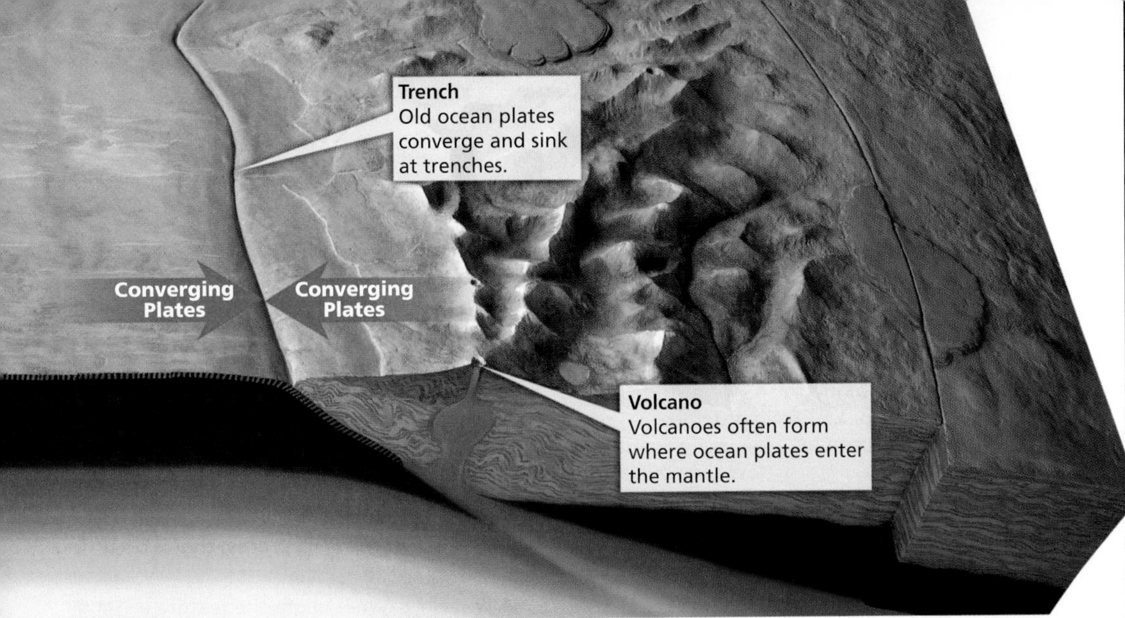

Trench
Old ocean plates converge and sink at trenches.
Converging Plates
Converging Plates
Volcano
Volcanoes often form where ocean plates enter the mantle.

Section 1 Assessment

Target Reading Skill Building Vocabulary Use your definitions to help answer the questions below.

Reviewing Key Concepts

1. a. Reviewing What features of the ocean have modern scientists investigated?
   b. Relating Cause and Effect Why has this investigation been difficult?
   c. Problem Solving What is sonar? Explain how it has helped scientists solve problems associated with ocean investigation.
2. a. Listing List the four main sections of the ocean floor.
   b. Interpreting Diagrams Refer to Figure 2. Describe the characteristics of each of the four sections of the ocean floor that you listed above. Include specific features found in each section.
3. a. Defining What are Earth's plates?
   b. Relating Cause and Effect What is seafloor spreading? How does it relate to the behavior of Earth's plates?
   c. Comparing and Contrasting Compare the process of seafloor spreading to the process that occurs when plates converge.

Lab zone At-Home Activity

Mapping the Ocean With a family member, choose a room in your house and make a "room-floor" map based on depth readings. Imagine that the ceiling is the ocean surface and the floor is the bottom of the ocean. Follow a straight path across the middle of the room from one wall to another. At regular intervals, use a carpenter's measuring tape to take a depth reading from the ceiling to the floor or to the top of any furniture in that spot. Plot the depths on a graph. Then challenge another family member to identify the room by looking at the graph.

Lab zone At-Home Activity

Mapping the Ocean L2 Have volunteers demonstrate the measuring process in the classroom and then make a graph from the data. Point out that students should use a line graph and plot the distances from the ceiling on the vertical axis and the distances from the "start" wall on the horizontal axis. The points will show the locations and heights of objects in the classroom.

Monitor Progress L2

Answers

Figure 5 The magma cools and hardens to form new seafloor.

Reading Checkpoint Magma flows into the crack between separating plates, cools, and hardens. New seafloor forms through this process.

Assess

Reviewing Key Concepts

1. a. Scientists have investigated characteristics of ocean water and the ocean floor. **b.** The investigation has been difficult because the ocean is deep, dark, and has high pressures. **c.** Sonar is sound navigation ranging. Sound waves are bounced off of the ocean bottom and the travel times are used to calculate depth of the ocean floor.

2. a. continental shelf, continental slope, abyssal plain, and mid-ocean ridge

b. continental shelf, shallow, gently sloping edge of continent; continental slope, more steeply sloping edge of continent; abyssal plain, relatively flat, deep ocean bottom; mid-ocean ridge, long range of high underwater mountains

3. a. Earth's plates are large pieces of Earth's outer layer. **b.** Sea-floor spreading is the process by which ocean floor moves away from ridges. **c.** Sea-floor spreading produces new ocean floor, whereas plate convergence pushes ocean floor back into Earth's interior.

Reteach L1

With the class, make a diagram showing the features of the ocean floor. Have volunteers describe the characteristics of each feature.

Performance Assessment

Drawing Have each student draw and label a simple sketch showing plate divergence at a mid-ocean ridge and plate convergence at a trench.

All in One Teaching Resources

- Section Summary: *Exploring the Ocean*
- Review and Reinforcement: *Exploring the Ocean*
- Enrich: *Exploring the Ocean*

The Shape of the Ocean Floor

Prepare for Inquiry

Key Concept

A profile of the ocean floor can be made by plotting depths on a graph.

Skills Objectives

Students will be able to

- graph depth data
- infer the identify of ocean-floor features.

Prep Time 5 minutes

Class Time 30 minutes

All in One Teaching Resources

- Lab Worksheet: *The Shape of the Ocean Floor*

Guide Inquiry

Introduce the Procedure

- Show students a large globe or world map and ask: **What are longitude lines?** *(Lines running vertically from pole to pole)* Explain that these lines are used to measure distances east and west of the Prime Meridian, which passes through Greenwich, England.
- Emphasize that the longitudes listed in the table should be plotted on the horizontal axis and that the depths should be plotted on the vertical axis. Ask: **What would be a good interval to mark on the horizontal axis?** *(Every 5° from 65° W to 0°W)* **What would be a good interval for the vertical axis?** *(Every 500 m from 0 to –5,000)*
- Students might want to use large sheets of paper or tape together two smaller sheets.

Expected Outcome

- Students' graphs would pass over an ocean-floor landscape similar to the one in figure 2 on pages 134–135 and should look similar to the one shown.

The Shape of the Ocean Floor

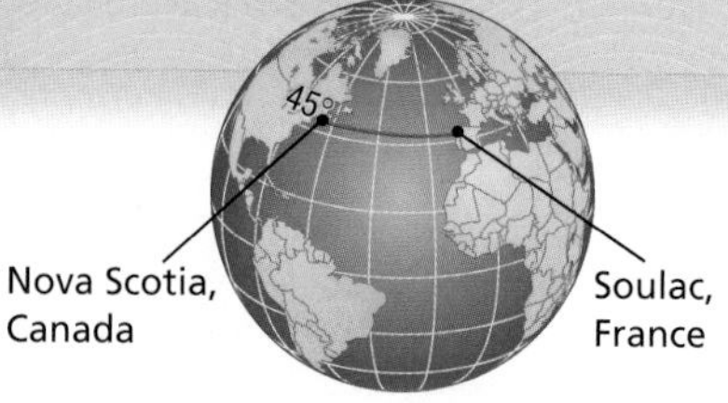

Problem

Imagine you are an oceanographer traveling across the Atlantic along the 45° N latitude line marked on the map. You are gathering data on the depth of the ocean between Nova Scotia, Canada, and Soulac, France. How can you use data to determine the shape of the ocean floor?

Skills Focus

graphing, predicting, inferring

Materials

- pencil
- graph paper

Procedure

1. Draw the axes of a graph. Label the horizontal axis *Longitude*. Mark from 65° W to 0° from left to right. Label the vertical axis *Ocean Depth*. Mark 0 meters at the top of the vertical axis to represent sea level. Mark –5,000 meters at the bottom to represent the depth of 5,000 meters below sea level. Mark depths at equal intervals along the vertical axis.
2. Examine the data in the table. The numbers in the Longitude column give the ship's location at 19 points in the Atlantic Ocean. Location 1 is Nova Scotia, and Location 19 is Soulac. The numbers in the Ocean Depth column give the depth measurements recorded at each location. Plot each measurement on your graph. Remember that the depths are represented on your graph as numbers below 0, or sea level.
3. Connect the points you have plotted with a line to create a profile of the ocean floor.

Analyze and Conclude

1. **Graphing** On your graph, identify and label the continental shelf and continental slope.
2. **Predicting** Label the abyssal plain on your graph. How would you expect the ocean floor to look there?
3. **Graphing** Label the mid-ocean ridge on your graph. Describe the process that is occurring there.
4. **Inferring** What might the feature at 10° W be? Explain.
5. **Communicating** Imagine you are traveling along the ocean floor from Nova Scotia, Canada, to Soulac, France. Describe the features you would see along your journey.

More to Explore

Use the depth measurements in the table to calculate the average depth of the Atlantic Ocean between Nova Scotia and France.

Ocean Depth Sonar Data

Longitude	Ocean Depth (m)	Longitude	Ocean Depth (m)
1. 64° W	0	11. 28° W	1,756
2. 60° W	91	12. 27° W	2,195
3. 55° W	132	13. 25° W	3,146
4. 50° W	73	14. 20° W	4,244
5. 48° W	3,512	15. 15° W	4,610
6. 45° W	4,024	16. 10° W	4,976
7. 40° W	3,805	17. 05° W	4,317
8. 35° W	4,171	18. 04° W	146
9. 33° W	3,439	19. 01° W	0
10. 30° W	3,073		

Analyze and Conclude

1. Continental shelf: Locations 1–4 and 18–19; continental slope: Locations 4–5 and 17–18.

2. Abyssal plain: Locations 5–9 and 14–17. The ocean floor would look smooth and nearly flat.

3. Mid-ocean ridge: Locations 9–13. Sea-floor spreading; magma moves up between two plates, cools, and adds new rock to the ocean floor.

4. Students might infer that a trench exists at this location.

5. Students should describe in sequence the following features: continental shelf, continental slope, abyssal plain, mid-ocean ridge, abyssal plain, continental slope, continental shelf.

Extend Inquiry

More to Explore The average depth is 2,511 m

Section 2

Integrating Life Science

Ocean Habitats

Reading Preview

Key Concepts

- Into what zones do scientists divide the ocean?
- How are marine organisms classified?

Key Terms

- intertidal zone
- neritic zone
- open-ocean zone
- plankton
- nekton
- benthos
- food web

Target Reading Skill

Using Prior Knowledge Your prior knowledge is what you already know before you read about a topic. Before you read, write what you know about conditions that might determine where ocean organisms live. Use a graphic organizer like the one below. As you read, continue to write in what you learn.

What You Know
1. Many organisms need sunlight.
2.

What You Learned
1.
2.

Lab zone Discover Activity

How Complex Are Ocean Feeding Relationships?

1. Form a circle of five students. Each student will represent one of the following marine organisms: algae, shrimp, fish, sea otter, and whale. Each student should write the name of his or her organism on a card.
2. Discuss the possible feeding relationships among the five organisms. What might your organism eat? What might eat the organism you represent?
3. Use pieces of string to connect your card to the cards of all the organisms that may have feeding relationships with your organism.

Think It Over

Inferring Based on your results in Step 3, are the feeding relationships among ocean organisms simple or complex? Explain your answer.

At first glance, an ocean may seem lifeless. As you walk along the beach, your feet sink in the soft, wet sand. You may notice some dark, tangled seaweed that has washed up on the shore. A few sea gulls screech and swoop overhead. Otherwise, all is calm. You stop to gaze out at the horizon. The ocean stretches as far as the eye can see. Waves crash against the shore. But you see no sign of life in the water.

Look closer. Right beneath your feet you can see evidence of living things. Tiny, round holes are signs of burrowing clams. These clams dig down into the sand. This burrowing enables the clams to hide from predators and avoid being washed away by the tide. If you wade into the water, you may be able to spot a sand crab feeding in the surf. And far out to sea, a school of dolphins swims by. Their bodies form graceful arcs as they dive in and out of the water. An ocean may seem lifeless, but many different organisms inhabit this vast, watery environment.

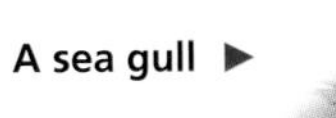

A sea gull ▶

H ◆ 141

Section 2

Ocean Habitats

Objectives

After this lesson, students will be able to

H.4.2.1 Identify the zones into which scientists divide the ocean.

H.4.2.2 Describe how marine organisms are classified.

Target Reading Skill

Using Prior Knowledge Explain that using prior knowledge helps students connect what they already know to what they are about to read.

Answers

What You Know

1. Many organisms need sunlight.
2. Marine organisms obtain oxygen from the water.

What You Learned

1. The ocean is divided into three zones.
2. Marine organisms are classified by where they live and how they move.

All in One Teaching Resources

- Transparency H46

Preteach

Build Background Knowledge L1

Marine Organisms

Ask students to describe marine organisms that they have observed either directly, such as at aquariums, or in movies, TV shows and nature magazines. Ask questions such as, **What do marine organisms look like? How do the organisms move? What do marine organisms eat?**

Lab zone Discover Activity

Skills Focus Inferring L1

Materials string, index cards

Time 10 minutes

Tips You might want to use different colors of yarn to show the complex feeding relationships.

Expected Outcome Students will note that all of the organisms depend, either directly or indirectly, on the algae. Shrimp feed on algae. Fish feed on shrimp and algae. Sea otters feed on fish, and whales could feed on all of the organisms listed depending on the species of whale.

Think It Over Students might say that the feeding relationships are complex because the relationships form a web.

Instruct

Ocean Zones and Conditions

Teach Key Concepts L1

Comparing and Contrasting Ocean Zones

Focus Remind students about different ecosystems on land, such as forest, prairie, and desert. Ask: **Why do different types of organisms live in these different zones?** *(The conditions are different within each.)* Tell them that the same thing is true about ocean zones.

Teach Identify each ocean zone for students. Prompt students to infer conditions within each of these zones. *(Intertidal; wet or dry, salinity variations, temperature variations, sunlight; neritic, light available, more constant temperature and salinity, some wave action on bottom; deep-ocean zone; stable temperature and salinity, no light at depth)*

Apply Challenge students to infer how the type of organisms varies from zone to zone. *(Hearty organisms that can survive changing conditions live in the intertidal zone; the neritic zone includes photosynthetic plants on the bottom along with a variety of bottom-living and swimming animals. The open-ocean zone cannot support bottom-living plants; photosynthetic algae live near the surface)*

All in One Teaching Resources

- Transparency H47

Independent Practice L2

All in One Teaching Resources

- Guided Reading and Study Worksheet: *Ocean Habitats*

Student Edition on Audio CD

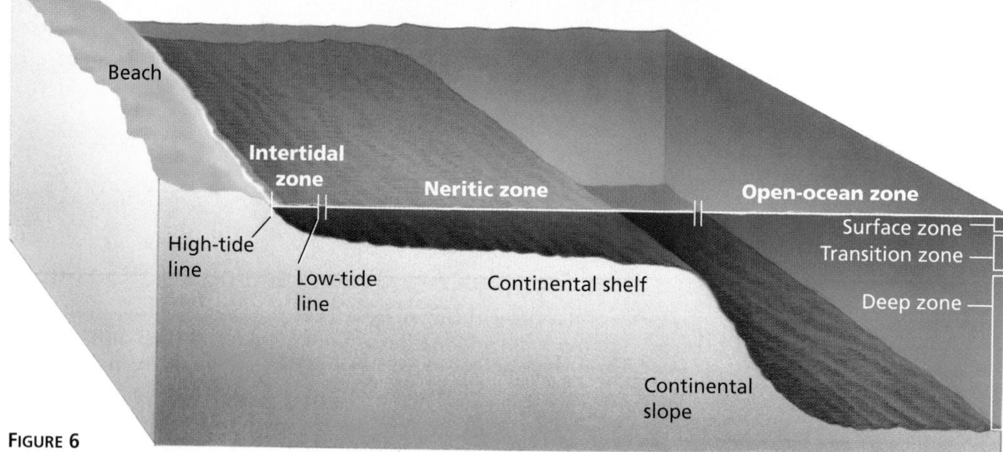

FIGURE 6
Ocean Zones
The three ocean zones are the intertidal zone, the neritic zone, and the open-ocean zone.
Classifying *Into what three zones is the open-ocean zone divided?*

Ocean Zones and Conditions

You can think of the ocean as a huge community that includes living and nonliving things. In some ways, the ocean community resembles a human city or town. Typically, cities and towns are divided into several zones. Some zones consist mostly of houses and apartment buildings. Other zones have stores and shops or factories and office buildings.

Ocean Zones The ocean, too, can be divided into zones, as shown in Figure 6. Your walk on the sandy beach, for example, took place in the intertidal zone. **Ocean zones include the intertidal zone, the neritic zone, and the open-ocean zone.** At the highest high-tide line on land, the **intertidal zone** begins. From there, the zone stretches out to the point on the continental shelf exposed by the lowest low tide. The **neritic zone** extends from the low-tide line out to the edge of the continental shelf. Beyond the edge of the continental shelf lies the **open-ocean zone.** This zone includes the deepest, darkest part of the ocean. You will learn more about these ocean zones in Section 3 and Section 4.

Physical Conditions Each ocean zone has its characteristic physical conditions. These conditions help determine which organisms can live in that zone. For example, light does not penetrate very far beneath the ocean's surface. Organisms that need light for photosynthesis must live near the surface of the ocean. In contrast, in the deep ocean, pressure is high. Organisms that live deep in the ocean must be able to withstand this force.

Reading Checkpoint Which ocean zone is farthest from shore?

Lab zone Try This Activity

Feeling the Pressure

1. Use a pen to poke two similar holes in an empty milk carton. One hole should be about one third of the way from the bottom. The other hole should be about two thirds of the way from the bottom.
2. Cover the holes with tape. Then fill the carton with water.
3. Hold the carton over a sink. Remove the tape. Note any differences in the flow of water from the two holes.

Making Models What physical condition in the ocean does this activity model? In which ocean zone is this condition most significant?

Lab zone Try This Activity

Skills Focus Making models L2

Materials ball-point pen, milk carton, water

Time 10 minutes

Tips Caution students to use care when poking holes in the milk carton.

Expected Outcome Students will notice that water flows with greater force from the hole that is closer to the bottom of the carton. This activity models pressure in the ocean. Pressure is higher at greater depth. Pressure is most significant in the open-ocean zone.

Extend Have students make a generalized graph showing how pressure varies with depth. Graphs should show pressure increasing linearly with depth.

Life in the Ocean

On land, most organisms live on or near the surface. The ocean, on the other hand, is inhabited by organisms at every depth. **Scientists classify marine organisms according to where they live and how they move.** Figure 7 shows the three categories of ocean organisms—plankton, nekton, and benthos.

Plankton **Plankton** are tiny algae and animals that float in the water and are carried by waves and currents. Algae plankton include geometrically shaped diatoms. Animal plankton include microscopic crustaceans and some tiny young fish.

Nekton **Nekton** are free-swimming animals that can move throughout the water column. Squid, most fishes, and marine mammals such as whales and seals are nekton.

Benthos **Benthos** are organisms that inhabit the ocean floor. Some benthos, like crabs, sea stars, octopus, and lobsters, move from place to place. Others, like sponges and sea anemones, stay in one location.

Reading Checkpoint Are sharks plankton, nekton, or benthos? Why?

FIGURE 7
Marine Organisms
Marine organisms can be classified as plankton, nekton, or benthos.

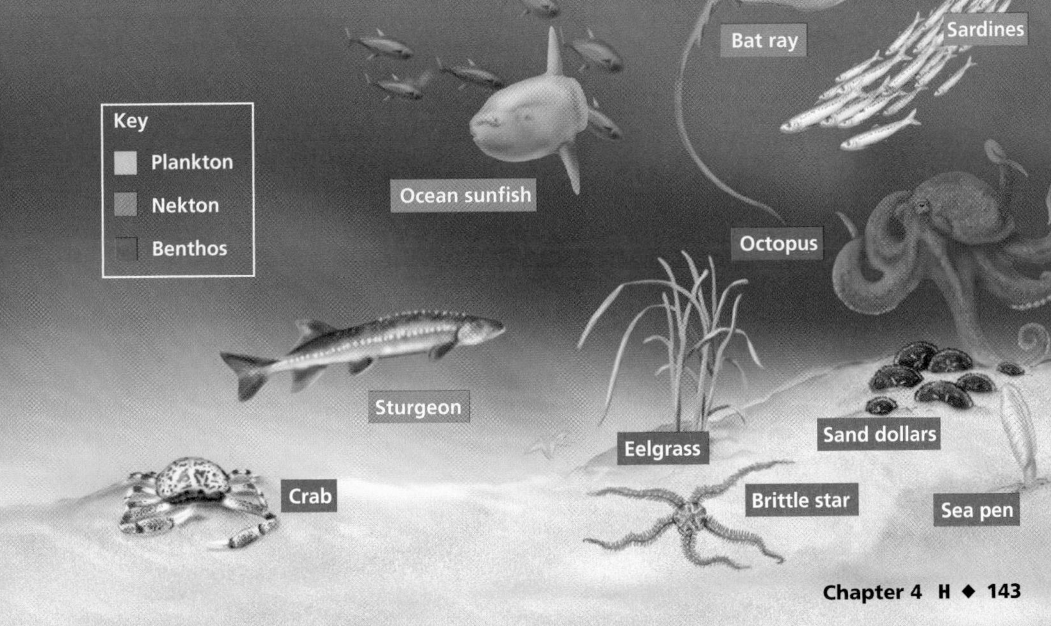

Life in the Ocean

Teach Key Concepts L2

Plankton, Nekton, and Benthos

Focus Remind students that the ocean has a surface, water column, and bottom. Tell them that ocean species are sometimes classified on the basis of the region the species inhabits.

Teach Tell students that floating organisms are called plankton, swimming organisms are nekton, and that bottom-dwelling organisms are called benthos. Ask: **Which species could move easily from place to place?** *(Nekton)* **Which are stationary or move only short distances?** *(Benthos)* **Which drift with the currents?** *(Plankton)*

Apply Challenge students to describe how the feeding habits of plankton, nekton, and benthos would differ. *(Plankton must make their own food or consume other plankton in their immediate vicinity; nekton can swim and chase prey or graze on algae; stationary benthos must get food as it drifts by or filter it from the water, mobile benthos feed on other nearby organisms)* **learning modality: logical/mathematical**

All in One Teaching Resources
- Transparency H48

Differentiated Instruction

Special Needs L1

Designing an Organism Have students design an organism that is to live as plankton, nekton, or benthos. Students can draw their organism or make a three-dimensional model. Make certain that students explain how their organism's characteristics would be of benefit. **learning modality: kinesthetic**

Gifted and Talented L3

Provide students with a photograph of an organism. Have students identify the organism as plankton, nekton, or benthos. After students have made their identification, have them list adaptations that make the organism well-suited to its way of living. **learning modality: kinesthetic**

Monitor Progress L1

Skills Check Have each student draw a concept map that includes the three types of marine organisms, their characteristics, and examples.

Portfolio

Answers

Figure 6 The surface zone, the transition zone, and the deep zone

Reading Checkpoint The open-ocean zone is farthest from shore.

Reading Checkpoint Sharks are nekton because they are free- swimming animals.

For: Ocean Food Web Activity
Visit: PHSchool.com
Web Code: cfp-3042

Students can interact with the art about ocean food webs online.

Use Visuals: Figure 8 L1

An Ocean Food Web

Focus Direct attention to the illustration and have a volunteer read aloud the caption.

Teach Point out that in a diagram of a food web, each arrow points from the organism being eaten to the organism doing the eating. Ask: **Which organisms are eaten by the ringed seal?** *(Animal plankton, Arctic cod, crab)* **Which organism eats the seal?** *(polar bear)* Remind students that a food web is a pattern of feeding relationships in a habitat. Food webs consist of overlapping food chains. Ask: **What is one food chain in this food web?** *(Example: algae plankton → animal plankton → silversides → Arctic cod → beluga whale)*

Apply Ask: **Which organism starts the food web?** *(Algae plankton)* **How do algae plankton get energy to make food?** *(From the sun)* **learning modality: visual**

All in One Teaching Resources

- Transparency H49

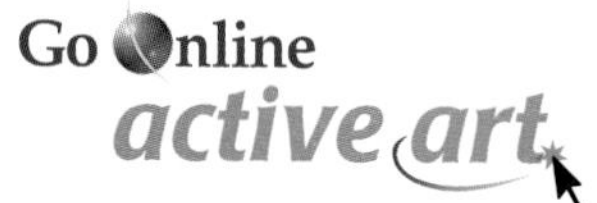

For: Ocean Food Web activity
Visit: PHSchool.com
Web Code: cfp-3042

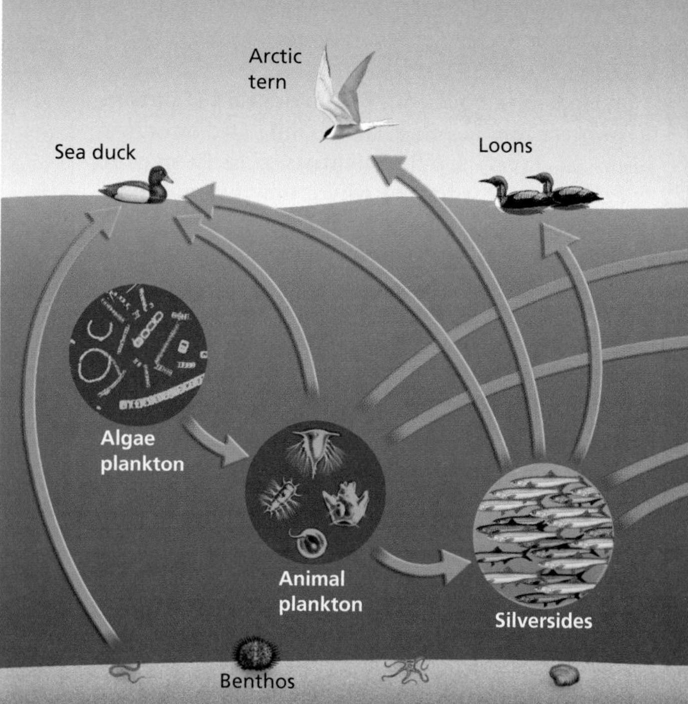

FIGURE 8
An Ocean Food Web
This ocean food web includes typical organisms found in the Arctic Ocean. The arrows indicate what each organism eats. **Interpreting Diagrams** *Which organisms feed directly on the Arctic cod? Which organisms depend indirectly on the cod?*

Relationships Among Organisms Plankton, nekton, and benthos are all found in most marine habitats. Many plankton and benthos are algae. Like plants, algae use sunlight to produce their own food through photosynthesis. Photosynthetic plankton are called producers. Other plankton and benthos, as well as all nekton, eat either algae or other organisms. They are called consumers. Finally, some organisms, including many benthos, break down wastes and the remains of other organisms. They are called decomposers.

Ocean Food Webs All of the feeding relationships that exist in a habitat make up a **food web.** A typical ocean food web is shown in Figure 8. Each organism in this Arctic food web depends either directly or indirectly on the algae plankton. Throughout the ocean, plankton are a source of food for other organisms of all sizes. If you think of sharks as sharp-toothed, meat-eating hunters, you might be surprised to learn that the biggest sharks of all feed directly on tiny plankton! Many whales, including Earth's largest animal—the blue whale—also feed only on plankton.

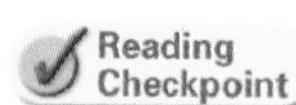
Which organisms in an ocean food web are the producers?

Differentiated Instruction

English Learners/Beginning L1
Vocabulary: Link to Visual Photocopy Figure 8. Then cover the names of the organisms that make up the food web. Provide students with a list of the names, and have them write the correct name in the space next to each organism. **learning modality: verbal**

English Learners/Intermediate L2
Vocabulary: Link to Visual Have students write sentences describing the relationships shown in the visual For example, *Polar bears feed on ringed seals.* **learning modality: verbal**

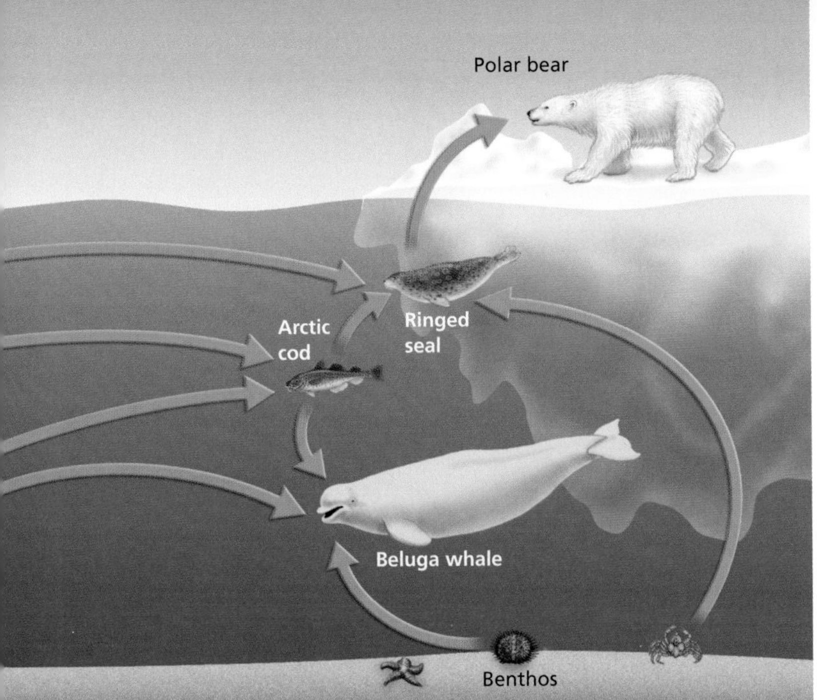

Section 2 Assessment

Target Reading Skill **Using Prior Knowledge** Review your graphic organizer and revise it based on what you just learned in the section.

Reviewing Key Concepts

1. a. **Identifying** Identify the three ocean zones.
   b. **Sequencing** Put the ocean zones in order, beginning with the zone in which the water is least deep and ending with the zone that is deepest.
   c. **Inferring** Which zone probably has the greatest variety of living things? How is this variety related to the water's depth?
2. a. **Reviewing** What characteristics do scientists use to classify ocean organisms?
   b. **Describing** Identify the three categories of ocean organisms and describe their characteristics.
   c. **Classifying** Sea cucumbers are small animals that crawl along the ocean floor. To which category of ocean organisms do they belong? Explain.

Writing in Science

Cause and Effect Paragraph Write a brief paragraph describing how the ocean food web in Figure 8 might be affected by a decrease in the Arctic cod population. Which populations might increase as a result and why? Which populations might decrease and why? To help plan your writing, you might use a cause-and-effect graphic organizer.

Monitor Progress L1

Answers

Figure 8 The beluga whale and ringed seal feed directly on Arctic cod. The polar bear depends indirectly on the cod because it eats seals.

Reading Checkpoint Algae plankton are the producers.

Assess

Reviewing Key Concepts

1. a. Three ocean zones are the intertidal zone, the neritic zone, and the open-ocean zone. **b.** From shallowest to deepest, the zones are these: intertidal zone, neritic zone, open-ocean zone **c.** The neritic zone probably has the greatest variety of organisms because the shallow water allows sunlight to penetrate so that plants and algae can carry out photosynthesis.

2. a. Scientists classify ocean organisms according to where they live and how they move. **b.** Plankton include algae plankton and animal plankton—many are microscopic organisms. Nekton include free-swimming animals such as fish and marine mammals. Benthos include bottom-dwellers that move from place to place or stay in one place. **c.** They are benthos because they inhabit the ocean floor.

Reteach L1

With the class, make a chart describing the three ocean zones. Then discuss organisms that live in each zone.

Performance Assessment

Classifying Provide students with names of marine organisms. Have students classify the organisms as plankton, nekton, or benthos and give reasons for their choices.

All in One Teaching Resources

- Section Summary: *Ocean Habitats*
- Review and Reinforcement: *Ocean Habitats*
- Enrich: *Ocean Habitats*

Lab zone Chapter Project

Keep Students on Track By now students should have selected the marine environment that they will create. They should make a list of the physical features they will need to represent and draw a scale diagram. Monitor students' choices to avoid repetition and encourage variety.

Writing in Science

Writing Mode Exposition

Scoring Rubric

4 Exceeds criteria by including a complete description and specific details about causes and effects

3 Meets criteria by including a description and some specific details

2 Description or some details only

1 Incomplete description or Inaccurate details only

Section 3 Intertidal Zone

Objectives
After this lesson, students will be able to

H.4.3.1 Identify the conditions that organisms in the rocky intertidal zone must tolerate.

H.4.3.2 List and describe the major types of coastal wetlands.

Target Reading Skill
Outlining Explain that using an outline format helps students organize information by main topic, subtopic, and details.

Answers

Intertidal Zone
- I. Rocky shores
  - A. Along the rocks
  - B. In Tide pools
- II. Where river meets ocean
  - A. Mangrove Forests
  - B. Salt Marshes
  - C. Protecting Estuaries

All in One Teaching Resources
- Transparency H50

Preteach

Build Background Knowledge L1
Ask: **What happens at high tide?** *(Water flows onto the land.)* **What happens at low tide?** *(Water flows off of the land.)* Ask students to describe the region over which this water flows. Tell them that this region is the topic of this section.

Help Students Read L2
Directed Reading/Thinking Activity
Have students preview the section's title, headings, visuals, and boldfaced type. Then ask them to read the introductory and concluding paragraphs. Have students predict what they will learn and formulate questions to be answered. Refer to page 128H in this chapter for the guidelines for the Directed Reading/Thinking Activity. **learning modality: verbal**

Section 3 Intertidal Zone

Reading Preview
Key Concepts
- What conditions must organisms in the rocky intertidal zone tolerate?
- What are the major types of coastal wetlands?

Key Term
- estuary

Target Reading Skill
Outlining As you read, make an outline about the intertidal zone. Use the red headings for the main topics and the blue headings for the subtopics.

Intertidal Zone
I. Rocky shores
A. Along the rocks
B.
II. Where river meets ocean

Lab zone Discover Activity
Can Your Animal Hold On?
1. Your teacher will give you a ping-pong ball, a rock, and some other materials. The ping-pong ball represents an ocean animal. Design a way for the animal to cling to the rock.
2. Attach the ping-pong ball to the rock.
3. Place the rock in a sink or deep pan. Run water over the rock. Observe how well your animal stays in place on the rock.

Think It Over
Inferring How might the ability to "hold on" be important to an animal that lives on the shore?

Imagine that your home has no walls or roof. Twice a day, a huge storm passes through, bringing a drenching downpour and winds so strong you can hardly keep your balance. At other times, the sun beats down, heating you and leaving you dry. This is what life is like for organisms that live on rocky shores, where the land meets the sea.

Rocky Shores
A rocky shore is one type of habitat found in the intertidal zone. You read about sandy shores, another type, in Section 2. **Organisms that live in the rocky intertidal zone must be able to tolerate the pounding of the waves and changes in both salinity and temperature. They must also withstand periods of being underwater and periods of being exposed to the air.** They must avoid drying out, hide from predators, and find food in this harsh setting. Luckily, they are well suited to these tasks.

Lab zone Discover Activity
Skills Focus Inferring L1

Materials ping-pong ball, rock, box of common materials (such as suction cups, glue, tape, string, rubber bands, plastic wrap, hooks, clay), sink or deep pan, water

Time 15 minutes

Tips Encourage students to model animal-like structures rather than simply wrapping the ball and rock together.

Expected Outcome Students' solutions will vary. Some solutions will be similar to strategies used by animals along a rocky coastline.

Think It Over If the animal could not "hold on" to the rock, waves could batter it against the rock, or move it onto dry land or out to sea.

Along the Rocks Rocky shores are found along much of both coasts of the United States. Figure 9 shows some of the colorful organisms that typically live along the California coast.

The highest rocks, above the highest high-tide line, make up the spray zone. The spray zone is never completely covered with water, but it gets wet as the waves break against the rocks. A stripe of black algae indicates the highest high-tide line.

The rocks below this level are covered with barnacles. Barnacles can close up their hard shells. This action traps a drop of water inside to carry the barnacles through the dry period until the next high tide. The rocks are also home to flat animals called limpets. Limpets have a large, muscular foot that allows them to hold tightly to the rocks. They release drops of mucus around the edges of their shells. The mucus forms a tight seal.

In Tide Pools When the tide goes out, some water remains in depressions among the rocks called tide pools. As the water in a tide pool is warmed by the sun, the water begins to evaporate. The remaining water becomes saltier. If it rains, however, the salinity quickly decreases. Organisms in the tide pool must be able to withstand these changes in temperature and salinity. Tide-pool organisms must also withstand the force of the waves when the tide comes in again.

Sea stars cling to the rocks with rows of tiny suction cups. Spiny sea urchins crawl slowly along the bottom of the tide pool. If the bottom is sandy, a sea urchin can use its spines to dig a hole. The sea urchin buries itself in the hole during heavy surf.

Under shady rock ledges, sponges and sea anemones wait for the incoming tide to bring a fresh supply of plankton and other food particles. Most sea anemones look delicate. However, some sea anemones can survive out of water for more than two weeks. When out of the water, the anemone pulls its tentacles inside and folds up into a round blob.

Reading Checkpoint: How are sea stars able to cling to rocks?

FIGURE 9
A Rocky Shore
The constantly changing water level along a rocky shore in the intertidal zone creates different habitats.
Comparing and Contrasting *How are conditions different for organisms near the top of the rocks compared to organisms at the bottom?*

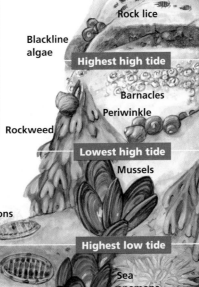

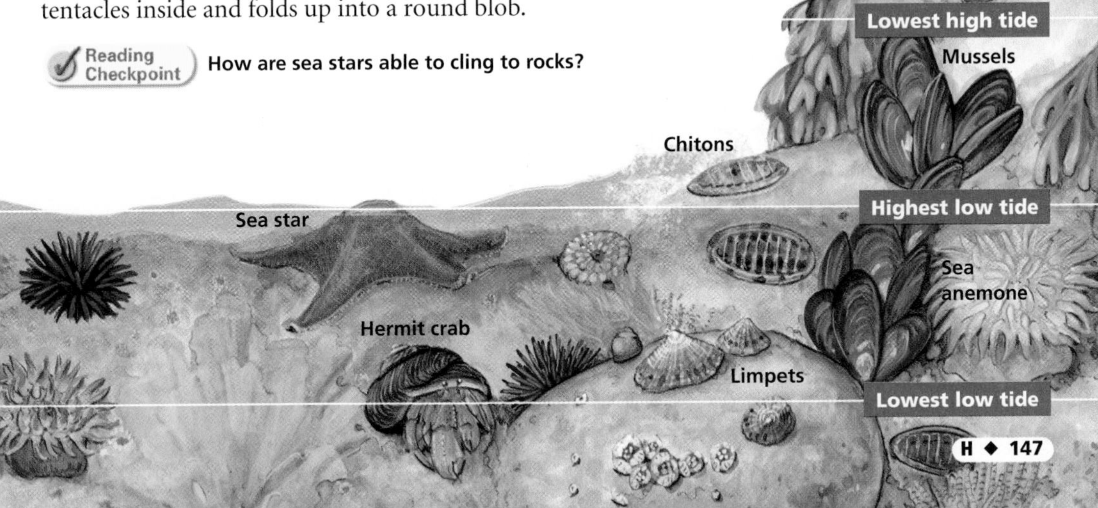

Instruct

Rocky Shores

Teach Key Concepts L2

Life on the Rocky Shore

Focus Tell students that today they will be battered by waves, bake in the hot sun, take a salty bath, and then be rinsed by fresh water. As they object, remind them that intertidal organisms tolerate these same conditions every day.

Teach Ask: **How could intertidal organisms survive being battered by waves?** *(By clinging tightly to rock, burrowing into the beach, having a protective shell)* **How could they survive the baking sun?** *(Trapping moisture in a shell, burrowing in the sand)* **Why must these organisms be able to tolerate varying salinity?** *(Evaporation and precipitation change the salinity in tide pools.)*

Apply Ask: **Why might the number of different types of organisms be less in the intertidal zone than in the neritic zone?** *(Fewer types of organisms are able to tolerate the harsh conditions of the intertidal zone.)* **learning modality: logical/mathematical**

All in One Teaching Resources

- Transparency H51

Independent Practice L2

All in One Teaching Resources

- Guided Reading and Study Worksheet: *Intertidal Zone*

Student Edition on Audio CD

Differentiated Instruction

Less Proficient Readers L1

Answering Questions As students read the section, have them summarize content by finding answers these questions: *What kinds of organisms live along rocky coasts? What kinds of organisms live in tide pools? What are mangrove forests? What are salt marshes?* **learning modality: verbal**

Gifted and Talented L3

Design an Experiment Challenge students to design an experiment to test how the salinity of a saltwater solution changes as the water evaporates. Students might design tests that include leaving a saltwater solution in a sunlit place to evaporate. Students then could determine the solution's density to detect changes in salinity. **learning modality: logical/mathematical**

Monitor Progress L1

Drawing Have students draw an intertidal zone environment, such as a beach, tide pool, or rocky coast.

Answers

Figure 9 Organisms near the top of the rocks are never completely covered with water, whereas those at the bottom are always covered with water, although its temperature and salinity might vary.

Reading Checkpoint: Sea stars cling to rocks with rows of tiny suction cups.

For: More on the Intertidal Zone
Visit: PHSchool.com
Web Code: cfd-3043

Students can review the intertidal zone in an online interactivity.

Where River Meets Ocean

Teach Key Concepts L1

Saltwater Wetlands

Focus Ask: **What's the difference between a forest and a marsh?** *(Forests have trees, and marshes have grass.)* Tell students that forests and marshes are common along the coast.

Teach Tell students that fresh water from land and salt water from the ocean often mix along the coast and that this mixed water provides a habitat for special kinds of plants, such as mangrove trees and cord grass.

Apply Ask: **How could trees and grass protect the coastline from erosion?** *(The roots bind the soil, and the plants reduce the energy of waves.)* **Why are young animals safer from predators in an estuary?** *(The shallow water and harsh conditions exclude many potential predators.)* **learning modality: verbal**

L2

Observing Estuaries

Materials maps of coastal regions

Time 25 minutes

Focus Point out that estuaries are a "meeting place" of salt and fresh water, and that coastal wetlands habitats exist in and around estuaries.

Teach Provide students with maps that represent coastal regions. Have students locate estuaries and coastal wetlands on the maps.

Apply Ask: **Where do estuaries occur?** *(Where rivers flow into the ocean)* **Where are coastal wetlands located?** *(Near estuaries and in a narrow belt along some parts of the coast)* **learning modality: visual**

For: More on the intertidal zone
Visit: PHSchool.com
Web Code: cfd-3043

Where River Meets Ocean

Other important environments along the ocean's edge are estuaries. **Estuaries** are coastal inlets or bays where fresh water from rivers mixes with the salty ocean water. Water that is partly salty and partly fresh is brackish.

Coastal wetlands are found in and around estuaries. **Along the coasts of the United States, most wetlands are either mangrove forests or salt marshes.** Mangrove forests are found in southern Florida and along the coast of the Gulf of Mexico. Salt marshes are especially abundant along the east coast from Massachusetts to Florida.

Mangrove Forests Mangroves are short, gnarled trees that grow well in brackish water. These trees fringe the coastline of southern Florida. The mangroves' prop roots, shown in Figure 10, anchor the trees to the land. Mangroves can withstand all but the strongest hurricane winds. The mangroves break the action of winds and waves, protecting the coastline during storms. The prop roots also trap sediment from the land. They create a protected nursery, rich in nutrients, for many young animals.

Salt Marshes A salt marsh oozes with smelly mud. The mud is made up of sediments, animal and plant matter, and nutrients carried into the marsh by fresh water and tides.

Cordgrass is the most common plant in the marsh. Unlike most plants, cordgrass can survive in salt water. The plant releases salt through small openings in its long, narrow leaves. Some cordgrass is eaten by animals. The rest of the cordgrass is decomposed by bacteria and fungi in the water. The decomposed material supplies nutrients to marsh organisms.

FIGURE 10
A Mangrove Forest
Arching prop roots anchor these mangrove trees firmly in the soft, sandy soil.
Relating Cause and Effect *How do mangrove forests protect the coastline?*

▲ Roseate spoonbill

▼ American crocodile

148 ◆ H

Differentiated Instruction

Gifted and Talented L3

Chesapeake Bay Encourage students to learn more about the health of the Chesapeake Bay. Much scientific research has been carried out in this area. Students can research the causes and effects of pollution in the Chesapeake Bay and the results of cleanup efforts.

Special Needs L1

Visual Aids Many students will have experience with organisms that live in intertidal zones, but most will not have observed organisms in mangrove forests or salt marshes. Provide a variety of visual resources that will enable students to see the variety of organisms that live in these wetlands habitats.

Tidal channels run through the cordgrass. Waves break up as they enter the channels, so that organisms in the marsh are protected from the surf. Within the marsh, fish, crabs, shrimp, and oysters hatch and feed before entering the harsher ocean environment offshore. As the tide retreats, mud flats are exposed. Many crabs search for food in the rich mud. Herons, stilts, and egrets stalk across the mud to prey on the crabs and other benthos exposed by the low tide.

Protecting Estuaries The rivers that flow into estuaries can carry harmful substances. Pollutants such as pesticides, sewage, and industrial waste may end up in an estuary. Organisms that live in the estuary are affected by these pollutants.

For example, the Chesapeake Bay is a huge estuary located on the mid-Atlantic coast. It has been a rich source of oysters, clams, and blue crabs. However, pollutants from inland sources accumulated in the bay for years. Pollution, along with overfishing, greatly reduced the numbers of blue crabs in the Chesapeake Bay. When people realized the threat to the estuary, they took action. Laws were passed to regulate the water quality of rivers that empty into the Chesapeake Bay. Cleanup efforts have reduced much of the pollution in the bay. Today, pollution is less of a problem in the Chesapeake Bay than it once was.

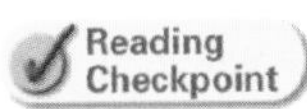
What has been done to help reduce pollution in the Chesapeake Bay?

FIGURE 11
Food From an Estuary
A crabber in the Chesapeake Bay pulls up the last trap of the day. As the health of the estuary improves, the blue crab population is increasing again.

Section 3 Assessment

Target Reading Skill **Outlining** Use the information in your outline about the intertidal zone to help you answer the questions below.

Reviewing Key Concepts

1. a. **Describing** What are conditions like in the rocky intertidal zone?
   b. **Explaining** Explain what a sea anemone does when it is not covered by water.
   c. **Applying Concepts** How does this behavior help the sea anemone survive in the intertidal zone?
2. a. **Identifying** Identify two types of coastal wetlands.
   b. **Comparing and Contrasting** List two ways that these environments are alike and two ways they are different.
   c. **Making Judgments** A builder has proposed filling in a salt marsh to create a seaside resort. What positive and negative impacts might this action have on wildlife and local residents? Would you support the proposal? Explain.

Writing in Science

Fact Sheet Suppose you work for a national or state park that contains salt marshes. Your job is to take people on guided tours of a salt marsh. Before the tour, you distribute a fact sheet that points out the sights that visitors can expect to see. Write a fact sheet on salt marshes to distribute to park visitors. If you want, you can illustrate your fact sheet.

Monitor Progress L1

Answers

Figure 10 Mangroves break the action of winds and waves.

Reading Checkpoint Laws were passed to reduce the amount of pollutants entering the bay, and the bay has been cleaned up.

Assess

Reviewing Key Concepts

1. a. Answers could include pounding waves, changes in salinity and water temperature, and exposure to sunlight and air. **b.** When a sea anemone is uncovered, it pulls its tentacles inside. **c.** This behavior protects the animal from exposure.
2. a. Two types of coastal wetlands are mangrove forests and salt marshes.
b. *Similarities*: brackish water, shallow water, high nutrients, plants break up waves and shelter organisms. *Differences*: Salt marshes have cordgrass and a muddy bottom; mangrove forests have mangrove trees and sandy soil and are located farther south.
c. Accept a variety of responses as long as students support their viewpoints with specific details. Sample answer: I would not support the proposal. Filling in the salt marsh would destroy natural habitats and thus eliminate most wildlife.

Reteach L1

Ask students to describe conditions in a tidal pool.

Performance Assessment L2

Organizing Information Have each student make a two-column table to summarize and contrast the characteristics of a rocky coastline and an estuary.

All in One Teaching Resources

- Section Summary: *Intertidal Zone*
- Review and Reinforcement: *Intertidal Zone*
- Enrich: *Intertidal Zone*

Writing in Science

Writing Mode Description

Scoring Rubric

4 Exceeds criteria by including a complete description of a salt marsh and descriptions of the important animal and plant life that visitors would see
3 Meets criteria by describing a salt marsh and some plant and animal life
2 Describes a salt marsh or describes some plant and animal life
1 Description is incomplete or inaccurate

Lab zone Chapter Project

Keep Students on Track Each group should have completed its plan for the habitat model, chosen the materials to use, and begun building. Individual students should have selected an organism to model and begun research to determine its physical characteristics. Encourage students to draw a picture of their model to help them plan.

Section 4

Neritic Zone and Open Ocean

Objectives

After this lesson, students will be able to

H.4.4.1 Describe the conditions in the neritic zone.

H.4.4.2 Describe two neritic zone habitats—coral reefs and kelp forests.

H.4.4.3 Describe the conditions in the open ocean.

Target Reading Skill

Relating Cause and Effect Explain that cause is the reason for what happens. The effect is what happens because of the cause. Relating cause and effect helps students relate the reason for what happens to what happens as a result.

Answers

Causes

Sunlight penetrates shallow water.

Nutrients from the land enter the ocean.

Effect

The neritic zone contains a wide variety of organisms.

All in One Teaching Resources

- Transparency H52

Preteach

Build Background Knowledge L1

Neritic and Open-Ocean Zones

Unlike intertidal areas, the neritic zone and open ocean are not directly observable by most students. Question students to elicit what they know about these areas—for example: **What kinds of animals live in the deep ocean? What do these animals feed on? How deep is the water beyond the continental slope?** *(Record students' responses and have students review and revise the responses as they read the section.)*

Section 4

Neritic Zone and Open Ocean

Reading Preview

Key Concepts

- What are the conditions in the neritic zone?
- What environments support coral reefs and kelp forests?
- What are the conditions in the open ocean?

Key Terms

- atoll
- bioluminescence
- hydrothermal vent

Target Reading Skill

Relating Cause and Effect As you read, identify the conditions that affect life in the neritic zone. Write the information in a graphic organizer like the one below.

Causes	Effect
	The neritic zone has a wide variety of organisms.

Lab zone Discover Activity

How Deep Can You See?

1. With a permanent marker, divide a white plastic lid into four quarters. Shade in two quarters as shown.
2. Use a pair of scissors to carefully poke a small hole in the center of the lid.
3. Tie a piece of string to a paper clip. Place the clip underneath the lid and thread the string up through the hole.
4. Tape the string tightly to a meterstick so that the lid presses against the bottom of the meterstick.
5. Fill a large, deep bucket with tap water. While stirring the water, add one teaspoon of flour to represent the dissolved substances in seawater. The water should be slightly cloudy.
6. Lower the lid into the water so that it is 5 cm below the surface. Note whether the lid is still visible in the water.
7. Lower the lid 10 cm below the surface, then 15 cm, and so on until the lid is no longer visible.

Think It Over

Observing At what depth could you no longer see the lid? Based on your results, how do you think visibility changes with depth in the ocean?

Floating mats of algae on the ocean surface mark the location of a kelp forest. Bright-orange sheephead fish dart about. Young sea lions chase each other around the kelp stalks. A sea otter dives down to the rocky ocean bottom. When it rises, the otter is clutching a sea urchin between its paws. On the surface again, the otter rolls onto its back among the kelp. The otter skillfully uses its paws to scoop out the meat from the soft parts of the sea urchin.

▼ Sea otter in a kelp forest

Lab zone Discover Activity

Skills Focus Observing L1

Materials permanent marker, white plastic lid, scissors, string, paper clip, tape, meterstick, bucket, tap water, flour, plastic spoon, stirring rod

Time 20 minutes

Tips You might want to construct one device to use as a model. Remind students to record their observations at each depth.

Expected Outcome At some depth, the flour particles suspended in the water will obscure the viewing of the lid.

Think It Over Students should infer that visibility decreases as water depth increases.

FIGURE 12
Organisms in the Neritic Zone
Because it is so rich in nutrients, the neritic zone supports a huge variety of organisms. These include sea lions (left) and herring (below). **Inferring** *Why is the neritic zone so rich in nutrients?*

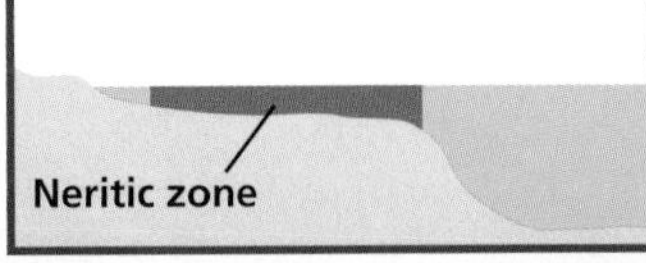

Conditions in the Neritic Zone

A kelp forest is one type of habitat found in the neritic zone. Remember that the neritic zone extends from the low-tide line out to the edge of the continental shelf. A huge variety of organisms are found in the neritic zone, more than in any other ocean zone. Most of the world's major fishing grounds are found in this zone.

Why is the neritic zone home to so many living things? The answer has to do with its location over the continental shelf. **The shallow water over the continental shelf receives sunlight and a steady supply of nutrients washed from the land into the ocean. The light and nutrients enable large plantlike algae to grow.** These algae serve as a food source and shelter for other organisms.

In many parts of the neritic zone, upwelling currents bring additional nutrients from the bottom to the surface. These nutrients support large numbers of plankton, which form the base of ocean food webs. Schools of fish such as sardines and herrings feed on the plankton. Major fisheries in upwelling areas include Monterey Canyon off the California coast, Newfoundland's Grand Banks, and Georges Bank off the New England coast.

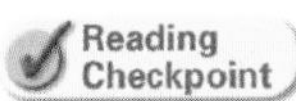
Reading Checkpoint **What are two ways that nutrients may be supplied to the neritic zone?**

Instruct

Conditions in the Neritic Zone

Teach Key Concepts L1

The Neritic Zone

Focus Compare the neritic zone to the shallow end of a swimming pool. Close to the shallow end, the pool's bottom slopes gently. It then slopes down rapidly to the deep end of the pool.

Teach Ask: **Why does sunlight penetrate to the bottom of the neritic zone?** *(It has shallow water.)* **How does sunlight help life in the neritic zone?** *(It allows photosynthesis to occur. Both algae plankton and bottom plants are able to thrive in this zone.)* **How does a high level of nutrients help life?** *(Plants and algae plankton needs nutrients to grow. These organisms are the base of the food web.)*

Apply Remind students that upwelling provides nutrients to some parts of the neritic zone. Ask: **What can you infer about life in these areas?** *(Life is very abundant.)* **learning modality: logical/mathematical**

Independent Practice L2

All in One **Teaching Resources**

- Guided Reading and Study Worksheet: *Neritic Zone and Open Ocean*

Student Edition on Audio CD

Differentiated Instruction

Less Proficient Readers L1

Conditions in the Neritic Zone Have student groups prepare and present a "weather report" for the bottom of the neritic zone at a particular area. Students could address temperature, pressure, sunlight, currents, waves, and water clarity. When students have questions, refer them to appropriate passages in the textbook. **learning modality: verbal**

Gifted and Talented L3

Conditions in the Neritic Zone Have student groups prepare and present a "fishing report" for the neritic zone at a particular region. Reports might include abundance and variety of life, availability of nutrients, and any problems, such as over-fishing or pollution. Students also might consider the effects of El Niño and La Niña. **learning modality: verbal**

Monitor Progress L1

Oral Presentation Have students explain why a huge variety of life exists in the neritic zone.

Answers

Figure 12 Rivers contribute nutrients from the land. Upwelling contributes nutrients to some parts of the neritic zone.

Reading Checkpoint Nutrients are washed into the neritic zone from land, and nutrients from deep water enter the neritic zone where upwelling occurs.

Coral Reefs

Teach Key Concepts

L1

Coral Reef Environments

Focus Remind students that each type of organism is adapted to certain environmental conditions. Ask: **What are some important environmental conditions?** *(Temperature, amount of light, depth)*

Teach Tell students that coral animals can live only in water with the following characteristics: warm, shallow, clear, clean, sunlit. Ask: **In which part of the world could coral animals live?** *(In the tropics)* **In which ocean zone could coral animals live?** *(The neritic zone)* **Why do coral animals need shallow water?** *(Enough sunlight must reach the animals.)* **Why might coral animals not survive near a large river?** *(The water would be cloudy with sediment.)*

Apply Ask: **How could humans affect the health of a coral reef?** *(Pollute the water; cause excess sediment to enter the water)* **learning modality: logical/mathematical**

All in One Teaching Resources

- Transparency H53

L2

Modeling Coral Reefs

Focus Discuss the differences between a fringing reef, a barrier reef, and an atoll.

Materials aluminum baking pans, clay or plaster of Paris

Time 20 minutes

Teach Challenge groups of students to build models of the three different kinds of coral reefs. Students can decorate and label their models.

Apply Ask: **When does a barrier reef become an atoll?** *(When the top of the volcanic island is no longer above the surface of the ocean.)* **learning modality: kinesthetic**

FIGURE 13
How an Atoll Forms
An atoll develops in stages, beginning with a fringing reef that surrounds a volcanic island. **Relating Cause and Effect** *For an atoll to form, what must happen to the volcanic island?*

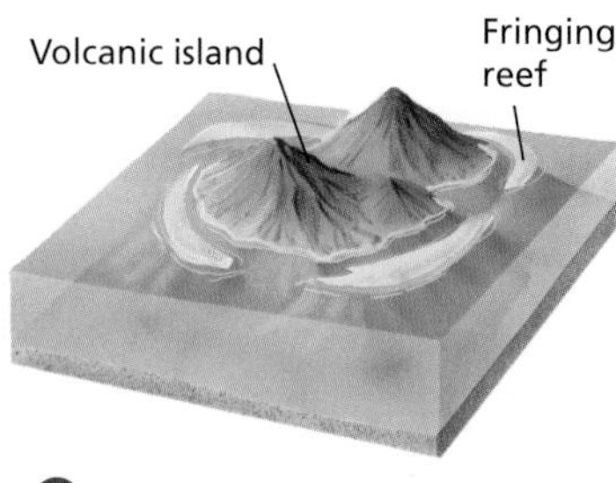

1 A fringing reef closely surrounds an island.

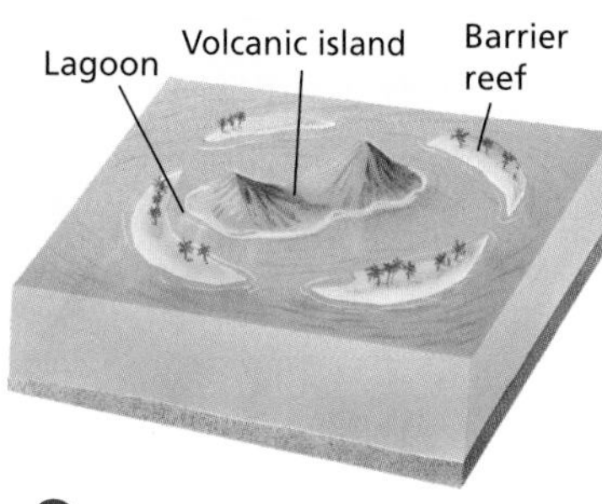

2 As the island sinks, a lagoon forms inside the barrier reef.

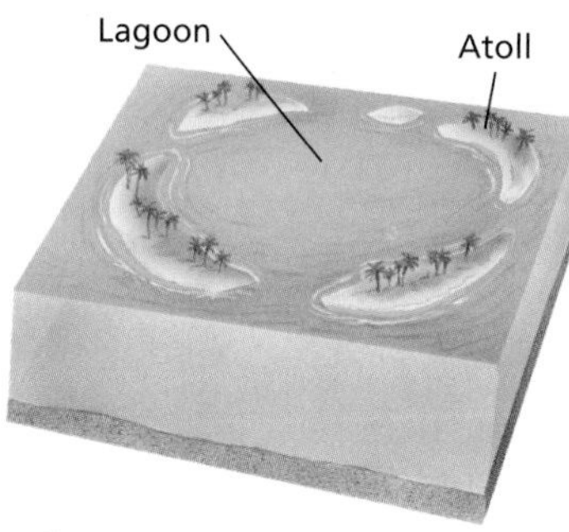

3 Finally, the island sinks, leaving a ring-shaped atoll.

Coral Reefs

A coral reef is another type of diverse habitat found in the neritic zone. Although a coral reef may look as if it is made of rock, it is actually made of living things. Coral reefs are created by colonies of tiny coral animals, each of which is not much larger than a pencil eraser. Each coral animal produces a hard structure that surrounds its soft body. After the coral dies, the empty structure remains. New coral animals attach and grow on top of it. Over many years, a reef is built.

Environment of Coral Reefs Microscopic algae live in the bodies of the coral animals and provide food for the corals. The algae need warm temperatures and sunlight. **Therefore, coral reefs can form only in shallow, tropical ocean waters.** The reefs grow above continental shelves or around volcanic islands, where the water is shallow.

Ring-Shaped Reefs In areas where the seafloor is sinking, a reef may develop over time into an atoll. An **atoll** is a ring-shaped reef surrounding a shallow lagoon. Figure 13 shows the development of an atoll. It begins as a fringing reef that closely surrounds the edges of the island. As the sea floor sinks, the island sinks with it, and the reef continues to grow upward. Water separates the top of the barrier reef from the island. The island continues to sink until it is entirely underwater, forming the atoll.

Life Around a Reef Coral can form a variety of shapes. These shapes are suggested by the names of coral species—elkhorn, brain, plate, star. Many animals live in and around a coral reef. Coral-reef animals include octopuses, spiny lobsters, shrimp, and fishes in all colors and sizes. Parrotfish scrape coral off the reef to eat. The parrotfish grind up the broken coral inside their bodies, producing the fine, soft sand commonly found around the reef.

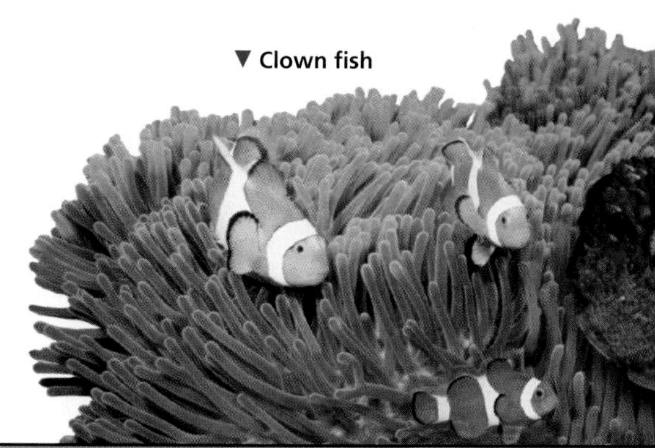

▼ Clown fish

Coral Reefs and Humans Coral reefs are like natural aquarium exhibits, displaying a colorful diversity of life that people can enjoy and study. Reefs also protect coastlines during violent storms. The reefs break up the surf, preventing waves from severely eroding the land. However, human activities can harm the fragile reefs. Boat anchors dragging across a reef can damage it. Divers can accidentally break off pieces of the reef. Even brushing against a reef can harm coral animals. Because coral grows only a few millimeters a year, a reef cannot quickly recover.

Changes in water temperature and clearness also affect algae, and therefore, endanger coral reefs. For example, if the water becomes too warm, the corals release the algae that live inside them. Cloudy water endangers the algae by reducing the amount of light that reaches them. If sediments produced by storms or human activities bury a reef, the algae in the living coral cannot survive. Without the algae, the coral animals die.

Today many people understand the importance of coral reefs and try to protect them. Many reef areas have been set aside as marine sanctuaries. In a marine sanctuary, the amount of diving and other activity near the reef is limited. Scientists are also studying the effects of temperature change and pollution on the reefs in order to preserve them.

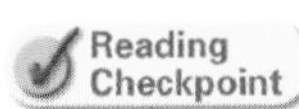

How can human activities impact a coral reef?

For: Links on coral reefs
Visit: www.SciLinks.org
Web Code: scn-0844

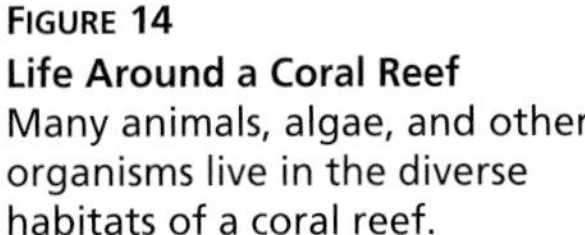

FIGURE 14
Life Around a Coral Reef
Many animals, algae, and other organisms live in the diverse habitats of a coral reef.

For: Links on coral reefs
Visit: www.SciLinks.org
Web Code: scn-0844

Download a worksheet that will guide students' review of Internet resources on coral reefs.

Integrating Life Science

The United States government has made a number of sites national marine sanctuaries. These include Stellwagen Bank, Monitor, and Gray's Reef in the Atlantic Ocean; Florida Keys and Flower Garden Banks in the Gulf of Mexico; and Olympic Coast, Cordell Bank, Gulf of Farallones, Monterey Bay, Channel Islands, Humpback Whale, and Fagatele Bay in the Pacific Ocean. Invite interested students to research one of the sanctuaries and discover how marine environments are protected there. **learning modality: logical/mathematical**

Help Students Read L1

Active Comprehension Read aloud the paragraphs about coral reefs and humans. After the reading, prompt students to verbally summarize the passage. Tell them that they may refer to the text if necessary.

Differentiated Instruction

Special Needs L1

Observing Coral Samples Provide samples of several different types of coral for students to examine. Emphasize that these pieces are coral skeletons, not coral animals. Ask: **Where do you think the coral animals lived?** *(In the tiny holes)* **How do you think this hard structure helps coral animals survive?** *(It provides protection for the animals' soft bodies and anchors them to the ocean floor.)* **learning modality: visual**

Monitor Progress L1

Writing Have each student write a paragraph explaining why coral reefs are fragile.

Answers

Figure 13 The volcanic island must sink below the surface of the ocean.

Reading Checkpoint Possible answers: Boat anchors can be dragged across a reef. Divers can break off pieces or injure coral animals by brushing against them. Human activities can make the water cloudy, which reduces the amount of sunlight. Humans can pollute the water.

Life in a Kelp Forest

Teach Key Concepts

L1

Kelp Forest Environments

Focus Ask: **Why is a kelp environment like a forest?** *(The stalks rise above the ocean bottom like trees rise above the soil.)*

Teach Tell students to imagine that they are divers swimming through a kelp forest. As a class, describe the environment and organisms that students would see. Remind students that a kelp forest is a thriving ecosystem, just like a forest on land.

Apply Ask: **What organism forms the base of the food web in a kelp forest?** *(The kelp)* **learning modality: visual**

Modeling Kelp

Focus Point out that kelp are adapted that to life in the neritic zone.

Materials string, heavy washers or nuts, tape, plastic bucket or aquarium tank, water, small balloons, ping-pong balls, clay

Time 15 minutes

Teach Give each student or group a piece of string and challenge them to devise a way to keep the string upright in water with its lower end on the bottom and its upper end near the surface. Students may use any of the listed materials to accomplish this task. A typical solution might include tying a weight on one end of the string and tying ping-pong balls at intervals along its length.

Apply Ask: **How is your model similar to giant kelp strands?** *(The balloons or ping-pong balls are like the gas-filled bulbs on kelp stalks, and the weight is like the holdfast.)* **learning modality: kinesthetic**

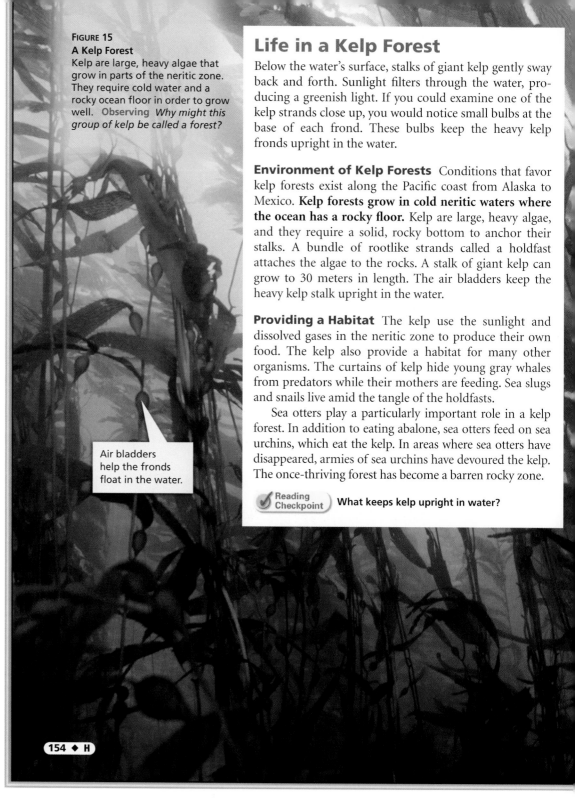

FIGURE 15
A Kelp Forest
Kelp are large, heavy algae that grow in parts of the neritic zone. They require cold water and a rocky ocean floor in order to grow well. **Observing** *Why might this group of kelp be called a forest?*

Air bladders help the fronds float in the water.

Life in a Kelp Forest

Below the water's surface, stalks of giant kelp gently sway back and forth. Sunlight filters through the water, producing a greenish light. If you could examine one of the kelp strands close up, you would notice small bulbs at the base of each frond. These bulbs keep the heavy kelp fronds upright in the water.

Environment of Kelp Forests Conditions that favor kelp forests exist along the Pacific coast from Alaska to Mexico. **Kelp forests grow in cold neritic waters where the ocean has a rocky floor.** Kelp are large, heavy algae, and they require a solid, rocky bottom to anchor their stalks. A bundle of rootlike strands called a holdfast attaches the algae to the rocks. A stalk of giant kelp can grow to 30 meters in length. The air bladders keep the heavy kelp stalk upright in the water.

Providing a Habitat The kelp use the sunlight and dissolved gases in the neritic zone to produce their own food. The kelp also provide a habitat for many other organisms. The curtains of kelp hide young gray whales from predators while their mothers are feeding. Sea slugs and snails live amid the tangle of the holdfasts.

Sea otters play a particularly important role in a kelp forest. In addition to eating abalone, sea otters feed on sea urchins, which eat the kelp. In areas where sea otters have disappeared, armies of sea urchins have devoured the kelp. The once-thriving forest has become a barren rocky zone.

Reading Checkpoint **What keeps kelp upright in water?**

FIGURE 16
An Open-Ocean Organism
Orcas, or killer whales, are fierce predators of the surface zone.

Conditions in the Open Ocean

The open ocean begins where the neritic zone ends, at the edge of the continental shelf. **The open ocean differs from the neritic zone in two important ways. First, only a small part of the open ocean receives sunlight. Second, the water has fewer nutrients.** As a result, the open ocean supports fewer organisms.

Diving into the open ocean is like walking down a long staircase that has a light only at the top. Sunlight penetrates only a short distance into the water. If the water is cloudy, sunlight does not reach as far. In clear tropical waters, however, sunlight may reach as deep as a few hundred meters.

Recall that the neritic zone receives a constant supply of nutrients from shore. In contrast, dissolved nutrients are less abundant in the open ocean.

The Surface Zone You have read that the water column in the open ocean can be divided into three zones. The surface zone extends as far as sunlight reaches below the surface. The surface zone is the only part of the open ocean that receives enough sunlight to support the growth of algae. These microscopic algae are the base of open-ocean food webs. Animal plankton that feed on the algae include shrimplike krill, as well as the young of crabs, mollusks, and fishes.

The Transition Zone The transition zone extends from the bottom of the surface zone to a depth of about 1 kilometer. The water here is darker and colder than in the surface zone.

Lab zone Skills Activity

Inferring

To keep from sinking, many plankton rely on the friction between their bodies and the surrounding water. More friction is needed to stay afloat in warm water than in denser cold water. One of the copepods below is found in tropical ocean waters, while the other is found near the poles. Which do you think is which? Explain your reasoning. (*Hint:* More streamlined shapes create less friction with their surroundings.)

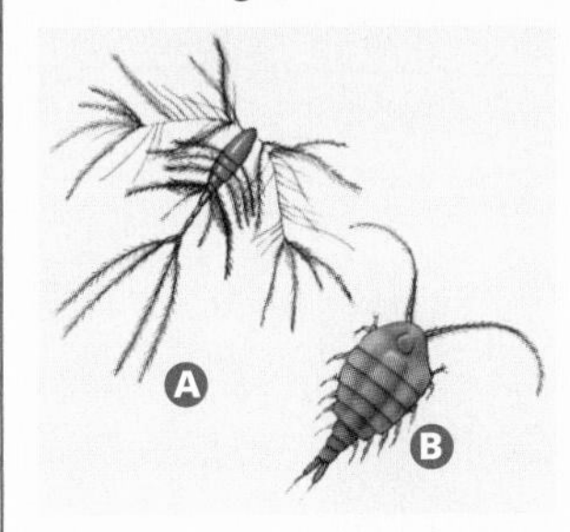

Conditions in the Open Ocean

Teach Key Concepts L2

The Open Ocean

Focus Help students recall that the open ocean is vertically divided into three zones—the surface zone, the transition zone, and the deep zone.

Teach Ask: **In which zone can algae use sunlight to make food?** *(Surface zone)* **Which zone has the coldest water?** *(Deep zone)* **In which zone do conditions gradually change?** *(Transition zone)*

Apply Ask: **Where is most of the food produced in the open ocean?** *(In the surface zone)* **Why do you think fewer organisms live in the deep zone?** *(Because algae cannot use sunlight to make food and because conditions are harsh)* **learning modality: verbal**

Lab zone Skills Activity

Skills Focus Inferring L2

Time 10 minutes

Tips Make sure that students note the three major clues needed to solve the problem: 1) more friction is needed to stay afloat in warm water, 2) more streamlined shapes create less friction, 3) copepod B is more streamlined than copepod A.

Expected Outcome Students infer that copepod A lives in warm, tropical waters, and copepod B lives in cold, polar waters.

Extend Challenge students to devise a model to demonstrate how different shapes behave in water. **learning modality: visual**

Monitor Progress L1

Skills Check Have students make a two-column chart to compare and contrast the characteristics of the surface zone and the deep zone.

Answers

Figure 15 The kelp forest is made up of many long, tree-like stalks of algae growing close together that resemble a forest on land.

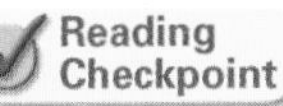

Gas-filled bulbs keep kelp upright in water.

L3

Modeling a Hydrothermal Vent Food Web

Focus Tell students that some microorganisms can make food without sunlight and that these bacteria support some of the strangest organisms in the ocean.

Materials index cards, colored yarn

Time 20 minutes

Teach Have students research the marine organisms that live near hydrothermal vents. Challenge students to use note cards and yarn to model the feeding relationships among the organisms.

Apply Ask: **Which organisms form the base of this food web?** *(Bacteria.)* **How are these bacteria similar to algae in surface zone food webs?** *(They, like the algae plankton of the surface zone, produce food.)* **How are they different?** *(Algae plankton produce food through photosynthesis. Hydrothermal-vent bacteria produce food by using chemicals in the hot water.)* **learning modality: kinesthetic**

The Deep Zone In the deep zone, the water is even darker and colder than in the transition zone. Because of its harsh conditions, the deep ocean is often compared to a desert. Few organisms live in the deep zone, compared to other ocean and land environments. But unlike a desert, which bakes under the bright sun, the deep ocean is cold, dark, and wet.

Finding food in the darkness is a challenge. Many deep-sea fishes produce their own light. The production of light by living things is called **bioluminescence.** Chemical reactions in the cells of organisms produce bioluminescence.

In some cases, light is produced by bioluminescent bacteria that live on the bodies of fishes. In other cases, the chemical reactions take place in the bodies of the fishes, as they do in fireflies on land. For example, tiny light-producing structures are scattered over the surfaces of some fishes. Other fishes, such as the anglerfish, have light-producing organs. The anglerfish has a light organ on its head. The anglerfish lurks in the shadows below the pool of light created by its light organ. Shrimp and fishes that are attracted to the light become prey of the anglerfish.

The food supply in most of the deep ocean is much more limited than in shallower water. Therefore, animals in this zone must be good hunters to survive. The gaping mouths of many deep-sea fishes are filled with fanglike teeth. Rows of sharp teeth stick out at angles, ensuring that any animal it bites cannot escape.

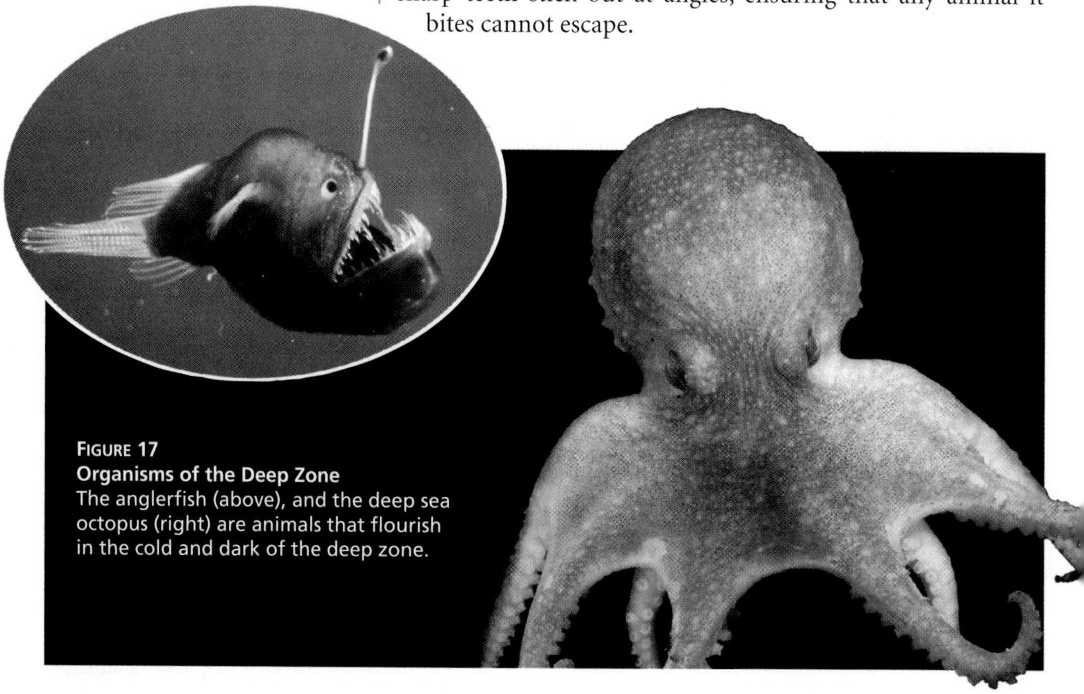

Figure 17
Organisms of the Deep Zone
The anglerfish (above), and the deep sea octopus (right) are animals that flourish in the cold and dark of the deep zone.

Differentiated Instruction

English Learners/Beginning L1
Vocabulary: Word Analysis Write the word *hydrothermal* on the board and circle the word parts *hydro-* (water), and *–thermal* (heat). Have students combine the word parts to understand that *hydrothermal* means "water that is heated." **learning modality: verbal**

English Learners/Intermediate L2
Vocabulary: Word Analysis Write the word *bioluminescence* on the board and circle the word parts *bio-* (living), *lumin* (light), and *-escence* (to become). Have students combine the word parts to understand that *bioluminescence* means "a living thing that becomes light." **learning modality: verbal**

Hydrothermal Vents In the deep zone, food is very scarce. As a result, organisms there tend to be small and slow-moving. However, there is one kind of deep-zone environment—a hydrothermal vent—that supports organisms of an unusual number, variety, and size. At a **hydrothermal vent,** hot water rises out of cracks in the ocean floor. This rising water has been heated by hot rock magma beneath the ocean floor. These vents are located along ocean ridges, where the plates are moving apart and new ocean floor is forming.

A hydrothermal vent is far from sunlight. What could organisms around a hydrothermal vent find to eat? The heated water coming from a vent carries gases and minerals from Earth's interior. Bacteria feed directly on these chemical nutrients. Like the algae in the surface zone that use sunlight to produce food, these bacteria use chemical nutrients to produce food.

These bacteria form the base of the food web at a hydrothermal vent. Other organisms, such as giant clams, feed on the bacteria. The giant red-tipped tube worms are supplied with food by bacteria living within their tissues. Meanwhile, the crabs feed on the remains of the other inhabitants of their unusual habitat.

FIGURE 18
A Hydrothermal Vent
Giant tube worms and crabs cluster around a hydrothermal vent on the ocean floor.

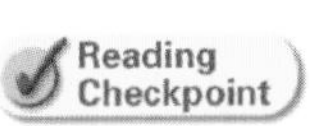

What is a hydrothermal vent?

Section 4 Assessment

Target Reading Skill **Relating Cause and Effect** Refer to your graphic organizer about conditions in the neritic zone to help you answer Question 1 below.

Reviewing Key Concepts

1. a. **Describing** Describe the physical conditions in the neritic zone.
   b. **Relating Cause and Effect** Explain how neritic-zone conditions support the growth of plankton.
   c. **Making Generalizations** Why are food webs in the neritic zone especially complex? (*Hint:* What is the role of plankton in food webs?)
2. a. **Describing** Describe life near a coral reef and life in a kelp forest.
   b. **Comparing and Contrasting** Compare and contrast the physical conditions that support coral reefs and kelp forests.
3. a. **Reviewing** How do conditions in the open ocean and the neritic zone differ?
   b. **Summarizing** Summarize the conditions that exist around hydrothermal vents.
   c. **Applying Concepts** Are the organisms around a hydrothermal vent typical of deep-zone organisms? Explain.

Writing in Science

Editorial You are a scientist studying a coral reef located near a tropical island. A forest on the island has been cut down. As a result, soil erosion is increasing. Write an editorial for the local newspaper explaining how this could affect the coral reef.

Lab zone Chapter Project

Keep Students on Track As students build their models, meet with them regularly to discuss their progress and any problems they may be encountering.

Writing in Science

Writing Mode Persuasion

Scoring Rubric

4 Explains and connects the events, including effects on the ocean and water clarity.
3 Meets expectations by explaining how soil erosion might lead to the death of the reef
2 Explains without connecting the events
1 Is incomplete or inaccurate

Monitor Progress L2

Answer

Reading Checkpoint A hydrothermal vent is an area in the deep ocean where ocean water that circulated into rock and was heated by nearby magma rises back into the ocean.

Assess

Reviewing Key Concepts

1. a. The physical conditions in the neritic zone include shallow water, sunlight, and a steady supply of nutrients. **b.** Plankton depend on the sunlight and rich nutrient supply of the neritic zone to live and produce food. **c.** Many organisms depend, either directly or indirectly, on plankton as a source of energy. Many food chains overlap to form complex food webs.
2. a. Coral reefs have a wide variety of marine life. Organisms that live in coral reefs include octopuses, spiny lobsters, shrimp, and fish. Organisms that live in kelp forests include sea slugs, sea urchins, otters, and baby whales that take refuge among the giant kelp. **b.** Coral reefs grow in shallow, tropical waters, but kelp forests grow in cold, neritic environments with rocky bottoms.
3. a. The neritic zone receives sunlight throughout and has high amounts of nutrients. In the open-ocean zone, sunlight penetrates only a short distance, and the water has few nutrients. **b.** The water coming from hydrothermal vents is extremely hot and contains chemicals that bacteria use to make food. Tube worms, crabs, and giant clams live near the vents. **c.** No, the organisms are part of isolated ecosystems that exist only near hydrothermal vents.

Reteach L1

With the class, draw a diagram of the ocean labeling the intertidal, neritic and open-ocean zones and the surface, transition, and deep zones. Discuss the conditions that exist in each zone.

All in One Teaching Resources

- Section Summary: *Neritic Zone and Open Ocean*
- Review and Reinforcement: *Neritic Zone and Open Ocean*
- Enrich: *Neritic Zone and Open Ocean*

Section 5 Resources from the Ocean

Objectives

After this lesson, students will be able to

H.4.5.1 Explain how people use living resources from the ocean.

H.4.5.2 Identify the ocean's nonliving resources.

H.4.5.3 Identify sources of ocean pollution.

Target Reading Skill

Identifying Main Ideas Explain that identifying main ideas and details helps students sort the facts from the information into groups. Each group can have a main topic, subtopics, and details.

Answers

Main Idea: Nonliving resources include…

- Water from desalination
- Fuels from the remains of animals
- Valuable minerals

All in One Teaching Resources

- Transparency H54

Preteach

Build Background Knowledge L1

Ocean Resources

Ask: **What kinds of foods do people obtain from the ocean?** *(Students should name a variety of fishes, shellfish, and other marine organisms such as seaweeds.)* **Besides food, what other ocean resources do people use?** *(Accept all reasonable responses.)* Write students' responses on the board for students to add to or revise as they read the section.

Section 5 Resources From the Ocean

Reading Preview

Key Concepts

- How do people use living resources from the ocean?
- What are some nonliving ocean resources?
- What are the sources of ocean pollution?

Key Terms

- aquaculture
- nodule

Target Reading Skill

Identifying Main Ideas As you read the Nonliving Resources section, write the main idea—the biggest or most important idea—in a graphic organizer like the one below. Then write three supporting details that give examples of the main idea.

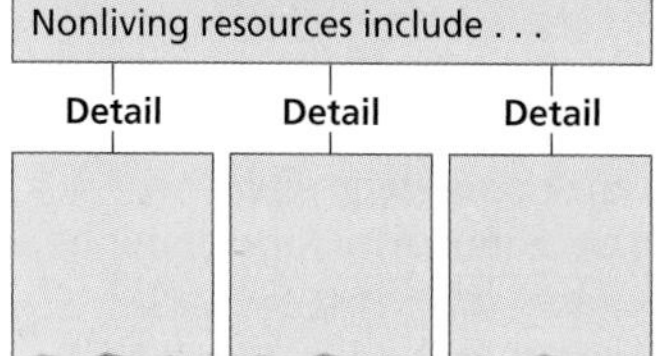

Lab zone Discover Activity

Is It From the Ocean?

1. Your teacher will give you some labels from common household products. Read the ingredient information on each label.
2. Divide the products into two piles—those you think include substances that come from the ocean and those that do not.

Think It Over

Classifying For each product you classified as coming from the ocean, name the ocean resource that is used to produce it. In which ocean zone is it found?

When European explorers began sailing to North America, they were astounded by the huge number of codfish off its eastern coast. Sailors reported that this area was so "swarming with fish that they could be taken not only with a net but in baskets let down and weighted with a stone." Others reported sailing through schools of cod so thick they slowed the boats down!

This cod fishery stretched from Newfoundland to a hook of land appropriately named Cape Cod. For more than 400 years, the seemingly endless supply of "King Cod" supported a thriving fishing industry. But starting in the early 1900s, it became clear that the cod population was decreasing. With the price of cod rising, there was more competition to catch fewer fish. In 1992, the Canadian government closed the fishery.

A cod catch ▶

Lab zone Discover Activity

Skills Focus Classifying L1

Materials labels from household products such as thickeners used in cooking, foods, abrasives, polishes, shampoos, and spice mixes containing sea salt

Time 15 minutes

Tips Students should consider both the living and nonliving resources in the ocean.

Expected Outcome Students will identify resources that come from the ocean, including foods and salt. They might also identify products, such as stabilizers, that are made from algae and abrasives that are made from diatoms.

Think It Over Sample answer: clam chowder—clams, intertidal zone; polish—diatoms, neritic and open-ocean zones; chocolate milk—kelp, neritic zone

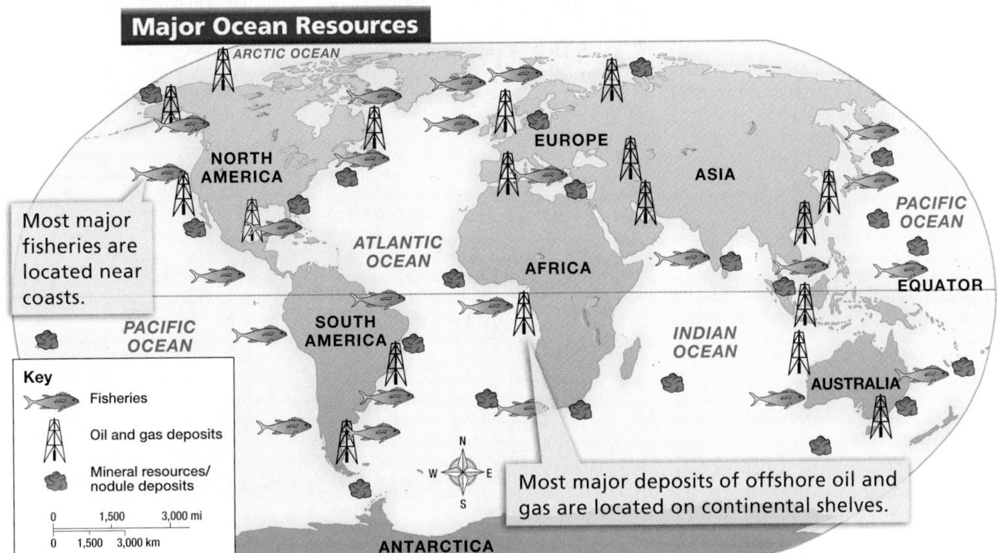

FIGURE 19
Resources From the Ocean
All over the world, the oceans are an important source of food, oil and gas, and minerals.
Interpreting Maps *Where are Africa's major fisheries located?*

Living Resources

Cod are just one example of a living resource from the ocean. How many other kinds of seafood have you tasted: tuna, shrimp, flounder, lobster, clams, squid, oysters, seaweed, or mussels? **People depend heavily on fishes and other ocean organisms for food. Ocean organisms also provide materials that are used in products such as detergents and paints.**

Harvesting Fish Many kinds of fishes are caught to be eaten. Anchovies, pollock, mackerel, herring, and tuna make up most of the worldwide catch. Locate the world's major fisheries in Figure 19. You can see that they are all located close to coasts. Nearly all fishes caught are harvested from coastal waters or areas of upwelling. These waters contain nutrients and plankton on which the fish feed.

If used wisely, fisheries naturally renew themselves each year. New fish are born, replacing those that are caught, but only as long as the fishery is not overfished. Overfishing causes the supply of fish to decrease.

Better technology has enabled people to catch large numbers of fish very quickly. Sometimes the fish can be caught faster than they can reproduce. When fish reproduction decreases, there are fewer and fewer fish each season. Eventually, the fish in the fishery may become very scarce. This is what happened in the cod fishery you read about earlier.

For: Links on ocean resources
Visit: www.SciLinks.org
Web Code: scn-0845

For: Links on ocean resources
Visit: www.SciLinks.org
Web Code: scn-0845

Download a worksheet that will guide students' review of Internet resources on ocean resources

Instruct

Living Resources

Teach Key Concepts L2

Ocean Resources

Focus Tell students that people have used resources from the oceans for thousands of years and that people use more of these resources today than ever before.

Teach Have students recall their previous three meals and identify any foods from the sea. Ask: **How important are seafoods to our society?** *(Very important)* **What other important products come from ocean organisms?** *(Polishes, abrasives, medicines)*

Apply Ask: **How might this use of ocean organisms affect their numbers?** *(If too many organisms are taken, populations will be reduced. The resource might become limited, and the species might become endangered.)*
learning modality: verbal

Independent Practice

All in One Teaching Resources

- Guided Reading and Study Worksheet: *Resources from the Ocean*
- Transparency H55

Student Edition on Audio CD

Differentiated Instruction

Gifted and Talented L3

Ocean Food Sources Invite a group of volunteers to visit a fish market or the seafood section of a supermarket at a time when the store is not busy. Have students list the names of the fish on display. Also have them interview the manager to obtain answers to these questions: **From what region is each type of fish caught? From what source(s) does the store buy the foods? Does the store buy each item fresh, frozen, or dried? Are any foods hard to obtain, and why?** Encourage students to add their own questions and report to the class.

Monitor Progress L2

Writing Have each student write a paragraph explaining the effects of overfishing.

Answer

Figure 19 Africa's major fisheries are located off its west coast and southwest coast.

Teacher Demo

L2

Materials diatomite, stereomicroscope, microscope lamp

Time 15 minutes

Focus Remind students that ocean organisms provide many types of resources, not just food.

Teach Place a small sample of diatomite under a stereomicroscope and allow students to observe. Students will see the tiny shells produced by these algae.

Apply Ask: **How could these shells be useful?** *(The shells are used in abrasives, polishes, and to kill insects.)* **learning modality: visual**

Integrating Technology

Aquaculture is an important and expanding technology. Oysters are farmed for food and for pearls. Other farmed organisms include clams, fish, and algae. Encourage students to learn more about marine aquaculture and report to the class. **learning modality: verbal**

Address Misconceptions

Unlimited Resources

L1

Focus Tell students that some resources, such as sunlight, will be available for billions of years, but that other resources are available in limited supply.

Teach Some students have the misconception that the ocean has an unlimited supply of resources. Help students understand that organisms can be harvested faster than they can reproduce. Even resources such as oil and minerals are present in limited supply.

Apply Have students speculate about how society can prevent shortages of ocean resources from occurring and how society can adapt if shortages do occur.

FIGURE 20
Aquaculture
These "farmers" are raising catfish in fenced-in areas near the mouth of the Mississippi River.

Try This Activity

Seaweed Candy

Make an Asian dessert whose main ingredient is algae. You will need a 0.5-ounce package of agar (a substance obtained from algae), 1 cup sugar, 4 cups guava juice or other fruit juice, and food coloring. Remember to prepare food only in a nonscience classroom and to get permission before using a stove.

1. Rinse the agar. Then break the agar into cubes and place them in a saucepan.
2. Add the sugar and juice to the pan. Bring the mixture to a boil. Turn down the heat and cook, stirring until the agar dissolves.
3. Remove the pan from the heat and stir in a few drops of food coloring. Pour the mixture into a shallow pan. Let it cool.
4. Refrigerate the candy until it is firm. Cut it into blocks and serve.

Inferring What purpose does the agar serve in this recipe?

Aquaculture As fish stocks decrease, **aquaculture,** the farming of saltwater and freshwater organisms, is likely to become more common. Aquaculture has been practiced in some Asian countries for centuries.

Aquaculture involves creating an environment for the organisms. To help the organisms thrive, nutrient levels, water temperature, light, and other factors must be controlled. Oysters, abalone, and shrimp have successfully been farmed in artificial saltwater ponds and protected bays. Even landlocked regions can produce seafood using aquaculture. For example, salmon are now being raised in Nebraska fields that once were cattle ranches.

Other Ocean Products People harvest ocean organisms for many purposes besides food. Algae is an ingredient in many household products. Its gelatin-like texture makes it an ideal base for detergents, shampoos, cosmetics, paints, and even ice cream! Sediments containing the hard pieces of diatoms are used for abrasives and polishes. Many researchers believe that other marine organisms may be important sources of chemicals for medicines in the future.

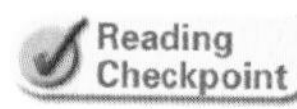

Reading Checkpoint What is aquaculture?

Try This Activity

Skills Focus Inferring L2

Materials 0.5-ounce package of agar, 1 cup sugar, 4 cups guava juice or other fruit juice, food coloring, water, saucepan, shallow pan, kitchen spatula

Time 20 minutes to prepare, several hours to set, 5 minutes to serve

Tips Supervise students closely when working with the heated mixture. Make sure they wear goggles and mitts. **CAUTION:** *Check for food allergies before allowing students to taste the candy.*

Expected Outcome The mixture will set in a gelatinlike consistency. The agar binds the ingredients together in a smooth gel. The sugar and juice add flavor.

Extend Let students make the candy without agar to see what happens.

Nonliving Resources

In addition to living organisms, the ocean contains valuable nonliving resources. **Some nonliving ocean resources include water, fuels, and minerals.**

Water You have read how fresh water can be extracted from ocean water using desalination. Desalination provides fresh water for many dry areas and islands.

Fuels The remains of dead marine organisms are the source of another nonliving resource. The remains sink to the bottom of the ocean, where they are buried by sediments. As more sediments accumulate, the buried remains decompose. Over hundreds of thousands of years, the heat and pressure from the overlying layers gradually transform the organisms' remains into oil and natural gas.

As you know, many organisms live in the part of the ocean above the continental shelf. The thick sediments on the continental shelves bury the remains of living things. As a result, the richest deposits of oil and gas are often located on the continental shelves.

Oil rigs like the one in Figure 21 drill the rocky ocean floor as much as 300 meters below the surface. Imagine trying to dig a hole in the concrete bottom of a swimming pool, while standing on a raft floating on the surface of the water. You can see why drilling the ocean floor is very difficult! Ocean drilling is made even harder by strong currents, winds, and violent storms.

FIGURE 21
An Oil Rig
Lit up like a city at night, this Norwegian oil-drilling platform rises above the icy waters of the North Sea. Hundreds of people may live and work on an oil rig.
Relating Cause and Effect *How did oil deposits form beneath the ocean?*

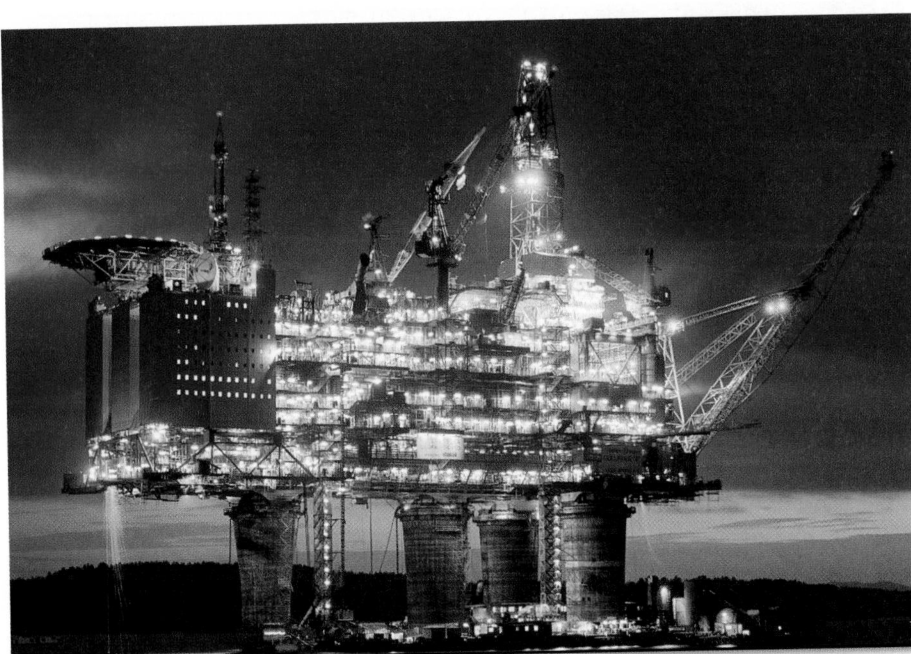

Nonliving Resources

Teach Key Concepts L2

Water, Fuels, and Minerals

Focus Point out that in addition to living resources, there are many nonliving resources that people use from the oceans.

Teach Ask: **Do you think that it is easier or more difficult to get water, fuel, and minerals from the ocean compared to the land?** *(It is more difficult.)* **Then why do people get these resources from the oceans?** *(Supplies on land are limited or not available in a particular region.)*

Apply Ask: **Where on Earth might people want to desalinate ocean water?** *(Desert regions)* **learning modality: logical/mathematical**

Differentiated Instruction

English Learners/Beginning L1
Vocabulary: Word Analysis Write the word *aquaculture* on the board and circle the prefix *aqua-*. Many students will recognize that this word means *water.* Tell students that *culture* is a word that has different meanings. In this case, it means "to develop, or grow."

English Learners/Intermediate L2
Vocabulary: Word Analysis Expand on the beginning activity above by having students create a concept map using the word *aquaculture*. Have them use the following connecting phrases: *is defined as, can raise animals such as,* and *has been practiced for centuries in.*

Monitor Progress L2

Oral Presentation Ask students to explain the importance of nonliving resources from the ocean.

Answers

Figure 21 Oil deposits formed through long periods of time from the remains of dead organisms that sank to the bottom of the ocean and were buried by layers of sediment.

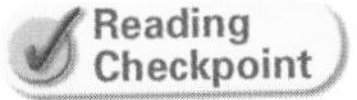
Aquaculture is the farming of saltwater and freshwater organisms.

Ocean Pollution

Teach Key Concepts L2

Sources of Pollution

Focus Review with students the definition of pollution—contamination of an environment with harmful substances.

Teach Ask: **How can humans cause pollution of the ocean?** *(Growing crops, manufacturing products, releasing sewage, spilling oil)* **Can pollution also occur naturally?** *(Yes. Examples include excess fresh water runoff and toxins released by some algae)*

Apply Tell students that much of the ocean belongs to no country and that many countries border the ocean. Have them explain why controlling ocean pollution is so difficult and why cooperation between nations is important. **learning modality: verbal**

Math Analyzing Data

Math Skill Interpreting Graphs

Focus Remind students that the top of a bar in a bar graph indicates the value on the vertical axis.

Teach Ask: **What is shown on the horizontal axis?** *(Sources of ocean oil pollution)* **What is shown on the vertical axis?** *(Oil pollution in millions of liters)*

Answers

1. Six sources of pollution are shown.
2. Street runoff causes the most pollution, and offshore drilling causes the least.
3. All sources of pollution are caused by human actions except natural seeps.
4. Possible answer: Student can reduce air pollution by walking or riding a bike instead of riding in a car or truck.

Minerals Minerals are solid substances that are obtained from the ground and the water. When fresh water is removed from ocean water, the salts that are left behind are a valuable mineral resource. More than half of the world's supply of magnesium, a strong, light metal, is obtained from seawater in this way.

The ocean floor is another source of mineral resources. From the sediments covering the continental shelves, gravel and sand are mined for use in building construction. In some areas of the world, diamonds and gold are mined from sand deposits. Metals such as manganese also accumulate on the ocean floor. The metals concentrate around pieces of shell, forming black lumps called **nodules** (NAHJ oolz). Nodules sometimes occur in waters as deep as 5,000 meters. Therefore, recovering the nodules is a difficult process. The technology to gather them is still being developed.

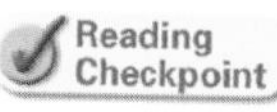

What minerals are obtained from the oceans?

Ocean Pollution

The ocean is a self-cleaning system that can absorb some wastes without permanent damage. But dumping large amounts of wastes into the ocean threatens many marine organisms. Most ocean pollution comes from the land. **Although some ocean pollution is the result of natural occurrences, most pollution is related to human activities.**

Math Analyzing Data

Ocean Oil Pollution

The bar graph shows the main sources of oil pollution in the ocean. The source *Natural Seeps* refers to the natural process by which oil leaks out of oil deposits in the oceans. Study the graph, and then answer the following questions.

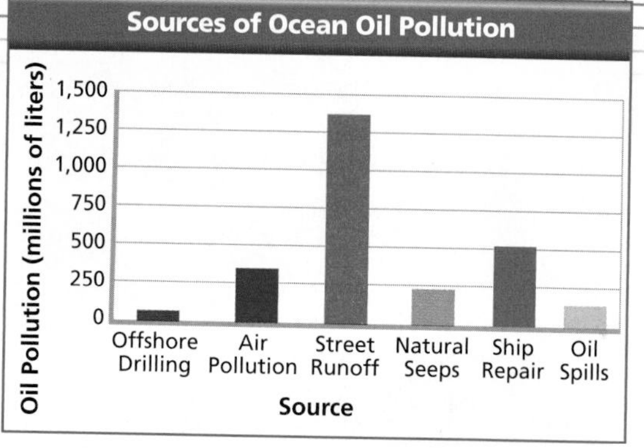

1. **Reading Graphs** How many sources of ocean oil pollution are shown on the graph?
2. **Interpreting Data** Which source causes the most oil pollution? The least?
3. **Classifying** Classify each source of oil pollution as either a natural cause or one that is caused by human actions.
4. **Problem Solving** Which source or sources of ocean oil pollution could you personally reduce? What actions could you take to reduce the sources?

162 ◆ H

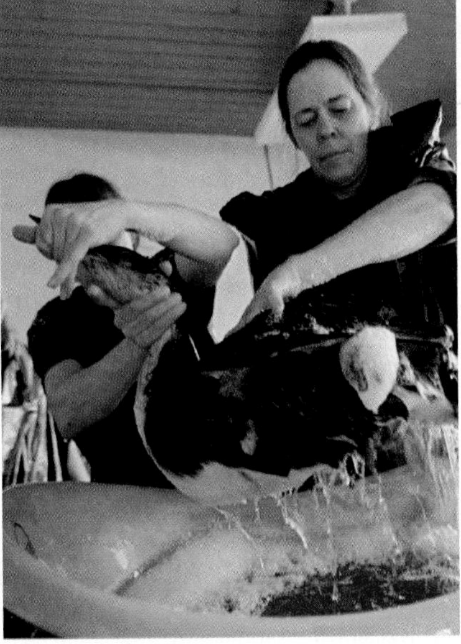

Figure 22
Cleaning Up Oil
This cleanup worker is using absorbent mops to remove oil from the sand (left). On the right, two workers try to clean oil from a bird's beak and feathers.
Inferring *What might have caused this oil pollution?*

Natural Occurrences Some pollution is the result of weather. For example, heavy rains wash fresh water into estuaries and out into the water offshore. This surge of fresh water pollutes the ocean by lowering its salinity. A sudden change in salinity may kill ocean animals that are unable to adjust to it.

Human Activities Sewage, chemicals, and trash dumped into coastal waters all come from human sources. Substances that run off fields and roads often end up in the ocean. These substances can harm ocean organisms directly. The pollutants can also build up in the organisms' bodies and poison other animals, including people, that feed on them. Trash can cause serious problems, too. Air-breathing marine mammals can drown if they get tangled in fishing lines or nets. Other animals are harmed when they swallow plastic bags that block their stomachs.

Another major threat to ocean life is oil pollution. When an oil tanker or drilling platform is damaged, oil leaks into the surrounding ocean. Oil is harmful to many organisms. As Figure 22 shows, oil from a spill can coat the bodies of animals that live near the spill. This destroys their natural insulation and affects their ability to float. Oil is also harmful to animals that swallow it.

There is a natural cleaning process that slowly takes place after oil spills. Certain bacteria that live in the ocean feed on the oil and multiply. It takes many years, but these bacteria can eventually clean an oil-covered beach. Of course, oil can cause much damage to an area in that time, so people often help to clean up large spills.

Ocean Trash

Materials tangled fishing line, plastic bags, old tennis shoe, empty plastic bottle (rinsed), cloth netting, plastic holder from a six-pack of canned soft drink

Time 10 minutes

Focus Display the items listed above. Ask students to guess what they represent. *(Trash that often pollutes the ocean)*

Teach Ask: **How can these materials damage ocean life?** *(Animals can get tangled or swallow harmful items.)* **What other negative effects does ocean trash have?** *(It makes the ocean or beach look bad; Some items contain harmful substances.)*

Apply Have students suggest ways to reduce the amount of ocean trash. **learning modality: visual**

Differentiated Instruction

Gifted and Talented L3

Debating Ocean Rights Have students imagine that they are delegates to the United Nations and that they are meeting to discuss a major mineral deposit that has been discovered in the mid-Atlantic Ocean. Have student teams represent the nation that discovered the deposit, the nation with the technology to mine it, and the closest nations to the deposit. As you serve as monitor, let students debate which country owns the deposit and which has the right to mine it. **learning modality: verbal**

Monitor Progress L1

Skills Check Have each student draw a concept map about ocean pollution. The map should include natural and human causes of ocean pollution, their sources, and their effects.

Answers

Figure 22 An oil spill from a tanker or offshore rig caused the pollution.

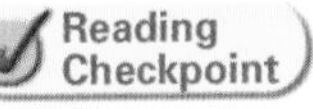

Magnesium minerals, diamonds, gold

Monitor Progress L1

Answer

Reading Checkpoint: Much of the ocean is "high seas."

Assess

Reviewing Key Concepts

1. a. People use ocean organisms for food and for materials that are used in many products. **b.** Aquaculture is the raising of fresh and saltwater organisms. It helps address the problem of overfishing.
2. a. Three nonliving ocean resources are water, fuels, and minerals. **b.** Oil is obtained from the ocean floor by drilling from offshore platforms. **c.** It is more difficult to obtain oil from the ocean because of the difficulty of drilling in deep water, and problems caused by strong ocean currents, winds, and storms.
3. a. One natural occurrence is heavy rain that washes fresh water into estuaries. Human activities include releasing sewage, chemicals, trash, or oil. **b.** The ocean is shared by many nations. **c.** Accept either viewpoint as long as students support it with reasonable arguments.

Reteach L1

Have students make a compare and contrast chart showing living and nonliving resources obtained from the ocean.

Performance Assessment

Writing Have each student describe one way that a nation could prevent overfishing in its waters.

All in One Teaching Resources

- Section Summary: *Ocean Resources*
- Review and Reinforcement: *Ocean Resources*
- Enrich: *Ocean Resources*

FIGURE 23
A Marine Refuge
This scientist is tagging an elephant seal in a marine refuge in California. Scientists will then be able to monitor the seal's travels.

Protecting Earth's Oceans Who owns the ocean and its resources? Who has the responsibility of protecting them? These are questions that nations have been struggling to answer for hundreds of years. Because the world ocean is a continuous body of water that has no boundaries, it is difficult to determine who, if anyone, should control portions of it. Nations must cooperate to manage and protect the oceans.

The United Nations has established different boundaries in the oceans. According to one treaty, a nation now controls the first 22 kilometers out from its coasts. The nation also controls the resources in the waters or on the continental shelf within 370 kilometers of shore. This treaty leaves approximately half of the ocean's surface waters as "high seas," owned by no nation. Ownership of the ocean floor beneath the high seas is still under debate.

Other international efforts have resulted in cooperation aimed at reducing ocean pollution. Examples include the establishment of marine refuges and regulations for building safer oil tankers.

Why is it difficult to determine who controls ocean resources?

Section 5 Assessment

Target Reading Skill Identifying Main Ideas Use your graphic organizer about Nonliving Resources to help you answer Question 2 below.

Reviewing Key Concepts

1. a. **Reviewing** What are two ways in which people use ocean organisms?
   b. **Summarizing** What is aquaculture? What problem does it help address?
2. a. **Listing** List three nonliving ocean resources.
   b. **Describing** How is oil obtained from the ocean floor?
   c. **Inferring** Oil deposits are found beneath dry land as well the ocean. From which location—ocean or dry land—is it more difficult to obtain oil? Explain your answer.
3. a. **Reviewing** Identify one natural occurrence and three human activities that can pollute the oceans.
   b. **Explaining** Explain why one nation by itself cannot control ocean pollution.
   c. **Making Judgments** Should mineral resources on the ocean floor belong to whomever finds them, or to the closest nation? Consider each position and write a short paragraph stating your opinion.

Lab zone At-Home Activity

Modeling Ocean Pollution Have a family member hook one end of a rubber band around his or her wrist. Stretch the rubber band across the back of the hand and hook the free end over three fingers as shown. Now ask the person to try to remove the rubber band without using the other hand. Explain that this shows how difficult it is for seals or dolphins to free themselves from a plastic beverage ring or piece of net. Can you propose any ways to reduce this threat to marine mammals?

Lab zone At-Home Activity

Modeling Ocean Pollution L1 Let students do the activity in class before they try it at home with family members. Give students an opportunity to present their responses to the question during a class discussion.

Lab zone **Skills Lab**

Cleaning Up an Oil Spill

Problem
How can an oil spill be cleaned up?

Skills Focus
making models, observing

Materials
- water
- feather
- marking pen
- shallow pan
- paper towels
- paper cup
- cotton balls
- vegetable oil
- plastic dropper
- wooden sticks
- graduated cylinder, 100-mL

Procedure
1. Place a pan on a table or desk covered with newspaper. Label one end of the pan "Beach" and the other end "Open Ocean."
2. Pour water into the pan to a depth of 2 cm.
3. Gently pour 20 mL of vegetable oil into the center of the pan. Record your observations.
4. Dip a feather and your finger into the oil. Observe how each is affected by the oil.
5. Try to wipe oil off the feather and your finger using cotton balls or paper towels. Record whether any oil is left on the feather or your skin.
6. Now try to clean up the spill. First, using the wooden sticks, try to keep the oil from reaching the "beach." Next, gently blow across the surface of the water from the "open ocean" side to simulate wind and waves. Then use the cotton balls, paper towels, and dropper to recover as much of the oil as possible. Record your observations with each step.
7. When you are finished, dispose of the oil and used items in the paper cup. Wash your hands.

Analyze and Conclude
1. **Observing** How successful were you in cleaning up the oil? Did the water end up as clean as it was at the start?
2. **Making Models** How well were you able to keep the oil from reaching the beach? How does this activity model the problems that actual cleanup workers encounter?
3. **Inferring** Describe what happened when you cleaned the feather and your finger. What might happen to fish, birds, and other animals if they were coated with oil as a result of an oil spill?
4. **Predicting** Predict how storms with strong winds and waves would affect the cleanup of an oil spill.
5. **Communicating** Look at the used cleanup materials in the paper cup. What additional problems does this suggest for cleanup crews? Write instructions for procedures that cleanup crews might follow to deal with these problems.

More to Explore
One way to reduce the threat of oil spills is to transport less oil across the oceans. To make that possible, people would need to use less oil in their daily lives. Use reference materials or the Internet to find tips on oil conservation. Then list at least three ways to reduce the amount of oil you and your family use.

Lab zone **Skills Lab** L2

Cleaning Up an Oil Spill

Prepare for Inquiry

Key Concept
Oil is difficult to remove from water, beaches, and organisms.

Skills Objectives
After this lab, students will be able to
- model oil-spill cleanup using a variety of materials
- observe how winds and waves affect an oil spill

Prep Time 30 minutes
Class Time 40 minutes

Advance Planning
Obtain a feather for each group.

All in One Teaching Resources
- Lab Worksheets: *Cleaning Up an Oil Spill*

Guide Inquiry

Invitation
Give each group a small paper cup of dark molasses. Tell students that molasses has similar consistency to crude oil—the oil usually carried by tankers. Encourage students to examine the molasses by tilting the cup and by dipping a finger into it and rubbing it against their thumb.

Introduce the Procedure
Ask: **If you were a volunteer cleaning an oil spill, what things would you expect to clean?** *(Possible answer: Birds.)*

Expected Outcome
Students will not be able to completely clean the oil from the feather and will be able to recover only a small amount of the oil.

Analyze and Conclude
1. Students will not be able to completely clean the oil. An observable film of oil will remain.

2. Students' success will vary, but some oil probably will reach the beach. The activity models how wind and waves can move an oil spill onto shore.

3. A light film of oil remains on the finger and feather. Heavily coated animals cannot survive. The insulation that fur and feathers provide is destroyed by the oil coating. Heavily coated birds cannot fly.

4. Winds and waves would wash the oil onto the beach and would spread the spill more widely over the water.

5. Cleanup materials are coated or saturated with oil and have to be disposed of in a way that they will not create more pollution. Students might suggest that all cleanup materials be gathered and deposited in a properly lined landfill.

Extend Inquiry
More to Explore Some methods of conserving oil are combining errands to reduce driving, recycling materials made from oil, and keeping the thermostat at the lowest comfortable setting.

Science and Society

Shrimp Farms—At What Cost?

Key Concept

Students discuss ways in which shrimp farming affects the environment and propose a solution that addresses shrimp farmers' needs and the environment.

Build Background Knowledge

Help students recall that aquaculture is raising fresh and saltwater organisms for human consumption. Ask: **What are the benefits of aquaculture?** *(It reduces overfishing. It provides an adequate supply of many foods.)*

Introduce the Debate

After students have read the introductory text and the three paragraphs beneath *The Issues*, ask: **If you were a shrimp farmer who used the usual farming methods, would you want to change your methods? Why or why not?** Let students discuss this question freely until opposing viewpoints are clear.

Facilitate the Debate

- Organize the class into small groups. Have each group member represent a different viewpoint—for example, a shrimp farmer who does not want to change his or her methods, another farmer who thinks new methods should be tried, an owner of a seafood company that sells shrimp, and a science advisor or government official who wants to protect the mangrove forests.
- Tell students that each group's goal is to arrive at an agreement about how shrimp farming should be done.

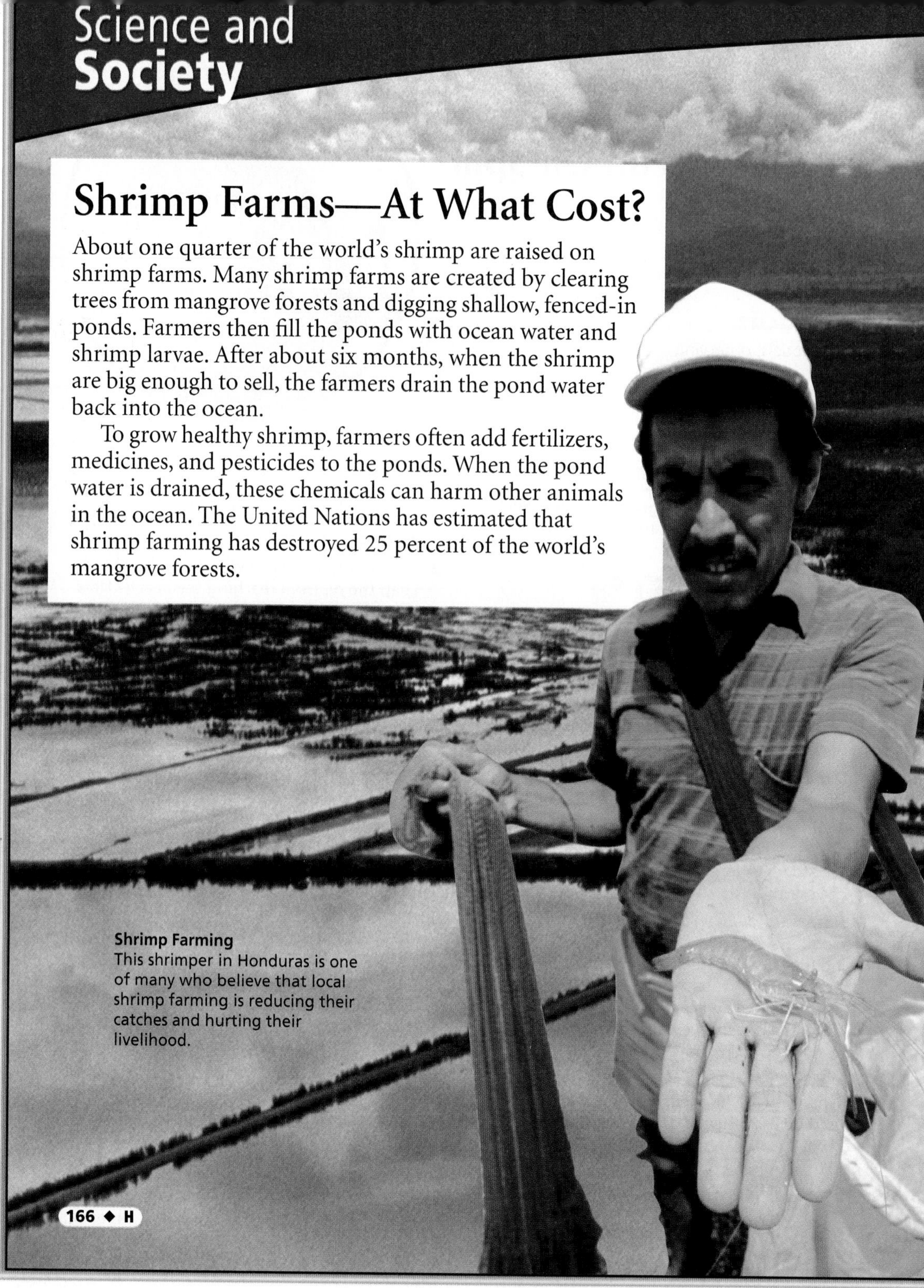

Science and Society

Shrimp Farms—At What Cost?

About one quarter of the world's shrimp are raised on shrimp farms. Many shrimp farms are created by clearing trees from mangrove forests and digging shallow, fenced-in ponds. Farmers then fill the ponds with ocean water and shrimp larvae. After about six months, when the shrimp are big enough to sell, the farmers drain the pond water back into the ocean.

To grow healthy shrimp, farmers often add fertilizers, medicines, and pesticides to the ponds. When the pond water is drained, these chemicals can harm other animals in the ocean. The United Nations has estimated that shrimp farming has destroyed 25 percent of the world's mangrove forests.

Shrimp Farming
This shrimper in Honduras is one of many who believe that local shrimp farming is reducing their catches and hurting their livelihood.

166 ◆ H

The Issues

How Important Is Shrimp Farming?

For many people in the world, shrimp is more than luxury food: It is a staple of their diet and their main source of animal protein. The current demand for shrimp is greater than the natural supply in the oceans. To meet the demand, many countries, including the United States, have turned to shrimp farming. Some people believe that the food and jobs that shrimp farms provide are worth a certain amount of damage to the environment.

Can the Pollution be Reduced?

Shrimp farmers are exploring ways to reduce the impact of their farms on the coastal environment. Better pond construction can help stop chemicals from leaking into the surrounding waters. Some governments have passed laws regulating where shrimp farms may be built. Farmers must investigate the impact their ponds will have on nearby mangrove forests and get approval before choosing a location. These methods of reducing environmental damage, however, are expensive and time-consuming for shrimp farmers.

Should Farmers Use Alternative Methods?

In some parts of Asia, a less destructive method of shrimp farming has been practiced for centuries. Shrimp are raised in ditches dug around clusters of mangroves. This provides the young shrimp with a natural nutrient supply that includes debris from the trees. A gate keeps the shrimp from escaping and allows the motion of the tides to replenish the water in the ditches. The disadvantage of this method is that it is much less profitable than the constructed shrimp ponds. Many shrimp farmers could not afford to switch to this method. If they did, the price of shrimp worldwide would rise.

You Decide

1. Identify the Problem
In your own words, summarize the problem facing shrimp farmers.

2. Analyze the Options
Make a list of the solutions mentioned. List the advantages and drawbacks of each. Who would benefit from each plan? Who might suffer?

3. Find a Solution
Write a brochure or pamphlet for shrimp farmers that states your proposed solution to their problem. After you have written the text, illustrate your brochure.

For: More on shrimp farms
Visit: PHSchool.com
Web Code: cfh-3040

You Decide

1. Students should summarize the need to raise food while still maintaining a clean environment.
2. (1) Better pond construction—advantage: chemicals stop leaking into surrounding water; drawback: expensive and may harm nearby mangrove forests; (2) regulating where farms can be built—advantage: impact on nearby mangrove forests is investigated; drawback: time-consuming; (3) raising shrimp in ditches—advantage: better for environment; disadvantage: not as profitable.
3. Students can share their solutions by displaying the brochures or pamphlets on a bulletin board.

For: More on shrimp farms
Visit: PHSchool.com
Web Code: cfh-3040

Students can research this issue online.

Extend

Students could survey a local supermarket to see whether fresh, frozen, and/or canned shrimp are available and, if so, how much they cost. Suggest that students talk with the seafood department's manager or clerk to find out whether any fresh shrimp are obtained from shrimp farms in this country or overseas.

Study Guide

- Complete student edition
- Section and chapter self-assessments
- Assessment reports for teachers

Help Students Read

Building Vocabulary

Word Origins Explain that the word *nekton* comes from a Greek word meaning "to swim." *Benthos* is from a Greek word meaning "depth of the sea," and *plankton* is from a Greek word meaning "wandering." Ask students how the origins of these words can help them remember their scientific meanings.

Word-Part Analysis Ask students what words they know that begin with the prefix *bio-*. *(Possible answers: biology, biodegradable, biosphere)* Tell students that the Greek meaning of *bio-* is "to live." Have students apply this knowledge to the word *bioluminescence.*

Connecting Concepts

Concept Maps Help students develop one way to show how the information in this chapter is related. The characteristics of the ocean floor and the ocean's zones give rise to a variety of habitats and marine life. Have students brainstorm to identify the key concepts, key terms, details, and examples, then write each one on a sticky note and attach it at random on chart paper or on the board.

Tell students that this concept map will be organized in hierarchical order and begin at the top with key concepts. Ask students these questions to guide them to categorize the information on the stickies: **What are the features of the ocean floor? What are the characteristics of the ocean zones and how are marine organisms that live there classified? What are the living and nonliving resources that people obtain from the ocean? What are the main sources of ocean pollution?** Prompt students by using connecting words or phrases, such as "occur in" "result in," and "includes," to indicate the basis for the organization of the map. The phrases should form a sentence between or among a set of concepts.

Answer

Accept logical presentations by students.

All in One Teaching Resources

- Key Terms Review: *Ocean Zones*
- Connecting Concepts: *Ocean Zones*

Chapter 4

Study Guide

1 Exploring the Ocean

Key Concepts

- People have studied the ocean since ancient times, because the ocean provides food and serves as a route for trade and travel. Modern scientists have studied the characteristics of the ocean's waters and the ocean floor.
- If you could travel along the ocean floor, you would see the continental shelf, the continental slope, the abyssal plain, and the mid-ocean ridge.
- Plate movements have shaped many of the most dramatic features of Earth, both on land and under the ocean.

Key Terms

sonar
continental shelf
continental slope
abyssal plain
mid-ocean ridge
trench
plate
seafloor spreading

2 Ocean Habitats

Key Concepts

- Ocean zones include the intertidal zone, the neritic zone, and the open-ocean zone.
- Scientists classify marine organisms according to where they live and how they move.

Key Terms

intertidal zone
neritic zone
open-ocean zone
plankton
nekton
benthos
food web

3 Intertidal Zone

Key Concepts

- Organisms that live in the rocky intertidal zone must be able to tolerate the pounding of the waves and changes in both salinity and temperature. They must also withstand periods of being underwater and periods of being exposed to the air.
- Along the coasts of the United States, most wetlands are mangrove forests or salt marshes.

Key Term

estuary

4 Neritic Zone and Open Ocean

Key Concepts

- The shallow water over the continental shelf receives sunlight and a steady supply of nutrients washed from the land into the ocean. The light and nutrients enable large plantlike algae to grow.
- Coral reefs can form only in shallow, tropical ocean waters. Kelp forests grow in cold neritic waters where the ocean has a rocky floor.
- The open ocean differs from the neritic zone in two important ways. First, only a small part of the open ocean receives sunlight. Second, the water has fewer nutrients.

Key Terms

atoll
bioluminescence
hydrothermal vent

5 Resources From the Ocean

Key Concepts

- People depend heavily on fishes and other ocean organisms for food. Ocean organisms also provide materials that are used in products such as detergents and paints.
- Some nonliving ocean resources include water, fuels, and minerals.
- Although some ocean pollution is the result of natural occurrences, most pollution is related to human activities.

Key Terms

aquaculture
nodule

Review and Assessment

Go Online PHSchool.com
For: Self-Assessment
Visit: PHSchool.com
Web Code: cfa-3040

Organizing Information

Comparing and Contrasting Copy the table about ocean habitats onto a separate sheet of paper. Then complete it and add a title. (For more on Comparing and Contrasting, see the Skills Handbook.)

Habitat	Zone	Conditions	Organisms
Tide pool	Intertidal	a. ___?___	b. ___?___
Coral reef	c. ___?___	d. ___?___	Coral, fishes, shrimp, eels
Surface zone	Open ocean	e. ___?___	f. ___?___
Hydrothermal vent	g. ___?___	High pressure, dark, warm	h. ___?___

Reviewing Key Terms

Choose the letter of the best answer.

1. A smooth, nearly flat region of the ocean floor is called a(n)
   a. trench.
   b. mid-ocean ridge.
   c. abyssal plain.
   d. sea mount.
2. Free-swimming animals that can move throughout the water column are called
   a. plankton.
   b. benthos.
   c. coral.
   d. nekton.
3. An area where rivers flow into the ocean and fresh water and salt water mix is a(n)
   a. tide pool.
   b. hydrothermal vent.
   c. estuary.
   d. kelp forest.
4. Hydrothermal vents are located
   a. in coral reefs.
   b. in the intertidal zone.
   c. in kelp forests.
   d. along ocean ridges.
5. Nodules consist of
   a. metals.
   b. algae.
   c. sediments.
   d. chemical nutrients.

If the statement is true, write *true*. If it is false, change the underlined word or words to make the statement true.

6. The mid-ocean ridge is formed where two plates converge.
7. The area between the high- and low-tide lines is the neritic zone.
8. An estuary is a coastal inlet or bay where fresh water mixes with salt water.
9. Many deep-sea fishes use their bioluminescence to attract prey.
10. Aquaculture is the farming of saltwater and freshwater organisms.

Writing in Science

Firsthand Account Suppose you were going to travel to the deepest part of the ocean floor in a submersible. Write about your journey, describing each feature of the ocean floor that you see along the way.

Ocean Zones
Video Preview
Video Field Trip
▶ Video Assessment

Go Online PHSchool.com
For: Self-assessment
Visit: PHSchool.com
Web Code: cfa-3040

Students can take a practice test online that is automatically scored.

Review and Assessment

Organizing Information

Sample title: Ocean Habitats
a. varying salinity, exposure to sunlight, varying temperature, rough wave action
b. barnacles, mussels, sea stars, sea urchins, sponges, sea anemones
c. neritic
d. warm, shallow water, receives sunlight, clean water
e. receives sunlight, nutrients less abundant than in the neritic zone
f. microscopic algae, copepods, krill, animal larvae, jellyfish fishes
g. deep
h. crabs, clams, tube worms, bacteria

Reviewing Key Terms

1. c **2.** d **3.** c **4.** d **5.** a
6. diverge
7. intertidal zone
8. true
9. true
10. true

Video Assessment

Ocean Zones

Show the Video Assessment to review chapter content and as a prompt for the writing assignment. Discussion questions: **How do fish use bioluminescence?** *(To find each other for mating and to attract prey)* **What are the three ocean life zones?** *(Intertidal, neritic, and open-ocean)*

Writing in Science

Writing Mode Description

Scoring Rubric

4 Exceeds expectations by writing about a journey to the deepest part of the ocean in a submersible and describing all of the important features seen on the trip.
3 Meets expectations by describing the journey and many important features
2 Describes the journey but omits many of the important features
1 Description is incomplete or inaccurate

All in One Teaching Resources

- Transparency H56
- Chapter Test
- Performance Assessment Teacher Notes
- Performance Assessment Student Worksheet
- Performance Assessment Scoring Rubric

ExamView® Computer Test Bank CD-ROM

Checking Concepts

11. Scientists use indirect methods to study the ocean floor because the darkness, coldness, and high pressure of very deep water pose problems for human survival.

12. Seafloor spreading is the process that produces the ocean floor. It is caused by magma moving up between diverging continental plates. As the magma cools and hardens, it adds new rock to the ocean floor.

13. A typical marine food web consists of producers, consumers, and decomposers. Many plankton and benthos make their own food through photosynthesis. These organisms usually begin the food chain.

14. Possible answers: They must overcome pounding waves, changes in salinity and temperature, and alternating periods of being underwater and exposed to air.

15. The rivers that flow into estuaries can carry pollutants such as pesticides, sewage, and industrial wastes.

16. An atoll is a ring-shaped coral reef surrounding a shallow lagoon. It begins as a fringing reef around an island and forms when the island sinks and the reef grows upward.

17. Hydrothermal vents occur in the deepest parts of the ocean far from sunlight, where food is scarce and organisms tend to be small, slow-moving, and of limited variety. Around the vents, however, the number, size, and variety of organisms are unusually high.

Review and Assessment

Checking Concepts

11. Why do scientists use indirect methods to study the ocean floor?
12. What is seafloor spreading, and what causes it?
13. Describe a typical marine food web.
14. Describe three physical factors that organisms in the rocky intertidal zone must overcome.
15. Explain why estuaries are especially vulnerable to pollution.
16. What is an atoll? How is it formed?
17. Explain why scientists were surprised to discover the variety of organisms living around hydrothermal vents.

Thinking Critically

18. **Drawing Conclusions** Mauna Kea projects about 4,200 meters above sea level. Its base is on the floor of the Pacific Ocean, about 6,000 meters below sea level. Mt. Everest rises 8,850 meters from base to summit. Its base is located on land. Which mountain is taller: Mauna Kea or Mt. Everest?
19. **Classifying** Classify the organisms in each photo below as plankton, nekton, or benthos.

20. **Making Generalizations** Explain why many of the world's fisheries are located in the neritic zone.
21. **Relating Cause and Effect** How might fertilizers used on farmland result in ocean pollution near shore?

Applying Skills

Use the diagram of a portion of the ocean floor to answer Questions 22–25.

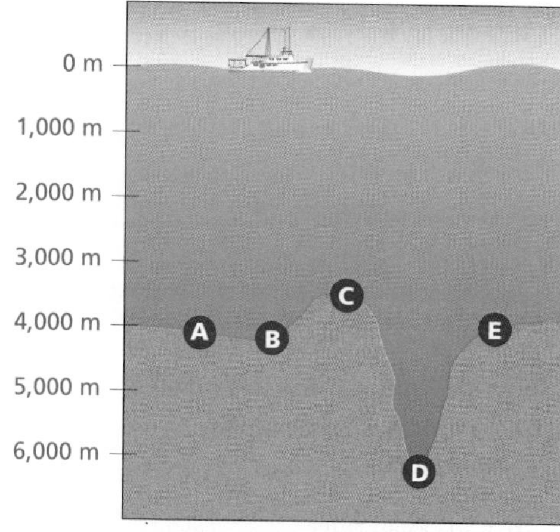

22. **Interpreting Diagrams** What is the approximate depth of the ocean floor at point A? At point C?
23. **Inferring** What might the feature between locations A and B be? The feature at point D?
24. **Describing** What would you expect the physical conditions at point D to be like?
25. **Posing Questions** What other information would help you determine which point—A or E—is closer to the mid-ocean ridge? Explain.

Lab zone Chapter Project

Performance Assessment Prepare a guided tour of your marine environment. First, rehearse the tour with your group. As you rehearse, check to see that your marine environment is complete. Make any final changes now. Then take your classmates through your tour.

Lab zone Chapter Project L3

Performance Assessment Allow each group time to give a "guided" tour of its marine habitat. Each student should also describe the characteristics of the particular organism that he or she modeled including its specific physical and behavior adaptations to that habitat and, possibly, the organism's role in the food web. Allow time for questions and discussion after each presentation. Emphasize that each group member is responsible for discussing the groups' habitat, in addition to his or her own organism. After students have described any difficulties they encountered while building the habitat, ask them to suggest other methods or materials they could have used.

Standardized Test Prep

Test-Taking Tip

Choosing Among Similar Answers

Sometimes two or more answer choices appear similar or closely related. You must read the question and all the answer choices carefully in order to select the correct answer.

Sample Question

What is the shallow, gently sloping area of the ocean floor that extends outward from the shoreline?

A the abyssal plain
B the continental shelf
C the continental slope
D the mid-ocean ridge

Answer

The correct answer is **B.** If you read the answer choices quickly, choices **B** and **C** might appear similar. However, the continental slope, answer choice **C,** does not extend from the shoreline, it is not a shallow area, and it has a steeper slope than the continental shelf.

Choose the letter of the best answer.

1. In which category of ocean organisms do sharks, tuna, killer whales, and squid belong?
A plankton
B nekton
C benthos
D none of the above

2. Use your knowledge of ocean zones to infer which adaptation would be most important for organisms in the intertidal zone.
F the ability to use bioluminescence
G the ability to withstand high pressures
H the ability to use chemical nutrients in the water
J the ability to withstand periods underwater and periods exposed to the air

Use the diagram below and your knowledge of science to answer Questions 3–4.

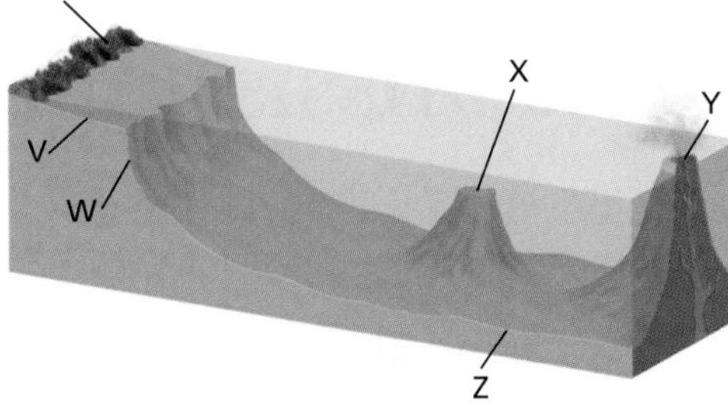

3. What is the feature labeled **X** on the diagram above?
A seamount
B abyssal plain
C mid-ocean ridge
D continental slope

4. In which part of the diagram would the greatest variety of organisms be found?
F part V
G part W
H part X
J part Z

5. If you were constructing a model of an estuary, which of the following elements would be the most important?
A the depth of water to which sunlight can penetrate
B the water temperature
C the mix of fresh water and salt water
D the presence of hydrothermal vents

Constructed Response

6. The coral reef ecosystem has a higher diversity of organisms than any other ecosystem. Explain the conditions necessary for coral reefs to form. Include in your explanation the relationship between coral and algae. Predict whether a coral reef would be likely to form near the mouth of a major river. Explain why or why not.

Thinking Critically

18. Mauna Kea is taller.

19. A: Sea star: benthos; B: fish: nekton

20. The neritic zone lies above the continental shelf. Here, the water is shallower, warmer, and contains more nutrients than in the deep zone. These conditions support a large number and wide variety of marine organisms.

21. Runoff from land could wash fertilizers into streams and rivers, which would eventually carry the substances into the ocean. Near land, the fertilizers would cause excess growth of plants and algae, upsetting the natural balance in coastal habitats.

Applying Skills

22. A: about 4,000 m; C: about 3,600 m

23. Between A and B: abyssal plain; at point D: trench

24. Dark, cold, extremely high pressure

25. The age of the rock on the seafloor at each point would help you determine which is closer to the mid-ocean ridge.

Standardized Test Prep

1. B **2.** J **3.** A **4.** F **5.** C

6. Coral reefs require warm, shallow water and plenty of sunlight. The animals require sunlight because microscopic algae live inside their bodies. These algae provide food for the coral animals. Coral reefs would not grow near the mouth of a river because of the excess sediment and possible salinity variations.

Interdisciplinary Exploration

The Mississippi

This interdisciplinary feature presents the central theme of transportation on the Mississippi River by connecting four different disciplines: science, social studies, mathematics, and language arts. The four explorations are designed to capture students' interest and help them understand how the content they are studying in science relates to other school subjects and to real-world events. The unit is particularly suitable for team teaching.

All in One Teaching Resources

- Interdisciplinary Exploration: *Social Studies*
- Interdisciplinary Exploration: *Science*
- Interdisciplinary Exploration: *Mathematics*
- Interdisciplinary Exploration: *Language Arts*

Build Background Knowledge

Help students recall what they have learned about Earth's waters. Ask: **What are the main parts of a river system?** *(The main river, its tributaries, and lakes, ponds, and wetlands along the river)* **How does a river's flow change from its source to its mouth?** *(Students should identify differences in the river's speed, width, and depth, as well as features such as the flood plain and the delta.)* **What do you know about the Mississippi River?** *(Accept all responses without comment at this time.)*

Introducing the Exploration

Display a large map of the United States, and invite a volunteer to point out the Mississippi River. Ask: **In which direction does the Mississippi flow?** *(From north to south)* Draw students' attention to the map on this page and have them trace the river's course from its headwaters to its mouth. Ask: **Which states have the Mississippi River as a natural boundary?** *(Minnesota, Wisconsin, Iowa, Illinois, Missouri, Kentucky, Tennessee, Arkansas, Mississippi, and Louisiana)*

Interdisciplinary Exploration

The Mississippi

What would you name a river that—

- **carries about 420 million metric tons of cargo a year,**
- **drains 31 states and 2 Canadian provinces,**
- **flows at about 18,100 cubic meters of water per second?**

Native Americans called the river *misi sipi*, an Algonquin name meaning "big water," or "father of waters."

You might have traveled on a river or lake that feeds into the mighty Mississippi but never realized it. The map below shows the watershed of this great river. From the west, the Missouri River—the "Big Muddy"—carries soft silt eroded from the Great Plains. The Missouri joins the Mississippi near St. Louis, turning the river's clear water to muddy brown. From the east, the Ohio River flows in from the rocky Appalachian plateau, nearly doubling the volume of water in the river. In all, the huge Mississippi watershed drains about 40 percent of the United States.

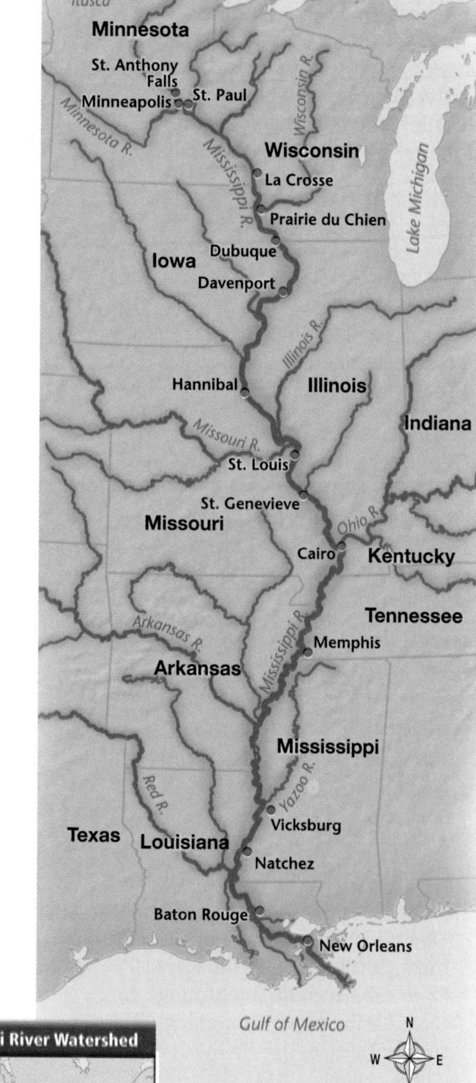

The Mississippi River
The Mississippi starts at Lake Itasca and flows through 10 states to the Gulf of Mexico. The river is a drainage point for hundreds of tributaries in the Mississippi watershed.

A National Trade Route

Since Native Americans settled in villages along the Mississippi around 1,200 years ago, the river has served as a water highway for trade and travel.

In the late 1600s, French explorers, fur traders, and soldiers arrived in the Mississippi Valley. They chose strategic sites for forts and fur-trading posts —Prairie du Chien, St. Louis, and St. Genevieve. At first, traders used canoes, rafts, and flatboats to carry goods downstream. But traveling up the river was difficult. Crews had to use long poles to push narrow keelboats upstream against the current.

In 1811, the arrival of *The New Orleans,* the first steamboat on the Mississippi River, changed the river forever. Within 40 years, there were hundreds more steamboats and many new river towns. On the upper Mississippi, the city of Minneapolis grew up around flour mills near St. Anthony Falls. Farther downstream, Memphis became a center for transporting cotton. Later, it was a stopping point for showboats and musicians. New Orleans quickly became a world port. It received cotton, tobacco, and sugar cane from southern plantations and exported corn, wheat, and indigo to Europe. Imported luxury items, such as soap, coffee, shoes, and textiles, traveled upstream from the port of New Orleans. Up and down the river townspeople eagerly waited for the cry, "Steamboat comin'!"

Flatboats
Flatboat crews rode the river currents, steering with long oars.

New Orleans
The city has been a major trading port since its founding in 1718.

The Mississippi River in Minnesota

Social Studies Activity

Research a city on the Mississippi River. Imagine that you are an early settler there. Write a letter to convince relatives to move to your city. Before writing, research the city's history by finding the answers to these questions:

- Who founded the city? When was it founded? Why did settlers move there? Where did they come from?
- What part did the Mississippi River play in the city's founding?
- What other physical features were important to the city?
- Where did the city's name come from?
- What products were grown, bought, or sold there?

Background

History The first European to see the Mississippi River was a Spaniard, Hernando de Soto, in 1541. French explorer and fur trader René-Robert Cavelier, Sieur de La Salle, canoed down the length of the river to the Gulf of Mexico. In 1682 he claimed the entire area for France and named it Louisiana in honor of the French king. Early French settlements on the river included New Orleans (1718), St. Louis (1764), and Memphis (1819). In the late 1700s, France, Spain, and the United States fought for control of navigation on the Mississippi, including the right to use the port of New Orleans. In the Louisiana Purchase of 1803, the United States purchased from France all of the land from the Mississippi River westward to the Rockies.

Social Studies

Explore Social Studies Concepts

Use Maps Have students refer to the map on the previous page to find each settlement named in the text. Ask: **Why do you think people chose these places to settle and build towns?** *(The locations provided easy access to the river for travel and transporting goods.)* **How did steamboats change the river?** *(People no longer had to depend on their own strength to move boats.)*

Research Encourage interested students to create a bulletin board display that shows the various types of boats used on the river from earliest times to today.

Extend Challenge students to construct a timeline of important events that have occurred in the Mississippi River Valley since early times.

Social Studies Activity

Focus Remind students that people often move from the area in which they were born. Ask: **Why do you think that people in the early 1800s would have moved from cities already established elsewhere to live in new settlements along the Mississippi?** *(To start a business, to buy cheap land, or to be with relatives who had already moved to the area; accept all reasoned responses.)*

Teach Allow students to work individually. To provide more choices of cities, suggest that they consult other, more detailed maps of the area. Caution students to choose cities that are large enough to merit entries in encyclopedias or other readily available reference books.

Scoring Rubric

4 Exceeds criteria; includes all items in activity, contains correct information, and is written persuasively
3 Meets criteria; includes all items and accurate information
2 Includes at least four of the five basic criteria
1 Is inaccurate and incomplete

Science

Explore Science Concepts

Use Visuals Remind students of the hazards involved in boating on a river. Ask: **Have you ever gone canoeing on a river or seen a movie that shows people rafting through river rapids? What can people do to make a river safer for travel and transportation?** *(Accept all reasonable responses. Point out that this page describes a way of "taming" rivers.)*

Review Relate the content of this page to what students have learned about surface water in Earth's Waters. Ask: **How does a river change from its headwaters to its mouth?** *(It may begin as a trickle of water. Later, after it is fed by several tributaries, it flows toward the ocean.)* Remind students that rivers increase in size and power and that the steady flow of most rivers is broken up by rapids and falls.

Extend Suggest that students research the building of the Panama Canal, which includes six pairs of locks. Encourage students to focus on the construction problems posed by the terrain and how engineers solved them. Also, have students compare and contrast the locks on the Panama Canal with those on the Mississippi River.

Science Activity

Materials cardboard milk container, modeling wax, cork or pen cap, duct tape

Focus Review the diagrams on this page step by step to make sure that students understand the purpose of a lock and how it works.

Teach Tell students that the four "L" shapes on the drawing represent modeling wax, which makes the model watertight. Complete instructions on how to build the model can be found in the All-in-One Teaching Resources.

Expected Outcome Focus on evaluating students' understanding of the "locking through" process, rather than on their skill in building models that operate without such flaws as leaks or sticky gates.

Science

Taming the River

Navigating the sandbars, shallow water, and rocky rapids on the upper Mississippi River was treacherous in the 1800s. To make traveling easier, engineers in the early 1900s built a "water staircase," a series of 29 locks and dams between Minneapolis, Minnesota, and Alton, Illinois, above St. Louis.

A lock is an enclosed basin, with gates at each end. Locks allow engineers to raise or lower the water level in a certain area of the river. Between the locks on the upper Mississippi, the river forms wide pools of quiet water, maintaining a channel deep enough for large boats. Use the diagrams to trace how a boat "locks through" as it travels upstream.

1 The lock gate opens.
Your boat moves in and you tie up to the wall.

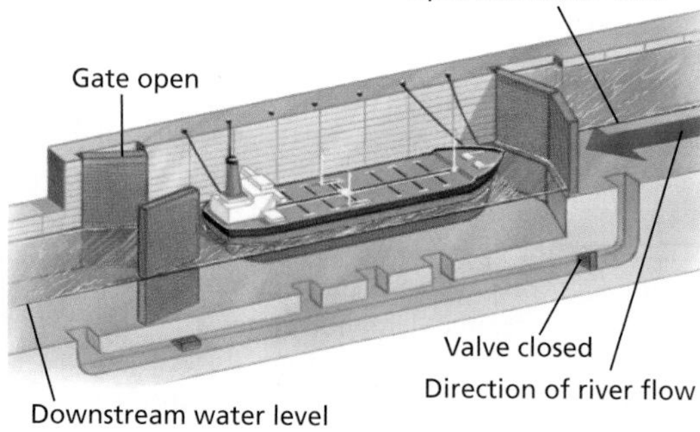

2 The gate closes, and water pours in.
As water fills the lock—like a bathtub filling—it lifts the boat a meter or more. When the water in the lock is even with the water level upstream, the gates at the upstream end open. You untie your boat and move out into the river.

If you were going downstream, you would "lock through" in reverse. The water would empty out of the lock, lowering the water level to match the level downstream.

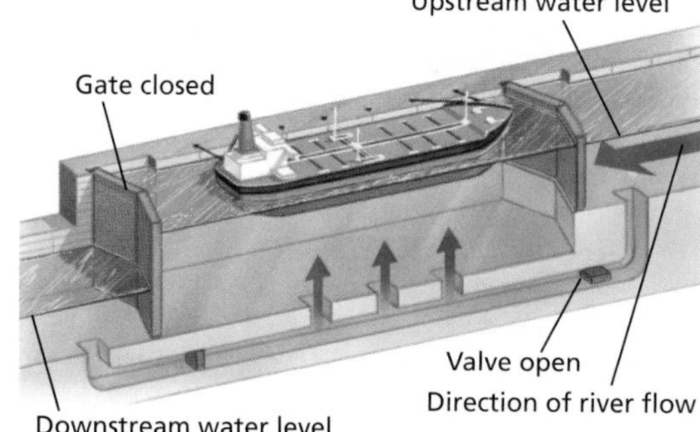

Science Activity

Use a cardboard milk container to build a working model of a lock. Set up your lock following the illustration. Then demonstrate how your lock works, using a cork or pen cap as your ship and sailing it through the lock.

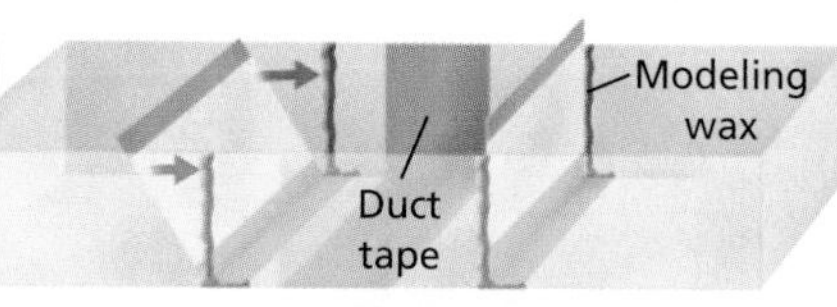

Cut-out side view

174 ◆ H

Background

Facts and Figures Some students may wonder why the natural topography of the upper Mississippi differed so markedly from that of the lower Mississippi before the locks and dams were constructed. The answer lies in the river's ancient history. The upper Mississippi is much older than the lower Mississippi. Millions of years ago, the mouth of the ancestral Mississippi was located near what is today Cape Girardeau, Missouri. The river deposited silt in the ocean gulf, over time creating a delta stretching southward more than 1,900 km to the Gulf of Mexico. As the delta built up, the river created a channel through the new land. Today's lower Mississippi winds through these ancient sediments on its way to the ocean.

All Aboard

The whistle blows. The gleaming white steamboat pulls away from the dock just below Fort Snelling, Minnesota. You head downstream toward New Orleans. As you watch the paddlewheel splashing in the water, you think of the old-time steamboats that traveled the Mississippi River in the 1800s.

Today you are cruising at a speed of 11.3 kilometers per hour. You want to stay awake until you enter Lock 3 at Red Wing, Minnesota. It's 4:30 P.M. on Monday now. You know that it's about 78.8 kilometers to Red Wing. It should take about 7 hours to reach the lock. So you'll be there at 11:30 P.M. and through the lock by midnight.

As your boat travels along the river, it will follow the schedule you see below. You will arrive in Mark Twain's hometown of Hannibal, Missouri, on Friday.

Look at the Upper Mississippi River schedule to answer the questions below. Distances are given from Fort Snelling.

- What is your average speed between Dubuque and Hannibal? Use the following equation:

$$\text{Speed} = \frac{\text{Distance}}{\text{Time}}$$

  Round to the nearest tenth.

- How long will you spend in Prairie du Chien?
- About how long does it take to travel from Prairie du Chien to Dubuque?

Upper Mississippi Riverboat Schedule May–Sept.

Port	Arrival Time	Departure Time	Distance From Fort Snelling
Fort Snelling, MN		4:30 P.M. Mon.	0 km
Lock 3, Red Wing, MN	11:30 P.M. Mon.	12:00 midnight	78.8 km
Prairie du Chien, WI	11:00 P.M. Tues.	10:30 A.M. Wed.	337.8 km
Dubuque, IA	6:30 P.M. Wed.	7:00 P.M. Wed.	426.3 km
Hannibal, MO	1:00 A.M. Fri.	______	863.9 km

Math Activity

Now complete the riverboat schedule for the Lower Mississippi. Your boat will leave Hannibal at 6 P.M. Friday and will travel at a speed of 14.7 kilometers per hour for the rest of the journey.

- When will you arrive at Lock 26?
- You spend 34 minutes in the lock. When will you depart from Lock 26? Your boat travels on. When will it arrive in St. Louis?
- The boat will spend 4 hours in St. Louis and head to Cape Girardeau, arriving at 6:30 A.M. Sunday. How far is it from St. Louis to Cape Girardeau?

Lower Mississippi Riverboat Schedule May–Sept.

Port	Arrival Time	Departure Time	Distance From Fort Snelling
Hannibal, MO		6 P.M. Fri.	863.9 km
Lock 26, Alton, IL	a. __?__	b. __?__	1,033.0 km
St. Louis, MO	c. __?__	d. __?__	1,070.7 km
Cape Girardeau, MO	6:30 A.M. Sun.	______	e. __?__

Mathematics

Explore Mathematics Concepts

Use Math Skills Before students begin to work on their schedules, have them find the ports listed in the schedule on the map in this feature. Cape Girardeau, not shown on the map, is at the river's bend, above Cairo.

Discuss Point out that on the schedule, each segment of the journey lasts from the departure time listed for one port to the arrival time listed for the next port. Also, emphasize that the distances listed in the right column are all from the original departure point at Fort Snelling.

Math Activity

Focus Help students learn to read the schedule. Ask: **How far is it from Dubuque to Hannibal?** *(863.9 – 426.3 km, or 437.6 km)* **How long does that part of the trip take?** *(30 hours—from 7:00 P.M. Wednesday to 1:00 A.M. Friday.)*

Teach As a whole-class activity, have students work through the three questions in the left column. *(Average speed between Dubuque and Hannibal, 437.6 km ÷ 30 hrs = 14.6 km/hr; time spent in Prairie du Chien, 11.5 hrs; travel time from Prairie du Chien to Dubuque, 8 hrs)*

Before starting the activity, remind students that to convert parts of hours expressed as decimal fractions, they must multiply the fraction by 60.

Answers

a. 5:30 A.M. Saturday (169.1 km ÷ 14.7 km/hr = 11.5 hrs from 6 P.M. Friday) **b.** 6:04 A.M. Saturday (5:30 + 34 min) **c.** 8:40 A.M. Saturday (37.7 km ÷ 14.7 km/hr = 2.6 hrs from 6:04 A.M.) **d.** 12:40 P.M. Saturday **e.** 1332.4 km from Fort Snelling (261.7 km from St. Louis to Cape Girardeau)

Background

Integrating Science and Technology Today, modern versions of the fabled steamboats offer cruises on the Mississippi and several of its major tributaries, including the Illinois, Ohio, Tennessee, and Arkansas Rivers. The *Delta Queen, Mississippi Queen,* and *American Queen* offer cruises with a variety of itineraries on the upper and lower Mississippi.

Today's steamboats look like those of Mark Twain's day, but they have air conditioning, elevators between decks, electronic navigation aids, and hulls of welded steel. They are powered in part by steam engines that turn colorful paddle wheels. These vessels also have powerful auxiliary diesel engines as well as devices that make steering the big boats much easier than it was 100 years ago.

Language Arts

Explore Language Arts Concepts

Descriptive Writing Ask students whether they recognize the name of Mark Twain or have read any of his books or stories. If they have, invite them to briefly describe the plots and characters.

Discussion Allow students to read the excerpt from Twain's *Life on the Mississippi*. Ask: **Have you ever had to walk around your home in the dark? How did you keep from running into things?** *(Students will probably say that they already knew the layout from seeing it so many times in the light.)* **Why did Mr. Bixby use the image of a dark hall?** *(To relate the new task to a familiar experience)*

Language Arts Activity

Focus Encourage students to share their responses to the questions posed in the text. *(A river pilot must know the river's shape so well that he can navigate safely even when he cannot see the shore. Mr. Bixby respects the river and is proud of his knowledge of it. This is indicated by what he says.)* Ask: **After reading this excerpt, how would you describe Mr. Bixby?** *(Experienced, tough, no-nonsense, forceful, insistent)* **How would you describe the young Mark Twain?** *(Nervous, overwhelmed, unsure of himself, reluctant, somewhat negative)*

Teach Before students begin writing, encourage them to think about the ending. Ask: **How do you think the excerpt should end?** *(Because students know that Twain eventually became a river pilot, they should realize that the excerpt will end on a positive note, with Twain resolving to do his best.)* Remind students of the following points: (1) The characters should talk as people did in Mark Twain's time; (2) the dialogue should move the story along and bring it to a natural conclusion; (3) each time there is a change of speaker, a new paragraph should begin; and (4) the speaker's words should be set off by quotation marks.

Scoring Rubric

4 Exceeds criteria; includes details and colorful adjectives, addresses all four points
3 Meets all four criteria but does not go beyond basic expectations
2 Writing is descriptive but does not include all criteria
1 Is inaccurate and incomplete

Language Arts

Mark Three! Mark Twain!

To steer a boat on the Mississippi, early riverboat pilots had to memorize landmarks at every bend and curve of the river, going both upstream and down. They had to know where the channel was deep enough for the boat, where the current was strong, and where there were sandbars or sunken logs.

When Samuel Clemens was growing up in the small river town of Hannibal, Missouri, his ambition was to become a Mississippi River steamboat pilot. He was a pilot for a while. Later he became one of America's most famous writers, using the pen name Mark Twain. In the passage at right from his book *Life on the Mississippi*, Twain describes a lesson he learned from an experienced pilot, Mr. Bixby.

"My boy," [Bixby said] "you've got to know the shape of the river perfectly. It is all there is left to steer by on a very dark night. Everything else is blotted out and gone. But mind you, it hasn't the same shape in the night that it has in the daytime."

"How on earth am I ever going to learn it, then?"

"How do you follow a hall at home in the dark? Because you know the shape of it. You can't see it."

"Do you mean to say that I've got to know all the million trifling variations of shape in the banks of this interminable [endless] river as well as I know the shape of the front hall at home?"

"On my honor, you've got to know them better than any man ever did know the shapes of the halls in his own house."

"I wish I was dead!"

"Now I don't want to discourage you, but— . . . . You see, this has got to be learned; there isn't any getting around it. . . .

What's in a Name?
Mark Twain's name comes from a term that steamboat crews used to measure the depth of river water. *Twain* means "two." Dropping a weighted line, they would call out the depth:
"Mark twain!"—2 fathoms deep;
"Mark three!"—3 fathoms deep.
(Note: One fathom equals 1.8 meters.)

Sunrise over the Mississippi River in Iowa

Background

History "Mark Twain" is one of the literary world's most famous pen names. Samuel Clemens—in *Life on the Mississippi*, written in 1883—claimed that another riverboat pilot had used the name for a series of articles and that he (Clemens) had borrowed it. However, most editors and critics do not accept this account, particularly because Clemens had first used the pen name 20 years earlier.

Clemens never forgot the Mississippi River and his years as a river pilot. As a journalist, humorist, and lecturer, he traveled throughout the United States and abroad. His most popular works for young people are *The Adventures of Tom Sawyer, The Adventures of Huckleberry Finn,* and "The Celebrated Jumping Frog of Calaveras County."

"The river is a very different shape on a pitch-dark night from what it is on a starlight night. All shores seem to be straight lines, then, and mighty dim ones, too; and you'd run them for straight lines, only you know better. Then there's your gray mist. You take a night when there's one of these grisly, drizzly gray mists, and then there isn't any particular shape to a shore. A gray mist would tangle the head of the oldest man that ever lived. Well, then, different kinds of moonlight change the shape of the river in different ways. You see—"

"Oh, don't say any more, please! Have I got to learn the shape of the river according to all these five hundred thousand different ways? If I tried to carry all that cargo in my head, it would make me stoop-shouldered."

"No! You only learn the shape of the river; and you learn it with such absolute certainty that you can always steer by the shape that's in your head, and never mind the one that's before your eyes."

Language Arts Activity

Read the excerpt, focusing on what the dialogue tells you about the characters of Mark Twain and Mr. Bixby.

- What lesson does Mark Twain learn?
- How does Mr. Bixby feel about the Mississippi River?

How can you tell?

Now, use dialogue to write an ending to this riverboat excerpt. Before you begin writing, think carefully about the characters, setting, and your conclusion.

Tie It Together

Celebrate the River

Plan a class fair featuring cities on the Mississippi River today, such as St. Louis (above). Set up a booth for each city and create a travel brochure to persuade people to visit.

Choose a city to represent. Then, research the city to find information on

- interesting attractions and events— zoos, museums, parks, sports events, and music festivals.
- influences of different groups on food, customs, music, and architecture.
- physical features around the city.
- famous people—writers, political figures, entertainers—who lived there.
- historic places to visit—monuments, houses, battlefields, and statues.
- illustrations and pictures of special attractions.
- maps of walking tours and historic areas.
- native plants and animals in the area.

Before starting your brochure, decide which attractions to highlight. Then set up your booth, display your brochure, and celebrate life on the Mississippi today.

Tie It Together

Celebrate the River

Time 1 week (2 days for research, 2 days for preparing the brochure and booth, 1 day for the fair)

Tips Have students work in groups of four or five. Encourage groups to choose a city that can be researched easily with readily available resource materials. If necessary, help each group divide the tasks and work out a plan for researching and compiling information. Guide students through the writing process as follows:

- In the research stage, suggest that they narrow the topics by listing all of their ideas and then selecting those that are most interesting.
- In the drafting stage, remind students to begin the brochure with a general introduction, followed by topic-specific information such as key attractions, famous people, and historic sites.
- In the editing stage, remind students to read the draft carefully, looking for errors and ways to improve the brochure.

Extend Suggest that groups choose one cultural aspect to research across different cities. For example, one group could find out about (and possibly prepare for class tasting) foods representing different ethnic and regional groups—a Cajun dish for Louisiana, Scandinavian food for Minnesota, and so on. Another group could research the music in river cities, including jazz and ragtime in New Orleans, country and rock in Memphis, and bluegrass in Kentucky. Still another group could explore various types of arts and crafts characteristic of different cities and regions along the river.

Think Like a Scientist

The Skills Handbook is designed as a reference for students to use whenever they need to review inquiry, reading, or math skills. You can use the activities in this part of the Skills Handbook to teach or reinforce inquiry skills.

Observing

Focus Remind students that an observation is what they can see, hear, smell, taste, or feel.

Teach Invite students to make observations of the classroom. List these observations on the board. Challenge students to identify the senses they used to make each observation. Then, ask: **Which senses will you use to make observations from the photograph on this page?** *(Sight is the only sense that can be used to make observations from the photograph.)*

Activity

Some observations that students might make include that the boy is skateboarding, wearing a white helmet, and flying in the air. Make sure that students' observations are confined to only things that they can actually see in the photograph.

Inferring

Focus Choose one or two of the classroom observations listed on the board, and challenge students to interpret them. Guide students by asking why something appears as it does.

Teach Encourage students to describe their thought processes in making their inferences. Point out where they used their knowledge and experience to interpret the observations. Then invite students to suggest other possible interpretations for the observations. Ask: **How can you find out whether an inference is correct?** *(By further investigation)*

Activity

One possible inference is that the boy just skated off a ramp at a skate park. Invite students to share their experiences that helped them make the inference.

Predicting

Focus Discuss the weather forecast for the next day. Point out that this prediction is an inference about what will happen in the future based on observations and experience.

Teach Help students differentiate between a prediction and an inference. You might organize the similarities and differences in a Venn diagram on the board. Both are interpretations of observations using experience and knowledge, and both can be incorrect. Inferences describe current or past events. Predictions describe future events.

Activity

Students might predict that the boy will land and skate to the other side. Others might predict that the boy will fall. Students should also describe the evidence or experience on which they based their predictions.

SKILLS Handbook

Think Like a Scientist

Scientists have a particular way of looking at the world, or scientific habits of mind. Whenever you ask a question and explore possible answers, you use many of the same skills that scientists do. Some of these skills are described on this page.

Observing

When you use one or more of your five senses to gather information about the world, you are **observing.** Hearing a dog bark, counting twelve green seeds, and smelling smoke are all observations. To increase the power of their senses, scientists sometimes use microscopes, telescopes, or other instruments that help them make more detailed observations.

An observation must be an accurate report of what your senses detect. It is important to keep careful records of your observations in science class by writing or drawing in a notebook. The information collected through observations is called evidence, or data.

Inferring

When you interpret an observation, you are **inferring,** or making an inference. For example, if you hear your dog barking, you may infer that someone is at your front door. To make this inference, you combine the evidence—the barking dog—and your experience or knowledge—you know that your dog barks when strangers approach—to reach a logical conclusion.

Notice that an inference is not a fact; it is only one of many possible interpretations for an observation. For example, your dog may be barking because it wants to go for a walk. An inference may turn out to be incorrect even if it is based on accurate observations and logical reasoning. The only way to find out if an inference is correct is to investigate further.

Predicting

When you listen to the weather forecast, you hear many predictions about the next day's weather—what the temperature will be, whether it will rain, and how windy it will be. Weather forecasters use observations and knowledge of weather patterns to predict the weather. The skill of **predicting** involves making an inference about a future event based on current evidence or past experience.

Because a prediction is an inference, it may prove to be false. In science class, you can test some of your predictions by doing experiments. For example, suppose you predict that larger paper airplanes can fly farther than smaller airplanes. How could you test your prediction?

Activity

Use the photograph to answer the questions below.

Observing Look closely at the photograph. List at least three observations.

Inferring Use your observations to make an inference about what has happened. What experience or knowledge did you use to make the inference?

Predicting Predict what will happen next. On what evidence or experience do you base your prediction?

Classifying

Could you imagine searching for a book in the library if the books were shelved in no particular order? Your trip to the library would be an all-day event! Luckily, librarians group together books on similar topics or by the same author. Grouping together items that are alike in some way is called **classifying.** You can classify items in many ways: by size, by shape, by use, and by other important characteristics.

Like librarians, scientists use the skill of classifying to organize information and objects. When things are sorted into groups, the relationships among them become easier to understand.

Activity

Classify the objects in the photograph into two groups based on any characteristic you choose. Then use another characteristic to classify the objects into three groups.

Activity

This student is using a model to demonstrate what causes day and night on Earth. What do the flashlight and the tennis ball in the model represent?

Making Models

Have you ever drawn a picture to help someone understand what you were saying? Such a drawing is one type of model. A model is a picture, diagram, computer image, or other representation of a complex object or process. **Making models** helps people understand things that they cannot observe directly.

Scientists often use models to represent things that are either very large or very small, such as the planets in the solar system, or the parts of a cell. Such models are physical models—drawings or three-dimensional structures that look like the real thing. Other models are mental models—mathematical equations or words that describe how something works.

Communicating

Whenever you talk on the phone, write a report, or listen to your teacher at school, you are communicating. **Communicating** is the process of sharing ideas and information with other people. Communicating effectively requires many skills, including writing, reading, speaking, listening, and making models.

Scientists communicate to share results, information, and opinions. Scientists often communicate about their work in journals, over the telephone, in letters, and on the Internet. They also attend scientific meetings where they share their ideas with one another in person.

Activity

On a sheet of paper, write out clear, detailed directions for tying your shoe. Then exchange directions with a partner. Follow your partner's directions exactly. How successful were you at tying your shoe? How could your partner have communicated more clearly?

Inquiry Skills

Classifying

Focus Encourage students to think of common things that are classified.

Teach Ask: **What things at home are classified?** *(Clothing might be classified in order to place it in the appropriate dresser drawer; glasses, plates, and silverware are grouped in different parts of the kitchen; screws, nuts, bolts, washers, and nails might be separated into small containers.)* **What are some things that scientists classify?** *(Scientists classify many things they study, including organisms, geological features and processes, and kinds of machines.)*

Activity

Some characteristics students might use include color, pattern of color, use of balls, and size. Students' criteria for classification should clearly divide the balls into two, and then three, distinct groups.

Making Models

Focus Ask: **What are some models you have used to study science?** *(Students might have used human anatomical models, solar system models, maps, or stream tables.)* **How have these models helped you?** *(Models can help you learn about things that are difficult to study because they are very large, very small, or highly complex.)*

Teach Be sure students understand that a model does not have to be three-dimensional. For example, a map is a model, as is a mathematical equation. Have students look at the photograph of the student modeling the causes of day and night on Earth. Ask: **What quality of each item makes this a good model?** *(The flashlight gives off light, and the ball is round and can be rotated by the student.)*

Activity

The flashlight represents the sun and the ball represents Earth.

Communicating

Focus Have students identify the methods of communication they have used today.

Teach Ask: **How is the way you communicate with a friend similar to and different from the way scientists communicate about their work to other scientists?** *(Both may communicate using various methods, but scientists must be very detailed and precise, whereas communication between friends may be less detailed and precise.)* Encourage students to communicate like a scientist as they carry out the activity.

Activity

Students' answers will vary but should identify a step-by-step process for tying a shoe. Help students identify communication errors such as leaving out a step, putting steps in the wrong order, or disregarding the person's handedness.

Making Measurements

Students can refer to this part of the Skills Handbook whenever they need to review how to make measurements with SI units. You can use the activities here to teach or reinforce SI units.

Measuring in SI

Focus Review SI units with students. Begin by providing metric rulers, graduated cylinders, balances, and Celsius thermometers. Use these tools to reinforce that the meter is the unit of length, the liter is the unit of volume, the gram is the unit of mass, and the degree Celsius is the unit of temperature.

Teach Ask: **If you want to measure the length and the width of the classroom, which SI unit would you use?** *(Meter)* **Which unit would you use to measure the amount of mass in your textbook?** *(Gram)* **Which would you use to measure how much water a drinking glass holds?** *(Liter)* **When would you use the Celsius scale?** *(To measure the temperature of something)* Then use the measuring equipment to review SI prefixes. For example, ask: **What are the smallest units on the metric ruler?** *(Millimeters)* **How many millimeters are there in one centimeter?** *(10 millimeters)* **How many in 10 centimeters?** *(100 millimeters)* **How many centimeters are there in one meter?** *(100 centimeters)* **What does 1,000 meters equal?** *(One kilometer)*

Activity

Length The length of the shell is 7.8 centimeters, or 78 millimeters. If students need more practice measuring length, have them use meter sticks and metric rulers to measure various objects in the classroom.

Activity

Liquid Volume The volume of water in the graduated cylinder is 62 milliliters. If students need more practice, have them use a graduated cylinder to measure different volumes of water.

Making Measurements

By measuring, scientists can express their observations more precisely and communicate more information about what they observe.

Measuring in SI

The standard system of measurement used by scientists around the world is known as the International System of Units, which is abbreviated as SI (**Système International d'Unités,** in French). SI units are easy to use because they are based on multiples of 10. Each unit is ten times larger than the next smallest unit and one tenth the size of the next largest unit. The table lists the prefixes used to name the most common SI units.

Common SI Prefixes

Prefix	Symbol	Meaning
kilo-	k	1,000
hecto-	h	100
deka-	da	10
deci-	d	0.1 (one tenth)
centi-	c	0.01 (one hundredth)
milli-	m	0.001 (one thousandth)

Length To measure length, or the distance between two points, the unit of measure is the **meter (m).** The distance from the floor to a doorknob is approximately one meter. Long distances, such as the distance between two cities, are measured in kilometers (km). Small lengths are measured in centimeters (cm) or millimeters (mm). Scientists use metric rulers and meter sticks to measure length.

Common Conversions

1 km	=	1,000 m
1 m	=	100 cm
1 m	=	1,000 mm
1 cm	=	10 mm

Activity

The larger lines on the metric ruler in the picture show centimeter divisions, while the smaller, unnumbered lines show millimeter divisions. How many centimeters long is the shell? How many millimeters long is it?

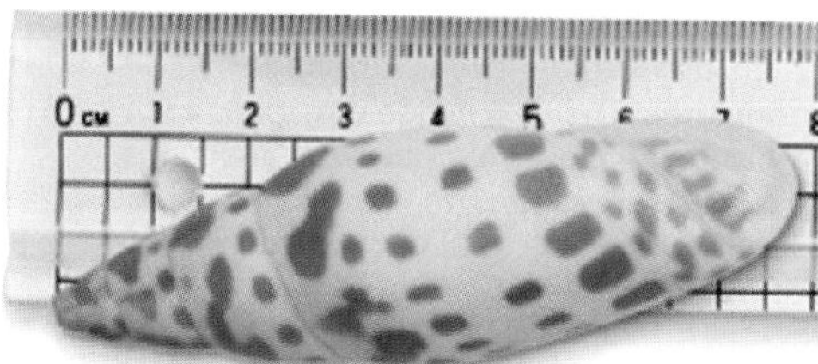

Liquid Volume To measure the volume of a liquid, or the amount of space it takes up, you will use a unit of measure known as the **liter (L).** One liter is the approximate volume of a medium-size carton of milk. Smaller volumes are measured in milliliters (mL). Scientists use graduated cylinders to measure liquid volume.

Activity

The graduated cylinder in the picture is marked in milliliter divisions. Notice that the water in the cylinder has a curved surface. This curved surface is called the *meniscus*. To measure the volume, you must read the level at the lowest point of the meniscus. What is the volume of water in this graduated cylinder?

Common Conversion

1 L = 1,000 mL

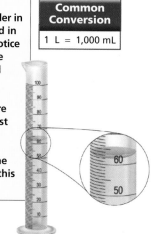

Mass To measure mass, or the amount of matter in an object, you will use a unit of measure known as the **gram (g).** One gram is approximately the mass of a paper clip. Larger masses are measured in kilograms (kg). Scientists use a balance to find the mass of an object.

Common Conversion
1 kg = 1,000 g

Activity

The mass of the potato in the picture is measured in kilograms. What is the mass of the potato? Suppose a recipe for potato salad called for one kilogram of potatoes. About how many potatoes would you need?

0.25KG

Temperature To measure the temperature of a substance, you will use the **Celsius scale.** Temperature is measured in degrees Celsius (°C) using a Celsius thermometer. Water freezes at 0°C and boils at 100°C.

Time The unit scientists use to measure time is the **second (s).**

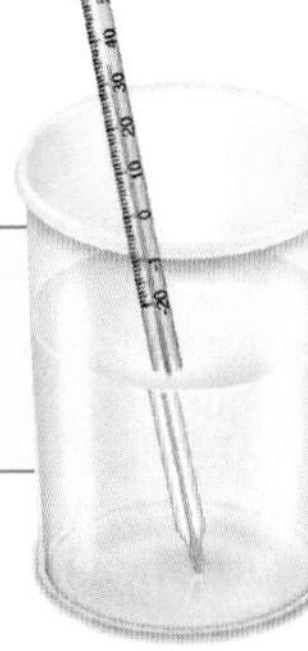

Activity

What is the temperature of the liquid in degrees Celsius?

Converting SI Units

To use the SI system, you must know how to convert between units. Converting from one unit to another involves the skill of **calculating,** or using mathematical operations. Converting between SI units is similar to converting between dollars and dimes because both systems are based on multiples of ten.

Suppose you want to convert a length of 80 centimeters to meters. Follow these steps to convert between units.

1. Begin by writing down the measurement you want to convert—in this example, 80 centimeters.
2. Write a conversion factor that represents the relationship between the two units you are converting. In this example, the relationship is 1 meter = 100 centimeters. Write this conversion factor as a fraction, making sure to place the units you are converting from (centimeters, in this example) in the denominator.
3. Multiply the measurement you want to convert by the fraction. When you do this, the units in the first measurement will cancel out with the units in the denominator. Your answer will be in the units you are converting to (meters, in this example).

Example

80 centimeters = ■ meters

$$80 \text{ centimeters} \times \frac{1 \text{ meter}}{100 \text{ centimeters}} = \frac{80 \text{ meters}}{100}$$

$$= 0.8 \text{ meters}$$

Activity

Convert between the following units.

1. 600 millimeters = ■ meters
2. 0.35 liters = ■ milliliters
3. 1,050 grams = ■ kilograms

Inquiry Skills

Activity

Mass The mass of the potato is 0.25 kilograms. You would need 4 potatoes to make one kilogram. If students need more practice, give them various objects, such as coins, paper clips, and books, to measure mass.

Activity

Temperature The temperature of the liquid is 35°C. Students who need more practice can measure the temperatures of various water samples.

Converting SI Units

Focus Review the steps for converting SI units, and work through the example with students.

Teach Ask: **How many millimeters are in 80 centimeters?** *(With the relationship 10 millimeters = 1 centimeter, students should follow the steps to calculate that 80 centimeters is equal to 800 millimeters.)* Have students do the conversion problems in the activity.

Activity

1. *600 millimeters = 0.6 meters*
2. *0.35 liters = 350 milliliters*
3. *1,050 grams = 1.05 kilograms*

If students need more practice converting SI units, have them make up conversion problems to trade with partners.

Conducting a Scientific Investigation

Students can refer to this part of the Skills Handbook whenever they need to review the steps of a scientific investigation. You can use the activities here to teach or reinforce these steps.

Posing Questions

Focus Ask: **What do you do when you want to learn about something?** *(Answers might include asking questions about it or looking for information in books or on the Internet.)* Explain that scientists go through the same process to learn about something.

Teach Tell students that the questions scientists ask may have no answers or many different answers. To answer their questions, scientists often conduct experiments. Ask: **Why is a scientific question important to a scientific investigation?** *(It helps the scientist decide if an experiment is necessary; the answer might already be known. It also helps focus the idea so that the scientist can form a hypothesis.)* **What is the scientific question in the activity on the next page?** *(Is a ball's bounce affected by the height from which it is dropped?)*

Developing a Hypothesis

Focus Emphasize that a hypothesis is one possible explanation for a set of observations. It is *not* a guess. It is often based on an inference.

Teach Ask: **On what information do scientists base their hypotheses?** *(Their observations and previous knowledge or experience)* Point out that a hypothesis does not always turn out to be correct. Ask: **When a hypothesis turns out to be incorrect, do you think the scientist wasted his or her time? Explain.** *(No. The scientist learned from the investigation and will develop another hypothesis that could prove to be correct.)*

Designing an Experiment

Focus Have a volunteer read the Experimental Procedure in the box. Invite students to identify the manipulated variable *(amount of salt)*, the variables kept constant *(amount and temperature of water, location of containers)*, the control *(Container 3)*, and the responding variable *(time required for the water to freeze)*.

Conducting a Scientific Investigation

In some ways, scientists are like detectives, piecing together clues to learn about a process or event. One way that scientists gather clues is by carrying out experiments. An experiment tests an idea in a careful, orderly manner. Although experiments do not all follow the same steps in the same order, many follow a pattern similar to the one described here.

Posing Questions

Experiments begin by asking a scientific question. A scientific question is one that can be answered by gathering evidence. For example, the question "Which freezes faster—fresh water or salt water?" is a scientific question because you can carry out an investigation and gather information to answer the question.

Developing a Hypothesis

The next step is to form a hypothesis. A **hypothesis** is a possible explanation for a set of observations or answer to a scientific question. In science, a hypothesis must be something that can be tested. A hypothesis can be worded as an *If . . . then . . .* statement. For example, a hypothesis might be *"If I add salt to fresh water, then the water will take longer to freeze."* A hypothesis worded this way serves as a rough outline of the experiment you should perform.

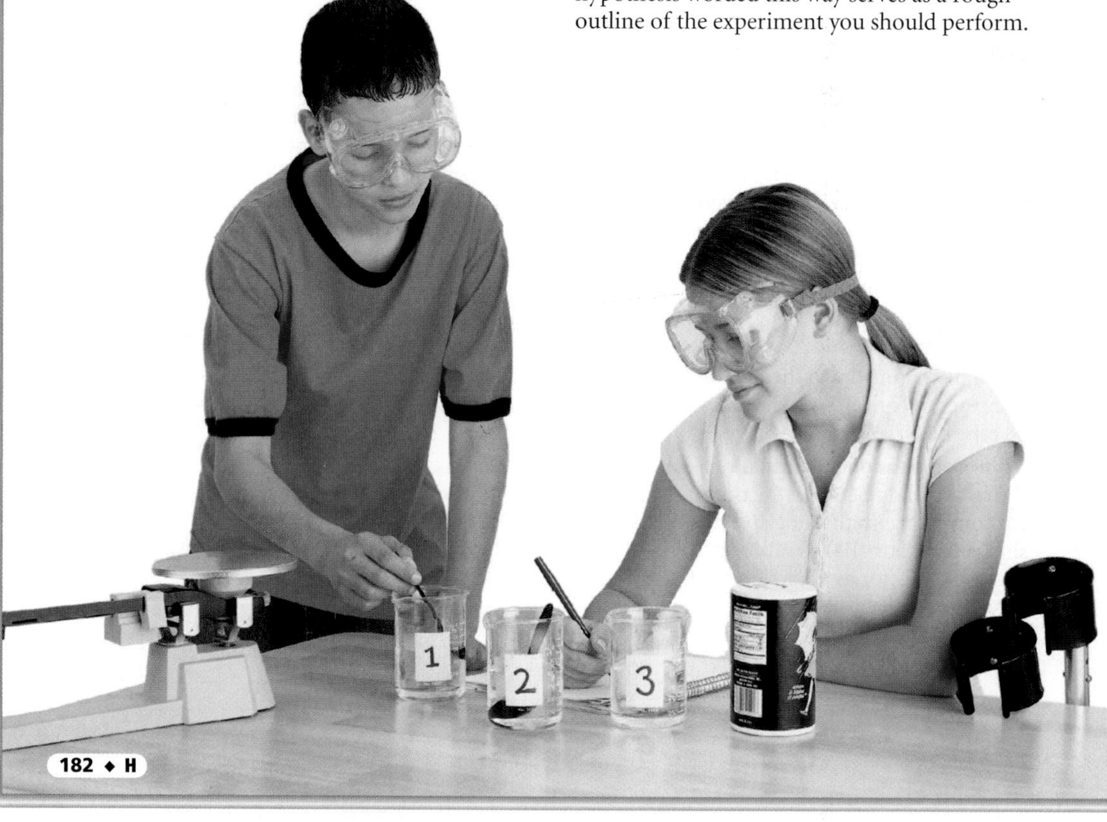

Teach Ask: **How might the experiment be affected if Container 1 had only 100 milliliters of water?** *(It wouldn't be an accurate comparison with the containers that have more water.)* Also make sure that students understand the importance of the control. Then, ask: **What operational definition is used in this experiment?** *("Frozen" means the time at which a wooden stick can no longer move in a container.)*

Designing an Experiment

Next you need to plan a way to test your hypothesis. Your plan should be written out as a step-by-step procedure and should describe the observations or measurements you will make.

Two important steps involved in designing an experiment are controlling variables and forming operational definitions.

Controlling Variables In a well-designed experiment, you need to keep all variables the same except for one. A **variable** is any factor that can change in an experiment. The factor that you change is called the **manipulated variable.** In this experiment, the manipulated variable is the amount of salt added to the water. Other factors, such as the amount of water or the starting temperature, are kept constant.

The factor that changes as a result of the manipulated variable is called the **responding variable.** The responding variable is what you measure or observe to obtain your results. In this experiment, the responding variable is how long the water takes to freeze.

An experiment in which all factors except one are kept constant is called a **controlled experiment.** Most controlled experiments include a test called the control. In this experiment, Container 3 is the control. Because no salt is added to Container 3, you can compare the results from the other containers to it. Any difference in results must be due to the addition of salt alone.

Forming Operational Definitions Another important aspect of a well-designed experiment is having clear operational definitions. An **operational definition** is a statement that describes how a particular variable is to be measured or how a term is to be defined. For example, in this experiment, how will you determine if the water has frozen? You might decide to insert a stick in each container at the start of the experiment. Your operational definition of "frozen" would be the time at which the stick can no longer move.

Experimental Procedure

1. Fill 3 containers with 300 milliliters of cold tap water.
2. Add 10 grams of salt to Container 1; stir. Add 20 grams of salt to Container 2; stir. Add no salt to Container 3.
3. Place the 3 containers in a freezer.
4. Check the containers every 15 minutes. Record your observations.

Interpreting Data

The observations and measurements you make in an experiment are called **data.** At the end of an experiment, you need to analyze the data to look for any patterns or trends. Patterns often become clear if you organize your data in a data table or graph. Then think through what the data reveal. Do they support your hypothesis? Do they point out a flaw in your experiment? Do you need to collect more data?

Drawing Conclusions

A **conclusion** is a statement that sums up what you have learned from an experiment. When you draw a conclusion, you need to decide whether the data you collected support your hypothesis or not. You may need to repeat an experiment several times before you can draw any conclusions from it. Conclusions often lead you to pose new questions and plan new experiments to answer them.

Activity

Is a ball's bounce affected by the height from which it is dropped? Using the steps just described, plan a controlled experiment to investigate this problem.

Activity

You might wish to have students work in pairs to plan the controlled experiment. Students should develop a hypothesis, such as, "If I increase the height from which a ball is dropped, then the height of its bounce will increase." They can test the hypothesis by dropping a ball from varying heights (the manipulated variable). All trials should be done with the same kind of ball and on the same surface (constants). For each trial, they should measure the height of the bounce (responding variable). After students have designed the experiment, provide rubber balls, and invite them to carry out the experiment so they can collect and interpret data and draw conclusions.

Interpreting Data

Focus Ask: **What kind of data would you collect from the experiment with freezing salt water?** *(Time and state of the water)*

Teach Ask: **What if you forgot to record some data during an investigation?** *(You wouldn't be able to draw valid conclusions because some data are missing.)* Then, ask: **Why are data tables and graphs a good way to organize data?** *(They make it easier to record data accurately, as well as compare and analyze data.)* **What kind of data table and graph might you use for this experiment?** *(A table would have columns for each container with a row for each time interval in which the state of water is recorded. A bar graph would show the time elapsed until water froze for each container.)*

Drawing Conclusions

Focus Help students understand that a conclusion is not necessarily the end of a scientific investigation. A conclusion about one experiment may lead right into another experiment.

Teach Point out that in scientific investigations, a conclusion is a summary and explanation of the results of an experiment. For the Experimental Procedure described on this page, tell students to suppose that they obtained the following results: Container 1 froze in 45 minutes, Container 2 in 80 minutes, and Container 3 in 25 minutes. Ask: **What conclusions can you draw from this experiment?** *(Students might conclude that water takes longer to freeze as more salt is added to it. The hypothesis is supported, and the question of which freezes faster is answered—fresh water.)*

Technology Design Skills

Students can refer to this part of the Skills Handbook whenever they need to review the process of designing new technologies. You can use the activities here to teach or reinforce the steps in this process.

Identify a Need

Focus Solicit from students any situations in which they have thought that a tool, machine, or other object would be really helpful to them or others. Explain that this is the first step in the design of new products.

Teach Point out that identifying specific needs is very important to the design process. Ask: **If it was specified that the toy boat be wind-powered, how might that affect the design?** *(The boat would likely be designed with sails.)*

Research the Problem

Focus Explain that research focuses the problem so that the design is more specific.

Teach Ask: **What might happen if you didn't research the problem before designing the solution?** *(Answers include developing a design that has already been found to fail, using materials that aren't the best, or designing a solution that already exists.)* **What would you research before designing your toy boat?** *(Students might research designs and materials.)*

Design a Solution

Focus Emphasize the importance of a design team. Ask: **Why are brainstorming sessions important in product design?** *(A group will propose more new ideas than one person.)*

Teach Divide the class into teams to design the toy boat. Instruct them to brainstorm design ideas. Then, ask: **Why do you think engineers evaluate constraints after brainstorming?** *(Evaluating constraints while brainstorming often stops the flow of new ideas.)* **What design constraints do you have for your toy boat?** *(Materials must be readily available and teacher-approved. The boat must be 15 centimeters or less in length and must travel 2 meters in a straight line carrying a load of 20 pennies.)*

Technology Design Skills

Engineers are people who use scientific and technological knowledge to solve practical problems. To design new products, engineers usually follow the process described here, even though they may not follow these steps in the exact order. As you read the steps, think about how you might apply them in technology labs.

Identify a Need

Before engineers begin designing a new product, they must first identify the need they are trying to meet. For example, suppose you are a member of a design team in a company that makes toys. Your team has identified a need: a toy boat that is inexpensive and easy to assemble.

Research the Problem

Engineers often begin by gathering information that will help them with their new design. This research may include finding articles in books, magazines, or on the Internet. It may also include talking to other engineers who have solved similar problems. Engineers often perform experiments related to the product they want to design.

For your toy boat, you could look at toys that are similar to the one you want to design. You might do research on the Internet. You could also test some materials to see whether they will work well in a toy boat.

Drawing for a boat design ▼

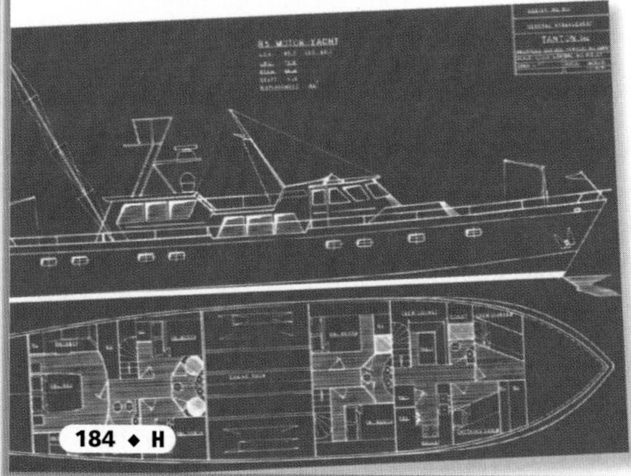

Design a Solution

Research gives engineers information that helps them design a product. When engineers design new products, they usually work in teams.

Generating Ideas Often design teams hold brainstorming meetings in which any team member can contribute ideas. **Brainstorming** is a creative process in which one team member's suggestions often spark ideas in other group members. Brainstorming can lead to new approaches to solving a design problem.

Evaluating Constraints During brainstorming, a design team will often come up with several possible designs. The team must then evaluate each one.

As part of their evaluation, engineers consider constraints. **Constraints** are factors that limit or restrict a product design. Physical characteristics, such as the properties of materials used to make your toy boat, are constraints. Money and time are also constraints. If the materials in a product cost a lot, or if the product takes a long time to make, the design may be impractical.

Making Trade-offs Design teams usually need to make trade-offs. In a **trade-off,** engineers give up one benefit of a proposed design in order to obtain another. In designing your toy boat, you will have to make trade-offs. For example, suppose one material is sturdy but not fully waterproof. Another material is more waterproof, but breakable. You may decide to give up the benefit of sturdiness in order to obtain the benefit of waterproofing.

Build and Evaluate a Prototype

Once the team has chosen a design plan, the engineers build a prototype of the product. A **prototype** is a working model used to test a design. Engineers evaluate the prototype to see whether it works well, is easy to operate, is safe to use, and holds up to repeated use.

Think of your toy boat. What would the prototype be like? Of what materials would it be made? How would you test it?

Troubleshoot and Redesign

Few prototypes work perfectly, which is why they need to be tested. Once a design team has tested a prototype, the members analyze the results and identify any problems. The team then tries to **troubleshoot,** or fix the design problems. For example, if your toy boat leaks or wobbles, the boat should be redesigned to eliminate those problems.

Communicate the Solution

A team needs to communicate the final design to the people who will manufacture and use the product. To do this, teams may use sketches, detailed drawings, computer simulations, and word descriptions.

Activity

You can use the technology design process to design and build a toy boat.

Research and Investigate

1. Visit the library or go online to research toy boats.
2. Investigate how a toy boat can be powered, including wind, rubber bands, or baking soda and vinegar.
3. Brainstorm materials, shapes, and steering for your boat.

Design and Build

4. Based on your research, design a toy boat that
   - is made of readily available materials
   - is no larger than 15 cm long and 10 cm wide
   - includes a power system, a rudder, and an area for cargo
   - travels 2 meters in a straight line carrying a load of 20 pennies
5. Sketch your design and write a step-by-step plan for building your boat. After your teacher approves your plan, build your boat.

Evaluate and Redesign

6. Test your boat, evaluate the results, and troubleshoot any problems.
7. Based on your evaluation, redesign your toy boat so it performs better.

Activity

The design possibilities are endless. Students might use small plastic containers, wood, foil, or plastic drinking cups for the boat. Materials may also include toothpicks, straws, or small wooden dowels. Brainstorm with students the different ways in which a toy boat can be propelled. The boats may be any shape, but must be no longer than 15 centimeters.

As student groups follow the steps in the design process, have them record their sources, brainstorming ideas, and prototype design in a logbook. Also give them time to troubleshoot and redesign their boats. When students turn in their boats, they should include assembly directions with a diagram, as well as instructions for use.

Build and Evaluate a Prototype

Focus Explain that building a prototype enables engineers to test design ideas.

Teach Relate building and testing a prototype to conducting an experiment. Explain that engineers set up controlled experiments to test the prototype. Ask: **Why do you think engineers set up controlled experiments?** *(From the data, they can determine which component of the design is working and which is failing.)* **How would you test your prototype of the toy boat?** *(Answers will vary depending on the toy boat's propulsion system.)*

Troubleshoot and Redesign

Focus Make sure students know what it means to troubleshoot. If necessary, give an example. One example is a stapler that isn't working. In that case, you would check to see if it is out of staples or if the staples are jammed. Then you would fix the problem and try stapling again. If it still didn't work, you might check the position of staples and try again.

Teach Explain that engineers often are not surprised if the prototype doesn't work. Ask: **Why isn't it a failure if the prototype doesn't work?** *(Engineers learn from the problems and make changes to address the problems. This process makes the design better.)* Emphasize that prototypes are completely tested before the product is made in the factory.

Communicate the Solution

Focus Inquire whether students have ever read the instruction manual that comes with a new toy or electronic device.

Teach Emphasize the importance of good communication in the design process. Ask: **What might happen if engineers did not communicate their design ideas clearly?** *(The product might not be manufactured correctly or used properly.)*

Creating Data Tables and Graphs

Students can refer to this part of the Skills Handbook whenever they need to review the skills required to create data tables and graphs. You can use the activities provided here to teach or reinforce these skills.

Data Tables

Focus Emphasize the importance of organizing data. Ask: **What might happen if you didn't use a data table for an experiment?** *(Possible answers include that data might not be collected or they might be forgotten.)*

Teach Have students create a data table to show how much time they spend on different activities during one week. Suggest that students first list the main activities they do every week. Then they should determine the amount of time they spend on each activity each day. Remind students to give the data table a title. A sample data table is shown below.

Bar Graphs

Focus Have students compare and contrast the data table and the bar graph on this page. Ask: **Why would you make a bar graph if the data are already organized in a table?** *(The bar graph organizes the data in a visual way that makes them easier to interpret.)*

Teach Students can use the data from the data table they created to make a bar graph that shows the amount of time they spend on different activities during a week. The vertical axis should be divided into units of time, such as hours. Remind students to label both axes and give their graph a title. A sample bar graph is shown below.

Creating Data Tables and Graphs

How can you make sense of the data in a science experiment? The first step is to organize the data to help you understand them. Data tables and graphs are helpful tools for organizing data.

Data Tables

You have gathered your materials and set up your experiment. But before you start, you need to plan a way to record what happens during the experiment. By creating a data table, you can record your observations and measurements in an orderly way.

Suppose, for example, that a scientist conducted an experiment to find out how many Calories people of different body masses burn while doing various activities. The data table shows the results.

Notice in this data table that the manipulated variable (body mass) is the heading of one column. The responding variable (for Experiment 1, the number of Calories burned while bicycling) is the heading of the next column. Additional columns were added for related experiments.

Calories Burned in 30 Minutes

Body Mass	Experiment 1: Bicycling	Experiment 2: Playing Basketball	Experiment 3: Watching Television
30 kg	60 Calories	120 Calories	21 Calories
40 kg	77 Calories	164 Calories	27 Calories
50 kg	95 Calories	206 Calories	33 Calories
60 kg	114 Calories	248 Calories	38 Calories

Bar Graphs

To compare how many Calories a person burns doing various activities, you could create a bar graph. A bar graph is used to display data in a number of separate, or distinct, categories. In this example, bicycling, playing basketball, and watching television are the three categories.

To create a bar graph, follow these steps.

1. On graph paper, draw a horizontal, or x-, axis and a vertical, or y-, axis.
2. Write the names of the categories to be graphed along the horizontal axis. Include an overall label for the axis as well.
3. Label the vertical axis with the name of the responding variable. Include units of measurement. Then create a scale along the axis by marking off equally spaced numbers that cover the range of the data collected.
4. For each category, draw a solid bar using the scale on the vertical axis to determine the height. Make all the bars the same width.
5. Add a title that describes the graph.

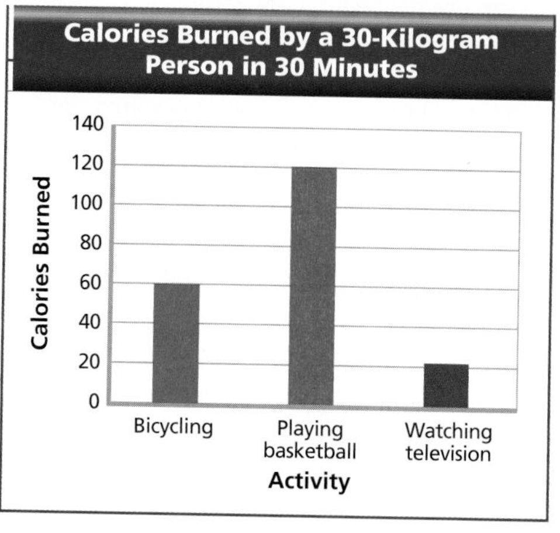

Time Spent on Different Activities in a Week

	Going to Classes	Eating Meals	Playing Soccer	Watching Television
Monday	6	2	2	0.5
Tuesday	6	1.5	1.5	1.5
Wednesday	6	2	1	2
Thursday	6	2	2	1.5
Friday	6	2	2	0.5
Saturday	0	2.5	2.5	1
Sunday	0	3	1	2

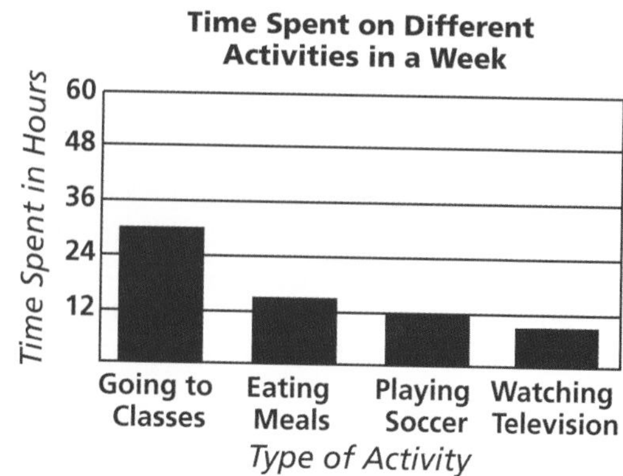

Line Graphs

To see whether a relationship exists between body mass and the number of Calories burned while bicycling, you could create a line graph. A line graph is used to display data that show how one variable (the responding variable) changes in response to another variable (the manipulated variable). You can use a line graph when your manipulated variable is **continuous,** that is, when there are other points between the ones that you tested. In this example, body mass is a continuous variable because there are other body masses between 30 and 40 kilograms (for example, 31 kilograms). Time is another example of a continuous variable.

Line graphs are powerful tools because they allow you to estimate values for conditions that you did not test in the experiment. For example, you can use the line graph to estimate that a 35-kilogram person would burn 68 Calories while bicycling.

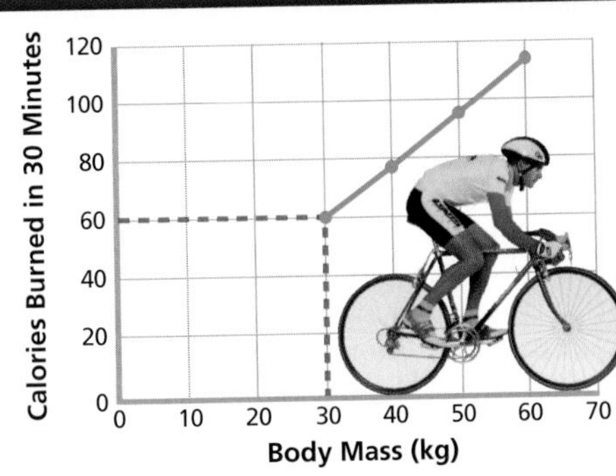

To create a line graph, follow these steps.

1. On graph paper, draw a horizontal, or *x*-, axis and a vertical, or *y*-, axis.
2. Label the horizontal axis with the name of the manipulated variable. Label the vertical axis with the name of the responding variable. Include units of measurement.
3. Create a scale on each axis by marking off equally spaced numbers that cover the range of the data collected.
4. Plot a point on the graph for each piece of data. In the line graph above, the dotted lines show how to plot the first data point (30 kilograms and 60 Calories). Follow an imaginary vertical line extending up from the horizontal axis at the 30-kilogram mark. Then follow an imaginary horizontal line extending across from the vertical axis at the 60-Calorie mark. Plot the point where the two lines intersect.
5. Connect the plotted points with a solid line. (In some cases, it may be more appropriate to draw a line that shows the general trend of the plotted points. In those cases, some of the points may fall above or below the line. Also, not all graphs are linear. It may be more appropriate to draw a curve to connect the points.)
6. Add a title that identifies the variables or relationship in the graph.

Activity

Create line graphs to display the data from Experiment 2 and Experiment 3 in the data table.

Activity

You read in the newspaper that a total of 4 centimeters of rain fell in your area in June, 2.5 centimeters fell in July, and 1.5 centimeters fell in August. What type of graph would you use to display these data? Use graph paper to create the graph.

Inquiry Skills

Line Graphs

Focus Ask: **Would a bar graph show the relationship between body mass and the number of Calories burned in 30 minutes?** *(No. Bar graphs can only show data in distinct categories.)* Explain that line graphs are used to show how one variable changes in response to another variable.

Teach Walk students through the steps involved in creating a line graph using the example illustrated on the page. For example, ask: **What is the label on the horizontal axis? On the vertical axis?** *(Body Mass (kg); Calories Burned in 30 Minutes)* **What scale is used on each axis?** *(10 kg on the x-axis and 20 Calories on the y-axis)* **What does the second data point represent?** *(77 Calories burned for a body mass of 40 kg)* **What trend or pattern does the graph show?** *(The number of Calories burned in 30 minutes of cycling increases with body mass.)*

Activity

Students should make a different graph for each experiment. Each graph should have a different *x*-axis scale that is appropriate for the data. See sample graphs below.

Activity

Students should conclude that a bar graph would be best for displaying the data.

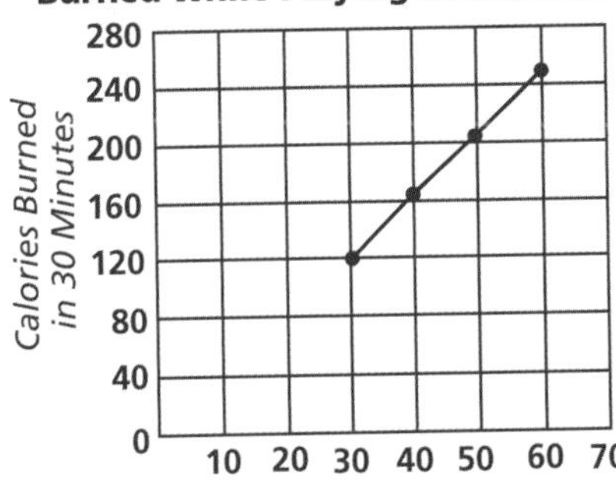

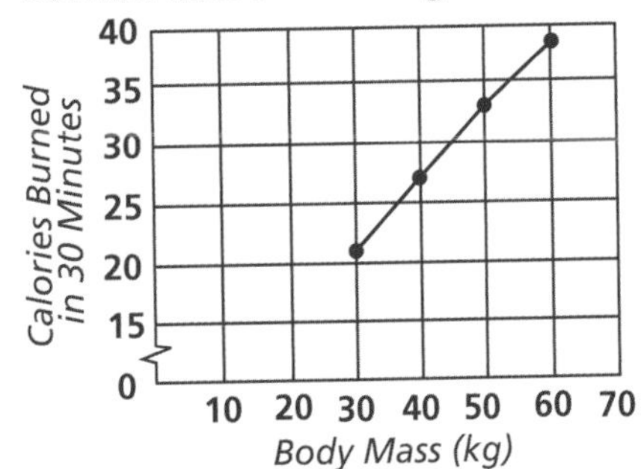

Circle Graphs

Focus Emphasize that a circle graph must include 100 percent of the categories for the topic being graphed. For example, ask: **Could the data in the bar graph titled "Calories Burned by a 30-kilogram Person in Various Activities" (on the previous page) be shown in a circle graph? Why or why not?** *(No. It does not include all the possible ways a 30-kilogram person can burn Calories.)*

Teach Walk students through the steps for making a circle graph. If necessary, help them with the compass and the protractor. Use the protractor to illustrate that a circle has 360 degrees. Make sure students understand the mathematical calculations involved in making a circle graph.

Activity

You might have students work in pairs to complete the activity. Students' circle graphs should look like the graph below.

Ways Students Get to School

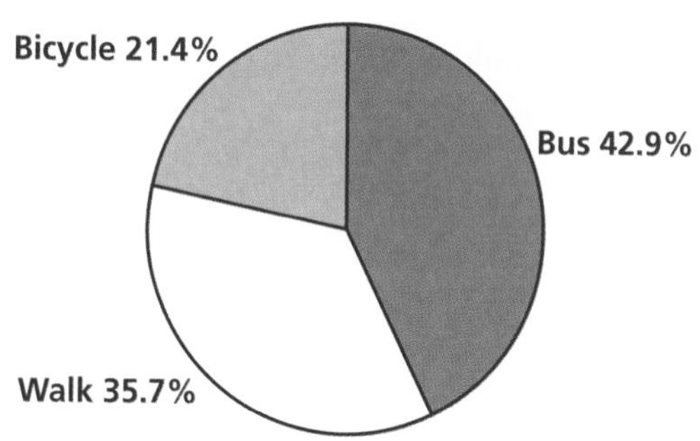

Circle Graphs

Like bar graphs, circle graphs can be used to display data in a number of separate categories. Unlike bar graphs, however, circle graphs can only be used when you have data for *all* the categories that make up a given topic. A circle graph is sometimes called a pie chart. The pie represents the entire topic, while the slices represent the individual categories. The size of a slice indicates what percentage of the whole a particular category makes up.

The data table below shows the results of a survey in which 24 teenagers were asked to identify their favorite sport. The data were then used to create the circle graph at the right.

Favorite Sports

Sport	Students
Soccer	8
Basketball	6
Bicycling	6
Swimming	4

To create a circle graph, follow these steps.

1. Use a compass to draw a circle. Mark the center with a point. Then draw a line from the center point to the top of the circle.
2. Determine the size of each "slice" by setting up a proportion where x equals the number of degrees in a slice. (*Note:* A circle contains 360 degrees.) For example, to find the number of degrees in the "soccer" slice, set up the following proportion:

$$\frac{\text{Students who prefer soccer}}{\text{Total number of students}} = \frac{x}{\text{Total number of degrees in a circle}}$$

$$\frac{8}{24} = \frac{x}{360}$$

Cross-multiply and solve for x.

$$24x = 8 \times 360$$

$$x = 120$$

The "soccer" slice should contain 120 degrees.

Sports That Teens Prefer

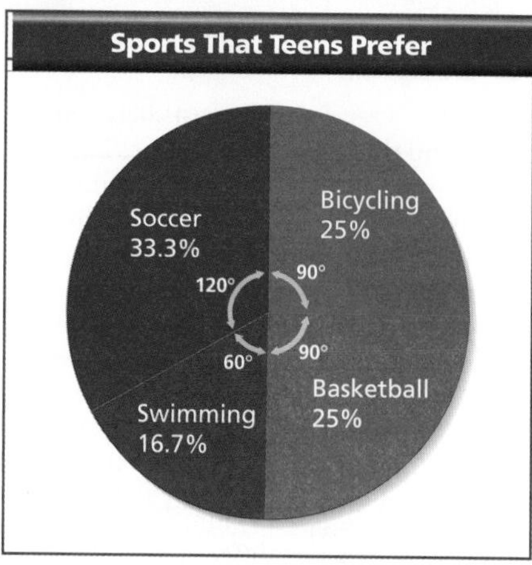

3. Use a protractor to measure the angle of the first slice, using the line you drew to the top of the circle as the 0° line. Draw a line from the center of the circle to the edge for the angle you measured.
4. Continue around the circle by measuring the size of each slice with the protractor. Start measuring from the edge of the previous slice so the wedges do not overlap. When you are done, the entire circle should be filled in.
5. Determine the percentage of the whole circle that each slice represents. To do this, divide the number of degrees in a slice by the total number of degrees in a circle (360), and multiply by 100%. For the "soccer" slice, you can find the percentage as follows:

$$\frac{120}{360} \times 100\% = 33.3\%$$

6. Use a different color for each slice. Label each slice with the category and with the percentage of the whole it represents.
7. Add a title to the circle graph.

Activity

In a class of 28 students, 12 students take the bus to school, 10 students walk, and 6 students ride their bicycles. Create a circle graph to display these data.

Math Review

Scientists use math to organize, analyze, and present data. This appendix will help you review some basic math skills.

Mean, Median, and Mode

The **mean** is the average, or the sum of the data divided by the number of data items. The middle number in a set of ordered data is called the **median.** The **mode** is the number that appears most often in a set of data.

Example

A scientist counted the number of distinct songs sung by seven different male birds and collected the data shown below.

Male Bird Songs

Bird	A	B	C	D	E	F	G
Number of Songs	36	29	40	35	28	36	27

To determine the mean number of songs, add the total number of songs and divide by the number of data items—in this case, the number of male birds.

$$\text{Mean} = \frac{231}{7} = 33 \text{ songs}$$

To find the median number of songs, arrange the data in numerical order and find the number in the middle of the series.

27 28 29 35 36 36 40

The number in the middle is 35, so the median number of songs is 35.

The mode is the value that appears most frequently. In the data, 36 appears twice, while each other item appears only once. Therefore, 36 songs is the mode.

Practice

Find out how many minutes it takes each student in your class to get to school. Then find the mean, median, and mode for the data.

Probability

Probability is the chance that an event will occur. Probability can be expressed as a ratio, a fraction, or a percentage. For example, when you flip a coin, the probability that the coin will land heads up is 1 in 2, or $\frac{1}{2}$, or 50 percent.

The probability that an event will happen can be expressed in the following formula.

$$P(\text{event}) = \frac{\text{Number of times the event can occur}}{\text{Total number of possible events}}$$

Example

A paper bag contains 25 blue marbles, 5 green marbles, 5 orange marbles, and 15 yellow marbles. If you close your eyes and pick a marble from the bag, what is the probability that it will be yellow?

$$P(\text{yellow marbles}) = \frac{\text{15 yellow marbles}}{\text{50 marbles total}}$$

$$P = \frac{15}{50}, \text{ or } \frac{3}{10}, \text{ or } 30\%$$

Practice

Each side of a cube has a letter on it. Two sides have *A*, three sides have *B*, and one side has *C*. If you roll the cube, what is the probability that *A* will land on top?

Math Skills

Math Review

Students can refer to this part of the Skills Handbook whenever they need to review some basic math skills. You can use the activities provided here to teach or reinforce these skills.

Mean, Median, and Mode

Focus Remind students that data from an experiment might consist of hundreds or thousands of numbers. Unless analyzed, the numbers likely will not be helpful.

Teach Work through the process of determining mean, median, and mode using the example in the book. Make sure students realize that these three numbers do not always equal each other. Point out that taken together, these three numbers give more information about the data than just one of the numbers alone.

Practice

Answers will vary based on class data. The mean should equal the total number of minutes divided by the number of students. The median should equal the number in the middle after arranging the data in numerical order. The mode should equal the number of minutes that is given most frequently.

Probability

Focus Show students a coin and ask: **What is the chance that I will get tails when I flip the coin?** *(Some students might know that there is a 1 in 2, or 50 percent, chance of getting tails.)*

Teach Set up a bag of marbles like the one in the example. Allow students to practice determining the probabilities of picking marbles of different colors. Then, encourage them to actually pick marbles and compare their actual results with those results predicted by probability.

Practice

$P(A) = 2$ sides with $\frac{A}{6}$ sides total

$P = \frac{2}{6}$, or $\frac{1}{3}$, or 33%

Area

Focus Ask: **Who knows what area is?** *(Area is equal to the number of square units needed to cover a certain shape or object.)* On the board, write the formulas for the area of a rectangle and a circle.

Teach Give students various objects of different shapes. Have them measure each object and determine its area based on the measurements. Point out that the units of the answer are squared because they are multiplied together. If students are interested, you might also explain that π is equal to the ratio of the circumference of a circle to its diameter. For circles of all sizes, π is approximately equal to the number 3.14, or $\frac{22}{7}$.

Practice

The area of the circle is equal to 21 m × 21 m × $\frac{22}{7}$, or 1,386 m^2.

Circumference

Focus Draw a circle on the board. Then trace the outline with your finger and explain that this is the circumference of the circle, or the distance around it.

Teach Show students that the radius is equal to the distance from the center of the circle to any point on it. Point out that the diameter of a circle is equal to two times the radius. Give students paper circles of various sizes, and have them calculate the circumference of each.

Practice

The circumference is equal to 2 × 28 m × $\frac{22}{7}$, or 176 m.

Volume

Focus Fill a beaker with 100 milliliters of water. Ask: **What is the volume of water?** *(100 milliliters)* Explain that volume is the amount of space that something takes up. Then point out that one milliliter is equal to one cubic centimeter (cm^3).

Teach Write on the board the formulas for calculating the volumes of a rectangle and a cylinder. Point out that volume is equal to the area of an object multiplied by its height. Then measure the beaker to show students the relationship between liquid volume (100 milliliters) and the number of cubic units it contains (100 cubic centimeters).

Area

The **area** of a surface is the number of square units that cover it. The front cover of your textbook has an area of about 600 cm^2.

Area of a Rectangle and a Square To find the area of a rectangle, multiply its length times its width. The formula for the area of a rectangle is

$$A = \ell \times w, \text{ or } A = \ell w$$

Since all four sides of a square have the same length, the area of a square is the length of one side multiplied by itself, or squared.

$$A = s \times s, \text{ or } A = s^2$$

Example

A scientist is studying the plants in a field that measures 75 m × 45 m. What is the area of the field?

$A = \ell \times w$

$A = 75 \text{ m} \times 45 \text{ m}$

$A = 3{,}375 \text{ m}^2$

Area of a Circle The formula for the area of a circle is

$$A = \pi \times r \times r, \text{ or } A = \pi r^2$$

The length of the radius is represented by r, and the value of π is approximately $\frac{22}{7}$.

Example

Find the area of a circle with a radius of 14 cm.

$A = \pi r^2$

$A = 14 \times 14 \times \frac{22}{7}$

$A = 616 \text{ cm}^2$

Practice

Find the area of a circle that has a radius of 21 m.

Circumference

The distance around a circle is called the circumference. The formula for finding the circumference of a circle is

$$C = 2 \times \pi \times r, \text{ or } C = 2\pi r$$

Example

The radius of a circle is 35 cm. What is its circumference?

$C = 2\pi r$

$C = 2 \times 35 \times \frac{22}{7}$

$C = 220 \text{ cm}$

Practice

What is the circumference of a circle with a radius of 28 m?

Volume

The volume of an object is the number of cubic units it contains. The volume of a wastebasket, for example, might be about 26,000 cm^3.

Volume of a Rectangular Object To find the volume of a rectangular object, multiply the object's length times its width times its height.

$$V = \ell \times w \times h, \text{ or } V = \ell wh$$

Example

Find the volume of a box with length 24 cm, width 12 cm, and height 9 cm.

$V = \ell wh$

$V = 24 \text{ cm} \times 12 \text{ cm} \times 9 \text{ cm}$

$V = 2{,}592 \text{ cm}^3$

Practice

What is the volume of a rectangular object with length 17 cm, width 11 cm, and height 6 cm?

Practice

The volume of the rectangular object is equal to 17 cm × 11 cm × 6 cm, or 1,122 cm^3.

Fractions

A **fraction** is a way to express a part of a whole. In the fraction $\frac{4}{7}$, 4 is the numerator and 7 is the denominator.

Adding and Subtracting Fractions To add or subtract two or more fractions that have a common denominator, first add or subtract the numerators. Then write the sum or difference over the common denominator.

To find the sum or difference of fractions with different denominators, first find the least common multiple of the denominators. This is known as the least common denominator. Then convert each fraction to equivalent fractions with the least common denominator. Add or subtract the numerators. Then write the sum or difference over the common denominator.

Example

$\frac{5}{6} - \frac{3}{4} = \frac{10}{12} - \frac{9}{12} = \frac{10-9}{12} = \frac{1}{12}$

Multiplying Fractions To multiply two fractions, first multiply the two numerators, then multiply the two denominators.

Example

$\frac{5}{6} \times \frac{2}{3} = \frac{5 \times 2}{6 \times 3} = \frac{10}{18} = \frac{5}{9}$

Dividing Fractions Dividing by a fraction is the same as multiplying by its reciprocal. Reciprocals are numbers whose numerators and denominators have been switched. To divide one fraction by another, first invert the fraction you are dividing by—in other words, turn it upside down. Then multiply the two fractions.

Example

$\frac{2}{5} \div \frac{7}{8} = \frac{2}{5} \times \frac{8}{7} = \frac{2 \times 8}{5 \times 7} = \frac{16}{35}$

Practice

Solve the following: $\frac{3}{7} \div \frac{4}{5}$.

Decimals

Fractions whose denominators are 10, 100, or some other power of 10 are often expressed as decimals. For example, the fraction $\frac{9}{10}$ can be expressed as the decimal 0.9, and the fraction $\frac{7}{100}$ can be written as 0.07.

Adding and Subtracting With Decimals To add or subtract decimals, line up the decimal points before you carry out the operation.

Example

$$\begin{array}{r} 27.4 \\ +\ 6.19 \\ \hline 33.59 \end{array} \qquad \begin{array}{r} 278.635 \\ -\ 191.4 \\ \hline 87.235 \end{array}$$

Multiplying With Decimals When you multiply two numbers with decimals, the number of decimal places in the product is equal to the total number of decimal places in each number being multiplied.

Example

$$\begin{array}{rl} 46.2 & \text{(one decimal place)} \\ \times\ 2.37 & \text{(two decimal places)} \\ \hline 109.494 & \text{(three decimal places)} \end{array}$$

Dividing With Decimals To divide a decimal by a whole number, put the decimal point in the quotient above the decimal point in the dividend.

Example

$15.5 \div 5$

$$5\overline{)15.5} = 3.1$$

To divide a decimal by a decimal, you need to rewrite the divisor as a whole number. Do this by multiplying both the divisor and dividend by the same multiple of 10.

Example

$1.68 \div 4.2 = 16.8 \div 42$

$$42\overline{)16.8} = 0.4$$

Practice

Multiply 6.21 by 8.5.

Fractions

Focus Draw a circle on the board, and divide it into eight equal sections. Shade in one of the sections, and explain that one out of eight, or one eighth, of the sections is shaded. Also use the circle to show that four eighths is the same as one half.

Teach Write the fraction $\frac{3}{4}$ on the board. Ask: **What is the numerator?** *(Three)* **What is the denominator?** *(Four)* Emphasize that when adding and subtracting fractions, the denominators of the two fractions must be the same. If necessary, review how to find the least common denominator. Remind students that when multiplying and dividing, the denominators do not have to be the same.

Practice

$\frac{3}{7} \div \frac{4}{5} = \frac{3}{7} \times \frac{5}{4} = \frac{15}{28}$

Decimals

Focus Write the number *129.835* on the board. Ask: **What number is in the ones position?** *(9)* **The tenths position?** *(8)* **The hundredths position?** *(3)* Make sure students know that 0.8 is equal to $\frac{8}{10}$ and 0.03 is equal to $\frac{3}{100}$.

Teach Use the examples in the book to review addition, subtraction, multiplication, and division with decimals. Make up a worksheet of similar problems to give students additional practice. Also show students how a fraction is converted to a decimal by dividing the numerator by the denominator. For example, $\frac{1}{2}$ is equal to 0.5.

Practice

$6.21 \times 8.5 = 52.785$

Ratio and Proportion

Focus Differentiate a ratio from a fraction. Remind students that a fraction tells how many parts of the whole. In contrast, a ratio compares two different numbers. For example, $\frac{12}{22}$, or $\frac{6}{11}$, of a class are girls. But the ratio of boys to girls in the class is 10 to 12, or $\frac{5}{6}$.

Teach Use the example in the book to explain how to use a proportion to find an unknown quantity. Provide students with additional practice problems, if needed.

Practice

$6 \times 49 = 7x$

$294 = 7x$

$294 \div 7 = x$

$x = 42$

Percentage

Focus On the board, write $50\% = \frac{50}{100}$. Explain that a percentage is a ratio that compares a number to 100.

Teach Point out that when calculating percentages, you are usually using numbers other than 100. In this case, you set up a proportion. Go over the example in the book. Emphasize that the number representing the total goes on the bottom of the ratio, as does the 100%.

Practice

Students should set up the proportion $\frac{42 \text{ marbles}}{300 \text{ marbles}} = \frac{x\%}{100\%}$

$42 \times 100 = 300x$

$4200 = 300x$

$4200 \div 300 = 14\%$

Ratio and Proportion

A **ratio** compares two numbers by division. For example, suppose a scientist counts 800 wolves and 1,200 moose on an island. The ratio of wolves to moose can be written as a fraction, $\frac{800}{1,200}$, which can be reduced to $\frac{2}{3}$. The same ratio can also be expressed as 2 to 3 or 2 : 3.

A **proportion** is a mathematical sentence saying that two ratios are equivalent. For example, a proportion could state that $\frac{800 \text{ wolves}}{1,200 \text{ moose}} = \frac{2 \text{ wolves}}{3 \text{ moose}}$. You can sometimes set up a proportion to determine or estimate an unknown quantity. For example, suppose a scientist counts 25 beetles in an area of 10 square meters. The scientist wants to estimate the number of beetles in 100 square meters.

Example

1. Express the relationship between beetles and area as a ratio: $\frac{25}{10}$, simplified to $\frac{5}{2}$.
2. Set up a proportion, with x representing the number of beetles. The proportion can be stated as $\frac{5}{2} = \frac{x}{100}$.
3. Begin by cross-multiplying. In other words, multiply each fraction's numerator by the other fraction's denominator.

   $5 \times 100 = 2 \times x$, or $500 = 2x$
4. To find the value of x, divide both sides by 2. The result is 250, or 250 beetles in 100 square meters.

Practice

Find the value of x in the following proportion: $\frac{6}{7} = \frac{x}{49}$.

Percentage

A **percentage** is a ratio that compares a number to 100. For example, there are 37 granite rocks in a collection that consists of 100 rocks. The ratio $\frac{37}{100}$ can be written as 37%. Granite rocks make up 37% of the rock collection.

You can calculate percentages of numbers other than 100 by setting up a proportion.

Example

Rain falls on 9 days out of 30 in June. What percentage of the days in June were rainy?

$$\frac{9 \text{ days}}{30 \text{ days}} = \frac{d\%}{100\%}$$

To find the value of d, begin by cross-multiplying, as for any proportion:

$9 \times 100 = 30 \times d \qquad d = \frac{900}{30} \qquad d = 30$

Practice

There are 300 marbles in a jar, and 42 of those marbles are blue. What percentage of the marbles are blue?

Significant Figures

The **precision** of a measurement depends on the instrument you use to take the measurement. For example, if the smallest unit on the ruler is millimeters, then the most precise measurement you can make will be in millimeters.

The sum or difference of measurements can only be as precise as the least precise measurement being added or subtracted. Round your answer so that it has the same number of digits after the decimal as the least precise measurement. Round up if the last digit is 5 or more, and round down if the last digit is 4 or less.

Example

Subtract a temperature of 5.2°C from the temperature 75.46°C.

$$75.46 - 5.2 = 70.26$$

5.2 has the fewest digits after the decimal, so it is the least precise measurement. Since the last digit of the answer is 6, round up to 3. The most precise difference between the measurements is 70.3°C.

Practice

Add 26.4 m to 8.37 m. Round your answer according to the precision of the measurements.

Significant figures are the number of nonzero digits in a measurement. Zeroes between nonzero digits are also significant. For example, the measurements 12,500 L, 0.125 cm, and 2.05 kg all have three significant figures. When you multiply and divide measurements, the one with the fewest significant figures determines the number of significant figures in your answer.

Example

Multiply 110 g by 5.75 g.

$$110 \times 5.75 = 632.5$$

Because 110 has only two significant figures, round the answer to 630 g.

Scientific Notation

A **factor** is a number that divides into another number with no remainder. In the example, the number 3 is used as a factor four times.

An **exponent** tells how many times a number is used as a factor. For example, $3 \times 3 \times 3 \times 3$ can be written as 3^4. The exponent ^{4} indicates that the number 3 is used as a factor four times. Another way of expressing this is to say that 81 is equal to 3 to the fourth power.

Example

$$3^4 = 3 \times 3 \times 3 \times 3 = 81$$

Scientific notation uses exponents and powers of ten to write very large or very small numbers in shorter form. When you write a number in scientific notation, you write the number as two factors. The first factor is any number between 1 and 10. The second factor is a power of 10, such as 10^3 or 10^6.

Example

The average distance between the planet Mercury and the sun is 58,000,000 km. To write the first factor in scientific notation, insert a decimal point in the original number so that you have a number between 1 and 10. In the case of 58,000,000, the number is 5.8.

To determine the power of 10, count the number of places that the decimal point moved. In this case, it moved 7 places.

$$58{,}000{,}000 \text{ km} = 5.8 \times 10^7 \text{ km}$$

Practice

Express 6,590,000 in scientific notation.

Significant Figures

Focus Measure the length of a paper clip using two different rulers. Use one ruler that is less precise than the other. Compare the two measurements. Ask: **Which measurement is more precise?** *(The ruler with the smallest units will give the more precise measurement.)*

Teach Give students the opportunity to take measurements of an object using tools with different precision. Encourage students to add and subtract their measurements, making sure that they round the answers to reflect the precision of the instruments. Go over the example for significant digits. Check for understanding by asking: **How many significant digits are in the number 324,000?** *(Three)* **In the number 5,901?** *(Four)* **In the number 0.706?** *(Three)* If students need additional practice, create a worksheet with problems in multiplying and dividing numbers with various significant digits.

Practice

26.4 m + 8.37 m = 34.77 m

This answer should be rounded to 34.8 m because the least precise measurement has only one digit after the decimal. This number is rounded up to 8 because the last digit is more than 5.

Scientific Notation

Focus Write a very large number on the board, such as 100 million, using all the zeros. Then, write the number using scientific notation. Ask: **Why do you think scientists prefer to write very large numbers using scientific notation?** *(Possible answers include that it is easier to do calculations, convert units, and make comparisons with other numbers.)*

Teach Go over the examples, and ask: **In the second example, which numbers are the factors?** *(5.8 and 10^7)* **Which number is the exponent?** *(^{7})* Explain that very small numbers have a negative exponent because the decimal point is moved to the right to produce the first factor. For example, 0.00000628 is equal to 6.28×10^{-6}.

Practice

$6{,}590{,}000 = 6.59 \times 10^6$

Reading Comprehension Skills

Students can refer to this part of the Skills Handbook whenever they need to review a reading skill. You can use the activities provided here to teach or reinforce these skills.

Learning From Science Textbooks

Reading in a content area presents challenges different from those encountered when reading fiction. Science texts often have more new vocabulary and more unfamiliar concepts that place greater emphasis on inferential reasoning. Students who can apply reading skills and information-organizing strategies will be more successful in reading and understanding a science textbook.

Activity

Turn with students to the first page of any section. Walk through the Reading Preview with students, showing them the Key Concepts that provide a guiding set of questions that students can answer from the text. Next, point out the Key Terms list, which highlights the science vocabulary. Last, have students find the Target Reading Skill with graphic organizer. Make the connection for students to the help in this Skills Handbook.

All in One Teaching Resources

- Target Reading Skills Handbook

Building Vocabulary

Focus Explain to students that knowing the definitions of key concept words can help them understand what they read.

Teach List on the board strategies to learn the definitions of new terms. Also solicit from students strategies that work for them—drawing a picture for the term, acting it out, or using it in conversation. Challenge students to choose a new strategy to learn the Key Terms in your next section.

Using Prior Knowledge

Focus Explain to students that using prior knowledge helps connect what they already know to what they are about to read.

Teach Point out that prior knowledge might not be accurate because memories have faded or perspectives have changed. Encourage students to ask questions to resolve discrepancies between their prior knowledge and what they have learned.

Asking Questions

Focus Demonstrate to students how to change a text heading into a question to help them anticipate the concepts, facts, and events they will read about.

Teach Encourage students to use this reading skill for the next section they read. Instruct them to turn the text headings into questions. Also challenge students to write at least four *what, how, why, who, when,* or *where* questions. Then, have students evaluate the skill. Ask: **Did asking questions about the text help you focus on the reading and remember what you read?** *(Answers will vary, but encourage honesty.)* If this reading skill didn't help, challenge them to assess why not.

Reading Comprehension Skills

Your textbook is an important source of science information. As you read your science textbook, you will find that the book has been written to assist you in understanding the science concepts.

Learning From Science Textbooks

As you study science in school, you will learn science concepts in a variety of ways. Sometimes you will do interesting activities and experiments to explore science ideas. To fully understand what you observe in experiments and activities, you will need to read your science textbook. To help you read, some of the important ideas are highlighted so that you can easily recognize what they are. In addition, a target reading skill in each section will help you understand what you read.

By using the target reading skills, you will improve your reading comprehension—that is, you will improve your ability to understand what you read. As you learn science, you will build knowledge that will help you understand even more of what you read. This knowledge will help you learn about all the topics presented in this textbook.

And—guess what?—these reading skills can be useful whenever you are reading. Reading to learn is important for your entire life. You have an opportunity to begin that process now.

The target reading skills that will improve your reading comprehension are described below.

Building Vocabulary

To understand the science concepts taught in this textbook, you need to remember the meanings of the Key Terms. One strategy consists of writing the definitions of these terms in your own words. You can also practice using the terms in sentences and make lists of words or phrases you associate with each term.

Using Prior Knowledge

Your prior knowledge is what you already know before you begin to read about a topic. Building on what you already know gives you a head start on learning new information. Before you begin a new assignment, think about what you know. You might page through your reading assignment, looking at the headings and the visuals to spark your memory. You can list what you know in the graphic organizer provided in the section opener. Then, as you read, consider questions like the ones below to connect what you learn to what you already know.

- How does what you learn relate to what you know?
- How did something you already know help you learn something new?
- Did your original ideas agree with what you have just learned? If not, how would you revise your original ideas?

Asking Questions

Asking yourself questions is an excellent way to focus on and remember new information in your textbook. You can learn how to ask good questions.

One way is to turn the text headings into questions. Then your questions can guide you to identify and remember the important information as you read. Look at these examples:

Heading: Using Seismographic Data

Question: How are seismographic data used?

Heading: Kinds of Faults

Question: What are the kinds of faults?

You do not have to limit your questions to the text headings. Ask questions about anything that you need to clarify or that will help you understand the content. *What* and *how* are probably the most common question words, but you may also ask *why, who, when,* or *where* questions. Here is an example:

Properties of Waves

Question	Answer
What is amplitude?	Amplitude is . . .

Previewing Visuals

Visuals are photographs, graphs, tables, diagrams, and illustrations. Visuals, such as this diagram of a normal fault, contain important information. Look at visuals and their captions before you read. This will help you prepare for what you will be reading about.

Often you will be asked what you want to learn about a visual. For example, after you look at the normal fault diagram, you might ask: What is the movement along a normal fault? Questions about visuals give you a purpose for reading—to answer your questions. Previewing visuals also helps you see what you already know.

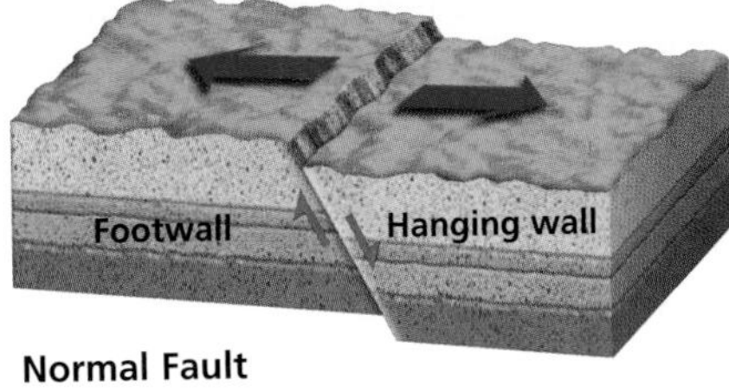

Normal Fault

Outlining

An outline shows the relationship between main ideas and supporting ideas. An outline has a formal structure. You write the main ideas, called topics, next to Roman numerals. The supporting ideas, sometimes called subtopics, are written under the main ideas and labeled A, B, C, and so on. An outline looks like this:

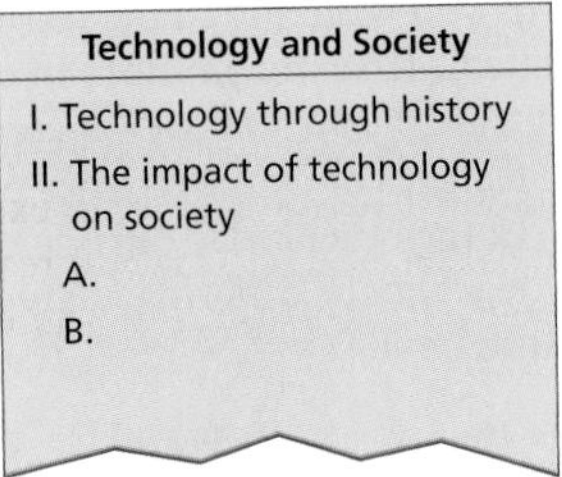

Technology and Society

I. Technology through history
II. The impact of technology on society
   A.
   B.

When you have completed an outline like this, you can see at a glance the structure of the section. You can use this outline as a study tool.

Identifying Main Ideas

When you are reading, it is important to try to understand the ideas and concepts that are in a passage. As you read science material, you will recognize that each paragraph has a lot of information and detail. Good readers try to identify the most important—or biggest—idea in every paragraph or section. That's the main idea. The other information in the paragraph supports or further explains the main idea.

Sometimes main ideas are stated directly. In this book, some main ideas are identified for you as key concepts. These are printed in boldface type. However, you must identify other main ideas yourself. In order to do this, you must identify all the ideas within a paragraph or section. Then ask yourself which idea is big enough to include all the other ideas.

Previewing Visuals

Focus Explain to students that looking at the visuals before reading will help them activate prior knowledge and predict what they are about to read.

Teach Assign a section for students to preview the visuals. First, instruct them to write a sentence describing what the section will be about. Then, encourage them to write one or two questions for each visual to give purpose to their reading. Also have them list any prior knowledge about the subject.

Outlining

Focus Explain that using an outline format helps organize information by main topic, subtopic, and details.

Teach Choose a section in the book, and demonstrate how to make an outline for it. Make sure students understand the structure of the outline by asking: **Is this a topic or a subtopic? Where does this information go in the outline? Would I write this heading next to a Roman numeral or a capital letter?** *(Answers depend on the section being outlined.)* Also show them how to indent and add details to the outline using numerals and lowercase letters.

Identifying Main Ideas

Focus Explain that identifying main ideas and details helps sort the facts from the information into groups. Each group can have a main topic, subtopics, and details.

Teach Tell students that paragraphs are often written so that the main idea is in the first or second sentence, or in the last sentence. Assign students a page in the book. Instruct them to write the main idea for each paragraph on that page. If students have difficulty finding the main idea, suggest that they list all of the ideas given in the paragraph, and then choose the idea that is big enough to include all the others.

Comparing and Contrasting

Focus Explain that comparing and contrasting information shows how concepts, facts, and events are similar or different. The results of the comparison can have importance.

Teach Point out that Venn diagrams work best when comparing two things. To compare more than two things, students should use a compare/contrast table. Have students make a Venn diagram or compare/contrast table using two or more different sports or other activities, such as playing musical instruments. Emphasize that students should select characteristics that highlight the similarities and differences in the activities.

Sequencing

Focus Tell students that organizing information from beginning to end will help them understand a step-by-step process.

Teach Encourage students to create a flowchart to show the things they did this morning to get ready for school. Remind students that a flowchart should show the correct order in which events occur. *(A typical flowchart might include: got up ➛ took a shower ➛ got dressed ➛ ate breakfast ➛ brushed teeth ➛ gathered books and homework ➛ put on jacket.)* Then explain that a cycle diagram shows a sequence of events that is continuous. Challenge students to create a cycle diagram that shows how the weather changes with the seasons where they live. *(Most cycle diagrams will include four steps, one for each season.)*

Comparing and Contrasting

When you compare and contrast, you examine the similarities and differences between things. You can compare and contrast in a Venn diagram or in a table. Your completed diagram or table shows you how the items are alike and how they are different.

Venn Diagram A Venn diagram consists of two overlapping circles. In the space where the circles overlap, you write the characteristics that the two items have in common. In one of the circles outside the area of overlap, you write the differing features or characteristics of one of the items. In the other circle outside the area of overlap, you write the differing characteristics of the other item.

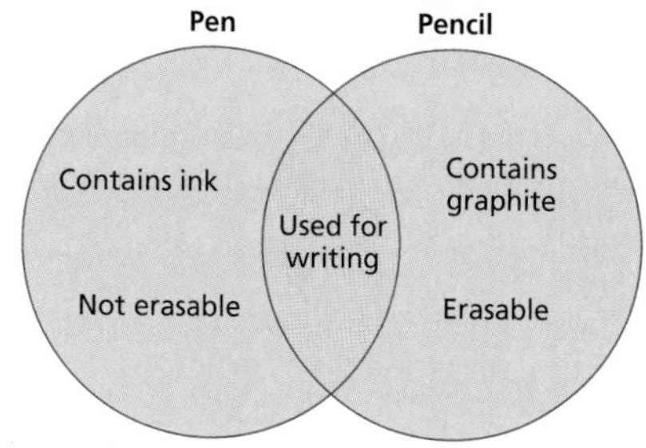

Table In a compare/contrast table, you list the items to be compared across the top of the table. Then list the characteristics or features to be compared in the left column. Complete the table by filling in information about each characteristic or feature.

Blood Vessel	Function	Structure of Wall
Artery	Carries blood away from heart	
Capillary		
Vein		

Sequencing

A sequence is the order in which a series of events occurs. Recognizing and remembering the sequence of events is important to understanding many processes in science. Sometimes the text uses words like *first, next, during*, and *after* to signal a sequence. A flowchart or a cycle diagram can help you visualize a sequence.

Flowchart To make a flowchart, write a brief description of each step or event in a box. Place the boxes in order, with the first event at the top of the page. Then draw an arrow to connect each step or event to the next.

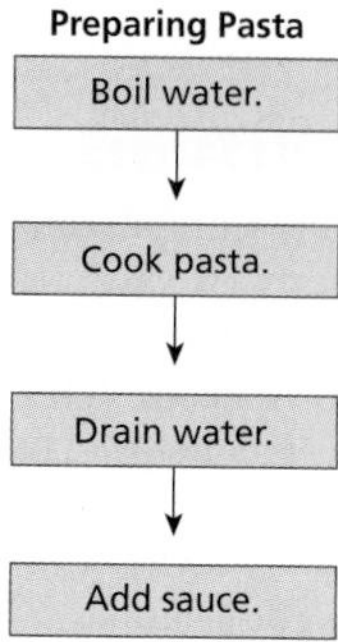

Cycle Diagram A cycle diagram shows a sequence that is continuous, or cyclical. A continuous sequence does not have an end because when the final event is over, the first event begins again. To create a cycle diagram, write the starting event in a box placed at the top of a page in the center. Then, moving in a clockwise direction around an imaginary circle, write each event in a box in its proper sequence. Draw arrows that connect each event to the one that occurs next, forming a continuous circle.

Identifying Supporting Evidence

A hypothesis is a possible explanation for observations made by scientists or an answer to a scientific question. A hypothesis is tested over and over again. The tests may produce evidence that supports the hypothesis. When enough supporting evidence is collected, a hypothesis may become a theory.

Identifying the supporting evidence for a hypothesis or theory can help you understand the hypothesis or theory. Evidence consists of facts—information whose accuracy can be confirmed by testing or observation.

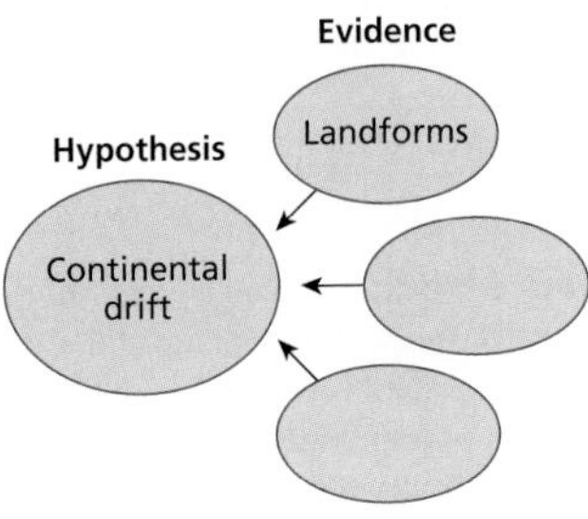

Relating Cause and Effect

Identifying causes and effects helps you understand relationships among events. A cause makes something happen. An effect is what happens. When you recognize that one event causes another, you are relating cause and effect. Words like *cause, because, effect, affect,* and *result* often signal a cause or an effect.

Sometimes an effect can have more than one cause, or a cause can produce several effects. For example, car exhaust and smoke from industrial plants are two causes of air pollution. Some effects of air pollution include breathing difficulties for some people, death of plants along some highways, and damage to some building surfaces.

Science involves many cause-and-effect relationships. Seeing and understanding these relationships helps you understand science processes.

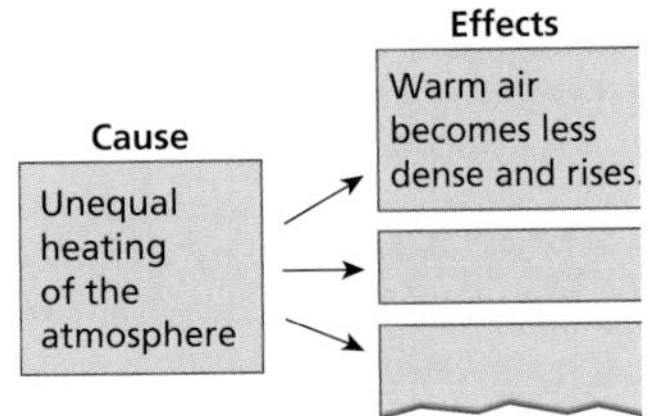

Concept Mapping

Concept maps are useful tools for organizing information on any topic. A concept map begins with a main idea or core concept and shows how the idea can be subdivided into related subconcepts or smaller ideas. In this way, relationships between concepts become clearer and easier to understand.

You construct a concept map by placing concepts (usually nouns) in ovals and connecting them with linking words. The biggest concept or idea is placed in an oval at the top of the map. Related concepts are arranged in ovals below the big idea. The linking words are often verbs and verb phrases and are written on the lines that connect the ovals.

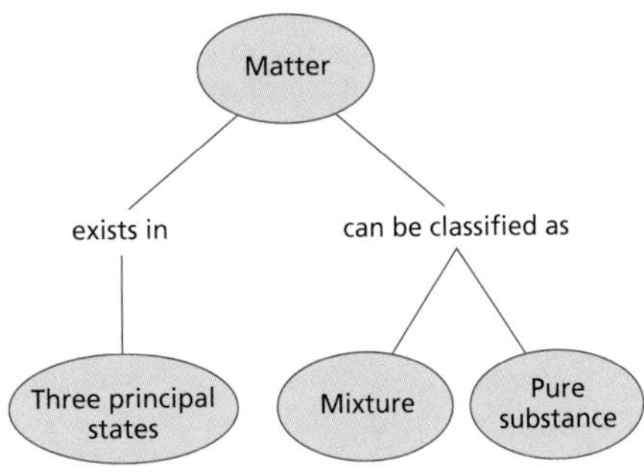

Identifying Supporting Evidence

Focus Explain to students that identifying the supporting evidence will help them to understand the relationship between the facts and the hypothesis.

Teach Remind students that a hypothesis is neither right nor wrong, but it is either supported or not supported by the evidence from testing or observation. If evidence is found that does not support a hypothesis, the hypothesis can be changed to accommodate the new evidence, or it can be dropped.

Relating Cause and Effect

Focus Explain to students that cause is the reason for what happens. The effect is what happens in response to the cause. Relating cause and effect helps students relate the reason for what happens to what happens as a result.

Teach Emphasize that not all events that occur together have a cause-and-effect relationship. For example, tell students that you went to the grocery store and your car stalled. Ask: **Is there a cause-and-effect relationship in this situation? Explain.** *(No. Going to the grocery store could not cause a car to stall. There must be another cause to make the car stall.)*

Concept Mapping

Focus Elicit from students how a map shows the relationship of one geographic area to another. Connect this idea to how a concept map shows the relationship between terms and concepts.

Teach Challenge students to make a concept map with at least three levels of concepts to organize information about types of transportation. All students should start with the phrase *Types of transportation* at the top of the concept map. After that point, their concepts may vary. *(For example, some students might place* private transportation *and* public transportation *at the next level, while other students might choose* human-powered *and* gas-powered.*)* Make sure students connect the concepts with linking words.

- Complete student edition
- Video and audio
- Simulations and activities
- Section and chapter activities

Laboratory Safety

Laboratory safety is an essential element of a successful science class. Students need to understand exactly what is safe and unsafe behavior and what the rationale is behind each safety rule.

All in One Teaching Resources

- Laboratory Safety Teacher Notes
- Laboratory Safety Rules
- Laboratory Safety Symbols
- Laboratory Safety Contract

General Precautions

- Post safety rules in the classroom, and review them regularly with students before beginning every science activity.
- Familiarize yourself with the safety procedures for each activity before introducing it to your students.
- For open-ended activities like Chapter Projects, have students submit their procedures or design plans in writing and check them for safety considerations.
- Always act as an exemplary role model by displaying safe behavior.
- Know how to use safety equipment, such as fire extinguishers and fire blankets, and always have it accessible.
- Have students practice leaving the classroom quickly and orderly to prepare them for emergencies.
- Explain to students how to use the intercom or other available means of communication to get help during an emergency.
- Never leave students unattended while they are engaged in science activities.
- Provide enough space for students to safely carry out science activities.
- Instruct students to report all accidents and injuries to you immediately.

Appendix A Laboratory Safety

Safety Symbols

These symbols warn of possible dangers in the laboratory and remind you to work carefully.

Safety Goggles Wear safety goggles to protect your eyes in any activity involving chemicals, flames or heating, or glassware.

Lab Apron Wear a laboratory apron to protect your skin and clothing from damage.

Breakage Handle breakable materials, such as glassware, with care. Do not touch broken glassware.

Heat-Resistant Gloves Use an oven mitt or other hand protection when handling hot materials such as hot plates or hot glassware.

Plastic Gloves Wear disposable plastic gloves when working with harmful chemicals and organisms. Keep your hands away from your face, and dispose of the gloves according to your teacher's instructions.

Heating Use a clamp or tongs to pick up hot glassware. Do not touch hot objects with your bare hands.

Flames Before you work with flames, tie back loose hair and clothing. Follow instructions from your teacher about lighting and extinguishing flames.

No Flames When using flammable materials, make sure there are no flames, sparks, or other exposed heat sources present.

Corrosive Chemical Avoid getting acid or other corrosive chemicals on your skin or clothing or in your eyes. Do not inhale the vapors. Wash your hands after the activity.

Poison Do not let any poisonous chemical come into contact with your skin, and do not inhale its vapors. Wash your hands when you are finished with the activity.

Fumes Work in a ventilated area when harmful vapors may be involved. Avoid inhaling vapors directly. Only test an odor when directed to do so by your teacher, and use a wafting motion to direct the vapor toward your nose.

Sharp Object Scissors, scalpels, knives, needles, pins, and tacks can cut your skin. Always direct a sharp edge or point away from yourself and others.

Animal Safety Treat live or preserved animals or animal parts with care to avoid harming the animals or yourself. Wash your hands when you are finished with the activity.

Plant Safety Handle plants only as directed by your teacher. If you are allergic to certain plants, tell your teacher; do not do an activity involving those plants. Avoid touching harmful plants such as poison ivy. Wash your hands when you are finished with the activity.

Electric Shock To avoid electric shock, never use electrical equipment around water, or when the equipment is wet or your hands are wet. Be sure cords are untangled and cannot trip anyone. Unplug equipment not in use.

Physical Safety When an experiment involves physical activity, avoid injuring yourself or others. Alert your teacher if there is any reason you should not participate.

Disposal Dispose of chemicals and other laboratory materials safely. Follow the instructions from your teacher.

Hand Washing Wash your hands thoroughly when finished with the activity. Use antibacterial soap and warm water. Rinse well.

General Safety Awareness When this symbol appears, follow the instructions provided. When you are asked to develop your own procedure in a lab, have your teacher approve your plan before you go further.

198 ◆ H

End-of-Experiment Rules

- Always have students use warm water and soap for washing their hands.

Heating and Fire Safety

- No flammable substances should be in use around hot plates, light bulbs, or open flames.
- Test tubes should be heated only in water baths.
- Students should be permitted to strike matches to light candles or burners *only* with strict supervision. When possible, you should light the flames, especially when working with younger students.
- Be sure to have proper ventilation when fumes are produced during a procedure.
- All electrical equipment used in the lab should have GFI (Ground Fault Interrupter) switches.

Science Safety Rules

General Precautions
Follow all instructions. Never perform activities without the approval and supervision of your teacher. Do not engage in horseplay. Never eat or drink in the laboratory. Keep work areas clean and uncluttered.

Dress Code
Wear safety goggles whenever you work with chemicals, glassware, heat sources such as burners, or any substance that might get into your eyes. If you wear contact lenses, notify your teacher.

Wear a lab apron or coat whenever you work with corrosive chemicals or substances that can stain. Wear disposable plastic gloves when working with organisms and harmful chemicals. Tie back long hair. Remove or tie back any article of clothing or jewelry that can hang down and touch chemicals, flames, or equipment. Roll up long sleeves. Never wear open shoes or sandals.

First Aid
Report all accidents, injuries, or fires to your teacher, no matter how minor. Be aware of the location of the first-aid kit, emergency equipment such as the fire extinguisher and fire blanket, and the nearest telephone. Know whom to contact in an emergency.

Heating and Fire Safety
Keep all combustible materials away from flames. When heating a substance in a test tube, make sure that the mouth of the tube is not pointed at you or anyone else. Never heat a liquid in a closed container. Use an oven mitt to pick up a container that has been heated.

Using Chemicals Safely
Never put your face near the mouth of a container that holds chemicals. Never touch, taste, or smell a chemical unless your teacher tells you to.

Use only those chemicals needed in the activity. Keep all containers closed when chemicals are not being used. Pour all chemicals over the sink or a container, not over your work surface. Dispose of excess chemicals as instructed by your teacher.

Be extra careful when working with acids or bases. When mixing an acid and water, always pour the water into the container first and then add the acid to the water. Never pour water into an acid. Wash chemical spills and splashes immediately with plenty of water.

Using Glassware Safely
If glassware is broken or chipped, notify your teacher immediately. Never handle broken or chipped glass with your bare hands.

Never force glass tubing or thermometers into a rubber stopper or rubber tubing. Have your teacher insert the glass tubing or thermometer if required for an activity.

Using Sharp Instruments
Handle sharp instruments with extreme care. Never cut material toward you; cut away from you.

Animal and Plant Safety
Never perform experiments that cause pain, discomfort, or harm to animals. Only handle animals if absolutely necessary. If you know that you are allergic to certain plants, molds, or animals, tell your teacher before doing an activity in which these are used. Wash your hands thoroughly after any activity involving animals, animal parts, plants, plant parts, or soil.

During field work, wear long pants, long sleeves, socks, and closed shoes. Avoid poisonous plants and fungi as well as plants with thorns.

End-of-Experiment Rules
Unplug all electrical equipment. Clean up your work area. Dispose of waste materials as instructed by your teacher. Wash your hands after every experiment.

Using Glassware Safely
- Use plastic containers, graduated cylinders, and beakers whenever possible. If using glass, students should wear safety goggles.
- Use only nonmercury thermometers with anti-roll protectors.

Using Chemicals Safely
- When students use both chemicals and microscopes in one activity, microscopes should be in a separate part of the room from the chemicals so that when students remove their goggles to use the microscopes, their eyes are not at risk.

Handling Organisms Safely
- In an activity where students are directed to taste something, be sure to store the material in clean, *nonscience* containers. Distribute the material to students in *new* plastic or paper dispensables, which should be discarded after the tasting. Tasting or eating should never be done in a lab classroom.
- When growing bacterial cultures, use only disposable petri dishes. After streaking, the dishes should be sealed and not opened again by students. After the lab, students should return the unopened dishes to you.
- Two methods are recommended for the safe disposal of bacterial cultures. *First method:* Autoclave the petri dishes and discard them without opening. *Second method:* If no autoclave is available, carefully open the dishes (never have a student do this), pour full-strength bleach into the dishes, and let them stand for a day. Then pour the bleach from the petri dishes down a drain, and flush the drain with lots of water. Tape the petri dishes back together, and place them in a sealed plastic bag. Wrap the plastic bag with a brown paper bag or newspaper, and tape securely. Throw the sealed package in the trash. Thoroughly disinfect the work area with bleach.
- To grow mold, use a new, sealable plastic bag that is two to three times larger than the material to be placed inside. Seal the bag and tape it shut. After the bag is sealed, students should not open it. To dispose of the bag and mold culture, make a small cut near an edge of the bag, and cook the bag in a microwave oven on a high setting for at least one minute. Discard the bag according to local ordinance, usually in the trash.
- Students should wear disposable nitrile, latex, or food-handling gloves when handling live animals or nonliving specimens.

The microscope is an essential tool in the study of life science. It allows you to see things that are too small to be seen with the unaided eye.

You will probably use a compound microscope like the one you see here. The compound microscope has more than one lens that magnifies the object you view.

Typically, a compound microscope has one lens in the eyepiece, the part you look through. The eyepiece lens usually magnifies 10 ×. Any object you view through this lens would appear 10 times larger than it is.

The compound microscope may contain one or two other lenses called objective lenses. If there are two objective lenses, they are called the low-power and high-power objective lenses. The low-power objective lens usually magnifies 10 ×. The high-power objective lens usually magnifies 40 ×.

To calculate the total magnification with which you are viewing an object, multiply the magnification of the eyepiece lens by the magnification of the objective lens you are using. For example, the eyepiece's magnification of 10 × multiplied by the low-power objective's magnification of 10 × equals a total magnification of 100 ×.

Use the photo of the compound microscope to become familiar with the parts of the microscope and their functions.

The Parts of a Compound Microscope

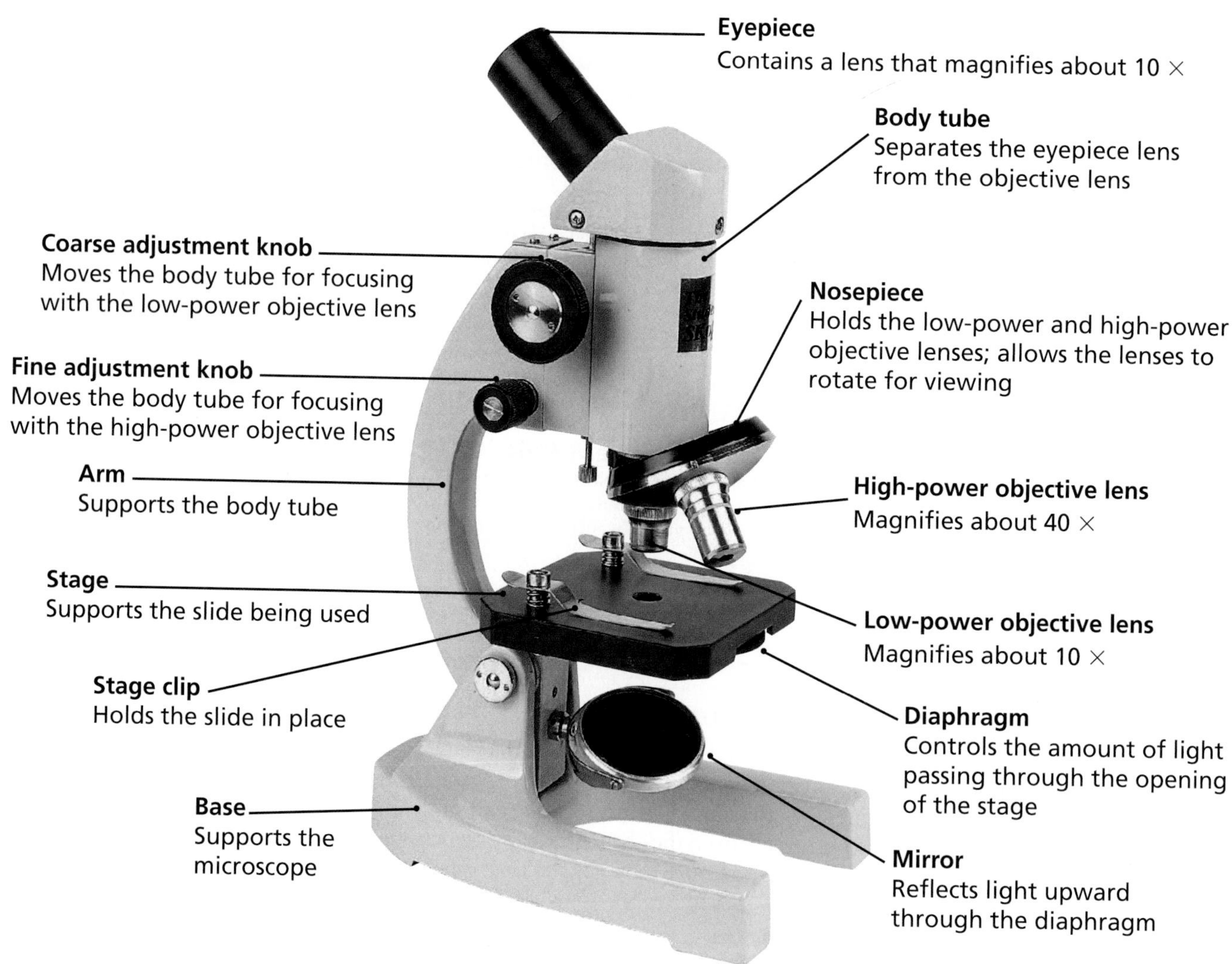

Using the Microscope

Use the following procedures when you are working with a microscope.

1. To carry the microscope, grasp the microscope's arm with one hand. Place your other hand under the base.
2. Place the microscope on a table with the arm toward you.
3. Turn the coarse adjustment knob to raise the body tube.
4. Revolve the nosepiece until the low-power objective lens clicks into place.
5. Adjust the diaphragm. While looking through the eyepiece, also adjust the mirror until you see a bright white circle of light. **CAUTION:** *Never use direct sunlight as a light source.*
6. Place a slide on the stage. Center the specimen over the opening on the stage. Use the stage clips to hold the slide in place. **CAUTION:** *Glass slides are fragile.*
7. Look at the stage from the side. Carefully turn the coarse adjustment knob to lower the body tube until the low-power objective almost touches the slide.
8. Looking through the eyepiece, very slowly turn the coarse adjustment knob until the specimen comes into focus.
9. To switch to the high-power objective lens, look at the microscope from the side. Carefully revolve the nosepiece until the high-power objective lens clicks into place. Make sure the lens does not hit the slide.
10. Looking through the eyepiece, turn the fine adjustment knob until the specimen comes into focus.

Making a Wet-Mount Slide

Use the following procedures to make a wet-mount slide of a specimen.

1. Obtain a clean microscope slide and a coverslip. **CAUTION:** *Glass slides and coverslips are fragile.*
2. Place the specimen on the slide. The specimen must be thin enough for light to pass through it.
3. Using a plastic dropper, place a drop of water on the specimen.
4. Gently place one edge of the coverslip against the slide so that it touches the edge of the water drop at a 45° angle. Slowly lower the coverslip over the specimen. If air bubbles are trapped beneath the coverslip, tap the coverslip gently with the eraser end of a pencil.
5. Remove any excess water at the edge of the coverslip with a paper towel.

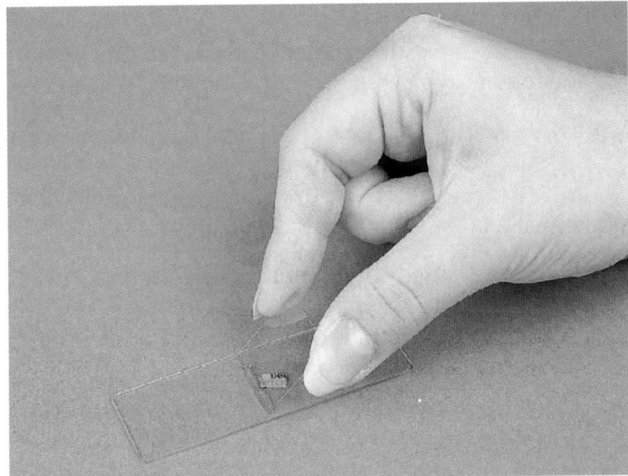

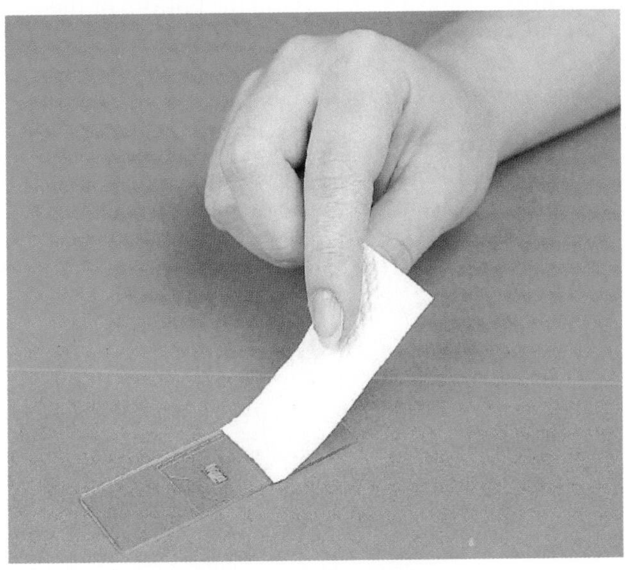

English and Spanish Glossary

A

abyssal plain A smooth, nearly flat region of the deep ocean floor. (p. 135)
llanura abisal Región llana, casi plana, de la cuenca oceánica profunda.

acid rain Rain or another form of precipitation that is more acidic than normal, caused by the release of molecules of sulfur dioxide and nitrogen oxide into the air. (p. 73)
lluvia ácida Lluvia u otra forma de precipitación que es más ácida de lo normal, debido a la contaminación del aire con moléculas de dióxido de azufre y óxido de nitrógeno.

aquaculture The farming of saltwater and freshwater organisms. (p. 160)
acuicultura Crianza de organismos de agua salada y dulce.

aquifer An underground layer of rock or sediment that holds water. (p. 36)
acuífero Capa subterránea de roca o sedimento que retiene agua.

artesian well A well in which water rises because of pressure within the aquifer. (p. 38)
pozo artesiano Pozo por el que el agua se eleva debido a la presión dentro del acuífero.

atoll A ring-shaped coral reef that surrounds a shallow lagoon. (p. 152)
atolón Arrecife coralino con forma de anillo que rodea a una laguna poco profunda.

B

benthos Organisms that live on the bottom of the ocean or other body of water. (p. 143)
bentos Organismos que viven en el fondo del océano u otro cuerpo de agua.

bioluminescence The production of light by living things. (p. 156)
bioluminiscencia Producción de luz por seres vivos.

C

capillary action The combined force of attraction among water molecules and with the molecules of surrounding materials. (p. 8)
acción capilar Fuerza de atracción combinada entre las moléculas de agua y entre esas moléculas y los materiales circundantes.

climate The pattern of temperature and precipitation typical of an area over a long period of time. (p. 118)
clima Patrón de temperatura y precipitación típico de un área a lo largo de mucho tiempo.

coagulation The process by which particles in a liquid clump together. (p. 60)
coagulación Proceso por el cual partículas presentes en un líquido forman cúmulos.

concentration The amount of one substance in a certain volume of another substance. (p. 58)
concentración Cantidad de una sustancia que hay en cierto volumen de otra sustancia.

condensation The process by which a gas changes to a liquid. (p. 11)
condensación Proceso por el cual un gas se convierte en líquido.

conservation The practice of using less of a resource so that it will not be used up. (p. 52)
conservación Práctica de usar menos de un recurso para que no se agote.

continental shelf A gently sloping, shallow area of the ocean floor that extends outward from the edge of a continent. (p. 134)
plataforma continental Área poco profunda con pendiente suave en la cuenca oceánica que se extiende desde los márgenes de un continente.

continental slope A steep incline of the ocean floor leading down from the edge of the continental shelf. (p. 134)
talud continental Región de la cuenca oceánica con pendiente empinada que baja del borde de la plataforma continental.

Coriolis effect The effect of Earth's rotation on the direction of winds and currents. (p. 117)
efecto Coriolis Efecto de la rotación terrestre sobre la dirección de los vientos y las corrientes.

current A large stream of moving water that flows through the oceans. (p. 116)
corriente Un gran volumen de agua que fluye por los océanos.

D

desalination The process of obtaining fresh water from salt water by removing the salt. (p. 54)
desalinización Proceso mediante el cual se obtiene agua dulce a partir de agua salada eliminando la sal.

divide A ridge of land that separates one watershed from another. (p. 21)
divisoria Elevación de terreno que separa una cuenca hidrográfica de otra.

drought A long period of scarce rainfall. (p. 78)
sequía Período largo de escasas lluvias.

E

El Niño An abnormal climate event that occurs every two to seven years in the Pacific Ocean, causing changes in winds, currents, and weather patterns for one to two years. (p. 119)
El Niño Suceso climático anormal que se presenta cada dos a siete años en el océano Pacífico y que causa cambios en los vientos, corrientes y patrones meteorológicos que duran uno o dos años.

estuary A coastal inlet or bay where fresh water from rivers mixes with salty ocean water. (p. 148)
estuario Ensenada o bahía costera donde el agua dulce de los ríos se mezcla con el agua salada del mar.

eutrophication The process by which nutrients in a lake build up over time and cause an increase in the growth of algae. (p. 26)
eutroficación Proceso por el cual se van acumulando nutrientes en un lago y producen un aumento en el crecimiento de algas.

evaporation The process by which molecules at the surface of a liquid absorb enough energy to change to the gaseous state. (p. 10)
evaporación Proceso por el cual las moléculas en la superficie de un líquido absorben suficiente energía para pasar al estado gaseoso.

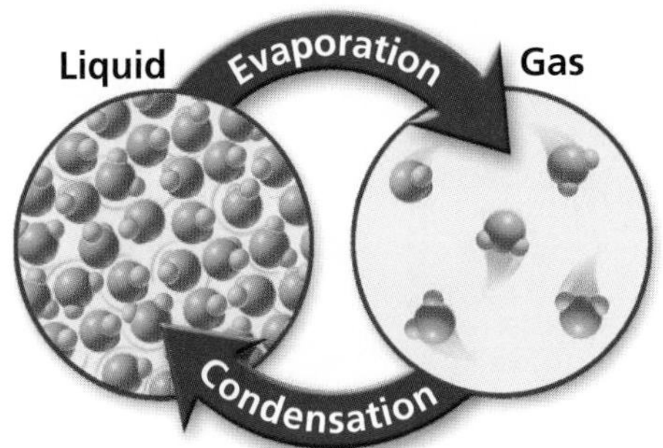

F

filtration The process of passing water through a series of screens that allow the water through, but not larger solid particles. (p. 60)
filtración Proceso en el que el agua pasa por una serie de mallas que impiden el paso de partículas sólidas grandes.

flash flood A sudden, violent flood that occurs within a few hours, or even minutes, of a storm. (p. 81)
torrente Inundación repentina y violenta que ocurre en unas pocas horas, o incluso minutos, después de iniciada una tormenta.

food web The feeding relationships in a habitat. (p. 144)
red alimentaria Relaciones de alimentación en un hábitat.

frequency The number of waves that pass a specific point in a given amount of time. (p. 96)
frecuencia Número de ondas u olas que pasan por un punto dado en cierto tiempo.

groin A wall made of rocks or concrete that is built outward from a beach to reduce erosion. (p. 101)
escollera Pared de piedra o concreto que se construye perpendicularmente a una playa para reducir la erosión.

groundwater Water that fills the cracks and spaces in underground soil and rock layers. (p. 15)
aguas freáticas Agua que llena las grietas y espacios de capas subterráneas de suelo y roca.

habitat The place where an organism lives and where it obtains all the things it needs to survive. (p. 13)
hábitat Lugar donde vive un organismo y donde obtiene todo lo que necesita para sobrevivir.

hardness The level of the minerals calcium and magnesium in water. (p. 59)
dureza Cantidad de los minerales calcio y magnesio que contiene el agua.

hydroelectric power Electricity produced by the kinetic energy of water moving over a waterfall or dam. (p. 85)
energía hidroeléctrica Electricidad producida a partir de la energía cinética del agua que baja por una catarata o presa.

hydrothermal vent An area where ocean water sinks through cracks in the ocean floor, is heated by the underlying magma, and rises again through the cracks. (p. 157)
chimenea hidrotermal Área en la que aguas oceánicas se cuelan por grietas del suelo oceánico, son calentadas por el magma subyacente y ascienden otra vez por las grietas.

impermeable A characteristic of materials, such as clay and granite, through which water does not easily pass. (p. 35)
impermeable Característica de los materiales, como la arcilla y el granito, que no dejan pasar fácilmente el agua.

intertidal zone An area that stretches from the highest high-tide line on land out to the point on the continental shelf exposed by the lowest low tide. (p. 142)
zona intermareal Área que se extiende desde la línea más alta de pleamar en tierra hasta el punto de la plataforma continental expuesto por la bajamar más baja.

irrigation The process of supplying water to areas of land to make them suitable for growing crops. (p. 51)
irrigación Proceso mediante el cual se suministra agua a áreas de terreno para que pueda sembrarse en ellas.

kinetic energy The form of energy that an object has when it is moving. (p. 85)
energía cinética Forma de energía que tiene un objeto cuando está en movimiento.

levee A long ridge formed by deposits of sediments alongside a river channel. (p. 83)
ribero Elevación larga formada por depósitos de sedimentos a lo largo del cauce de un río.

longshore drift The movement of sand along a beach. (p. 99)
deriva litoral Movimiento de arena a lo largo de una playa.

204 • H

mid-ocean ridge A continuous range of mountains on the ocean floor that winds around Earth. (p. 135)
dorsal oceánica Cordillera continua en el suelo oceánico que serpentea por todo la Tierra.

neap tide A tide with the least difference between low and high tide that occurs when the sun and moon pull at right angles to each other at the first and third quarters of the moon. (p. 104)
marea muerta Marea con la mínima diferencia entre pleamar y bajamar; se presenta cuando el Sol y la Luna ejercen su atracción en direcciones que forman un ángulo recto, durante los cuartos creciente y menguante de la Luna.

nekton Free-swimming animals that can move throughout the water column. (p. 143)
necton Animales que nadan libremente y pueden desplazarse por la columna de agua.

neritic zone The area of the ocean that extends from the low-tide line out to the edge of the continental shelf. (p. 142)
zona nerítica Área del océano que se extiende desde la línea de bajamar hasta el borde de la plataforma continental.

nodule A lump on the ocean floor that forms when metals such as manganese build up around pieces of shell. (p. 162)
nódulo Protuberancia formada en el suelo oceánico cuando metales, como el manganeso, se depositan sobre pedazos de concha.

nonpoint source A widely spread source of pollution that is difficult to link to a specific point of origin. (p. 69)
fuente dispersa Fuente muy extendida de contaminación que es difícil vincular a un punto específico de origen.

nutrient A substance such as nitrogen or phosphorus that enables plants and algae to grow. (p. 26)
nutriente Sustancia, como el nitrógeno o el fósforo, que permite el crecimiento de plantas y algas.

open-ocean zone The deepest, darkest area of the ocean beyond the edge of the continental shelf. (p. 142)
zona de mar abierto Zona más profunda y oscura del océano, más allá de la plataforma continental.

permeable A characteristic of materials, such as sand and gravel, through which water easily passes. (p. 35)
permeable Característica de materiales, como la arena y la grava, por los que pasa fácilmente el agua.

pesticide A chemical intended to kill insects and other organisms that damage crops. (p. 74)
pesticida Sustancia química empleada para matar insectos y otros organismos que dañan los cultivos.

pH The measurement of how acidic or basic a substance is, on a scale of 0 (very acidic) to 14 (very basic). (p. 58)
pH Medida de qué tan ácida o básica es una sustancia, en una escala de 0 (muy ácida) a 14 (muy básica).

photosynthesis The process by which plants use water, along with carbon dioxide and energy from the sun, to make their own food. (p. 13)
fotosíntesis Proceso por el cual las plantas usan el agua, el dióxido de carbono y la energía del Sol para elaborar su propio alimento.

plankton Tiny algae and animals that float in water and are carried by waves and currents. (p. 143)
plancton Algas y animales diminutos que flotan en el agua a merced de las olas y las corrientes.

plate One of the major pieces of solid rock that make up Earth's upper layer. (p. 137)
placa Una de las grandes piezas de roca sólida que componen la capa superior de la Tierra.

point source A specific source of pollution that can be identified. (p. 69)
fuente localizada Fuente específica de contaminación que puede identificarse.

polar molecule A molecule that has electrically charged areas. (p. 7)
molécula polar Molécula que posee áreas con carga eléctrica.

pollutant A substance that causes pollution. (p. 69)
contaminante Sustancia que causa contaminación.

potential energy Energy that is stored and waiting to be used. (p. 85)
energía potencial Energía que está almacenada para usarse posteriormente.

precipitation Water that falls to Earth as rain, snow, hail, or sleet. (p. 17)
precipitación Agua que cae a la superficie terrestre en forma de lluvia, nieve, granizo o aguanieve.

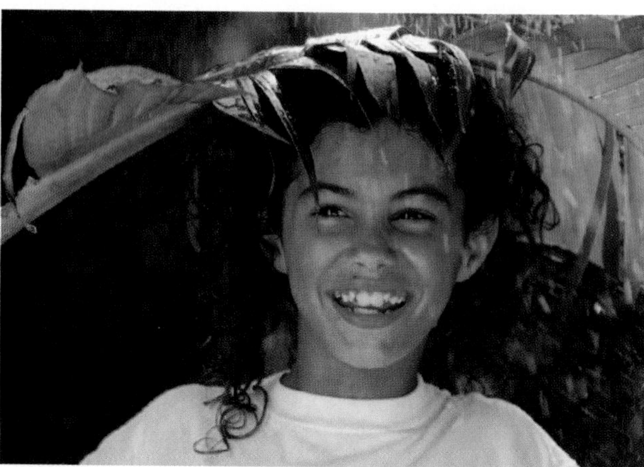

R

reservoir A lake that stores water for human use. (p. 25)
embalse Lago en el que se almacena agua para uso humano.

rip current A rush of water that flows rapidly back to sea through a narrow opening in a sandbar. (p. 99)
corriente de resaca Torrente de agua que fluye con fuerza desde una playa hacia mar adentro por un canal estrecho en un banco de arena.

S

salinity The total amount of dissolved salts in a water sample. (p. 109)
salinidad Cantidad total de sales disueltas en una muestra de agua.

saturated zone The area of permeable rock or soil in which the cracks and pores are totally filled with water. (p. 35)
zona saturada Área de roca o suelo permeable cuyas grietas y poros están totalmente llenos de agua.

seafloor spreading A process by which new rock is added to the ocean floor along the boundary between diverging plates. (p. 138)
expansión del suelo marino Proceso por el cual se añade roca nueva al suelo oceánico a lo largo de una frontera entre placas divergentes.

sewage Wastewater containing human wastes. (p. 62)
aguas residuales Aguas que contienen desechos humanos.

solution A mixture that forms when one substance dissolves another. (p. 8)
solución Mezcla que se forma cuando una sustancia disuelve a otra.

solvent A substance that dissolves another substance. (p. 8)
solvente Sustancia que disuelve otra sustancia.

sonar A system that uses sound waves to calculate the distance to an object, and that gets its name from *so*und *na*vigation and *r*anging. (p. 133)
sonar Sistema que utiliza ondas sonoras para calcular la distancia a la que está un objeto. Su nombre proviene de la frase en inglés "*so*und *na*vigation and *r*anging" (navegación y determinación de distancias por sonido).

specific heat The amount of heat needed to increase the temperature of a certain mass of a substance by 1°C. (p. 9)
calor específico Cantidad de calor necesaria para elevar en 1°C la temperatura de cierta masa de una sustancia.

spring tide A tide with the greatest difference between high and low tide that occurs when the sun and the moon are aligned with Earth at the new moon and the full moon. (p. 104)
marea viva Marea que presenta la mayor diferencia entre pleamar y bajamar; se presenta cuando el Sol y la Luna están alineados con la Tierra en la luna nueva y la luna llena.

submersible An underwater vehicle built of strong materials to resist pressure. (p. 113)
sumergible Vehículo submarino hecho de materiales fuertes para resistir la presión.

surface tension The tightness across the surface of water that is caused by the polar molecules pulling on one another. (p. 8)
tensión superficial Tirantez que hay en la superficie del agua debido a que sus moléculas polares tiran unas de otras.

tides The daily rise and fall of Earth's waters on its coastlines. (p. 103)
mareas Ascenso y descenso diario de las aguas de la Tierra en las costas.

transpiration The process by which plants give off water vapor through their leaves. (p. 16)
transpiración Proceso por el cual las plantas desprenden vapor de agua de sus hojas.

trench A deep, steep-sided canyon in the ocean floor.
fosa Cañón profundo, de lados empinados, en el suelo oceánico. (p. 136)

tributary A stream or smaller river that feeds into a main river. (p. 20)
afluente Arroyo o río más pequeño que desemboca en un río principal.

tsunami A giant wave usually caused by an earthquake beneath the ocean floor. (p. 98)
tsunami Ola gigantesca, casi siempre causada por un sismo bajo la cuenca oceánica.

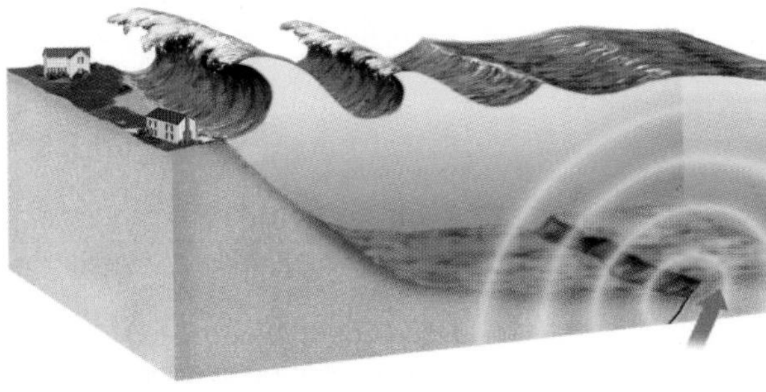

U

unsaturated zone The layer of rocks and soil above the water table in which the pores contain air as well as water. (p. 35)
zona insaturada Capa de rocas y suelo encima del nivel freático en la cual los poros contienen aire además de agua.

upwelling The movement of cold water upward from the deep ocean that is caused by wind. (p. 120)
corriente de ascenso Movimiento ascendente de aguas frías desde las profundidades del mar, causado por los vientos.

water cycle The continuous process by which water moves from Earth's surface to the atmosphere and back. (p. 16)
ciclo del agua Proceso continuo por el cual el agua pasa de la superficie terrestre a la atmósfera y regresa.

water pollution The addition of any substance that has a negative effect on water or the living things that depend on the water. (p. 69)
contaminación del agua Adición de cualquier sustancia que tiene un efecto negativo sobre el agua o los seres vivos que dependen de ella.

water quality The degree of purity of water, determined by measuring the substances in water besides water molecules. (p. 58)
calidad del agua Grado de pureza del agua, determinado por medición de las sustancias que el agua contiene además de sus propias moléculas.

watershed The land area that supplies water to a river system. (p. 21)
cuenca hidrográfica Área de terreno que suministra agua a un sistema fluvial.

water table The top of the saturated zone, or depth to the groundwater under Earth's surface. (p. 35)
nivel freático Límite superior de la zona saturada, o distancia hasta las aguas freáticas bajo la superficie terrestre.

wave The movement of energy through a body of water. (p. 95)
ola Movimiento de energía a través de un cuerpo de agua.

wave height The vertical distance from the crest of a wave to the trough. (p. 96)
altura de una ola Distancia vertical desde la cresta de una ola hasta el valle.

wavelength The horizontal distance between two wave crests. (p. 96)
longitud de una ola Distancia horizontal entre dos crestas de ola.

wetland A land area that is covered with a shallow layer of water during some or all of the year. (p. 28)
tierra cenagosa Área de terreno cubierta por una capa superficial de agua durante una parte del año, o todo el tiempo.

Index

Page numbers for key terms are printed in **boldface** type.
Page numbers for illustrations, maps, and charts are printed in *italics.*

Teacher's Edition entries appear in blue type. The page on which a term is defined is indicated in **boldface** type.

A

C

Index

Index

Page numbers for key terms are printed in **boldface** type.
Page numbers for illustrations, maps, and charts are printed in *italics*.

Index

Page numbers for key terms are printed in **boldface** type.
Page numbers for illustrations, maps, and charts are printed in *italics*.

T

U

V

W

Acknowledgments

Staff Credits

Scott Andrews, Jennifer Angel, Laura Baselice, Carolyn Belanger, Barbara A. Bertell, Suzanne Biron, Peggy Bliss, Stephanie Bradley, James Brady, Anne M. Bray, Kerry Cashman, Jonathan Cheney, Joshua D. Clapper, Lisa J. Clark, Bob Craton, Patricia Cully, Patricia M. Dambry, Kathy Dempsey, Emily Ellen, Thomas Ferreira, Jonathan Fisher, Patricia Fromkin, Paul Gagnon, Robert Graham, Ellen Granter, Barbara Hollingdale, Etta Jacobs, Linda Johnson, Anne Jones, John Judge, Kevin Keane, Kelly Kelliher, Toby Klang, Russ Lappa, Carolyn Lock, Rebecca Loveys, Constance J. McCarty, Carolyn B. McGuire, Ranida Touranont McKneally, Anne McLaughlin, Eve Melnechuk, Tania Mlawer, Janet Morris, Francine Neumann, Marie Opera, Jill Ort, Joan Paley, Dorothy Preston, Rashid Ross, Siri Schwartzman, Laurel Smith, Emily Soltanoff, Jennifer A. Teece, Diane Walsh, Amanda M. Watters, Merce Wilczek, Amy Winchester, Char Lyn Yeakley. **Additional Credits** Tara Allamilla, Terence Hegarty, Louise Gachet, Andrea Golden, Stephanie Rogers, Kim Schmidt, Joan Tobin.

Illustration

David Corrente: 127, 171; **John Edwards and Associates**: 64–65, 99, 143; **Kevin Jones and Associates**: 16, 76; **XNR Productions**: 49, 137. **All charts and graphs by Matt Mayerchak.**

Photography

Photo Research Paula Wehde

Cover Image top, Larry Ulrich; **bottom**, Stuart Westmoreland/Getty Images, Inc.

Page vi, Corbis; **vii**, Richard Haynes; **viii**, Richard Haynes; **x**, Norbert Wu; **1 both**, Norbert Wu; **2–3**, Dale Stokes/Norbert Wu; **3t**, Norbert Wu; **3b**, Dale Stokes/Norbert Wu.

Chapter 1
Pages 4–5, Larry Carver; **5 inset**, Richard Haynes; **6t**, Russ Lappa; **6–7b**, Randy Linchs/Sharpshooters; **8b**, Richard Haynes; **8m**, Visuals Unlimited; **8t**, Richard Haynes; **9**, Grafton Marshall-Smith/Corbis; **10l**, Karen Mancinelli; **10m**, Clive Streeter/Dorling Kindersley; **10r**, Japack/Leo de Wys; **12**, Rana Clamitans/Visuals Unlimited; **13**, AFP/Corbis; **17**, Norbert Schafer/Corbis; **18**, Richard Haynes; **19**, Dennis Welch/Imagestate; **24**, Dave G. Houser/Corbis; **25l**, Royalty Free/Corbis; **25r**, David Parker/Photo Researchers Inc.; **27**, AP/Wide World Photos; **28b**, Wolfgang Kaehler/Corbis; **28t**, Russ Lappa; **29l**, John Eastcott /Yva Momatiuk/Animals Animals/Earth Scenes; **29r**, Breck P. Kent/Animals Animals/Earth Scenes; **32**, Doug Perrine/Seapics; **33**, Salvatore Vasapolli/Earthscenes; **34**, Richard Haynes; **38**, John Paul Kay/Peter Arnold Inc.; **39**, Joseph Van Os/Getty Images, Inc.; **40**, Richard Haynes; **41**, Mark Thayer; **42**, Rana Clamitans/Visuals Unlimited.

Chapter 2
Pages 46–47, Julian Hirshowitz/Corbis; **47 inset**, Richard Haynes; **49b**, Jim Richardson; **49t**, Corbis; **50l**, Liba Taylor/Corbis; **50r**, O. Louis Mazzatenta/National Geographic Image Collection; **51l**, Tom Bean/Getty Images, Inc.; **51r**, Richard T. Nowitz/Corbis; **53**, L. Lefkowitz/Getty Images, Inc.; **55**, Ralph A. Clevenger/Corbis Westlight; **56**, Russ Lappa; **57**, Uniphoto; **58**, Richard Haynes; **59**, Jim Cummins/Getty Images, Inc..; **64–65 all**, Courtesy of Massachusetts Water Resources Authority, Boston, MA; **67**, Richard Haynes; **68t,** Russ Lappa; **68b,** Harrison Shull; **69**, Getty Images, Inc.; **71**, Bettmann/Corbis; **72 inset l**, Digital Vision/Getty Images, Inc.; **72 inset r**, Jouanne Thomas/Corbis; **72–73**, David Woodfall/Getty Images, Inc.; **73 inset l**, Getty Images, Inc.; **73 inset r**, Robert Goddyn/UPA; **74**, Tony Craddock/Photo Researchers, Inc.; **75**, Gabe Palmer/Corbis; **77**, Peter Essick/Aurora; **79**, AP/Wide World Photos; **79 inset**, Svenja-Foto/Masterfile; **80**, Comstock; **81**, Grant V. Faint/Getty Images, Inc.; **82**, AFP/Corbis; **84**, Julia Waterlow/Corbis; **85**, Hubert Stadler/Corbis; **87**, AP/Wide World Photos; **88**, Hubert Stadler/Corbis.

Chapter 3
Pages 92–93, Ron Sanford/Corbis; **93 inset**, Index Stock Imagery, Inc.; **94t**, Richard Haynes; **94–95b**, Aaron Chang/Corbis; **100l**, Robert Gill; Papilio/Corbis; **100r**, Jim Wark/Airphoto; **101**, Jim Wark/Airphoto; **102**, Gene Ahrens/Bruce Coleman, Inc.; **103**, Gene Ahrens/Bruce Coleman, Inc.; **104**, Fred Bruemmer/DRK Photo; **107**, Maher Attar/Corbis Sygma; **108–109**, Peter M. Fisher/Corbis; **110**, Alon Reininger/Corbis; **111b**, Norbert Wu; **111t**, Dave Fleetham/Seapics; **114**, Richard Haynes; **115**, Mark Thayer; **116**, Russ Lappa; **118**, Raven/Explorer/Photo Researchers, Inc.; **119**, Jeffrey Greenberg/Visuals Unlimited; **121**, Andrew J. Martinez; **123**, Richard Haynes; **124l**, Fred Bruemmer/DRK Photo; **124r**, Peter M. Fisher/Corbis.

Chapter 4
Pages 128–129, Darrell Gulin/Dembinsky Photo Associates; **129 inset**, Richard Haynes; **130b**, State Library of NSW; **130t**, Russ Lappa; **131**, Herb Kawainui/HawaiianEyes.com; **131 inset**, Photograph Courtesy Peabody Essex Museum; **132l**, Norbert Wu/Corbis; **132r**, Hulton Archive/Getty Images, Inc.; **133l**, Scott Camanzine/Photo Researchers, Inc.; **133r**, 2004 Jay Wade; **138–139t**, Dorling Kindersley; **139b**, Russ Lappa; **141**, Richard Dunoff/Corbis; **143l**, E.R. Degginger/Photo Researchers, Inc.; **143r**, Tim Heller/Mo Yung Productions; **148**, David R. Frazier; **148 inset l**, Corbis; **148 inset r**, George McCarthy/Nature Picture Library; **149b**, Andy Martinez/Photo Researchers, Inc.; **149t**, Lynda Richardson/Corbis; **150b**, Corbis; **150t**, Richard Haynes; **151l**, Doug Perrine/Seapics; **151r**, Andrew J. Martinez; **152**, Japack/Corbis; **153**, Australia Picture Library/Corbis; **153 inset l**, Seapics; **153 inset r**, Fred Bavendam; **154**, Corbis; **155**, Martin Ruegner/Image State/Picture Quest; **156**, Seapics; **156 inset**, Bruce Robinson/Corbis; **157**, WHOI; **158b**, Seapics; **158t**, Richard Haynes; **160b**, Russ Lappa; **160t**, Clyde H. Smith/Peter Arnold, Inc.; **161**, Arnulf Husmo/Getty Images, Inc.; **163l**, Bob Torrez/Getty Images, Inc.; **163r**, Bill Nation/Corbis Sygma; **164t**, Frans Lanting/Minden Pictures; **164b**, Richard Haynes; **165**, Richard Haynes; **166**, Corbis; **166–167 background**, Corbis;**168**, Russ Lappa; **170l**, Corbis; **170r**, Doug Perrine/Innerspace Visions.

Page 173b, Panoramic Images; **173m**, University Art Collection, Tulane; **173t**, North Wind Picture Archive; **175**, Richard Pasley/Liaison/Getty Images, Inc.; **176 inset**, Bettmann/Corbis; **176 journal page**, Russ Lappa; **176–177**, Clint Farlinger; **177 inset**, Richard Sisk/Panoramic Images; **178**, Tony Freeman/PhotoEdit; **179b**, Russ Lappa; **179m**, Richard Haynes; **179t**, Russ Lappa; **180**, Richard Haynes; **182**, Richard Haynes; **184**, Morton Beebe/Corbis; **185**, Richard Haynes; **187b**, Richard Haynes; **187t**, Dorling Kindersley; **189**, ImageStop/Phototake; **192**, Richard Haynes; **199**, Richard Haynes; **200**, Russ Lappa; **201 both**, Russ Lappa; **202**, Bruce Robinson/Corbis; **203**, AP/Wide World Photos; **204**, John Paul Kay/Peter Arnold Inc.; **205**, Doug Perrine/Seapics; **206**, Norbert Schafer/Corbis.